Stanley Gibbons CATALOGUE

of

King George VI

POSTAGE STAMPS

1998 Edition

Stanley Gibbons
London and Ringwood

By Appointment to Her Majesty The Queen
Stanley Gibbons Ltd, London
Philatelists

Published by **Stanley Gibbons Ltd**
Editorial, Publications Sales Offices and Distribution Centre:
5 Parkside, Christchurch Road, Ringwood,
Hants BH24 3SH.

1998 (6th edition) (extracted from 1998 edition
Part 1 (British Commonwealth) Stamp Catalogue
in two volumes)

© **Stanley Gibbons Ltd 1997**

ISBN:0-85259-434-8

Item No. 2884 (97)

Text assembled by Black Bear Press Limited, Cambridge
Made and Printed in Great Britain by The Alden Press, Oxford

Resurgam

It is rather unusual for there to be a gap of forty-five years between editions of a Stanley Gibbons catalogue. The 5th edition of the *King George VI Catalogue* appeared in November 1952, when it cost 4 shillings plus a 3d. post and packing charge. This 6th edition, costing a little more than 4 shillings, is to be published in November 1997.

A number of factors have played a part in this revival, but the primary influence has been the continued and growing interest in King George VI stamps. It is difficult to *exactly* gauge levels of popularity, but it certainly does appear that the number of collectors of these issues grows steadily each year. The period between 1936 and 1952 was crucially important, both in the evolution of the modern world and in the development of stamp production. The exigencies of wartime printing produced many provisionals and varieties which would not have appeared in more settled times and the post war years saw the rise of photogravure stamp printing to a position of prominence.

Although the King George VI listings appear in the annual *Part 1* (*British Commonwealth*) *Catalogue*, and now include many more shades, varieties, inverted watermarks and stamp booklets than was the case forty-five years ago, these encyclopaedic volumes are hardly easily portable so this pocket-sized publication has been produced especially for collectors of these popular issues.

The listings have been extracted directly from the 1998 edition of the *Part 1* (*British Commonwealth*) *Catalogue* and then reformatted to a smaller page size. Stamps are listed under the territory names used during the reign of King George VI. Some issues which appeared before December 1936, and which continued in use for a considerable time during the reign, are included as are printings of King George VI stamps which appeared after 1952. Such a selection must be somewhat arbitary, but hopefully all King George VI collectors will find what they require in these pages.

The publication of this catalogue is also something of an experiment. If it proves to be a success then other "extracts" may well follow in the future.

David J. Aggersberg

Stanley Gibbons Holdings Plc

STANLEY GIBBONS LIMITED, STANLEY GIBBONS AUCTIONS
399 Strand, London WC2R 0LX
Auction Room and Specialist Stamp Departments. Open Monday–Friday, 9.30 a.m. to 5 p.m.
Shop. Open Monday–Friday 8.30 a.m. to 6 p.m. and Saturday 10 a.m. to 4 p.m.
Telephone 0171 836 8444 and Fax 0171 836 7342 for all departments

STANLEY GIBBONS PUBLICATIONS
5 Parkside, Christchurch Road, Ringwood, Hants BH24 3SH
**Telephone 01425 472363 (24 hour answerphone service), Fax 01425 470247 and E-mail
info@stangib.demon.co.uk**
Publications Showroom (at above address). Open Monday–Friday 9 a.m. to 3 p.m.
Publications Mail Order. FREEPHONE 0800 611622. Trade Desk 01425 478776.
Both Monday–Friday 8.30 a.m. to 5 p.m.

Stanley Gibbons Publications has overseas licensees and distributors for Australia, Austria, Belgium,
Canada, Denmark, Finland, France, Germany, Hong Kong, Israel, Italy, Japan, Luxembourg,
Netherlands, New Zealand, Norway, Singapore, South Africa, Sweden, Switzerland, West Indies and
Caribbean. Please contact the Ringwood address for details.

URCH HARRIS & CO
(a division of Stanley Gibbons Ltd)
1 Denmark Avenue, Bristol BS1 5HD
UH New Issue Service
Telephone 0117 9349333 and Fax 0117 9273037
Monday–Friday 8.30 a.m. to 5 p.m.

FRASER'S
(a division of Stanley Gibbons Ltd)
399 Strand, London WC2R 0LX
Autographs, photographs, letters and documents
Telephone 0171 836 8444 and Fax 0171 836 7342
Monday–Friday 9 a.m. to 5.30 p.m. and Saturday 10 a.m. to 4 p.m.

Specialist Philatelic Society

King George VI Collectors Society. Secretary: Mr F. R. Lockyer, OBE, 98 Albany,
Manor Road, Bournemouth, Dorset BH1 3EW

Contents

General Philatelic Information

and Guidelines to the Scope of the Part 1
(British Commonwealth) Catalogue
from which this listing is taken

The notes which follow seek to reflect current practice in compiling the Part 1 (British Commonwealth) Catalogue.

It scarcely needs emphasising that the *Stanley Gibbons Stamp Catalogue* has a very long history and that the vast quantity of information it contains has been carefully built up by successive generations through the work of countless individuals. Philately itself is never static and the Catalogue has evolved and developed during this long time-span. Thus, while these notes are important for today's criteria, they may be less precise the further back in the listings one travels. They are not intended to inaugurate some unwanted series of piecemeal alterations in a widely respected work, but it does seem to us useful that Catalogue users know as exactly as possible the policies currently in operation.

PRICES

The prices quoted in this Catalogue are the estimated selling prices of Stanley Gibbons Ltd at the time of publication. They are, *unless it is specifically stated otherwise,* for examples in fine condition for the issue concerned. Superb examples are worth more; those of a lower quality considerably less.

All prices are subject to change without prior notice and Stanley Gibbons Ltd may from time to time offer stamps below catalogue price. Individual low value stamps sold at 399, Strand are liable to an additional handling charge. Purchasers of new issues are asked to note that the prices charged for them contain an element for the service rendered and so may exceed the prices shown when the stamps are subsequently catalogued. Postage and handling charges are extra.

No guarantee is given to supply all stamps priced, since it is not possible to keep every catalogued item in stock. Commemorative issues may, at times, only be available in complete sets and not as individual values.

Quotation of prices. The prices in the left-hand column are for unused stamps and those in the right-hand column are for used.

A dagger (†) denotes that the item listed does not exist in that condition and a blank, or dash, that it exists, or may exist, but no market price is known.

Prices are expressed in pounds and pence sterling. One pound comprises 100 pence (£1 = 100p).

The method of notation is as follows: pence in numerals (e.g. 10 denotes ten pence); pound and pence, up to £100, in numerals (e.g. 4·25 denotes four pounds and twenty-five pence); prices above £100 expressed in whole pounds with the "£" sign shown.

Unused stamps. Prices for unused stamps are for examples in unmounted mint condition.

Some stamps from the King George VI period are often difficult to find in unmounted mint condition. In such instances we would expect that collectors would need to pay a high proportion of the price quoted to obtain mounted mint examples. Generally speaking lightly mounted mint stamps from this reign, issued before 1945, are in considerable demand.

Used stamps. The used prices are normally for stamps postally used but may be for stamps cancelled-to-order where this practice exists.

A pen-cancellation on early issues can sometimes correctly denote postal use. Instances are individually noted in the Catalogue in explanation of the used price given.

Prices quoted for bisects on cover or on large piece are for those dated during the period officially authorised.

Stamps not sold unused to the public (e.g. some official stamps) are priced used only.

The use of "unified" designs, that is stamps inscribed for both postal and fiscal purposes, results in a number of stamps of very high face value. In some instances these may not have been primarily intended for postal purposes, but if they are so inscribed we include them. We only price such items used, however, where there is evidence of normal postal usage.

Minimum price. The minimum catalogue price quoted is 10p. For individual stamps prices between 10p. and 30p. are provided as a guide for catalogue users. The lowest price *charged* for individual stamps purchased from Stanley Gibbons Ltd is 30p.

Set prices. Set prices are generally for one of each value, excluding shades and varieties, but including major colour changes. Where there are alternative shades, etc., the cheapest is usually included. The number of stamps in the set is always stated for clarity. The mint prices for sets containing *se-tenant* pieces are based on the prices quoted for such combinations, and not on those for the individual stamps.

Varieties. Where plate or cylinder varieties are priced in a used condition the price quoted is for a fine used example with the cancellation well clear of the listed flaw.

Specimen stamps. The pricing of these items is explained under that heading.

Stamp booklets. Prices are for complete assembled booklets in fine condition with those issued before 1945 showing normal wear and tear. Incomplete booklets and those which have been "exploded" will, in general, be worth less than the figure quoted.

Repricing. Collectors will be aware that the market factors of supply and demand directly influence the prices quoted in this Catalogue. Whatever the scarcity of a particular stamp, if there is no one in the market who wishes to buy it it cannot be expected to achieve a high price. Conversely, the same item actively sought by numerous potential buyers may cause the price to rise.

All the prices in this Catalogue are examined during the preparation of each new edition by expert staff of Stanley Gibbons and repriced as necessary. They take many factors into account, including supply and demand, and are in close touch with the international stamp market and the auction world.

GUARANTEE

All stamps are guaranteed genuine originals in the following terms:

If not as described, and returned by the purchaser, we undertake to refund the price paid to us in the original transaction. If any stamp is certified as genuine by the Expert Committee of the Royal Philatelic Society, London, or by B.P.A. Expertising Ltd, the purchaser shall not be entitled to make any claim against us for any error, omission or mistake in such certificate.

Consumers' statutory rights are not affected by the above guarantee.

The recognised Expert Committees in this country are those of the Royal Philatelic Society, 41 Devonshire Place, London W1N 1PE, and B.P.A. Expertising Ltd, P.O. Box 137, Leatherhead, Surrey KT22 0RG. They do not undertake valuations under any circumstances and fees are payable for their services.

THE CATALOGUE IN GENERAL

Contents. The Catalogue is confined to adhesive postage stamps, including miniature sheets. For particular categories the rules are:

(*a*) Revenue (fiscal) stamps or telegraph stamps are listed only where they have been expressly authorised for postal duty.

(*b*) Stamps issued only precancelled are included, but normally issued stamps available additionally with precancel have no separate precancel listing unless the face value is changed.

(*c*) Stamps prepared for use but not issued, hitherto accorded full listing, are nowadays footnoted with a price (where possible).

(*d*) Bisects (trisects, etc.) are only listed where such usage was officially authorised.

(*e*) Stamps issued only on first day covers or in presentation packs and not available separately are not listed but may be priced in a footnote.

(*f*) New printings are only included in this Catalogue where they show a major philatelic variety, such as a change in shade, watermark or paper. Stamps which exist with or without imprint dates are listed separately; changes in imprint dates are mentioned in footnotes.

(*g*) Official and unofficial reprints are dealt with by footnote.

(*h*) Stamps from imperforate printings of modern issues which also occur perforated are covered by footnotes, but are listed where widely available for postal use.

Exclusions. The following are excluded: (*a*) non-postal revenue or fiscal stamps; (*b*) postage stamps used fiscally; (*c*) local carriage labels and private local issues; (*d*) telegraph stamps; (*e*) bogus or phantom stamps; (*f*) railway or airline letter fee stamps, bus or road transport company labels; (*g*) cut-outs; (*h*) all types of non-postal labels and souvenirs; (*i*) documentary labels for the postal service, e.g. registration, recorded delivery, air-mail etiquettes, etc.; (*j*) privately applied embellishments to official issues and privately commissioned items generally; (*k*) stamps for training postal officers.

Full listing. "Full listing" confers our recognition and implies allotting a catalogue number and (wherever possible) a price quotation.

In judging status for inclusion in the catalogue broad considerations are applied to stamps. They must be issued by a legitimate postal authority, recognised by the government concerned, and must be adhesives valid for proper postal use in the class of service for which they are inscribed. Stamps, with the exception of such categories as postage dues and officials, must be available to the general public, at face value, in reasonable quantities without any artificial restrictions being imposed on their distribution.

For errors and varieties the criterion is legitimate (albeit inadvertent) sale through a postal administration in the normal course of business. Details of provenance are always important; printers' waste and deliberately manufactured material are excluded.

Certificates. In assessing unlisted items due weight is given to Certificates from recognised Expert Committees and, where appropriate, we will usually ask to see them.

Date of issue. Where local issue dates differ from dates of release by agencies, "date of issue" is the local date. Fortuitous stray usage before the officially intended date is disregarded in listing. For ease of reference, the Catalogue displays in the top corner the date of issue of the first set listed on each page.

Catalogue numbers. Stamps of each country are catalogued chronologically by date of issue. Subsidiary classes are placed at the end of the country, as separate lists, with a distinguishing letter prefix to the catalogue number, e.g. D for postage due, O for official and E for express delivery stamps.

The catalogue number appears in the extreme left column. The boldface Type numbers in the next column are merely cross-references to illustrations. Catalogue numbers in the *Gibbons Stamp Monthly* Supplement are provisional only and may need to be altered when the lists are consolidated. For the numbering of miniature sheets and sheetlets *see* section below.

Once published in the Catalogue, numbers are changed as little as possible; really serious renumbering is reserved for the occasions when a complete country or an entire issue is being rewritten. The edition first affected includes cross-reference tables of old and new numbers.

Our catalogue numbers are universally recognised in specifying stamps and as a hallmark of status.

Illustrations. Stamps are illustrated at three-quarters linear size. Stamps not illustrated are the same size and format as the value shown, unless otherwise indicated. Stamps issued only as miniature sheets have the stamp alone illustrated but sheet size is also quoted. Overprints, surcharges, watermarks and postmarks are normally actual size. Illustrations of varieties are often enlarged to show the detail. Stamp booklet covers are illustrated half-size, unless otherwise indicated.

Designers. Designers' names are quoted where known, though space precludes naming every individual concerned in the production of a set. In particular, photographers supplying material are usually named only where they also make an active contribution in the design stage; posed photographs of reigning monarchs are, however, an exception to this rule.

CONTACTING THE CATALOGUE EDITOR

The editor is always interested in hearing from people who have new information which will improve or correct the Catalogue. As a general rule he must see and examine the actual stamps before they can be considered for listing; photo-

graphs or photocopies are insufficient evidence.

Submissions should be made in writing to the Catalogue Editor, Stanley Gibbons Publications at the Ringwood office. The cost of return postage for items submitted is appreciated, and this should include the registration fee if required.

Where information is solicited purely for the benefit of the enquirer, the editor cannot undertake to reply if the answer is already contained in these published notes or if return postage is omitted. Written communications are greatly preferred to enquiries by telephone and the editor regrets that he or his staff cannot see personal callers without a prior appointment being made. Correspondence may be subject to delay during the production period of each new edition.

The editor welcomes close contact with study circles and is interested, too, in finding reliable local correspondents who will verify and supplement official information in countries where this is deficient.

> We regret we do not give opinions as to the genuineness of stamps, nor do we identify stamps or number them by our Catalogue.

TECHNICAL MATTERS

The meanings of the technical terms used in the catalogue will be found in our *Philatelic Terms Illustrated* (3rd edition), (*price £7.50 plus postage and packing charge*).

References below to "more specialised" listings are to be taken to indicate, as appropriate, the Stanley Gibbons *Great Britain Specialised Catalogue* in 5 volumes or the *Great Britain Concise Catalogue*.

1. Printing

Printing errors. Errors in printing are of major interest to the Catalogue. Authenticated items meriting consideration would include: background, centre or frame inverted or omitted; centre or subject transposed; error of colour; error or omission of value; double prints and impressions; printed both sides; and so on. Designs *tête-bêche*, whether intentionally or by accident, are listable. *Se-tenant* arrangements of stamps are recognised in the listings or footnotes. Gutter pairs (a pair of stamps separated by blank margin) are not included in this volume. Colours only partially omitted are not listed. Stamps with embossing omitted and (for Commonwealth countries) stamps printed on the gummed side are reserved for our more specialised listings.

Printing varieties. Listing is accorded to major changes in the printing base which lead to completely new types. In recess-printing this could be a design re-engraved; in photogravure or photolithography a screen altered in whole or in part. It can also encompass flat-bed and rotary printing if the results are readily distinguishable.

To be considered at all, varieties must be constant.

Early stamps, produced by primitive methods, were prone to numerous imperfections: the lists reflect this, recognising re-entries, retouches, broken frames, misshapen letters, and so on. Printing technology has, however, radically improved over the years, during which time photogravure and lithography have become predominant. Varieties nowadays are more in the nature of flaws and these, being too specialised for this general catalogue, are almost always outside the scope. The development of our range of specialised catalogues allows us now to list those items which have philatelic significance in their appropriate volume.

In no catalogue, however, do we list such items as: dry prints, kiss prints, doctor-blade flaws, colour shifts or registration flaws (unless they lead to the complete omission of a colour from an individual stamp), lithographic ring flaws, and so on. Neither do we recognise fortuitous happenings like paper creases or confetti flaws.

Overprints (and surcharges). Overprints of different types qualify for separate listing. These include overprints in different colours; overprints from different printing processes such as litho and typo; overprints in totally different typefaces, etc. Major errors in machine-printed overprints are important and listable. They include: overprint inverted or omitted; overprint double (treble, etc.); overprint diagonal; overprint double, one inverted; pairs with one overprint omitted, e.g. from a radical shift to an adjoining stamp; error of colour; error of type fount; letters inverted or omitted, etc. If the overprint is handstamped, few of these would qualify and a distinction is drawn. We continue, however, to list pairs of stamps where one has a handstamped overprint and the other has not.

Varieties occurring in overprints will often take the form of broken letters, slight differences in spacing, rising spaces, etc. Only the most important would be considered for footnote mention.

Sheet positions. If space permits we quote sheet positions of listed varieties and authenticated data is solicited for this purpose.

2. Paper

All stamps listed are deemed to be on "ordinary" paper of the wove type and white in colour; only departures from this are normally mentioned.

Types. Where classification so requires we distinguish such other types of paper as, for example, vertically and horizontally laid; wove and laid bâtonné; card(board); carton; cartridge; glazed; granite; native; pelure; porous; quadrillé; ribbed; rice; and silk thread.

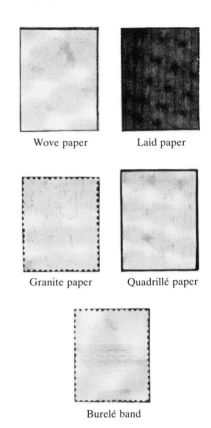

Wove paper   Laid paper

Granite paper   Quadrillé paper

Burelé band

The various makeshifts for normal paper are listed as appropriate. The varieties of double paper and joined paper are recognised. The security device of a printed burelé band on the back of a stamp, as in early Queensland, qualifies for listing.

Descriptive terms. The fact that a paper is handmade (and thus probably of uneven thickness) is mentioned where necessary. Such descriptive terms as "hard" and "soft"; "smooth" and 'rough"; "thick", "medium" and "thin" are applied where there is philatelic merit in classifying papers. We do not, for example, even in more specialised listings, classify paper thicknesses in the Wilding and Machin definitives of Great Britain. Weight standards for the paper apply to complete reels only, so that differences on individual stamps are acceptable to the printer provided the reel conforms overall.

Coloured, very white and toned papers. A coloured paper is one that is coloured right through (front and back of the stamp). In the Catalogue the colour of the paper is given in *italics*, thus:

black/*rose* = black design on rose paper.

Papers have been made specially white in recent years by, for example, a very heavy coating of chalk. We do not classify shades of whiteness of paper as distinct varieties. There does exist, however, a type of paper from early days called toned. This is off-white, often brownish or buffish, but it cannot be assigned any definite colour. A toning effect brought on by climate, incorrect storage or gum staining is disregarded here, as this was not the state of the paper when issued.

"Ordinary" and "Chalk-surfaced" papers. The availability of many postage stamps for revenue purposes made necessary some safeguard against the illegitimate re-use of stamps with removable cancellations. This was at first secured by using fugitive inks and later by printing on chalk-surfaced paper, both of which made it difficult to remove any form of obliteration without also damaging the stamp design.

This catalogue lists these chalk-surfaced paper varieties from their introduction in 1905. Where no indication is given, the paper is "ordinary".

Our chalk-surfaced paper is specifically one which shows a black mark when touched with a silver wire. The paper used during the Second World War for high values, as in Bermuda, the Leeward Islands, etc., was thinly coated with some kind of surfacing which does not react to silver and is therefore regarded (and listed) as "ordinary". Stamps on chalk-surfaced paper can easily lose this coating through immersion in water.

Another paper introduced during the War as a substitute for chalk-surfaced is rather thick, very white and glossy and shows little or no watermark, nor does it show a black line when touched with silver. In the Bahamas high values this paper might be mistaken for the chalk-surfaced (which is thinner and poorer-looking) but for the silver test.

Some modern coated papers show little or no reaction to the silver test and, therefore, cannot be classed as chalk-surfaced.

Green and yellow papers. Issues of the First World War and immediate postwar period occur on green and yellow papers and these are given separate Catalogue listing. The original coloured papers (coloured throughout) gave way to surface-coloured papers, the stamps having "white backs"; other stamps show one colour on the front and a different one at the back. Because of the numerous variations a grouping of colours is adopted as follows:

YELLOW PAPERS

(1) The original *yellow* paper (throughout), usually bright in colour. The gum is often sparse, of harsh consistency and dull-looking.

(2) The *white backs*.

(3) A bright *lemon* paper. The colour must have a pronounced greenish tinge, different from the "yellow" in (1). As a rule, the gum on stamps using this lemon paper is plentiful, smooth and shiny, and the watermark shows distinctly. Care is needed with stamps printed in green on yellow paper (1) as it may appear that the paper is this lemon.

(4) An *orange-buff* paper. The colour must have a distinct brownish tinge. It is not to be confused with a muddy yellow (1) nor the misleading appearance (on the surface) of stamps printed in red on yellow paper where an engraved plate has been insufficiently wiped.

(5) A *pale yellow* paper that has a creamy tone to the yellow.

GREEN PAPERS

(6) The original "green" paper, varying considerably through shades of *blue-green* and *yellow-green*, the front and back sometimes differing.

(7) The *white backs*.

(8) A paper blue-green on the surface with *pale olive* back. The back must be markedly paler than the front and this and the pronounced olive tinge to the back distinguish it from (6).

(9) Paper with a vivid green surface, commonly called *emerald-green*; it has the olive back of (8).

(10) Paper with *emerald-green* both back and front.

3. Perforation and Rouletting

Perforation gauge. The gauge of a perforation is the number of holes in a length of 2 cm. For correct classification the size of the holes (large or small) may need to be distinguished; in a few cases the actual number of holes on each edge of the stamp needs to be quoted.

Measurement. The Gibbons *Instanta* gauge is the standard for measuring perforations. The stamp is viewed against a dark background with the transparent gauge put on top of it. Though the gauge measures to decimal accuracy, perforations read from it are generally quoted in the Catalogue to the nearest half. For example:

Just over perf $12\frac{3}{4}$ to just under $13\frac{1}{4}$ = perf 13
Perf $13\frac{1}{4}$ exactly, rounded up   = perf $13\frac{1}{2}$
Just over perf $13\frac{1}{4}$ to just under $13\frac{3}{4}$ = perf $13\frac{1}{2}$
Perf $13\frac{3}{4}$ exactly, rounded up   = perf 14

However, where classification depends on it, actual quarter-perforations are quoted.

Notation. Where no perforation is quoted for an issue it is imperforate. Perforations are usually abbreviated (and spoken) as follows, though sometimes they may be spelled out for clarity. This notation for rectangular stamps (the majority) applies to diamond shapes if "top" is read as the edge to the top right.

P 14: perforated alike on all sides (read: "perf 14").

P 14 × 15: the first figure refers to top and bottom, the second to left and right sides (read: "perf 14 by 15"). This is a compound perforation. For an upright triangular stamp the first figure refers to the two sloping sides and second to the base. In inverted triangulars the base is first and the second figure refers to the sloping sides.

P 14–15: perforation measuring anything between 14 and 15: the holes are irregularly spaced, thus the gauge may vary along a single line or even along a single edge of the stamp (read: "perf 14 to 15").

P 14 *irregular*: perforated 14 from a worn perforator, giving badly aligned holes irregularly spaced (read: "irregular perf 14").

P comp(ound) 14 × 15: two gauges in use but not necessarily on opposite sides of the stamp. It could be one side in one gauge and three in the other; or two adjacent sides with the same gauge. (Read: "perf compound of 14 and 15".) For three gauges or more, abbreviated as "*P* 14, 14½, 15 *or compound*" for example.

P 14, 14½: perforated approximately 14¼ (read: "perf 14 or 14½"). It does *not* mean two stamps, one perf 14 and the other perf 14½. This obsolescent notation is gradually being replaced in the Catalogue.

Imperf: imperforate (not perforated).

Imperf × *P* 14: imperforate at top and bottom and perf 14 at sides.

P 14 × *imperf*: perf 14 at top and bottom and imperforate at sides.

Such headings as "*P* 13 × 14 (*vert*) and *P* 14 × 13 (*horiz*)" indicate which perforations apply to which stamp format—vertical or horizontal.

Some stamps are additionally perforated so that a label or tab is detachable; others have been perforated suitably for use as two halves. Listings are normally for whole stamps, unless stated otherwise.

Other terms. Perforation almost always gives circular holes; where other shapes have been used they are specified, e.g. square holes; lozenge perf. Interrupted perfs are brought about by the omission of pins at regular intervals. Perforations merely simulated by being printed as part of the design are of course ignored. With few exceptions, privately applied perforations are not listed.

In the nineteenth century perforations are often described as clean cut (clean, sharply incised holes), intermediate or rough (rough holes, imperfectly cut, often the result of blunt pins).

Perforation errors and varieties. Authenticated errors, where a stamp normally perforated is accidentally issued imperforate, are listed provided no traces of perforation (blind holes or indentations) remain. They must be provided as pairs, both stamps wholly imperforate, and are only priced in that form.

Stamps imperforate between stamp and sheet margin are not listed in this catalogue, but such errors on Great Britain stamps will be found in the *Great Britain Specialised Catalogue*.

Pairs described as "imperforate between" have the line of perforations between the two stamps omitted.

· *Imperf between* (*horiz pair*): a horizontal pair of stamps with perfs all around the edges but none between the stamps.

Imperf between (*vert pair*): a vertical pair of stamps with perfs all around the edges but none between the stamps.

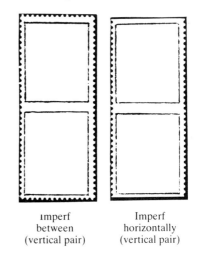

imperf   Imperf
between   horizontally
(vertical pair)   (vertical pair)

Where several of the rows have escaped perforation the resulting varieties are listable. Thus:

Imperf vert (*horiz pair*): a horizontal pair of stamps perforated top and bottom; all three vertical directions are imperf—the two outer edges and between the stamps.

Imperf horiz (*vert pair*): a vertical pair perforated at left and right edges; all three horizontal directions are imperf—the top, bottom and between the stamps.

Straight edges. Large sheets cut up before issue to post offices can cause stamps with straight edges, i.e. imperf on one side or on two sides at right angles. They are not usually listable in this condition and are worth less than corresponding stamps properly perforated all round. This does not, however, apply to certain stamps, mainly from coils and booklets, where straight edges on various sides are the manufacturing norm affecting every stamp. The listings and notes make clear which sides are correctly imperf.

Malfunction. Varieties of double, misplaced or partial perforation caused by error or machine malfunction are not listable, neither are freaks, such as perforations placed diagonally from paper folds, nor missing holes caused by broken pins.

Centering. Well-centred stamps have designs surrounded by equal opposite margins. Where this condition affects the price the fact is stated.

Types of perforating. Where necessary for classification, perforation types are distinguished. These include:

Line perforation from one line of pins punching single rows of holes at a time.

Comb perforation from pins disposed across the sheet in comb formation, punching out holes at three sides of the stamp a row at a time.

Harrow perforation applied to a whole pane or sheet at one stroke.

Rotary perforation from toothed wheels operating across a sheet, then crosswise.

Sewing-machine perforation. The resultant condition, clean-cut or rough, is distinguished where required.

Pin-perforation is the commonly applied term for pin-roulette in which, instead of being punched out, round holes are pricked by sharp-pointed pins and no paper is removed.

Mixed perforation occurs when stamps with defective perforations are re-perforated in a different gauge.

Punctured stamps. Perforation holes can be punched into the face of the stamp. Patterns of small holes, often in the shape of initial letters, are privately applied devices against pilferage. These "perfins" are outside the scope except for Canada where they were used as official stamps by the national administration.

Rouletting. In rouletting the paper is cut, for ease of separation, but none is removed. The gauge is measured, when needed, as for perforations. Traditional French terms descriptive of the type of cut are often used and types include:

Arc roulette (percé en arc). Cuts are minute, spaced arcs, each roughly a semicircle.

Cross roulette (percé en croix). Cuts are tiny diagonal crosses.

Line roulette (percé en ligne or en ligne droite). Short straight cuts parallel to the frame of the stamp. The commonest basic roulette. Where not further described, "roulette" means this type.

Rouletted in colour or coloured roulette (percé en lignes colorées or en lignes de couleur). Cuts with coloured edges, arising from notched rule inked simultaneously with the printing plate.

Saw-tooth roulette (percé en scie). Cuts applied zigzag fashion to resemble the teeth of a saw.

Serpentine roulette (percé en serpentin). Cuts as sharply wavy lines.

Zigzag roulette (percé en zigzags). Short straight cuts at angles in alternate directions, producing sharp points on separation. U.S. usage favours "serrate(d) roulette" for this type.

Pin-roulette (originally *percé en points* and now *perforés trous d'epingle*) is commonly called pin-perforation in English.

4. Gum

All stamps listed are assumed to have gum of some kind; if they were issued without gum this is stated. Original gum (o.g.) means that which was present on the stamp as issued to the public. Deleterious climates and the presence of certain chemicals can cause gum to crack and, with early stamps, even make the paper deteriorate. Unscrupulous fakers are adept in removing it and regumming the stamp to meet the unreasoning demand often made for "full o.g." in cases where such a thing is virtually impossible.

5. Watermarks

Stamps are on unwatermarked paper except where the heading to the set says otherwise.

Detection. Watermarks are detected for Catalogue description by one of four methods: (1) holding stamps to the light; (2) laying stamps face down on a dark background; (3) adding a few drops of petroleum ether 40/60 to the stamp laid face down in a watermark tray; (4) by use of the Morley-Bright Detector, or other equipment, which work by revealing the thinning of the paper at the watermark (Note that petroleum ether is highly inflammable in use and can damage photogravure stamps.)

Listable types. Stamps occurring on both watermarked and unwatermarked papers are different types and both receive full listing.

Single watermarks (devices occurring once on every stamp) can be modified in size and shape as between different issues; the types are noted but not usually separately listed. Fortuitous absence of watermark from a single stamp or its gross displacement would not be listable.

To overcome registration difficulties the device may be repeated at close intervals (a *multiple watermark*), single stamps thus showing parts of several devices. Similarly, a large *sheet watermark* (or *all-over watermark*) covering numerous stamps can be used. We give informative notes and illustrations for them. The designs may be such that numbers of stamps in the sheet automatically lack watermark: this is not a listable variety. Multiple and all-over watermarks sometimes undergo modifications, but if the various types are difficult to distinguish from single stamps notes are given but not separate listings.

Papermakers' watermarks are noted where known but not listed separately, since most stamps in the sheet will lack them. Sheet watermarks which are nothing more than officially adopted papermakers' watermarks are, however, given normal listing.

Marginal watermarks, falling outside the pane of stamps, are ignored except where misplacement caused the adjoining row to be affected, in which case they are footnoted.

Watermark errors and varieties. Watermark errors are recognised as of major importance. They comprise stamps intended to be on unwatermarked paper but issued watermarked by mistake, or stamps printed on paper with the wrong watermark. Varieties showing letters omitted from the watermark are also included, but broken or deformed bits on the dandy roll are not.

Watermark positions. The diagram shows how watermark position is described in the Catalogue. Paper has a side intended for printing and watermarks are usually impressed so that they read normally when looked through from that printed side. However, since philatelists customarily detect watermarks by looking at the back of the stamp the watermark diagram also makes clear what is actually seen.

Illustrations in the Catalogue are of watermarks in normal positions (from the front of the stamps) and are actual size where possible.

Differences in watermark position are collectable as distinct varieties. This Catalogue now lists inverted, sideways inverted and reversed watermark varieties on Commonwealth stamps issued after 1936 *except* where the watermark position is completely haphazard. It is hoped to extend such listings to earlier issues in due course.

Great Britain inverted and sideways inverted watermarks can be found in the *Great Britain Specialised Catalogue* and the *Great Britain Concise Catalogue.*

Where a watermark comes indiscriminately in various positions our policy is to cover this by a general note: we do not give separate listings because the watermark position in these circumstances has no particular philatelic importance.

Standard types of watermark. Some watermarks have been used generally for various British possessions rather than exclusively for a single colony. To avoid repetition the Catalogue classifies 17 general types, as under, with references in the headings throughout the listings being given either in words or in the form "*W* w **14**" (meaning "watermark type w **14**"). In those cases where watermark illustrations appear in the listings themselves, the respective reference reads, for example, *W* **153**, thus indicating that the watermark will be found in the normal sequence of illustrations as (type) **153**.

AS DESCRIBED (Read through front of stamp)		AS SEEN DURING WATERMARK DETECTION (Stamp face down and back examined)
GvR	Normal	ЯvƏ
ЯvƏ	Inverted	ɘʌЯ
ЯvƏ	Reversed	GvR
ɘʌЯ	Reversed and inverted	ЯvƏ
GvR (sideways)	Sideways	ЯvƏ (sideways)
GvR (sideways)	Sideways inverted	ЯvƏ (sideways)

w **8**
Multiple Crown CA

w **9**
Multiple Crown Script CA

Multiple watermarks began in 1904 with w **8**, *Multiple Crown CA,* changed from 1921 to w **9**, *Multiple Crown Script CA.* On stamps of ordinary size portions of two or three watermarks appear and on the large-sized stamps a greater number can be observed. The change to letters in script character with w **9** was accompanied by a Crown of distinctly different shape.

w **9a**: Error,
Crown missing

w **9b**: Error,
St. Edward's Crown

The *Multiple Crown Script CA* watermark, w **9**, is known with two errors recurring among the 1950–52 printings of several territories. In the first a crown has fallen away from the dandy-roll that impresses the watermark into the paper pulp. It gives w **9a**, *Crown missing*, but this omission has been found in both "Crown only" (*illustrated*) and "Crown CA" rows. The resulting faulty paper was used for Seychelles, Johore and the postage due stamps of nine colonies.

When the omission was noticed a second mishap occurred, which was to insert a wrong crown in the space, giving w **9b**, *St. Edward's Crown*. This produced varieties in Bahamas, St. Kitts-Nevis and Singapore and the incorrect crown likewise occurs in "Crown only" and "Crown CA" rows.

6. Colours

Stamps in two or three colours have these named in order of appearance, from the centre moving outwards. Four colours or more are usually listed as multicoloured.

In compound colour names the second is the predominant one, thus:

    orange-red = a red tending towards orange;
    red-orange = an orange containing more red than usual.

Standard colours used. The 200 colours most used for stamp identification are given in the Stanley Gibbons Stamp Colour Key. The Catalogue has used the Stamp Colour Key as standard for describing new issues for some years. The names are also introduced as lists are rewritten, though exceptions are made for those early issues where traditional names have become universally established.

Determining colours. When comparing actual stamps with colour samples in the Stamp Colour Key, view in a good north daylight (or its best substitute: fluorescent "colour-matching" light). Sunshine is not recommended. Choose a solid portion of the stamp design; if available, marginal markings such as solid bars of colour or colour check dots are helpful. Shading lines in the design can be misleading as they appear lighter than solid colour. Postmarked portions of a stamp appear darker than normal. If more than one colour is present, mask off the extraneous ones as the eye tends to mix them.

Errors of colour. Major colour errors in stamps or overprints which qualify for listing are: wrong colours; one colour inverted in relation to the rest; albinos (colourless impressions), where these have Expert Committee certificates; colours completely omitted, but only on unused stamps (if found on used stamps the information is footnoted) and with good credentials, missing colours being frequently faked.

Colours only partially omitted are not recognised. Colour shifts, however spectacular, are not listed.

Shades. Shades in philately refer to variations in the intensity of a colour or the presence of differing amounts of other colours. They are particularly significant when they can be linked to specific printings. In general, shades need to be quite marked to fall within the scope of this Catalogue; it does not favour nowadays listing the often numerous shades of a stamp, but chooses a single applicable colour name which will indicate particular groups of outstanding shades. Furthermore, the listings refer to colours as issued: they may deteriorate into something different through the passage of time.

Modern colour printing by lithography is prone to marked differences of shade, even within a single run, and variations can occur within the same sheet. Such shades are not listed.

Aniline colours. An aniline colour meant originally one derived from coal-tar; it now refers more widely to colour of a particular brightness suffused on the surface of a stamp and showing through clearly on the back.

Colours of overprints and surcharges. All overprints and surcharges are in black unless stated otherwise in the heading or after the description of the stamp.

7. Specimen Stamps

Originally, stamps overprinted SPECIMEN were circulated to postmasters or kept in official records, but after the establishment of the Universal Postal Union supplies were sent to Berne for distribution to the postal administrations of member countries. During the period 1884 to 1928 most of the stamps of British Crown Colonies required for this purpose were overprinted SPECIMEN in various shapes and sizes by their printers from typeset formes. Some locally produced provisionals were handstamped locally, as were sets prepared for presentation. From 1928 stamps were punched with holes forming the word SPECIMEN, each firm of printers using a different machine or machines. From 1948 the stamps supplied for U.P.U. distribution were no longer punctured.

Stamps of some other Commonwealth territories were overprinted or handstamped locally, while stamps of Great Britain and those overprinted for use in overseas postal agencies (mostly of the higher denominations) bore SPECIMEN overprints and handstamps applied by the Inland Revenue or the Post Office.

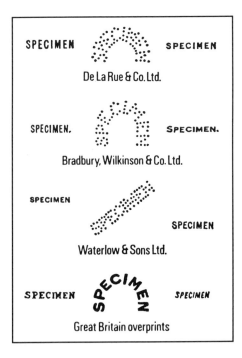

De La Rue & Co. Ltd.

Bradbury, Wilkinson & Co. Ltd.

Waterlow & Sons Ltd.

Great Britain overprints

Some of the commoner types of overprints or punctures are illustrated here. Collectors are warned that dangerous forgeries of the punctured type exist.

The *Part 1* (*British Commonwealth*) *Catalogue* records those Specimen overprints or perforations intended for distribution by the U.P.U. to member countries. In addition the Specimen overprints of Australia and its dependent territories, which were sold to collectors by the Post Office, are also included.

All other Specimens are outside the scope of this volume.

Specimens are not quoted in Great Britain as they are fully listed in the Stanley Gibbons *Great Britain Specialised Catalogue*.

In specifying type of specimen for individual high-value stamps, "H/S" means handstamped, "Optd" is overprinted and "Perf" is punctured. Some sets occur mixed, e.g. "Optd/Perf". If unspecified, the type is apparent from the date or it is the same as for the lower values quoted as a set.

Prices. Prices for stamps up to £1 are quoted in sets; higher values are priced singly after the colours, thus "(S. £20)". Where specimens exist in more than one type the price quoted is for the cheapest. Specimen stamps have rarely survived even as pairs; these and strips of three, four or five are worth considerably more than singles.

8. Coil Stamps

Stamps issued only in coil form are given full listing. If stamps are issued in both sheets and coils the coil stamps are listed separately only where there is some feature (e.g. perforation or watermark sideways) by which singles can be distinguished. Coil strips containing different stamps *se-tenant* are also listed.

Coil join pairs are too random and too easily faked to permit of listing; similarly ignored are coil stamps which have accidentally suffered an extra row of perforations from the claw mechanism in a malfunctioning vending machine.

9. Stamp Booklets

Stamp booklets (with the exception of those from Great Britain, for which see the current edition of the *Great Britain Concise Catalogue*) are now listed in this catalogue.

Single stamps from booklets are listed if they are distinguishable in some way (such as watermark or perforation) from similar sheet stamps.

Booklet panes are listed where they contain stamps of different denominations *se-tenant*, where stamp-size labels are included, or where such panes are otherwise identifiable. Booklet panes are placed in the listing under the lowest denomination present.

Particular perforations (straight edges) are covered by appropriate notes.

10. Forgeries and Fakes

Forgeries. Where space permits, notes are considered if they can give a concise description that will permit unequivocal detection of a forgery. Generalised warnings, lacking detail, are not nowadays inserted, since their value to the collector is problematic.

Fakes. Unwitting fakes are numerous, particularly "new shades" which are colour changelings brought about by exposure to sunlight, soaking in water contaminated with dyes from adherent paper, contact with oil and dirt from a pocketbook, and so on. Fraudulent operators, in addition, can offer to arrange: removal of hinge marks; repairs of thins on white or coloured papers; replacement of missing margins or perforations; reperforating in true or false gauges; removal of fiscal cancellations; rejoining of severed pairs, strips and blocks; and (a major hazard) regumming. Collectors can only be urged to purchase from reputable sources and to insist upon Expert Committee certification where there is any kind of doubt.

The Catalogue can consider footnotes about fakes where these are specific enough to assist in detection.

ABBREVIATIONS

Printers

A.B.N. Co	American Bank Note Co, New York.
A. & M.	Alden & Mowbray Ltd, Oxford.
Ashton-Potter	Ashton-Potter Ltd, Toronto.
Aspioti-Elka (Aspiotis)	Aspioti-Elka, Greece.
B.A.B.N.	British American Bank Note Co, Ottawa.
B.D.T.	B.D.T. International Security Printing Ltd, Dublin, Ireland.
B.W.	Bradbury Wilkinson & Co, Ltd.
Cartor	Cartor S.A., L'Aigle, France
C.B.N.	Canadian Bank Note Co, Ottawa.
Continental B.N. Co	Continental Bank Note Co.
Courvoisier	Imprimerie Courvoisier S.A., La-Chaux-de-Fonds, Switzerland.
D.L.R.	De La Rue & Co, Ltd, London, and (from 1961) Bogota, Colombia.
Edila	Editions de l'Aubetin, S.A.
Enschedé	Joh. Enschedé en Zonen, Haarlem, Netherlands.
Format	Format International Security Printers, Ltd, London.
Harrison	Harrison & Sons, Ltd, London
Heraclio Fournier	Heraclio Fournier S.A., Vitoria, Spain.
J.W.	John Waddington Security Print Ltd., Leeds
P.B.	Perkins Bacon Ltd, London.
Questa	Questa Colour Security Printers, Ltd., London
Ueberreuter	Ueberreuter (incorporating Bruder Rosenbaum), Korneuburg, Austria.
Walsall	Walsall Security Printers, Ltd.
Waterlow	Waterlow & Sons, Ltd, London.

General Abbreviations

Alph	Alphabet
Anniv	Anniversary
Comp	Compound (perforation)
Des	Designer; designed
Diag	Diagonal; diagonally
Eng	Engraver; engraved
F.C.	Fiscal Cancellation
H/S	Handstamped
Horiz	Horizontal; horizontally

Imp, Imperf	Imperforate
Inscr	Inscribed
L	Left
Litho	Lithographed
mm	Millimetres
MS	Miniature sheet
N.Y.	New York
Opt(d)	Overprint(ed)
P or P-c	Pen-cancelled
P, Pf or Perf	Perforated
Photo	Photogravure
Pl	Plate
Pr	Pair
Ptd	Printed
Ptg	Printing
R	Right
R.	Row
Recess	Recess-printed
Roto	Rotogravure
Roul	Rouletted
S	Specimen (overprint)
Surch	Surcharge(d)
T.C.	Telegraph Cancellation
T	Type
Typo	Typographed
Un	Unused
Us	Used
Vert	Vertical; vertically
W or wmk	Watermark
Wmk s	Watermark sideways

(†)=Does not exist.

(—) (or blank price column)=Exists, or may exist, but no market price is known.

/ between colours means "on" and the colour following is that of the paper on which the stamp is printed.

Colours of Stamps

Bl (blue); blk (black); brn (brown); car, carm (carmine); choc (chocolate); clar (claret); emer (emerald); grn (green); ind (indigo); mag (magenta); mar (maroon); mult (multicoloured); mve (mauve); ol (olive); orge (orange); pk (pink); pur (purple); scar (scarlet); sep (sepia); turq (turquoise); ultram (ultramarine); verm (vermilion); vio (violet); yell (yellow).

Colour of Overprints and Surcharges

(B.) = blue, (Blk.) = black, (Br.) = brown, (C.) = carmine, (G.) = green, (Mag.) = magenta, (Mve.) = mauve, (Ol.) = olive, (O.) = orange, (P.) = purple, (Pk.) = pink, (R.)=red, (Sil.) = silver, (V.) = violet, (Vm.) or (Verm.) = vermilion, (W.) = white, (Y.) = yellow.

Arabic Numerals

As in the case of European figures, the details of the Arabic numerals vary in different stamp designs, but they should be readily recognised with the aid of this illustration.

0	1	2	3	4	5	6	7	8	9

Great Britain

12 pence (d) = 1 shilling
20 shillings = 1 pound

PRINTERS. The following stamps were printed in photogravure by Harrison and Sons, *unless otherwise stated.*

126 King George VI and Queen Elizabeth

(Des E. Dulac)

1937 (13 May). *Coronation.* W **127**. P 15×14.
| 461 | 126 | 1½d. maroon | .. | .. | .. | .. | 40 | 30 |

127   **128**

129   **130**

King George VI and National Emblems

(Des T **128/9**, E. Dulac (head) and E. Gill (frames). T **130**, E. Dulac (whole stamp))

1937–47. W **127**. P 15×14.
462	128	½d. green (10.5.37)	..	..	10	15
		a. Wmk sideways (1.38)	..	..	25	25
		ab. Booklet pane of 4 (6.40)		..	25·00	
463		1d. scarlet (10.5.37)	..	..	10	15
		a. Wmk sideways (2.38)	..	..	13·00	4·50
		ab. Booklet pane of 4 (6.40)		..	65·00	
464		1½d. red-brown (30.7.37)	..	..	20	15
		a. Wmk sideways (2.38)	..	..	80	1·00
		b. Booklet pane. Four stamps plus two printed labels (8.37)		..	45·00	
		c. Imperf three sides (pair)	..			
465		2d. orange (31.1.38)	..	..	75	45
		a. Wmk sideways (2.38)	..	..	55·00	28·00
		b. Bisected (on cover)	..		†	22·00
466		2½d. ultramarine (10.5.37)	..	..	25	15
		a. Wmk sideways (6.40)	..	..	50·00	16·00
		b. *Tête-bêche* (horiz pair)	..			
467		3d. violet (31.1.38)	..	..	3·25	80
468	129	4d. grey-green (21.11.38)	..	..	50	40
		a. Imperf (pair)	..	..	£2000	
		b. Imperf three sides (horiz pair)	..	£2500	
469		5d. brown (21.11.38)	..	..	2·00	50
		a. Imperf (pair)	..	..	£2500	
		b. Imperf three sides (horiz pair)	..	£2000	
470		6d. purple (30.1.39)	..	..	1·25	40

471	130	7d. emerald-green (27.2.39)	..	3·25	50
		a. Imperf three sides (horiz pair)	..	£2000	
472		8d. bright carmine (27.2.39)	..	3·50	50
473		9d. deep olive-green (1.5.39)	..	5·50	60
474		10d. turquoise-blue (1.5.39)	..	..	5·00	60
		aa. Imperf (pair)	..	..	£3500	
474a		11d. plum (29.12.47)	..	..	2·00	1·50
475		1s. bistre-brown (1.5.39)	..	..	5·75	50
462/75		..	..	..	*Set of* 15	30·00	6·50

For later printings of the lower values in apparently lighter shades and different colours, see Nos. 485/90 and 503/8.

No. 465b was authorised for use in Guernsey. See notes on War Occupation Issues.

Nos. 468b and 469b are perforated at foot only and each occurs in the same sheet as Nos. 468a and 469a.

No. 471a is also perforated at foot only, but occurs on the top row of a sheet.

131 King George VI   **132** King George VI

133

(Des E. Dulac (T **131**) and Hon. G. R. Bellew (T **132**). Eng J. A. C. Harrison. Recess Waterlow)

1939–48. W **133**. P 14.
476	131	2s. 6d. brown (4.9.39)	..	..	38·00	6·00
476a		2s. 6d. yellow-green (9.3.42)	..	7·00	1·00
477		5s. red (21.8.39)	..	..	14·00	1·50
478	132	10s. dark blue (30.10.39)	..	£170	20·00
478a		10s. ultramarine (30.11.42)	..	35·00	5·00
478b		£1 brown (1.10.48)	..	..	10·00	22·00
476/8b		..	..	..	*Set of* 6	£250	50·00

134 Queen Victoria and King George VI

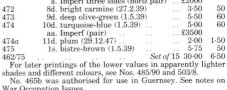

(Des H. L. Palmer)

1940 (6 May). *Centenary of First Adhesive Postage Stamps.*
W **127**. P 14½×14.

479	**134**	½d. green	..	..	..	30	20
480		1d. scarlet	..	..	..	1·00	40
481		1½d. red-brown	..	..	..	30	30
482		2d. orange	..	..	..	50	40
		a. Bisected (on cover)	..	..	†	16·00	
483		2½d. ultramarine	..	..	..	2·25	80
484		3d. violet	..	..	..	3·00	3·50
479/84				*Set of* 6	6·50	5·00	

No. 482a was authorised for use in Guernsey. See notes on War Occupation Issues.

1941-42. *Head as Nos. 462/7, but lighter background.* W **127**. P 15×14.

485	**128**	½d. pale green (1.9.41)	..	15	10	
		a. *Tête-bêche* (horiz pair)	..	£3000		
		b. Imperf (pair)	..	£1750		
486		1d. pale scarlet (11.8.41)	..	15	10	
		a. Wmk sideways (10.42)	..	3·50	5·00	
		b. Imperf (pair)	..	£2500		
		c. Imperf three sides (horiz pair)	..	£2500		
487		1½d. pale red-brown (28.9.42)	..	75	45	
488		2d. pale orange (6.10.41)	..	50	40	
		a. Wmk sideways (6.42)	..	22·00	14·00	
		b. *Tête-bêche* (horiz pair)	..	£2500		
		c. Imperf (pair)	..	£2000		
		d. Imperf pane*	..	£4500		
489		2½d. light ultramarine (21.7.41)	..	15	10	
		a. Wmk sideways (8.42)	..	12·00	10·00	
		b. *Tête-bêche* (horiz pair)	..	£2500		
		c. Imperf (pair)	..	£2250		
		d. Imperf pane*	..	£3500		
		e. Imperf three sides (horiz pair)	..	£3500		
490		3d. pale violet (3.11.41)	..	1·50	50	
485/90			..	*Set of* 6	2·75	1·50

The *tête-bêche* varieties are from defectively made-up stamp booklets.

Nos. 486c and 489e are perforated at foot only and occur in the same sheets as Nos. 486b and 489c.

*BOOKLET ERRORS. Those listed as "imperf panes" show one row of perforations either at the top or at the bottom of the pane of 6.

135

136 Symbols of Peace and Reconstruction

(Des H. L. Palmer (T **135**) and R. Stone (T **136**))

1946 (11 June). *Victory.* W **127**. P 15×14.

491	**135**	2½d. ultramarine	..	..	..	25	15
492	**136**	3d. violet	..	..	..	25	15

PRICES OF SETS

Set prices are given for many issues, generally those containing three stamps or more. Definitive sets include one of each value or major colour change, but do not cover different perforations, die types or minor shades. Where a choice is possible the set prices are based on the cheapest versions of the stamps included in the listings.

137

138 King George VI and Queen Elizabeth

(Des G. Knipe and Joan Hassall from photographs by Dorothy Wilding)

1948 (26 Apr). *Royal Silver Wedding.* W **127**. P 15×14 (2½d.) or 14×15 (£1).

493	**137**	2½d. ultramarine	..	..	30	30
494	**138**	£1 blue	..	..	38·00	35·00

139 Globe and Laurel Wreath

140 "Speed"

141 Olympic Symbol

142 Winged Victory

(Des P. Metcalfe (T **139**), A. Games (T **140**), S. D. Scott (T **141**) and E. Dulac (T **142**))

1948 (29 July). *Olympic Games.* W **127**. P 15×14.

495	**139**	2½d. ultramarine	..	..	..	10	1
496	**140**	3d. violet	..	..	..	30	3
497	**141**	6d. bright purple	..	..	..	60	3
498	**142**	1s. brown	..	..	..	1·25	1·5
495/8			..	..	*Set of* 4	2·00	2·0

143 Two Hemispheres

144 U.P.U. Monument, Berne

145 Goddess Concordia, Globe and Points of Compass

146 Posthorn and Globe

(Des Mary Adshead (T **143**), P. Metcalfe (T **144**), H. Fleury (T **145**) and Hon G. R. Bellew (T **146**))

1949 (10 Oct). *75th Anniv of Universal Postal Union.* W **127**. P 15×14.

499	143	2½d. ultramarine	..	..	..	10	10
500	144	3d. violet	..	..	..	30	40
501	145	6d. bright purple	..	..	..	60	75
502	146	1s. brown	..	..	..	1·25	1·50
499/502		..	..	..	Set of 4	2·00	2·75

1950–52. *4d. as Nos. 468 and others as Nos. 485/9, but colours changed.* W **127**. P 15×14.

503	128	½d. pale orange (3.5.51)	..	..	20	30
		a. Imperf (pair)	..	..		
		b. *Tête-bêche* (horiz pair)	..	.. £3000	
		c. Imperf pane*	..	.. £4000	
504		1d. light ultramarine (3.5.51)	..	20	30
		a. Wmk sideways (5.51)	..	50	60
		b. Imperf (pair)	..	.. £2000	
		c. Imperf three sides (horiz pair)	.. £1500	
		d. Booklet pane. Three stamps plus three printed labels (3.52)	..	15·00	
		e. Ditto. Partial *tête-bêche* pane	.. £2500	
505		1½d. pale green (3.5.51)	..	..	30	40
		a. Wmk sideways (9.51)	..	2·50	3·00
506		2d. pale red-brown (3.5.51)	..	30	30
		a. Wmk sideways (5.51)	..	1·25	1·40
		b. *Tête-bêche* (horiz pair)	.. £3000	
		c. Imperf three sides (horiz pair)	.. £1500	
507		2½d. pale scarlet (3.5.51)	..	30	30
		a. Wmk sideways (5.51)	..	1·25	1·25
		b. *Tête-bêche* (horiz pair)	..		
508	129	4d. light ultramarine (2.10.50)	..	2·00	1·25
		a. Double impression	..	† £5000	
503/8		..	..	..	Set of 6	3·00	2·50

No. 504c is perforated at foot only and occurs in the same sheet as No. 504b.

No. 506c is also perforated at foot only.

*BOOKLET ERRORS. Those listed as "imperf panes" show one row of perforations either at the top or at the bottom of the pane of 6.

147 H.M.S. *Victory*

148 White Cliffs of Dover

149 St. George and the Dragon

150 Royal Coat of Arms

(Des Mary Adshead (T **147/8**), P. Metcalfe (T **149/50**). Recess Waterlow)

1951 (3 May). W **133**. P 11×12.

509	147	2s. 6d. yellow-green	..	..	..	5·00	75
510	148	5s. red	..	..	..	28·00	1·50
511	149	10s. ultramarine	..	..	..	18·00	8·00
512	150	£1 brown	..	..	..	30·00	18·00
509/12		..	..	..	Set of 4	70·00	24·00

151 "Commerce and Prosperity"

152 Festival Symbol

(Des E. Dulac (T **151**), A. Games (T **152**))

1951 (3 May). *Festival of Britain.* W **127**. P 15×14.

513	151	2½d. scarlet	..	..	..	25	15
514	152	4d. ultramarine	..	..	..	50	45

STAMP BOOKLETS

For a full listing of Great Britain stamp booklets see the *Great Britain Concise Catalogue* published each Spring.

NEW INFORMATION

The editor is always interested to correspond with people who have new information that will improve or correct the Catalogue.

POSTAGE DUE STAMPS

PERFORATIONS. All postage due stamps are perf 14×15.

D 1

D 2

1937–38. W 127 (G VI R) *sideways.*

D27	D 1	¹⁄₂d. emerald (5.38)	..	.. 8·00	4·50
D28		1d. carmine (5.38) ..		.. 2·50	50
D29		2d. agate (5.38)	..	.. 2·50	50
D30		3d. violet (12.37) ..	..	.. 12·00	90
D31		4d. dull grey-green (9.37)	..	.. 65·00	10·00
D32		5d. yellow-brown (11.38)	..	.. 12·00	1·50
D33		1s. deep blue (10.37)	..	.. 60·00	1·50
D34	D 2	2s. 6d. purple/*yellow* (9.38) ..		.. 60·00	2·50
D27/34		.. .. ..	*Set of* 8	£200	19·00

The 2d. is known bisected in June 1951 (Boreham Wood,
Harpenden and St. Albans) and on 30 October 1954
(Harpenden).

1951–52. *Colours changed and new value* (1¹⁄₂d.). W **127**
(G VI R) *sideways.*

D35	D 1	¹⁄₂d. orange (18.9.51)	..	.. 1·00	2·50
D36		1d. violet-blue (6.6.51)	..	.. 1·50	1·25
D37		1¹⁄₂d. green (11.2.52) ..	..	.. 1·75	2·50
D38		4d. blue (14.8.51)	..	.. 30·00	11·00
D39		1s. ochre (6.12.51) ..	..	.. 35·00	13·00
D35/9			*Set of* 5	60·00	22·00

The 1d. is known bisected (Dorking, 1952, and Camberley,
6 April 1954).

CHANNEL ISLANDS

GENERAL ISSUE

C 1 Gathering Vraic

C 2 Islanders gathering Vraic

(Des J. R. R. Stobie (1d.) or from drawing by E. Blampied (2¹⁄₂d.).
Photo Harrison)

1948 (10 May). *Third Anniv of Liberation.* W **127** *of Great
Britain.* P 15×14.

C1	C 1	1d. scarlet	..	..	.. 20	20
C2	C 2	2¹⁄₂d. ultramarine	..	..	.. 30	30

GUERNSEY

WAR OCCUPATION ISSUES

Stamps issued under British authority during the German
Occupation

BISECTS. On 24 December 1940 authority was given, by Post
Office notice, that prepayment of penny postage could be
effected by using half a British 2d. stamp, diagonally bisected.
Such stamps were first used on 27 December 1940.

The 2d. stamps generally available were those of the Postal
Centenary issue, 1940 (S.G. 482) and the first colour of the King
George VI issue (S.G. 465). These are listed under Nos. 482a and
465b. A number of the 2d. King George V, 1912–22, and of the
King George V photogravure stamp (S.G. 442) which were in
the hands of philatelists, were also bisected and used.

1

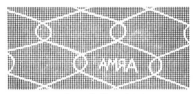

1a Loops (*half actual size*)

(Des E. W. Vaudin. Typo Guernsey Press Co Ltd)

1941–44. *Rouletted.* (a) *White paper. No wmk.*

1	1	¹⁄₂d. light green (7.4.41) ..	..	.. 2·75	2·00
		a. Emerald-green (6.41)	..	.. 3·25	2·25
		b. Bluish green (11.41)	..	.. 40·00	22·00
		c. Bright green (2.42)	..	.. 24·00	10·00
		d. Dull green (9.42)	..	.. 3·75	3·50
		e. Olive-green (2.43)	..	.. 29·00	18·00
		f. Pale yellowish green (7.43 and later)			
		(shades)	.. .. ..	.. 2·50	2·50
		g. Imperf (pair)	..	.. £150	
		h. Imperf between (horiz pair) ..		.. £600	
		i. Imperf between (vert pair)	..	.. £700	
2		1d. scarlet (18.2.41)	..	.. 2·00	1·00
		a. Pale vermilion (7.43) (etc.) ..		.. 2·00	1·50
		b. Carmine (1943)	..	.. 2·50	3·00
		c. Imperf (pair)	..	.. £150	75·00
		d. Imperf between (horiz pair) ..		.. £600	
		da. Imperf vert (centre stamp of horiz strip			
		of 3)	.. .. ..		
		e. Imperf between (vert pair) ..		.. £700	
		f. Printed double (scarlet shade) ..		75·00	
3		2¹⁄₂d. ultramarine (12.4.44)	..	.. 4·00	4·00
		a. Pale ultramarine (7.44)	..	.. 4·00	4·00
		b. Imperf (pair)	..	.. £350	
		c. Imperf between (horiz pair) ..		.. £800	

(b) *Bluish French bank-note paper.* W **1a** (*sideways*)

4	1	¹⁄₂d. bright green (11.3.42)	..	.. 18·00	19·00
5		1d. scarlet (9.4.42)	..	.. 9·00	21·00

The dates given for the shades of Nos. 1/3 are the months in
which they were printed as indicated on the printer's imprints.
Others are issue dates.

MINIMUM PRICE

The minimum price quote is 10p which represents
a handling charge rather than a basis for valuing
common stamps. For further notes about prices
see introductory pages.

JERSEY

WAR OCCUPATION ISSUES

Stamps issued under British authority during the German Occupation

1

(Des Major N. V. L. Rybot. Typo *Jersey Evening Post*, St. Helier)

1941–43. *White paper (thin to thick). No wmk. P* 11.

1	1	½d. bright green (29.1.42)	..	..	3·75	3·00
		a. Imperf between (vert pair)	..	..	£700	
		b. Imperf between (horiz pair)	..	..	£600	
		c. Imperf (pair) ..	..	..	£200	
		d. On greyish paper (1.43)	..	..	5·00	5·75
2		1d. scarlet (1.4.41)	..	..	4·00	3·00
		a. Imperf between (vert pair)	..	..	£700	
		b. Imperf between (horiz pair)	..	..	£600	
		c. Imperf (pair)	..	..	£225	
		d. On chalk-surfaced paper	..	..	40·00	38·00
		e. On greyish paper (1.43)	..	..	5·00	5·75

2 Old Jersey Farm   3 Portelet Bay

4 Corbière Lighthouse   5 Elizabeth Castle

6 Mont Orgueil Castle   7 Gathering Vraic
(seaweed)

(Des E. Blampied. Eng H. Cortot. Typo French Govt Works, Paris)

1943–44. *No wmk. P* 13½.

3	2	½d. green (1 June)	..	..	6·00	5·50
		a. Rough, grey paper (6.10.43)	..	8·50	8·50
4	3	1d. scarlet (1 June)	..	..	1·50	75
		a. On newsprint (28.2.44)	..	2·50	2·00
5	4	1½d. brown (8 June)	..	..	3·00	3·00
6	5	2d. orange-yellow (8 June)	..	4·00	3·00
7	6	2½d. blue (29 June)	..	..	2·00	1·75
		a. On newsprint (25.2.44)	..	1·00	1·50
		ba. Thin paper*	..	..	£200	
8	7	3d. violet (29 June)	..	..	1·00	2·75
3/8			..	*Set of* 6	15·00	15·00

*On No. 7ba the design shows clearly through the back of the stamp.

Aden

1937. 12 pies = 1 anna; 16 annas = 1 rupee
1951. 100 cents = 1 shilling

CROWN COLONY

1 Dhow   3 Aidrus Mosque, Crater

(Recess D.L.R.)

1937 (1 Apr). *Wmk Mult Script CA sideways. P* 13 × 12.

1	1	½ a. yellow-green	..	..	3·50	1·40
2		9 p. deep green	..		3·25	1·60
3		1 a. sepia		..	3·50	70
4		2 a. scarlet	..	..	3·25	2·00
5		2½ a. bright blue	..		3·25	80
6		3 a. carmine	..	..	9·00	6·50
7		3½ a. grey-blue	..	..	6·00	2·00
8		8 a. pale purple	..	..	19·00	5·50
9		1 r. brown	..	..	28·00	6·00
10		2 r. yellow	..	..	48·00	16·00
11		5 r. deep purple	..	..	90·00	65·00
12		10 r. olive-green	..	..	£200	£225
1/12				*Set of* 12	£375	£300
1/12 Perf "Specimen"				*Set of* 12	£275	

1937 (12 May). *Coronation. As Nos. 95/7 of Antigua, but ptd by D.L.R. P* 14.

13	1 a. sepia	..	..	..	75	80
14	2½ a. light blue	..	..	..	1·00	1·40
15	3½ a. grey-blue	..	..	..	1·25	2·50
13/15	..	..	..	*Set of* 3	2·75	4·25
13/15 Perf "Specimen"	..	..	*Set of* 3	70·00	

(Recess Waterlow)

1939 (19 Jan)–**48**. *Horiz designs as T* 3. *Wmk Mult Script CA. P* 12½.

16	½ a. yellowish green	..	..	..	50	60
	a. *Bluish green* (9.48)	..	..	1·75	3·25
17	¾ a. red-brown	..	..	1·25	1·25
18	1 a. pale blue	..	..	..	20	25
19	1½ a. scarlet	..	..	..	55	60
20	2 a. sepia	..	..	..	20	25
21	2½ a. deep ultramarine	..	..	40	30
22	3 a. sepia and carmine	..	..	60	25
23	8 a. red-orange	..	..	55	40
23a	14 a. sepia and light blue (15.1.45)	..	2·25	1·00
24	1 r. emerald-green	..	..	2·25	1·50
25	2 r. deep blue and magenta	..	4·75	1·75
26	5 r. red-brown and olive-green	..	11·00	6·50
27	10 r. sepia and violet	..	..	28·00	11·00
16/27	..	..	..	*Set of* 13	48·00	23·00
16/27 Perf "Specimen"	..	*Set of* 13	£170	

Designs:—½ a., 2 a., Type 3; ¾ a., 5 r. Adenese Camel Corps; 1 a., 2 r. The Harbour; 1½ a., 1 r. Adenese Dhow; 2½ a., 8 a. Mukalla; 3 a., 14 a., 10 r. "Capture of Aden, 1839" (Capt. Rundle).

1946 (15 Oct). *Victory. As Nos. 110/11 of Antigua.*

28	1½ a. carmine	..	..	..	15	60
29	2½ a. blue	..	..	..	15	30
	w. Wmk inverted	..	..	£300	
28/9 Perf "Specimen"	..	*Set of* 2	50·00	

1949 (7 Jan). *Royal Silver Wedding. As Nos. 112/13 of Antigua.*

30	1½ a. scarlet (*p* 14×15)	..	..	40	80
31	10 r. mauve (*p* 11½×11)	..	..	27·00	29·00

1949 (10 Oct). *75th Anniv of U.P.U. As Nos.* 114/17 *of Antigua, surch with new values by Waterlow.*

32	2½ a. on 20 c. ultramarine	..		75	1·50
33	3 a. on 30 c. carmine-red	..		1·75	1·50
34	8 a. on 50 c. orange			1·60	1·50
35	1 r. on 1 s. blue	..	..	2·10	2·75
32/5	..	..	..	*Set of* 4	5·75	6·50

(New Currency. 100 cents = 1 shilling)

5 CENTS

(12)

1951 (1 Oct). *Nos. 18 and 20/7 surch with new values, in cents or shillings, as T* 12, *or in one line between bars* (30 c.) *by Waterlow.*

36	5 c. on 1 a. pale blue	..	..	15	40
37	10 c. on 2 a. sepia	..	..	15	45
38	15 c. on 2½ a. deep ultramarine	..	20	1·00
	a. Surch double	..	..	£600	
39	20 c. on 3 a. sepia and carmine	..	25	40
40	30 c. on 8 a. red-orange (R.)	..	25	65
41	50 c. on 8 a. red-orange	..	25	35
42	70 c. on 14 a. sepia and light blue	..	1·75	1·25
43	1 s. on 1 r. emerald-green	..	35	30
44	2 s. on 2 r. deep blue and magenta	..	6·00	2·50
	a. Surch albino	..	..	£350	
45	5 s. on 5 r. red-brown and olive-green	..	16·00	7·00
46	10 s. on 10 r. sepia and violet	..	23·00	10·00
36/46	..	..	..	*Set of* 11	42·00	22·00

ADEN PROTECTORATE STATES

KATHIRI STATE OF SEIYUN

1 Sultan of Seiyun    2 Seiyun

(Recess D.L.R.)

1942 (July–Oct). *Designs as T* 1/2. *Wmk Mult Script CA. T* 1, *perf* 14; *others, perf* 12 × 13 (*vert*) *or* 13 × 12 (*horiz*).

1	½ a. blue-green	..	..	..	15	35
2	¾ a. brown	..	..	..	15	35
3	1 a. blue	..	..	..	20	35
4	1½ a. carmine	..	..	..	30	40
5	2 a. sepia	..	..	..	30	60
6	2½ a. blue	..	..	..	55	1·00
7	3 a. sepia and carmine	..	..	90	1·00
8	8 a. red	..	..	..	40	50
9	1 r. green	..	..	..	1·50	75
10	2 r. blue and purple	..	..	7·00	9·00
11	5 r. brown and green	..	..	17·00	12·00
1/11	..	..	..	*Set of* 11	25·00	23·00
1/11 Perf "Specimen"	..	*Set of* 11	£140	

Designs:—½ to 1 a. Type 1. *Vert as T* 2—2 a. Tarim; 2½ a. Mosque, Seiyun; 1 r. South Gate, Tarim; 5 r. Mosque entrance, Tarim. *Horiz as T* 2—3 a. Fortress, Tarim; 8 a. Mosque, Seiyun; 2 r. A Kathiri house.

VICTORY

ISSUE

8TH JUNE 1946

(10)

1946 (15 Oct). *Victory. No. 4 optd with T* **10**, *and No.* 6 *optd similarly but in four lines, by De La Rue.*

12	1½ a. carmine	..	10	30
13	2½ a. blue (R.)	..	10	10
	a. Opt inverted	..	£375	
12/13 Perf "Specimen"		Set of 2	55·00	

No. 13 is known with surcharge double but the second impression is almost coincident with the first.

1949 (17 Jan). *Royal Silver Wedding. As Nos.* 112/13 *of Antigua.*

14	1½ a. scarlet	..	30	2·00
15	5 r. green	..	12·00	9·00

1949 (10 Oct). *75th Anniv of U.P.U. As Nos.* 114/17 *of Antigua, surch with new values by Waterlow.*

16	2½ a. on 20 c. ultramarine	..	25	50
17	3 a. on 30 c. carmine-red	..	70	65
18	8 a. on 50 c. orange	..	40	75
19	1 r. on 1 s. blue	..	60	90
16/19	..	Set of 4	1·75	2·50

5 CTS

(11)

50 CENTS

(12)

5/-

(13)

1951 (1 Oct). *Currency changed. Nos.* 3 *and* 5/11 *surch as T* **11** (5 c.), **12** (10 c. ("CTS"), 15 c. ("CTS"), 20 c. and 50 c.) *or* 13 (1s. *to* 5s.), *by Waterlow.*

20	5 c. on 1 a. blue (R.)	..	15	20
21	10 c. on 2 a. sepia	..	30	20
22	15 c. on 2½ a. blue	..	15	20
23	20 c. on 3 a. sepia and carmine	..	15	30
24	50 c. on 8 a. red	..	15	20
25	1 s. on 1 r. green	..	20	40
26	2 s. on 2 r. blue and purple	..	2·25	13·00
27	5 s. on 5 r. brown and green	..	12·00	28·00
20/27	..	Set of 8	14·00	38·00

QU'AITI STATE OF SHIHR AND MUKALLA

1 Sultan of Shihr and Mukalla

2 Mukalla Harbour

VICTORY

ISSUE

8TH JUNE

1946

(10)

(Recess D.L.R.)

1942 (July)–**46**. *Wmk Mult Script CA. Designs as T* **1** (½ *to* 1 *a.*) *or T* **2** (*others*). *P* 14 (½ *to* 1 *a.*), 12 × 13 (1½, 2, 3 *a. and* 1 *r.*) *or* 13 × 12 (*others*).

1	½ a. blue-green	..	..	50	40
	a. Olive-green (12.46)	..	..	24·00	35·00
2	¾ a. brown	..	..	50	30
3	1 a. blue	..	..	60	50
4	1½ a. carmine	..	..	70	40
5	2 a. sepia	..	..	70	50
6	2½ a. blue	..	..	40	30
7	3 a. sepia and carmine	..	..	70	30
8	8 a. red	..	..	40	40
9	1 r. green	..	..	1·50	1·25
	a. "A" of "CA" missing from wmk	..	†		
10	2 r. blue and purple	..	10·00	8·00	
11	5 r. brown and green	..	13·00	10·00	
1/11		Set of 11	26·00	20·00	
1/11 Perf "Specimen"		Set of 11	£140		

Designs: *Vert*—2 a. Gateway of Shihr; 3 a. Outpost of Mukalla; 1 r. Du'an. *Horiz*—2½ a. Shibam; 8 a. 'Einat; 2 r. Mosque in Hureidha; 5 r. Meshhed.

1946 (15 Oct). *Victory. No. 4 optd. with T* **10** *and No.* 6 *optd similarly, but in three lines, by De La Rue.*

12	1½ a. carmine	..	10	30
13	2½ a. blue (R.)	..	10	10
12/13 Perf "Specimen"		Set of 2	55·00	

1949 (17 Jan). *Royal Silver Wedding. As Nos.* 112/13 *of Antigua.*

14	1½ a. scarlet	..	50	2·00
15	5 r. green	..	13·00	9·00

1949 (10 Oct). *75th Anniv of U.P.U. As Nos.* 114/17 *of Antigua, surch with new values, but in three lines, by Waterlow.*

16	2½ a. on 20 c. ultramarine	..	20	20
17	3 a. on 30 c. carmine-red	..	85	50
18	8 a. on 50 c. orange	..	55	60
19	1 r. on 1s. blue	..	60	50
	a. Surch omitted	..	£1000	
16/19	..	Set of 4	2·00	1·60

1951 (1 Oct). *Currency changed. Surch with new values in cents or shillings as T* **11** (5 c.), **12** (10 c. ("CTS"), 15 c., 20 c. and 50 c.) *or* 13 (1 s. *to* 5 s.) *of Seiyun, by Waterlow.*

20	5 c. on 1 a. blue (R.)	..	15	15
21	10 c. on 2 a. sepia	..	15	15
22	15 c. on 2½ a. blue	..	15	15
23	20 c. on 3 a. sepia and carmine	..	15	20
	a. Surch double, one albino	..	£170	
24	50 c. on 8 a. red	..	15	40
25	1 s. on 1 r. green	..	30	25
26	2 s. on 2 r. blue and purple	..	4·25	7·00
27	5 s. on 5 r. brown and green	..	7·00	13·00
20/27	..	Set of 8	11·00	19·00

Antigua

1937. 12 pence (d) = 1 shilling; 20 shillings = 1 pound
1951. 100 cents = 1 West Indian dollar

CROWN COLONY

14 King George VI and
Queen Elizabeth

(Des D.L.R.. Recess B.W.)

1937 (12 May). *Coronation. Wmk Mult Script CA. P* 11×11½.
95	**14**	1d. carmine	..	..	50	70
96		1½d. yellow-brown			60	70
97		2½d. blue	..	..	1·75	1·10
95/7		..		*Set of 3*	2·50	2·25
95/7 Perf "Specimen"	..	..		*Set of 3*	50·00	

15 English Harbour   **16** Nelson's Dockyard

(Recess Waterlow)

1938 (15 Nov)–**51**. *T* **15**, **16** *and similar designs. Wmk Mult
Script CA. P* 12½.
98	**15**	½d. green	..	..	20	60
99	**16**	1d. scarlet	..	..	2·75	1·25
		a. Red (8.42 and 11.47)	..		2·50	1·25
100		1½d. chocolate-brown	..		4·50	50
		a. Dull reddish brown (12.43)		..	2·25	1·10
		b. Lake-brown (7.49)			23·00	12·00
101	**15**	2d. grey	..	..	30	50
		a. Slate-grey (6.51)	..		5·00	4·00
102	**16**	2½d. deep ultramarine	..		55	80
103	–	3d. orange	..	..	45	70
104	–	6d. violet	..	..	90	60
105	–	1s. black and brown	..	..	2·75	85
		a. Black and red-brown (7.49)		30·00	9·50
		ab. Frame ptd double, once albino		£2500	
106	–	2s. 6d. brown-purple	..		38·00	7·50
		a. Maroon (8.42)	..		22·00	7·00
107	–	5s. olive-green	..		14·00	7·00
108	**16**	10s. magenta (1.4.48)	..		16·00	25·00
109	–	£1 slate-green (1.4.48)		..	25·00	32·00
98/109				*Set of 12*	75·00	65·00
98/109 Perf "Specimen"	..	..	*Set of 12*	£180	

Designs: *Horiz*—3d., 2s. 6d., £1 Fort James. *Vert*—6d., 1s., 5s.
St. John's Harbour.

17 Houses of Parliament,
London

(Des and recess D.L.R.)

1946 (1 Nov). *Victory. Wmk Mult Script CA. P* 13½×14.
110	**17**	1½d. brown	..	..	..	15	10
111		3d. red-orange	..	..	..	15	30
110/111 Perf "Specimen"	..	..	*Set of 2*	50·00	

18   **19**
King George VI and Queen Elizabeth

(Des and photo Waterlow (T **18**). Design recess; name typo
B.W. (T **19**))

1949 (3 Jan). *Royal Silver Wedding. Wmk Mult Script CA.*
112	**18**	2½d. ultramarine (*p* 14×15)	..	40	90
113	**19**	5s. grey-olive (*p* 11½×11)	..	8·00	5·50

20 Hermes, Globe and   **21** Hemispheres, Jet-
Forms of Transport   powered Vickers Viking
                              Airliner and Steamer

22 Hermes and Globe   **23** U.P.U. Monument

(Recess Waterlow (T **20**, **23**). Designs recess, name typo B.W.
(T **21/2**))

1949 (10 Oct). *75th Anniv of Universal Postal Union. Wmk Mult
Script CA.*
114	**20**	2½d. ultramarine (*p* 13½–14)	..	40	50
115	**21**	3d. orange (*p* 11 × 11½)	..	80	1·10
116	**22**	6d. purple (*p* 11 × 11½)	..	80	1·10
117	**23**	1s. red-brown (*p* 13½–14)	..	80	75
114/17	..	..	..	*Set of 4*	2·50	3·00

(New Currency. 100 cents = 1 West Indian, later Eastern Caribbean, dollar)

24 Arms of
University

25 Princess Alice

(Recess Waterlow)

1951 (16 Feb). *Inauguration of B.W.I. University College. Wmk Mult Script CA. P* 14×14½.

118	**24**	3 c. black and brown	..	..	..	45	40
119	**25**	12 c. black and violet	..	..	..	45	70

Ascension

12 pence (d) = 1 shilling; 20 shillings = 1 pound

DEPENDENCY OF ST. HELENA

1937 (19 May). *Coronation. As Nos. 95/7 of Antigua, but printed by D.L.R. P* 14.

35	1d. green			50	50
36	2d. orange			1·50	40
37	3d. bright blue			1·50	50
35/7			*Set of* 3	3·25	1·25
35/7 Perf "Specimen"			*Set of* 3	£130	

10 The Pier

Long centre bar to "E" in
"GEORGETOWN" (R. 2/3)

"Davit" flaw (R. 5/1) (all
ptgs of 1½d. and 2s. 6d.)

(Recess D.L.R.)

1938 (12 May)–**53**. *Horiz designs as King George V issue, but modified and with portrait of King George VI as in T* **10**. *Wmk Mult Script CA. P* 13½.

38	**3**	½d. black and violet		2·75	90
		a. Long centre bar to E		60·00	
		b. Perf 13. *Black and bluish violet*			
		(17.5.44)		65	1·50
		ba. Long centre bar to E		30·00	

39	–	1d. black and green		40·00	7·50
39a	–	1d. black and yellow-orange (8.7.40)		14·00	9·00
		b. Perf 13 (5.42)		45	60
		c. Perf 14 (17.2.49)		70	16·00
39d	–	1d. black and green, *p* 13 (1.6.49)		30	30
40	**10**	1½d. black and vermilion		2·75	1·40
		a. Davit flaw		£100	
		b. Perf 13 (17.5.44)		85	80
		ba. Davit flaw		65·00	
		c. Perf 14 (17.2.49)		2·75	13·00
		ca. Davit flaw		£110	
40d		1½d. black and rose-carmine, *p* 14 (1.6.49)		55	80
		da. Davit flaw		55·00	
		db. *Black and carmine*		6·00	5·00
		dba. Davit flaw		£140	
		e. Perf 13 (25.2.53)		45	5·50
		ea. Davit flaw		48·00	
41	–	2d. black and red-orange		3·50	1·00
		a. Perf 13 (17.5.44)		80	40
		b. Perf 14 (17.2.49)		3·25	35·00
41c	–	2d. black and scarlet, *p* 14 (1.6.49)		50	75
42	–	3d. black and ultramarine		£100	26·00
42a	–	3d. black and grey (8.7.40)		14·00	90
		b. Perf 13 (17.5.44)		70	80
42c	–	4d. black and ultramarine (8.7.40)		10·00	3·25
		d. Perf 13 (17.5.44)		4·50	3·00
43	–	6d. black and blue		9·00	90
		a. Perf 13 (17.5.44)		9·00	4·25
44	**3**	1s. black and sepia		12·00	1·25
		a. Perf 13 (17.5.44)		4·75	2·00
45	**10**	2s. 6d. black and deep carmine		40·00	7·50
		a. Frame printed double, once albino		£2000	
		b. Davit flaw		£425	
		c. Perf 13 (17.5.44)		35·00	32·00
		ca. Davit flaw		£375	
46	–	5s. black and yellow-brown		£110	7·50
		a. Perf 13 (17.5.44)		48·00	26·00
47	–	10s. black and bright purple		£110	42·00
		a. Perf 13 (17.5.44)		65·00	55·00
38/47a			*Set of* 16	£275	90·00
38/47 Perf "Specimen"			*Set of* 13	£450	

Designs: *Horiz*—½d., 1s. Georgetown; 1d. (Nos. 39/c), 2d., 4d. Green Mountain; 1d. (No. 39d), 6d., 10s. Three Sisters; 3d., 5s. Long Beach.

1946 (21 Oct). *Victory. As Nos. 110/11 of Antigua.*

48	2d. red-orange			40	30
49	4d. blue			40	30
48/9 Perf "Specimen"			*Set of* 2	£140	

1948 (20 Oct). *Royal Silver Wedding. As Nos. 112/13 of Antigua.*

50	3d. black			50	30
51	10s. bright purple			45·00	38·00

1949 (10 Oct). *75th Anniv of Universal Postal Union. As Nos. 114/17 of Antigua.*

52	3d. carmine			1·40	1·00
53	4d. deep blue			3·50	1·10
54	6d. olive			3·75	2·50
55	1s. blue-black			3·75	1·50
52/5			*Set of* 4	11·00	5·50

Australia

12 pence (d) = 1 shilling; 20 shillings = 1 pound

DOMINION

15

40 King George VI and Queen Elizabeth

Dies of 3d.:

Die I   Die Ia   Die II

Die I. The letters "TA" of "POSTAGE" at right are joined by a white flaw; the outline of the chin consists of separate strokes.

No. 168*a* is a preliminary printing made with unsuitable ink and may be detected by the absence of finer details; the King's face appears whitish and the wattles are blank. The greater part of this printing was distributed to the Press with advance notices of the issue.

Die Ia. As Die I, but "T" and "A" have been clearly separated by individual retouches made on the plates.

Die II. A completely new die. "T" and "A" are separate and a continuous line has been added to the chin. The outline of the cheek extends to about 1 mm above the lobe of the King's right ear.

Die III. Differs from Dies I and II in the King's left eyebrow which is shaded downwards from left to right instead of from right to left.

27 Wallaroo

28 Queen Elizabeth **28a**

29

30 King George VI

30a

31 King George VI

32 Koala

33 Merino Ram

Medal flaw
(Pl 2. Right pane R. 2/5)

4 Laughing Kookaburra **35** Platypus

36 Superb Lyrebird

38 Queen Elizabeth

39 King George VI

Line to Kangaroo's ear (Rt pane R. 6/8)

(Des R. A. Harrison (T **28/30**), F. D. Manley (T **27**, **31/6**), H. Barr (T **38/9**), H. Barr and F. D. Manley (T **40**). Eng F. D. Manley and T. C Duffell (T **34**), T. C Duffell (revised lettering for T **28**a, **30**a), F. D. Manley (others). All recess with John Ash, W. C. G. McCracken or "By Authority ..." imprints)

1937–49. *W* **15** (*sideways on* 5d., 9d., 5s. *and* 10s.). *Chalk-surfaced paper* (3d. (*No.* 168), 5s., 10s., £1).

(a) *P* 13½ × 14 (*vert designs*) *or* 14 × 13½ (*horiz*)

164	**27**	½d. orange (3.10.38)	..	.. 2·50	45
165	**28**	1d. emerald-green (10.5.37)	..	40	10
166	**29**	1½d. maroon (20.4.38)	..	.. 9·00	3·00
167	**30**	2d. scarlet (10.5.37)	..	40	10
168	**31**	3d. blue (Die I) (2.8.37)	..	.. 60·00	9·00
		a. "White wattles" (from 1st ptg)	..	£120	70·00
		b. Die Ia	..	£140	6·50
		c. Die II (3.38)	..	60·00	3·25
		ca. *Bright blue* (*ordinary thin paper*)			
		(20.12.38)	..	.. 55·00	2·25
170	**32**	4d. green (1.2.38)	..	.. 14·00	55
171	**33**	5d. purple (1.12.38)	..	.. 2·00	50
172	**34**	6d. purple-brown (2.8.37)	..	.. 23·00	90
173	**35**	9d. chocolate (1.9.38)	..	.. 6·00	90
174	**36**	1s. grey-green (2.8.37)	..	.. 48·00	1·90
175	**31**	1s. 4d. pale magenta (3.10.38)	..	.. 1·50	1·50
		a. *Deep magenta* (1943)	..	.. 3·25	2·00

(b) *P* 13½

176	**38**	5s. claret (1.4.38)	..	.. 14·00	1·25
		a. Thin rough ordinary paper			
		(4.2.48) ..		5·00	2·00
177	**39**	10s. dull purple (1.4.38) (Optd S. £30)	38·00	12·00
		a. Thin rough ordinary paper			
		(11.48)		48·00	28·00
178	**40**	£1 bl-slate (1.11.38) (Optd S. £400)	60·00	30·00
		a. Thin rough ordinary paper			
		(4.4.49) ..	..	85·00	60·00
164/78	..	..	..	*Set of* 14	£250 48·00

(c) *P* 15×14 (*vert designs*) *or* 14×15 (*horiz*) (1d. *and* 2d. *redrawn with background evenly shaded and lettering strengthened*)

179	**27**	½d. orange (28.1.42)	..	55	10
		a. Line to kangaroo's ear	..	10·00	
		b. Coil pair (1942)	..	15·00	17·00
		ba. Coil block of four	..	£130	
180	**28**a	1d. emerald-green (1.8.38) ..	..	2·00	10
181		1d. maroon (10.12.41)	..	1·25	10
		a. Coil pair (1942)	..	12·00	16·00
182	**29**	1½d. maroon (21.11.41)	..	4·50	7·50
183		1½d. emerald-green (10.12.41)	..	1·00	50
184	**30**a	2d. scarlet (11.7.38)	..	2·50	10
		a. Coil pair (10.41)	..	£325	£375
		b. Medal flaw	..	75·00	
		w. Wmk inverted (*from booklets*)	..	4·00	50
185		2d. bright purple (10.12.41)	..	50	60
		a. Coil pair (1942)	..	42·00	48·00
		b. Medal flaw	..	30·00	
		w. Wmk inverted (*from coils*)	..	60·00	20·00
186	**31**	3d. bright blue (Die III) (11.40)	..	45·00	2·25
187		3d. purple-brown (Die III) (10.12.41)	30	10
188	**32**	4d. green (10.42)	..	1·00	10
		w. Wmk inverted	..	.. †	£450
189	**33**	5d. purple (1.46)	..	45	1·50
190	**34**	6d. red-brown (6.42)	..	2·00	10
		a. *Purple-brown* (1944)	..	1·75	10
191	**35**	9d. chocolate (8.43)	..	1·00	20
192	**36**	1s. grey-green (3.41)	..	1·00	10
		w. Wmk inverted	..	£500	£130
179/92	..	..	..	*Set of* 14	55·00 11·00

For unwmkd issue, see Nos. 228/30d.

Thin paper. Nos. 176a, 177a, 178a. In these varieties the watermark is more clearly visible on the back and the design is much less sharp. On early printings of No. 176a the paper appears tinted.

SPECIAL COIL PERFORATION. This special perforation of large and small holes on the narrow sides of the stamps was introduced after 1939 for stamps issued in coils and was intended to facilitate separation. Where they exist they are listed as "Coil pairs".

The following with "special coil" perforation were placed on sale in *sheets*: Nos. 179, 205, 222a (1952), 228, 230, 237, 262 (1953), 309, 311, and 314. These are listed as "Coil blocks of four".

Coils with "normal" perforations also exist for Nos. 180 and 184.

41 "Governor Phillip at   "Tail" flaw
Sydney Cove" (J. Allcot)   (Left pane R. 7/1)

(Des and eng E. Broad and F. D. Manley. Recess J. Ash)

1937 (1 Oct). *150th Anniv of Foundation of New South Wales.* W **15**. *P* 13½ × 14.

193	**41**	2d. scarlet	..	..	..	.. 2·25	15
		a. "Tail" flaw	..	..	..	£200	50·00
194		3d. bright blue	..	..	..	7·50	2·75
195		9d. purple	..	..	..	15·00	9·50
193/5	..	..	..	..	*Set of* 3	22·00	11·00

42 A.I.F. and Nurse

(Des and eng F. D. Manley from drawing by Virgil Reilly. Recess W. C. G. McCracken)

1940 (15 July). *Australian Imperial Forces.* W **15** (*sideways*) *P* 14 × 13½.

196	**42**	1d. green	..	..	..	1·75	1·25
197		2d. scarlet	..	..	..	1·75	40
198		3d. blue ..	..	..	..	12·00	7·50
199		6d. brown-purple	..	..	..	22·00	13·00
196/9	..	..	..	..	*Set of* 4	35·00	20·00

 ≡ ≡

(43)   (44)   (45)

(Opts designed by F. D. Manley)

1941 (10 Dec). Nos. 184, 186 *and* 171 *surch with T* **43/5**.

200	**40**b	2½d. on 2d. scarlet (V.)	..	..	75	40
		a. Pair, one without surcharge	..	£3250	
		b. Medal flaw	..	..	80·00	
201	**31**	3½d. on 3d. bright blue (Y. on Black)	1·00	1·50
202	**33**	5½d. on 5d. purple (V.)	..	..	4·50	50
200/2		..	..	*Set of* 3	5·50	5·50

Nos 200/2 were prepared in connection with the imposition of a ½d. "war tax" increase on most postage rates.

One sheet of the 2½d on 2d. was discovered showing the surcharge omitted on R.1/4 and R.1/5.

46 Queen Elizabeth   46a   47 King George
                                          VI

53 Star and Wreath   56 Sir Thomas Mitchell
                                and Queensland

48 King George   49 King George VI   50 Emu
   VI

(Des F. D. Manley. Eng F. D. Manley and T. C. Duffell (T **46**/a)
or F. D. Manley (others))

1942–48. *Recess.* W **15**. *P* 15×14.
203	46	1d. brown-purple (2.1.43)	..	30	10
		a. Coil pair (1944)	..	17·00	20·00
204	46a	1½d. green (1.12.42) ..		30	10
205	47	2d. bright purple (4.12.44) ..		45	40
		b. Coil pair (4.48) ..	..	85·00	90·00
		ba. Coil block of four	..	£800	
206	48	2½d. scarlet (7.1.42)	..	30	10
		a. Imperf (pair)* ..	..	£2500	
		w. Wmk inverted *(from booklets)*	..	2·75	30
207	49	3½d. bright blue (3.42)	..	30	10
		a. *Deep blue*	..	50	10
208	50	5½d. slate-blue (12.2.42)	..	65	10
203/8		..	*Set of 6*	2·10	50

*No. 206a comes in horizontal pair with the right-hand stamp
completely imperforate and the left-hand stamp imperforate at
right only.
Coils with normal perforations exist for 1d.
For stamps as Nos. 204/5 but without watermark see Nos.
229/30.

52 Duke and Duchess of Gloucester

(Des F. D. Manley. Eng F. D. Manley and T. C. Duffell. Recess)
1945 (19 Feb). *Arrival of Duke and Duchess of Gloucester in
Australia.* W **15**. *P* 14½.
209	52	2½d. lake ..	..	10	10
210		3½d. ultramarine	..	15	40
211		5½d. indigo	..	20	40
209/11		..	*Set of 3*	40	75

A   B

1945 (24 Dec). *Kangaroo type, as No. 134, but re-engraved as
B.* W **15**. *P* 12.
212	1	2s. maroon	..	3·50	4·00
		w. Wmk inverted	..	†	£750

No. 134 has two background lines between the value circle and
"TWO SHILLINGS"; No. 212 has only one line in this position.
There are also differences in the shape of the letters.

(Des F. D. Manley (2½d.), F. D. Manley and G. Lissenden (3½d.),
G. Lissenden (5½d.). Eng F. D. Manley. Recess)

1946 (18 Feb). *Victory Commemoration. T* **53** *and similar designs.*
W **15** (*sideways on* 5½d.). *P* 14½.
213		2½d. scarlet	..	..	10	10
214		3½d. blue	..	..	25	75
215		5½d. green	..	..	30	50
213/15		..	..	*Set of 3*	60	1·25

Designs: *Horiz*—3½d. Flag and dove. *Vert*—5½d. Angel.
For these designs re-issued in 1995 with face values in
decimal currency see Nos. 1542/4.

(Des F. D. Manley. Eng F. D. Manley and T. C. Duffell. Recess)
1946 (14 Oct). *Centenary of Mitchell's Exploration of Central
Queensland.* W **15**. *P* 14½.
216	56	2½d. scarlet	..	..	10	10
217		3½d. blue ..	..	..	25	60
218		1s. grey-olive	..	..	30	25
216/18		..	..	*Set of 3*	60	80

57 Lt. John   58 Steel Foundry   59 Coal Carrier Cranes
Shortland R.N.

(Des and eng G. Lissenden (5½d.), F. D. Manley (others).
Recess)
1947 (8 Sept). *150th Anniv of City of Newcastle, New South
Wales.* W **15** (*sideways on* 3½d.). *P* 14½ *or* 15×14 (2½d.).
219	57	2½d. lake	..	..	10	10
220	58	3½d. blue	..	..	25	55
221	59	5½d. green	..	..	25	35
219/21		..	..	*Set of 3*	55	85

The following items are understood to have been the
subject of unauthorised leakages from the Commonwealth
Note and Stamp Printing Branch and are therefore not
listed by us.
It is certain that none of this material was distributed to
post offices for issue to the public.
Imperforate all round. 1d. Princess Elizabeth; 1½d.
Queen; 3d. King; 4d. Koala; 6d. Kookaburra; 9d. Platypus; 1s. Lyrebird (small) (also imperf three sides); 1s. 6d.
Air Mail (Type **22**); 2½d. Mitchell; 2½d. Newcastle (also
imperf three sides or imperf vertically).
Also 2½d. Peace, unwatermarked; 2½d. King, *tête-
bêche*; 3½d. Newcastle, in dull ultramarine; 2½d. King on
"toned" paper.

60 Queen Elizabeth II when Princess

(Des R. A. Harrison. Eng. F. D. Manley. Recess)

1947 (20 Nov)–**52.**   *Marriage of Princess Elizabeth. P* 14×15.

(a) W **15** *(sideways)*

222	**60**	1d. purple	..	..	15	10

(b) No wmk

222a	**60**	1d. purple (8.48)	..	..	10	10
		b. Coil pair (1.50)	..	..	2·00	4·50
		c. Coil block of four (9.52)	..	4·25	

61 Hereford Bull   **61a** Hermes and Globe

62 Aboriginal Art   **62a** Commonwealth
Coat of Arms

(Des G. Sellheim (T **62**), F. D. Manley (others). Eng G. Lissenden
(T **62**), F. D. Manley (1s. 3d., 1s. 6d., 5s.), F. D. Manley and R.
J. Becker (10s., £1, £2). Recess)

1948 (16 Feb)–**56.**   *(a)* W **15** *(sideways). P* 14½

223	**61**	1s. 3d. brown-purple	..	1·75	85
223a	**61a**	1s. 6d. blackish brown (1.9.49)	..	1·25	10
224	**62**	2s. chocolate	..	..	2·00	10

(b) W **15.** *P* 14½×13½

224a	**62a**	5s. claret (11.4.49)	..	3·75	20
		ab. Thin paper (1951)	..	22·00	1·00
224b		10s. purple (3.10.49)	..	20·00	50
224c		£1 blue (28.11.49)	..	35·00	3·25
224d		£2 green (16.1.50)	..	£110	14·00
224b/d	Optd "Specimen"	..	*Set of 3*	£150	

(c) No wmk. P 14½

224e	**61a**	1s. 6d. blackish brown (6.12.56)	..	16·00	1·25
224f	**62**	2s. chocolate (21.7.56)	..	16·00	50
223/4f		..	..	*Set of 9*	£180	19·00

No. 224ab is an emergency printing on white Harrison paper
instead of the toned paper used for No. 224a.

63 William J.   **64** F. von Mueller   **65** Boy Scout
Farrer

(Des and eng F. D. Manley. Recess)

1948 (12 July).   *William J. Farrer (wheat research) Commem-*
oration. W **15.** *P* 15×14.

225	**63**	2½d. scarlet	..	..	10	10

(Des and eng F. D. Manley. Recess)

1948 (13 Sept).   *Sir Ferdinand von Mueller (botanist) Comm-*
emoration. W **15.** *P* 15×14.

226	**64**	2½d. lake	..	..	10	10

(Des and eng F. D. Manley. Recess)

1948 (15 Nov).   *Pan-Pacific Scout Jamboree, Wonga Park.* W **15**
(sideways). P 14 × 15.

227	**65**	2½d. lake	..	..	10	10

See also No. 254.

Sky retouch (normally unshaded near hill) (Rt pane
R. 6/8) (No. 228a retouched in 1951)

"Green mist" retouch. A
large area to the left of
the bird's feathers is
recut (upper plate left
pane R. 9/3)

1948–56.   *No wmk. P* 15×14 *or* 14×15 (9d.).

228	**27**	½d. orange (15.9.49)	..	20	10
		a. Line to kangaroo's ear	..	6·00	
		b. Sky retouch	..	17·00	
		c. Coil pair (1950)	..	75	2·25
		ca. Line to kangaroo's ear	..	25·00	
		cb. Sky retouch (in pair)	..	90·00	
		d. Coil block of four (1953)	..	2·50	
229	**46a**	1½d. green (17.8.49)	..	1·25	85
230	**47**	2d. bright purple (1.49)	..	70	70
		aa. Coil pair	..	3·00	5·50
230a	**32**	4d. green (18.8.56)	..	2·00	70
230b	**34**	6d. purple-brown (18.8.56)	..	4·25	50
230c	**35**	9d. chocolate (13.12.56)	..	20·00	2·50
230d	**36**	1s. grey green (13.12.56)	..	8·00	90
		da. "Green mist" retouch	..	£550	
228/30d		..	..	*Set of 7*	32·00	5·75

 AUSTRALIA   3½

66 "Henry Lawson"   **67** Mounted Postman
(Sir Lionel Lindsay)   and Convair CV 240
Aircraft

(Des F. D. Manley. Eng. E. R. M. Jones. Recess)

1949 (17 June).   *Henry Lawson (poet) Commemoratio*
P 15×14.

231	**66**	2½d. maroon	..	..	15

(Des Sir Daryl Lindsay and F. D. Manley. Eng F. D. Manley. Recess)

1949 (10 Oct). *75th Anniv of Founding of U.P.U. P* 15 × 14.

232 67 3½d. ultramarine 20 30

| 68 | Lord Forrest of Bunbury | 69 | Queen Elizabeth | 70 | King George VI |

(Des and eng F. D. Manley. Recess)

1949 (28 Nov). *Lord Forrest of Bunbury (explorer and politician) Commemoration. W* 15. *P* 15×14.

233 68 2½d. lake 15 10

(Des and eng F. D. Manley. Recess)

1950 (12 Apr)–53. *P* 15×14. (*a*) W 15

234 70 2½d. scarlet (12.4.50) 10 10
235   3d. scarlet (28.2.51) 15 10
        aa. Coil pair (4.51) .. .. .. 17·00 19·00

(*b*) No wmk

236 69 1½d. green (19.6.50) 15 10
237   2d. yellow-green (28.3.51) 15 10
        a. Coil pair .. .. .. 5·00 7·50
        b. Coil block of four (8.53) .. .. 10·00
237c 70 2½d. purple-brown (23.5.51) 15 15
237d   3d. grey-green (14.11.51) 15 10
        da. Coil pair (12.51) .. .. .. 24·00 30·00
234/7d .. .. *Set of 6* 80 40

On 14 October 1951 No. 235 was placed on sale in sheets of 144 originally intended for use in stamp booklets. These sheets contain 3 panes of 48 (16×3) with horizontal gutter margin between.

71 Aborigine

72
Reproductions of First Stamps of New South Wales and Victoria

73

(Des and eng F. D. Manley. Recess)

1950 (14 Aug). W 15. *P* 15×14.

238 71 8½d. brown 15 45

For T **71** in a larger size, see Nos. 253/*b*.

(Des and eng G. Lissenden (T **72**), E. R. M. Jones (T **73**). Recess)

1950 (27 Sept). *Centenary of First Adhesive Postage Stamps in Australia. P* 15×14.

239 72 2½d. maroon 10 10
        a. Horiz pair. Nos. 239/40 .. .. 20 55
240 73 2½d. maroon 10 10

Nos. 239/40 were printed alternately in vertical columns throughout the sheet.

74 Sir Edmund Barton

75 Sir Henry Parkes

| 76 "Opening First Federal Parliament" (T. Roberts) | 77 Federal Parliament House, Canberra |

(Des and eng F. D. Manley. Recess)

1951 (1 May). *50th Anniv of Commonwealth of Australia. P* 15×14.

241 74 3d. lake 30 10
        a. Horiz pair. Nos. 241/2 .. .. 1·75 2·00
242 75 3d. lake 30 10
243 76 5½d. blue .. .. 20 1·50
244 77 1s. 6d. purple-brown 35 50
241/4 .. .. *Set of 4* 2·00 2·00

Nos. 241/2 are printed alternately in vertical columns throughout the sheet.

| 78 | E. H. Hargraves | 79 | C. J. Latrobe |

(Des and eng F. D. Manley. Recess)

1951 (2 July). *Centenaries of Discovery of Gold in Australia and of Responsible Government in Victoria. P* 15×14.

245 78 3d. maroon 30 10
        a. Horiz pair. Nos. 245/6 .. .. 70 95
246 79 3d. maroon 30 10

Nos. 245/6 were printed alternately in vertical columns throughout the sheet.

| 80 | 81 King George VI | 82 |

(Des and eng F. D. Manley. Recess)

1951–52. W 15 (*sideways on* 1s. 0½d.). *P* 14½ (1s. 0½d.) *or* 15×14 (*others*).

247 80 3½d. brown-purple (28.11.51) 10 10
        a. Imperf between (horiz pair) .. £5500
248   4½d. scarlet (20.2.52) 15 60
249   6½d. brown (20.2.52) 15 55
250   6½d. emerald-green (9.4.52) 10 15
251 81 7½d. blue (31.10.51) 15 45
        a. Imperf three sides (vert pr) .. £7000
252 82 1s. 0½d. indigo (19.3.52) 35 30
247/52 .. .. *Set of 6* 90 1·75

No. 251a occurs on the left-hand vertical row of one sheet.

(Des and eng F. D. Manley. Recess.)

1952 (19 Mar)–65. *P* 14½. (*a*) W 15 (*sideways**)

253   2s. 6d. deep brown .. .. 1·50 35
        aw. Wmk Crown to left of C of A .. † £600

(*b*) No wmk

253b   2s. 6d. deep brown (30.1.57) .. .. 5·00 45
        ba. Sepia (10.65) .. .. .. 12·00 12·00

Design:—2s. 6d. As T **71** but larger (21×25½ *mm*).

*The normal sideways watermark on No. 253 shows Crown to right of C of A, *as seen from the back of the stamp.*

No. 253ba was an emergency printing and can easily be distinguished from No. 253b as it is on white Harrison paper, No. 253b being on toned paper.

(Des and eng F. D. Manley. Recess)

1952 (19 Nov).   *Pan-Pacific Scout Jamboree, Greystanes. As T* **65**, *but inscr* "1952–53". *W* **15** (*sideways*). *P* 14 × 15.
254   3½d. brown-lake   10   10

STAMP BOOKLETS

1938 (Dec).   *Black on green cover with Commonwealth Savings Bank advertisement on front inscr* "WHEREVER THERE IS A MONEY ORDER POST OFFICE".
SB27   2s. booklet containing twelve 2d. (No. 184) in
        blocks of 6   ..   ..   £350
    a. With waxed interleaves £450
    b. Black on buff cover £400

1942 (Aug).   *Black on buff cover, size* 73×47½ *mm.*
SB28   2s. 6d. booklet containing twelve 2½d. (No. 206)
        in blocks of 6, upright within the booklet   ..   £110
    a. With waxed interleaves £200

1949 (Sept).   *Black on buff cover, size* 79½×42½ *mm including figure of Hermes.*
SB29   2s. 6d. booklet containing twelve 2½d. (No. 206)
        in blocks of 6, sideways within the booklet   80·00

B 1

1952 (24 June).   *Vermilion and deep blue on green cover as Type* B **1**.
SB30   3s. 6d. booklet containing twelve 3½d. (No. 247)
        in blocks of 6   ..   ..   12·00
    a. With waxed interleaves   ..   ..   85·00

POSTAGE DUE STAMPS

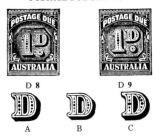

D 8   D 9

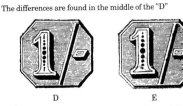

A   B   C

The differences are found in the middle of the "D"

D   E

Type E. Larger "1" with only three background lines above; hyphen more upright.

(Frame recess. Value typo J. Ash)

1938–39.   *W* **15**. *P* 14½×14.

D112 D **8**	½d. carmine and green (A) (1939)	..	3·75	2·50
D113	1d. carmine and green (A)	..	9·00	30
D114	2d. carmine and green (A)	..	9·00	1·00
D115	3d. carmine and green (B)	..	26·00	13·00
D116	4d. carmine and green (A)	..	12·00	30
D117	6d. carmine and green (A)	..	65·00	38·00
D118	1s. carmine and green (D)	..	60·00	12·00
D112/18	..	..	..	*Set of* 7	£170	60·00

Shades exist.

1946–57.   *Redrawn as Type* C *and* E (1s.). *W* **15**. *P* 14½ × 14.

D119 D **9**	½d. carmine and green (9.56)	..	85	3·00
D120	1d. carmine and green (11.1.47)	..	90	80
D121	2d. carmine and green (9.46)	..	4·50	95
D122	3d. carmine and green (25.9.46)	..	6·00	95
D123	4d. carmine and green (11.52)	..	8·50	1·75
D124	5d. carmine and green (12.48)	..	11·00	2·75
D125	6d. carmine and green (9.47)	..	10·00	1·50
D126	7d. carmine and green (26.8.53)	..	4·25	8·50
D127	8d. carmine and green (24.4.57)	..	10·00	25·00
D128	1s. carmine and green (9.47)	..	18·00	1·60
D119/28	..	..	..	*Set of* 10	65·00	42·00

There are many shades in this issue.

BRITISH COMMONWEALTH OCCUPATION FORCE (JAPAN)

Nos. J1/7 were used by the Australian forces occupying Japan after the Second World War. Initially their military post offices supplied unoverprinted Australian stamps, but it was decided to introduce the overprinted issue to prevent currency speculation.

B.C.O.F.
JAPAN
1946

(1)

B.C.O.F.
JAPAN
1946

(2)

Ɔ.F.Ɔ.F.

1946   AN AN

Wrong fount "6"   Normal   Narrow "N"
(left pane R. 9/4)   (right pane
                                       R. 1/8)

1946 (11 Oct)–**48.**   *Stamps of Australia optd as T* **1** (1d., 3d.) o〳 *T* **2** (*others*) *at Hiroshima Printing Co, Japan.*

J1 **27**	½d. orange (No. 179)	..	..	2·75	4·2〳
	a. Wrong fount "6"	..		50·00	60·0〳
	b. Narrow "N" ..	..		50·00	60·0〳
	c. Stop after "JAPAN" (right pane R.5/5)	50·00	60·0〳
J2 **46**	1d. brown-purple (No. 203)	..		2·25	1·5〳
	a. Blue-black overprint	..		60·00	95·C
J3 **31**	3d. purple-brown (No. 187)	..		1·75	1·〳
	a. Opt double	..	..		£350
J4 **34**	6d. purple-brown (No. 189a) (8.5.47)	..	14·00	9·C
	a. Wrong fount "6"	..	..		£150	£1〳
	b. Stop after "JAPAN" (right pane R. 5/5)	..	£150	£1〳
	c. Narrow "N" ..	..	..		£150	£1〳
J5 **36**	1s. grey-green (No. 191) (8.5.47)	..	14·00	10·〳
	a. Wrong fount "6"	..	..		£170	£1〳
	b. Stop after "JAPAN" (right pane R. 5/5)	..	£170	£1〳
	c. Narrow "N" ..	..	..		£170	£1〳
J6 **1**	2s. maroon (No. 212) (8.5.47)	..	42·00	45·〳
J7 **38**	5s. claret (No. 176) (8.5.47)	..	£120	£1〳
	a. Thin rough paper (No. 176a) (1948)	..	£130	£1〳
J1/7	..	..	..	*Set of* 7	£170	£1〳

The ½d., 1d. and 3d. values were first issued on 11 October 19〳 and withdrawn two days later, but were re-issued together with 〳 other values on 8 May 1947.

The following values with T **2** in the colours given were fr〳 proof sheets which, however, were used for postage: ½d. (re〳 1d. (red or black) and 3d. (gold, red or black). (*Prices for bl〳 opts* £100, *each, and for red or gold from* £300 *each, all un*)

The use of B.C.O.F. stamps ceased on 12 February 1949.

NAURU

AUSTRALIAN MANDATE

4 *Century* (freighter)   **6**

(Des R. A. Harrison. Eng T. S. Harrison. Recess Note Printing Branch of the Treasury, Melbourne and from 1926 by the Commonwealth Bank of Australia)

1924–48. *T* **4.** *No wmk. P* 11.
I. Rough surfaced, greyish paper (1924–34).
II. Shiny surfaced, white paper (1937–48).

				I		II	
26	¹/₂d. chestnut	..	..	1·00	2·75	8·00	13·00
	a. Perf 14 (1947)	..		†		1·40	8·50
27	1d. green	..	..	2·50	2·75	2·50	3·00
28	1¹/₂d. scarlet	..		3·00	3·75	90	1·50
29	2d. orange	..		3·00	8·00	1·75	8·00
30	2¹/₂d. slate-blue			4·25	17·00	†	
30a	2¹/₂d. greenish blue (1934)		4·25	12·00	†	
30b	2¹/₂d. dull blue (1948)			†		1·50	3·75
	ba. Imperf between (vert pair)	..	..	†	£4000	£4000
	bb. Imperf between (horiz pair)	..	..	†	£4000	£4000
31	3d. pale blue	..		2·50	10·00	†	
31a	3d. greenish grey (1947)	..		†	2·00	9·00
32	4d. olive-green	..		4·50	13·00	4·25	9·50
33	5d. brown	..		2·75	6·50	3·50	4·00
34	6d. dull violet	..		3·25	12·00	3·25	4·50
35	9d. olive-brown	..		7·50	19·00	7·50	20·00
36	1s. brown-lake	..		6·00	13·00	5·50	2·75
37	2s. 6d. grey-green	..		26·00	45·00	25·00	35·00
38	5s. claret	..		50·00	90·00	35·00	50·00
39	10s. yellow	..		£100	£140	£100	£110
26I/39I	..	..	*Set of* 14	£190	£350	†	
26II/39II	..	..	*Set of* 14	£170	£250		

(Recess John Ash, Melbourne)

1937 (10 May). *Coronation. P* 11.

44	**6**	1¹/₂d. scarlet	..	..	..	..	45	80
45		2d. orange	..	..	..	..	45	1·25
46		2¹/₂d. blue	..	..	..	..	45	40
47		1s. purple	..	..	..	..	1·10	90
44/7	..		..	..	*Set of* 4	2·25	3·00

Japanese forces invaded Nauru on 26 August 1942 and virtually all the inhabitants were removed to Truk in the Caroline Islands.

The Australian army liberated Nauru on 13 September 1945. After an initial period without stamps Australian issues were supplied during October 1945 and were used from Nauru until further supplies of Nos. 26/39 became available. The deportees did not return until early in 1946.

NEW GUINEA

AUSTRALIAN MANDATE

16 Bulolo Goldfields   **18**

(Recess John Ash, Melbourne)

1937 (18 May). *Coronation. P* 11.

208	**18**	2d. scarlet	..	..	..	..	50	30
209		3d. blue	..	..	..	..	80	45
210		5d. green	..	..	..	..	50	45
		a. Red-entry (design completely duplicated) (Pl 2a R. 5/2)	..	..	65·00	80·00
211		1s. purple	..	..	..		1·25	35
208/11	..		..	..	*Set of* 4	2·75	1·40

(Recess John Ash, Melbourne)

1939 (1 Mar). *Air. Inscr* "AIR MAIL POSTAGE" *at foot. P* 11.

212	**16**	¹/₂d. orange	..	..	..	1·75	4·25
213		1d. green	..	..	..	3·25	3·50
214		1¹/₂d. claret	..	..	..	1·75	6·50
215		2d. vermilion	..	..	7·00	3·00
216		3d. blue	..	..	..	9·00	15·00
217		4d. yellow-olive	..	..	7·00	7·50
218		5d. deep green	..	..	6·00	2·25
219		6d. bistre-brown	..	..	15·00	12·00
220		9d. violet	..	..	..	15·00	19·00
221		1s. pale blue-green	..	..	16·00	17·00
222		2s. dull lake	..	..	48·00	42·00
223		5s. olive-brown	..	..	£100	90·00
224		10s. pink	..	..	..	£300	£200
225		£1 olive-green	..	..	£100	£110
212/25		..	..	..	*Set of* 14	£550	£475

Civil Administration in New Guinea was suspended in 1942, following the Japanese invasion.

Various New Guinea stamps exist overprinted with an anchor and three Japanese characters in a style similar to the Japanese Naval Control Area overprints found on the stamps of Netherlands Indies. These overprints on New Guinea are bogus and are believed to have originated in Japan during 1947.

On resumption, after the Japanese defeat in 1945, Australian stamps were used until the appearance of the issue for the combined territories of Papua & New Guinea.

NORFOLK ISLAND

1 Ball Bay

(Recess Note Ptg Branch, Commonwealth Bank)

1947 (10 June)–59. *Toned paper. P* 14.

1	**1**	¹/₂d. orange	..	..	..	35	60
		a. White paper (11.56)	..	..	1·50	4·00
2		1d. bright violet	..	..	50	60
		a. White paper (11.56)	..	..	6·50	16·00
3		1¹/₂d. emerald-green	..	..	50	70
		a. White paper (11.56)	..	..	10·00	23·00
4		2d. reddish violet	..	..	55	40
		a. White paper (11.56)	..	..	£100	£130
5		2¹/₂d. scarlet	..	..	..	80	30
6		3d. chestnut	..	..	..	70	70
6a		3d. emerald-green (*white paper*) (6.7.59)	15·00	5·50
7		4d. claret	..	..	..	90	40
8		5¹/₂d. indigo	..	..	..	70	30
9		6d. purple-brown	..	..	70	30
10		9d. magenta	..	..	..	1·25	40
11		1s. grey-green	..	..	..	70	40
12		2s. yellow-bistre	..	..	2·00	1·00
12a		2s. deep blue (*white paper*) (6.7.59)	24·00	6·50
1/12a		..	..	..	*Set of* 14	45·00	16·00

Stamps of T **1**, perf 11, or in different colours, perf 11, are printer's waste which leaked from the Note Ptg Branch. They were never distributed to post offices for sale to the public.

PAPUA

37 Natives poling Rafts

35	**36** Port Moresby

(Recess J. Ash)

(Recess J. Ash)

1937 (14 May). *Coronation. P* 11.

154	**35**	1d. green					70	15
155		2d. scarlet					70	20
156		3d. blue . .					70	30
157		5d. purple			. .		70	80
154/7 . .		. .	. .	. .	. .	*Set of* 4	2·50	1·25

Some covers franked with these stamps and posted on 2 June 1937 were postmarked 2 April 1937 in error.

(Recess J. Ash)

1938 (6 Sept). *Air. 50th Anniv of Declaration of British Possession. P* 11.

158	**36**	2d. rose-red		. .		. .	3·75	2·25
159		3d. bright blue . .		. .		. .	3·75	2·25
160		5d. green		. .		. .	3·75	3·25
161		8d. brown-lake . .		. .		. .	11·00	14·00
162		1s. mauve		. .		. .	30·00	15·00
158/62		. .	. .	. .		*Set of* 5	48·00	32·00

1939 (6 Sept). *Air. P* 11.

163	**37**	2d. rose-red	. .	. .	. .	. .	7·00	3·75
164		3d. bright blue . .		. .	. .	. .	7·00	6·50
165		5d. green		. .	. .	. .	10·00	1·50
166		8d. brown-lake . .		. .	. .	. .	11·00	2·50
167		1s. mauve		. .	. .	. .	13·00	6·00

(Recess W. C. G. McCracken)

1941 (2 Jan). *Air. P* 11½.

168	**37**	1s. 6d. olive-green		. .	. .	45·00	32·00
163/168		. .	. .	. .	*Set of* 6	85·00	45·00

Civil Administration, in Papua, was suspended in 1942; on resumption, after the Japanese defeat in 1945, Australian stamps were used until the appearance of the issue of the combined territories of Papua & New Guinea.

Bahamas

12 pence (d) = 1 shilling; 20 shillings = 1 pound

CROWN COLONY

18

(Recess B.W.)

1931 (14 July)—**46.** *Wmk Mult Script CA. P* 12.

131	**18**	2s. slate-purple and deep ultramarine		..	20·00	22·00
		a. Slate-purple and indigo (9.42)	..		50·00	35·00
		b. Brownish black and indigo (13.4.43)			4·00	2·00
		c. Brownish black and steel-blue (6.44)		7·00	1·25
132		3s. slate-purple and myrtle-green		..	28·00	24·00
		a. Brownish black and green (13.4.43)		6·00	2·00
		b. Brownish blk & myrtle-grn (1.10.46)	3·00	2·00

131/2 Perf "Specimen" .. .. *Set of 2* 70·00

Most of the stamps from the September 1942 printing (No. 131a and further stocks of the 3s. similar to No. 132) were used for the 1942 "LANDFALL" overprints

1937 (12 May). *Coronation. As Nos. 95/7 of Antigua, but printed by D.L.R. P* 14.

146	½d. green	..	..	..	..	15	15
147	1½d. yellow-brown	..	..	..	30	45
148	2½d. bright blue	..	..	..	50	75
146/8 ..				*Set of 3*	85	1·25
146/8 Perf "Specimen"	..	..	*Set of 3* 60·00		

20 King George VI

Short "T" in "TWO"
(right pane R. 3/6)
(Retouched on No. 152c,
although bottom of letter
is still pointed)

(Typo D.L.R.)

1938 (11 Mar)—**52.** *Wmk Mult Script CA. Chalk-surfaced paper*
(1s. to £1). *P* 14.

149	**20**	½d. green	..	..	15	60
		a. Elongated "E"	..	..	28·00	
		b. Bluish green (11.9.42)	..	1·25	1·00
		ba. Elongated "E"	..	..	65·00	
		c. Myrtle-green (11.12.46)	..	4·00	4·00
		ca. Elongated "E"	..	..	£120	
149d		½d. brown-purple (18.2.52)	..	75	2·50
		da. Error. Crown missing	..	£2750	
		db. Error. St. Edward's Crown	£1700	
		dc. Elongated "E"	..	..	55·00	
150		1d. carmine	..	..	8·50	4·75
150a		1d. olive-grey (17.9.41)	..	3·00	3·00
		ab. Pale slate (11.9.42)	..	50	50
151		1½d. red-brown (19.4.38)	..	1·25	1·00
		a. Pale red-brown (19.4.48)	..	3·25	2·00
152		2d. pale slate (19.4.38)	..	18·00	7·00
		a. Short "T"	..	..	£325	

152b	**20**	2d. scarlet (17.9.41)	..	..	..	75	55
		ba. Short "T"	..	..	..	75·00	
		bb. "TWO PENCE" printed double	..	† £2750	
		bc. Dull rose-red (19.4.48)	..	2·00	2·00
152c		2d. green (1.5.51)	..	..	40	80
153		2½d. ultramarine	..	..	3·25	2·00
153a		2½d. violet (1.7.43)	..	..	1·25	70
		ab. "2½ PENNY" printed double	..	£2500	
154		3d. violet (19.4.38)	..	..	16·00	5·00
154a		3d. blue (4.43)	..	..	60	90
		ab. Bright ultramarine (19.4.48)	3·50	3·00
154b		3d. scarlet (1.2.52)	..	..	50	2·75
154c		10d. yellow-orange (18.11.46)	..	2·00	20
155		1s. grey-black and carmine (*thick paper*) (15.9.38) ..		12·00	4·50
		a. Brownish grey and scarlet (4.42)	£200	42·00
		b. Ordinary paper. Black and carmine (9.42) ..		15·00	5·50
		c. Ordinary paper. Grey-black and bright crimson (6.3.44) ..		7·00	50
		d. Pale brownish grey and crimson (19.4.48) ..	..	7·00	65
156		5s. lilac & blue (*thick paper*) (19.4.38)	£170	£100
		a. Reddish lilac and blue (4.42) ..		£850	£350
		b. Ordinary paper. Purple & bl (9.42)	25·00	9·50
		c. Ordinary paper. Dull mauve and deep blue (11.46) ..		60·00	24·00
		d. Brown-purple & dp brt bl (19.4.48)	25·00	8·00
		e. Red-purple & dp bright blue (8.51)	23·00	9·00
157		£1 deep grey-green and black (*thick paper*) (15.9.38) ..		£250	£140
		a. Ordinary paper. Blue-green and black (13.4.43) ..		60·00	42·00
		b. Ordinary paper. Grey-green and black (3.44) ..		80·00	50·00

149/57a .. .. *Set of 17* £130 65·00
149/57 Perf "Specimen" .. *Set of 14* £425

Nos. 149/50a exist in coils, constructed from normal sheets.

No. 149db occurs on a row in the watermark in which the crowns and letters "CA" alternate.

The thick chalk-surfaced paper, used for the initial printing of the 1s., 5s. and £1, was usually toned and had streaky gum. The April 1942 printing for the 1s. and 5s., which was mostly used for the "LANDFALL" overprints, was on thin, white chalk-surfaced paper with clear gum. Printings of the three values between September 1942 and November 1946 were on a thick, smooth, opaque ordinary paper.

21 Sea Garden, Nassau   **22** Fort Charlotte

23 Greater Flamingos in Flight   **(24)**

(Recess Waterlow)

1938 (1 July). *Wmk Mult Script CA. P* 12½.

158	**21**	4d. light blue and red-orange ..	..	1·00	60
159	**22**	6d. olive-green and light blue ..	..	60	60
160	**23**	8d. ultramarine and scarlet ..	..	5·00	1·75
158/60		..	..	..	*Set of 3*	6·00	2·75
158/60 Perf "Specimen"	..	..	*Set of 3* £100		

1940 (28 Nov). *No.* 153 *surcharged with T* 24 *by* The Nassau
Guardian.
161 **20** 3d. on 2¹/₂d. blue 65 40

**1 4 9 2
LANDFALL
OF
COLUMBUS
1 9 4 2**

(25)

"RENCE" flaw (Right
pane R. 9/3. Later
corrected so that it does
not occur on No. 154*a*)

1942 (12 Oct). *450th Anniv of Landing of Columbus in New
World. Optd as T* 25 *by* The Nassau Guardian.
162 **20** ¹/₂d. bluish green 30 60
        a. Elongated "E" .. .. . 25·00
163   1d. pale slate 30 60
164   1¹/₂d. red-brown 40 60
165   2d. scarlet 30 65
        a. Short "T" .. .. . 48·00
166   2¹/₂d. ultramarine 30 65
167   3d. ultramarine 30 65
        a. "RENCE" flaw .. .. . 50·00
168 **21** 4d. light blue and red-orange 40 90
        a. "COIUMBUS" £600 £600
169 **22** 6d. olive-green and light blue .. 40 1·75
        a. "COIUMBUS" £600 £650
170 **23** 8d. ultramarine and scarlet 90 70
        a. "COIUMBUS" £4000 £1900
171 **20** 1s. brownish grey and scarlet .. 4·50 3·25
        a. *Ordinary paper. Black and carmine* 3·75 2·25
        b. *Ordinary paper. Grey-black and
            bright crimson* .. .. .. 6·00 4·25
172 **18** 2s. slate-purple and indigo .. 15·00 16·00
        a. *Brownish black and indigo* .. 8·00 10·00
        b. *Brownish black and steel-blue* .. 16·00 16·00
        c. Stop after "COLUMBUS" (R. 2/12) £400
173   3s. slate-purple and myrtle-green 5·00 6·50
        a. *Brownish black and green* .. 40·00 32·00
        b. Stop after "COLUMBUS" (R. 2/12) £200
174 **20** 5s. reddish lilac and blue .. 26·00 12·00
        a. *Ordinary paper. Purple and blue* .. 18·00 10·00
175   £1 deep grey-green & blk (*thick paper*) 60·00 42·00
        a. *Ordinary paper. Grey-green & black* 30·00 25·00
162/75 .. .. *Set of* 14 60·00 55·00
162/75 Perf "Specimen" .. .. *Set of* 14 £400
  These stamps replaced the definitive series for a period of six
months. Initially stocks of existing printings were used, but
when further supplies were required for overprinting a number
of new printings were produced, some of which, including the
new colour of the 3d., did not appear without overprint until
much later.
  The "COIUMBUS" error (Nos. 168*a*, 169*a*, 170*a*) occurs on
R.5/2.

1946 (11 Nov). *Victory. As Nos.* 110/11 *of Antigua.*
176 1¹/₂d. brown 10 20
177 3d. blue 10 20
176/7 Perf "Specimen" .. .. *Set of* 5 5·00

26 Infant Welfare Clinic

(Recess C.B.N.)
1948 (11 Oct). *Tercentenary of Settlement of Island of Eleuthera.
T* **26** *and similar horiz designs. P* 12.
178 ¹/₂d. orange 30 60
179 1d. sage-green 30 35
180 1¹/₂d. yellow 30 80
181 2d. scarlet 30 40
182 2¹/₂d. brown-lake 45 75
183 3d. ultramarine 65 85
184 4d. black 60 70
185 6d. emerald-green .. .. .. 1·75 80
186 8d. violet 60 70
187 10d. carmine 60 35
188 1s. sepia 90 50
189 2s. magenta .. .. 4·00 8·50
190 3s. blue .. .. 7·50 8·50
191 5s. mauve .. .. 4·25 4·50
192 10s. grey .. .. 9·50 9·00
193 £1 vermilion .. .. .. 13·00 14·00
178/93 .. .. .. *Set of* 16 40·00 45·00
  Designs:—1d. Agriculture (combine harvester); 1¹/₂d. Sisal; 2d.
Straw work; 2¹/₂d. Dairy farm; 3d. Fishing fleet; 4d. Island settlement; 6d. Tuna fishing; 8d. Paradise Beach; 10d. Modern hotels; 1s.
Yacht racing; 2s. Water sports (skiing); 3s. Shipbuilding; 5s. Trans-
portation; 10s. Salt production; £1, Parliament Buildings.

1948 (1 Dec). *Royal Silver Wedding. As Nos.* 112/13 *of
Antigua.*
194 1¹/₂d. red-brown 20 25
195 £1 slate-green .. .. .. 32·00 32·00

1949 (10 Oct). *75th Anniv of Universal Postal Union. As Nos.*
114/17 *of Antigua.*
196 2¹/₂d. violet 35 40
197 3d. deep blue .. .. 1·00 1·75
198 6d. greenish blue .. .. .. 1·00 1·25
199 1s. carmine .. .. 1·00 75
196/9 .. .. *Set of* 4 3·00 3·75

STAMP BOOKLETS

1938. *Black on pink cover with map and* "BAHAMAS ISLES
OF JUNE" *on reverse. Stapled.*
SB1 2s. booklet containing twelve 1d. (No. 150) in
      blocks of 6 and eight 1¹/₂d. (No. 151) in folded
      block of 8 .. .. £5000

Bahrain

12 pies = 1 anna; 16 annas = 1 rupee

INDIAN AND SUBSEQUENTLY BRITISH POSTAL ADMINISTRATION

BAHRAIN   **BAHRAIN**

(1)   (2)

Stamps of India overprinted with T 1 or T 2 (rupee values)

1938–41. *King George VI.*

20	91	3 p. slate (5.38)			6·00	2·00
21		½ a. red-brown (5.38)			2·50	10
22		9 p. green (5.38)			2·50	1·75
23		1 a. carmine (5.38)			2·00	10
24	92	2 a. vermilion (1939)			6·50	90
26	–	3 a. yellow-green (1941)			45·00	4·50
27	–	3½ a. bright blue (7.38)			4·25	2·75
28	–	4 a. brown (1941)			£120	55·00
30	–	8 a. slate-violet (1940)			£140	35·00
31	–	12 a. lake (1940)			£100	48·00
32	93	1 r. grey and red-brown (1940)			2·75	1·40
33		2 r. purple and brown (1940)			15·00	2·50
34		5 r. green and blue (1940)			25·00	13·00
35		10 r. purple and claret (1941)			65·00	25·00
36		15 r. brown and green (1941)			45·00	45·00
37		25 r. slate-violet and purple (1941)			95·00	70·00
20/37				*Set of 16*	£600	£275

1942–45. *King George VI on white background.*

38	100*a*	3 p. slate			80	60
39		½ a. purple			3·50	90
40		9 p. green			9·50	9·50
41		1 a. carmine			3·50	50
42	101	1 a. 3 p. bistre			8·00	12·00
43		1½ a. dull violet			4·75	3·00
44		2 a. vermilion			3·50	1·50
45		3 a. bright violet			13·00	4·00
46		3½ a. bright blue			3·50	12·00
47	102	4 a. brown			1·50	1·00
48		6 a. turquoise-green			9·50	7·00
49		8 a. slate-violet			2·75	1·50
50		12 a. lake			4·50	3·00
38/50				*Set of 13*	60·00	50·00

Stamps of Great Britain surcharged

For similar surcharges without the name of the country, see BRITISH POSTAL AGENCIES IN EASTERN ARABIA.

BAHRAIN

I
ANNA

(3)

5 RUPEES

(4)

1948 (1 Apr)**–49.** *Surch as T 3, 4 (2 r. and 5 r.) or similar surch with bars at foot (10 r.).*

51	128	½ a. on ½d. pale green			40	40
52		1 a. on 1d. pale scarlet			40	65
53		1½ a. on 1½d. pale red-brown			40	70
54		2 a. on 2d. pale orange			40	20
55		2½ a. on 2½d. light ultramarine			50	1·60
56		3 a. on 3d. pale violet			40	10
57	129	6 a. on 6d. purple			40	10
58	130	1 r. on 1s. bistre-brown			1·25	10
59	131	2 r. on 2s. 6d. yellow-green			5·00	4·25
60		5 r. on 5s. red			5·50	4·50
60*a*	132	10 r. on 10s. ultramarine (4.7.49)			60·00	40·00
51/60*a*				*Set of 11*	65·00	48·00

BAHRAIN   BAHRAIN
2½   15
ANNAS   RUPEES

(5)   (6)

1948 (26 Apr). *Silver Wedding, surch as T 5 or 6.*

61	137	2½ a. on 2½d. ultramarine			30	30
62	138	15 r. on £1 blue			40·00	48·00

1948 (29 July). *Olympic Games, surch as T 5, but in one line (6 a.) or two lines (others); the 1 r. also has a square of dots as T 7*

63	139	2½ a. on 2½d. ultramarine			55	75
		a. Surch double			£650	£1100
64	140	3 a. on 3d. violet			55	1·50
65	141	6 a. on 6d. bright purple			1·50	2·25
66	142	1 r. on 1s. brown			1·50	2·25
63/6				*Set of 4*	3·75	6·00

Fourteen used examples of No. 63a are known, of which twelve were postmarked at Experimental P.O. K-121 (Muharraq).

BAHRAIN
3 ANNAS

(7)

1949 (10 Oct). *75th Anniv of U.P.U., surch as T 7, in one line (2½ a.) or in two lines (others).*

67	143	2½ a. on 2½d. ultramarine			55	1·75
68	144	3 a. on 3d. violet			85	2·25
69	145	6 a. on 6d. bright purple			75	2·50
70	146	1 r. on 1s. brown			1·60	1·50
67/70				*Set of 4*	3·25	7·00

BAHRAIN   BAHRAIN

2 RUPEES   **2 RUPEES**

(7*a*)   Type II

BAHRAIN

Extra bar (R. 6/1)

Three Types of 2 r.:

Type I.   As Type 7*a* showing "2" level with "RUPEES" and "BAHRAIN" sharp.

Type II.   "2" raised. "BAHRAIN" worn. 15 mm between "BAHRAIN" and "2 RUPEES".

Type III.   As Type II, but 16 mm between "BAHRAIN" and "2 RUPEES". Value is set more to the left of "BAHRAIN".

1950 (2 Oct)**–55.** *Surch as T 3 or 7a (rupee values).*

71	128	½ a. on ½d. pale orange (3.5.51)			30	40
72		1 a. on 1d. light ultramarine (3.5.51)			1·00	10
73		1½ a. on 1½d. pale green (3.5.51)			1·00	7·00
74		2 a. on 2d. pale red-brown (3.5.51)			40	30
75		2½ a. on 2½d. pale scarlet (3.5.51)			1·00	7·00
76	139	4 a. on 4d. light ultramarine			1·00	1·50
77	147	2 r. on 2s. 6d. yellow-green (3.5.51)			21·00	4·75
		a. Surch Type II (1953)			65·00	32·00
		b. Surch Type III (1955)			£700	75·00
		ba. "I" inverted and raised (R.2/1)			£2250	£550
78	148	5 r. on 5s. red (3.5.51)			13·00	3·75
		a. Extra bar			£200	
79	149	10 r. on 10s. ultramarine (3.5.51)			26·00	7·00
71/79				*Set of 9*	60·00	28·00

Barbados

1937. 12 pence (d) = 1 shilling; 20 shillings = 1 pound
1950. 100 cents = 1 West Indian dollar

CROWN COLONY

1937 (14 May). *Coronation. As Nos. 95/7 of Antigua, but printed by D.L.R. P* 14.

245	1d. scarlet	..	..	..	30	15
246	1½d. yellow-brown	..	..	..	40	30
247	2½d. bright blue	..	..	..	70	45
245/7	..	..	..	*Set of* 3 1·25		80
245/7 Perf "Specimen"				*Set of* 3 50·00		

21 Badge of the Colony

Recut line (R. 10/6)

Extra frame line (R. 11/9)

Mark on central ornament (R. 1/3, 2/3, 3/3)

Vertical line over horse's head (R. 4/10) (corrected on Dec 1947 ptg)

"Flying mane" (R. 4/1) (corrected on Dec 1947 ptg)

Curved line at top right (R. 7/8)

Cracked plate (extends to top right ornament) (R. 6/10))

(Recess D.L.R.)

1938 (3 Jan)–**47.** *Wmk Mult Script CA. P* 13½×13.

248	21	½d. green	..	..	..	4·50	15
		a. Recut line	..	..	..	75·00	
		b. Perf 14 (8.42)	..	..	70·00	1·25	
		ba. Recut line	..	..	£275		
248c		½d. yellow-bistre (16.10.42)	..	..	15	15	
		ca. "A" of "CA" missing from wmk	..				
		cb. Recut line	..	..	13·00		
249		1d. scarlet (1941)	..	..	£275	4·00	
		a. Perf 14 (3.1.38)	..	..	16·00	10	
249b		1d. blue-green (1943)	..	..	2·50	60	
		c. Perf 14 (16.10.42)	..	..	15	10	
		ca. "A" of "CA" missing from wmk	..				
250		1½d. orange	..	..	15	40	
		a. "A" of "CA" missing from wmk	..				
		b. Perf 14 (11.41)	..	..	3·75	40	
250c		2d. claret (3.6.41)	..	..	40	1·50	
		ca. Extra frame line	..	..	20·00		
250d		2d. carmine (20.9.43)	..	..	15	20	
		da. Extra frame line	..	..	15·00		
		e. Perf 14 (11.9.44)	..	..	15	75	
		ea. Extra frame line	..	..	15·00		
251		2½d. ultramarine	..	..	50	40	
		a. Mark on central ornament	..	29·00			
		b. Blue (17.2.44)	..	..	80	4·25	
		ba. "A" of "CA" missing from wmk	£1000				
		bb. Mark on central ornament	..	32·00			
252		3d. brown	..	..	20	1·90	
		a. Vertical line over horse's head	..	65·00			
		b. Perf 14 (4.41)	..	..	20	20	
		ba. Vertical line over horse's head	..	65·00			
252c		3d. blue (1.4.47)	..	..	20	1·00	
		ca. Vertical line over horse's head	..	70·00			
253		4d. black	..	..	20	10	
		a. Flying mane	..	..	65·00		
		b. Curved line at top right	..	50·00			
		c. Cracked plate	..	..	45·00		
		d. Perf 14 (11.9.44)	..	..	20	2·50	
		da. Flying mane	..	..	65·00		
		db. Curved line at top right	..	50·00			
		dc. Cracked plate	..	..	45·00		
254		6d. violet	..	..	80	10	
254a		8d. magenta (9.12.46)	..	..	55	1·40	
255		1s. olive-green	..	..	16·00	2·00	
		a. Deep brown-olive (19.11.45)	..	80	10		
256		2s. 6d. purple	..	..	5·50	1·00	
256a		5s. indigo (3.6.41)	..	..	3·25	5·00	
		ab. "A" of "CA" missing from wmk	..				
248/56a		..	..	*Set of* 16	30·00	10·00	
248/56a Perf "Specimen" ..		..	*Set of* 16	£180			

No. 249a was perforated by two machines, one gauging 13.8×14.1 (1938), the other 14.1 (1939).

Nos. 248/c and 249/c exist in coils constructed from normal sheets.

Nos. 249c and 256a both exist showing "A" of "CA" missing from a watermark on the sheet margin.

22 Kings Charles I, George VI, Assembly Chamber and Mace

(Recess D.L.R.)

1939 (27 June). *Tercentenary of General Assembly. Wmk Mult Script CA. P* 13½ × 14.

257	**22**	½d. green	..	..	1·60	30
258		1d. scarlet	..	..	1·60	30
259		1½d. orange	..	..	1·60	60
260		2½d. bright ultramarine ..		..	1·60	2·25
261		3d. brown	..	..	1·90	2·25
257/61			*Set of* 5	7·50	5·25
257/61 Perf "Specimen"		..	*Set of* 5 £140	

Two flags on tug
(R. 5/2)

1946 (18 Sept). *Victory. As Nos.* 110/11 *of Antigua.*

262	1½d. red-orange	..	..	..	15	15
	a. Two flags on tug .	..	..	20·00	
263	3d. brown	..	..	1·90	15
262/3 Perf "Specimen"		..	*Set of* 2 48·00	

ONE
PENNY
(23)

NY PEN

Short "Y" (R. 6/2)   Broken "E" (R. 7/4 and 11/4)

(Surch by Barbados Advocate Co)

1947 (21 Apr). *Surch with T* 23. (*a*) *P* 14.

264	**21**	1d. on 2d. carmine (No. 250e) ..	70	1·50
		a. Extra frame line	..	35·00
		b. Short "Y"	..	35·00
		c. Broken "E"	..	22·00

(*b*) *P* 13½×13

264*d*	**21**	1d. on 2d. carmine (No. 250*d*) ..	4·50	5·00
		da. Extra frame line	..	£120
		db. Short "Y" ..	..	£120
		dc. Broken "E"	..	80·00

The relationship of the two words in the surcharge differs on each position of the sheet.

1948 (24 Nov). *Royal Silver Wedding. As Nos.* 112/13 *of Antigua.*

265	1½d. orange	..	..	30	10
266	5s. indigo	..	..	9·50	6·00

1949 (10 Oct). *75th Anniv of Universal Postal Union. As Nos.* 114/17 *of Antigua.*

267	1½d. red-orange	..	..	30	35
268	3d. deep blue ..	..	..	70	90
269	4d. grey	..	..	70	1·25
270	1s. olive	..	..	80	60
267/70	..	..	..	*Set of* 4 2·25	2·75

MINIMUM PRICE

The minimum price quote is 10p which represents a handling charge rather than a basis for valuing common stamps. For further notes about prices see introductory pages.

(New Currency. 100 cents = 1 West Indian, later Barbados, dollar)

24 Dover Fort   27 Statue of Nelson

(Recess B.W.)

1950 (1 May). *T* **24**, **27** *and similar designs. Wmk Mult Script CA. P* 11 × 11½ (*horiz*), 13½ (*vert*).

271	1 c. indigo	..	..	15	2·00
272	2 c. emerald-green	..	..	15	1·50
273	3 c. reddish brown and blue-green ..		50	1·50
274	4 c. carmine	..	..	15	30
275	6 c. light blue	..	..	15	1·50
276	8 c. bright blue and purple-brown ..		65	1·25
277	12 c. greenish blue and brown-olive ..		90	70
278	24 c. scarlet and black	..	..	90	30
279	48 c. violet	..	..	8·00	4·50
280	60 c. green and claret..	..	..	6·00	6·00
281	$1.20, carmine and olive-green	..	8·50	2·50
282	$2.40, black ..	..	..	15·00	10·00
271/282		*Set of* 12	35·00	29·00

Designs: *Horiz*—2 c. Sugar cane breeding; 3 c. Public buildings; 6 c. Casting net; 8 c. *Frances W. Smith* (schooner); 12 c. Flying fish; 24 c. Old Main Guard Garrison; 60 c. Careenage; $2.40, Seal of Barbados. *Vert*—48 c. St. Michael's Cathedral; $1.20, Map of Barbados and wireless mast.

1951 (16 Feb). *Inauguration of B.W.I. University College. As Nos.* 118/19 *of Antigua.*

283	3 c. brown and blue-green	..	..	30	30
284	12 c. blue-green and brown-olive	..	..	55	95

36 King George VI and Stamp of 1852

(Recess Waterlow)

1952 (15 Apr). *Barbados Stamp Centenary. Wmk Mult Script CA. P* 13½.

285	**36**	3 c. green and slate-green	..	15	30
286		4 c. blue and carmine	..	15	75
287		12 c. slate-green and bright green	..	15	75
288		24 c. red-brown and brownish black	..	15	30
285/8 ..			*Set of* 4	55	1·90

STAMP BOOKLETS

1938 (3 Jan). *Black on light blue cover. Advocate Co. Ltd. advertisement on front. Stapled.*

SB7	2s. booklet containing ½d. and 1d. (Nos. 248, 249a) each in block of 10 and 1½d. (No. 250) in block of 6	.. £1300

POSTAGE DUE STAMPS

(Typo D.L.R.)

1934 (2 Jan)–47.   *Wmk Mult Script CA. P* 14.
D1	D 1	¹/₂d. green (10.2.35)	..	60	5·00
D2		1d. black	..	70	70
		a. Bisected (¹/₂d.) (on cover) ..		†	£600
D3		3d. carmine (13.3.47) ..		17·00	16·00
D1/3		..	*Set of* 3	17·00	20·00
D1/3 Perf "Specimen"			*Set of* 3	65·00	

The bisected 1d. was officially authorised for use between March 1934 and February 1935. Some specimens had the value "¹/₂d." written across the half stamp in red or black ink (*Price on cover* £700).

(Typo D.L.R.)

1950 (8 Dec)–**53**.   *Values in cents. Wmk Mult Script CA. Ordinary paper. P* 14.
D4	D 1	1 c. green	..	2·50	13·00
		a. Chalk-surfaced paper. *Deep green* (29.11.51)..		30	3·00
		ab. Error. Crown missing, W **9a**	..	£225	
		ac. Error. St. Edward's Crown, W **9b**		£150	

D5	D 1	2 c. black	..	5·50	8·00
		a. Chalk-surfaced paper (20.1.53)	..	40	3·25
		ac. Error. St. Edward's Crown, W **9b**	£225		
D6		6 c. carmine	..	13·00	13·00
		a. Chalk-surfaced paper (20.1.53)	..	1·50	8·50
		ab. Error. Crown missing, W **9a**	..	£150	
		ac. Error. St. Edward's Crown, W **9b**	..	£120	
D4/6		..	*Set of* 3	19·00	30·00
D4a/6a		..	*Set of* 3	2·00	13·00

The 1 c. has no dot below "c".

Basutoland

12 pence (d) = 1 shilling; 20 shillings = 1 pound

CROWN COLONY

1937 (12 May). *Coronation. As Nos. 95/7 of Antigua, but ptd by D.L.R. P* 14.

15	1d. scarlet	..	..	..	..	35	10
16	2d. bright purple	..	..	..	..	70	85
17	3d. bright blue	..	..	..	..	90	85
15/17 ..	..	..	..	*Set of* 3		1·75	1·60
15/17 Perf "Specimen"		..	..	*Set of* 3		55·00	

2 King George VI, Nile Crocodile and Mountains

Tower flaw (R. 2/4)

(Recess Waterlow)

1938 (1 Apr). *Wmk Mult Script CA. P* 12½.

18	**2**	½d. green	..	..	..	30	60
19		1d. scarlet	..	..	..	50	30
		a. Tower flaw ..	..	..	.. 60·00		
20		1½d. light blue	..	..	..	40	40
21		2d. bright purple	..	..	..	30	30
22		3d. bright blue ..	..	..	..	30	60
23		4d. grey ..	..	..	..	1·50	2·50
24		6d. orange-yellow	..	..	..	50	50
25		1s. red-orange ..	..	..	..	50	90
26		2s. 6d. sepia ..	..	..	..	8·00	6·00
27		5s. violet	..	..	.. ..	22·00	8·50
28		10s. olive-green ..	..	.. ..	22·00	16·00	
18/28 ..	..	..	..	*Set of* 11	50·00	32·00	
18/28 Perf "Specimen"			..	*Set of* 11	£190		

Basutoland
(3)

1945 (3 Dec). *Victory. Stamps of South Africa, optd with T* **3**, *inscr alternately in English and Afrikaans.*

				Un.	Used	Used
				pair	pair	single
29	**55**	1d. brown and carmine	..	..	30	30	10
30	**56**	2d. slate-blue and violet	..	30	30	10
31	**57**	3d. deep blue and blue	..	30	60	15
29/31	..	..	..	*Set of* 3	80	1·10	30

4 King George VI

5 King George VI and Queen Elizabeth

6 Queen Elizabeth II as Princess, and Princess Margaret

7 The Royal Family

(Recess Waterlow)

1947 (17 Feb). *Royal Visit. Wmk Mult Script CA. P* 12½.

32	**4**	1d. scarlet	..	..	..	10	10
33	**5**	2d. green	..	..	..	10	10
34	**6**	3d. ultramarine	..	..	..	10	10
35	**7**	1s. mauve	..	..	..	15	10
32/5 ..		..	..	..	*Set of* 4	40	30
32/5 Perf "Specimen"			..	*Set of* 4	80·00		

1948 (1 Dec). *Royal Silver Wedding. As Nos. 112/13 of Antigua.*

36	1½d. ultramarine ..		..	..	20	10
37	10s. grey-olive	..	..	.. ..	30·00	26·00

1949 (10 Oct). *75th Anniv of Universal Postal Union. As Nos. 114/17 of Antigua.*

38	1½d. blue	..	..	..	30	40
39	3d. deep blue ..	..	..	..	1·40	1·00
40	6d. orange	..	..	..	1·50	1·25
41	1s. red-brown	..	..	.. ..	1·25	90
38/41 ..	..	..	..	*Set of* 4	4·00	3·25

POSTAGE DUE STAMPS

D 1

Normal

Large "d."
(R. 9/6, 10/6)

(Typo D.L.R.)

1933 (1 Dec)–**52.** *Wmk Mult Script CA. Ordinary paper. P* 14.

D1	**D 1**	1d. carmine	..	..	..	1·75	5·50
		a. *Scarlet* (1938)	..	..	32·00	38·00
		b. Chalk-surfaced paper. *Deep carmine*				
		(24.10.51)	..	..	30	65
		ba. Error. Crown missing, W9*a*		95·00	
		bb. Error. St. Edward's Crown, W9*b*	..	55·00	
D2		2d. violet	..	..	7·50	11·00
		a. Chalk-surfaced paper (6.11.52)		30	3·75
		ab. Error. Crown missing, W9*a*	..	£100	
		ac. Error. St. Edward's Crown, W9*a*	..	55·00	
		ad. Large "d"	..	..	..	4·50	
D1/2 Perf "Specimen"		..	..	*Set of* 2	42·00	

Bechuanaland Protectorate

12 pence (d) = 1 shilling; 20 shillings = 1 pound

PROTECTORATE

1937 (12 May). *Coronation. As Nos. 95/7 of Antigua, but printed by D.L.R. P* 14.

115	1d. scarlet			45	40
116	2d. yellow-brown			85	65
117	3d. bright blue			85	80
115/17			*Set of* 3	1·90	1·75
115/17 Perf "Specimen"		*Set of* 3	55·00		

23 King George VI, Baobab Tree and Cattle drinking

(Recess Waterlow)

1938 (1 Apr)–**52.** *Wmk Mult Script CA. P* 12½.

118	**23**	½d. green		2·00	2·25
		a. Light yellowish green (1941)		3·00	4·50
		b. Yellowish green (4.43)		2·25	2·75
		c. Deep green (4.49)		1·50	4·25
119		1d. scarlet		30	40
120		1½d. dull blue		8·50	1·75
		a. Light blue (4.43)		40	70
121		2d. chocolate-brown		40	40
122		3d. deep ultramarine		30	1·25
123		4d. orange		1·10	2·00
124		6d. reddish purple		3·50	3·00
		a. Purple (1944)		2·75	2·50
125		1s. black and brown-olive		3·00	2·75
		a. Grey-black and olive-green (21.5.52)	8·50	11·00
126		2s.6d. black and scarlet		14·00	8·50
127		5s. black and deep ultramarine		30·00	8·50
		a. Grey-black & dp ultramarine (10.46)	65·00	35·00
128		10s. black and red-brown		14·00	16·00
118/28			*Set of* 11	60·00	40·00
118/28 Perf "Specimen"		*Set of* 11	£170		

Bechuanaland

(24)

24a King George VI and Queen Elizabeth

1945 (3 Dec). *Victory. Stamps of South Africa optd with T* 24. *Inscr alternately in English and Afrikaans.*

			Un. pair	Used pair	Used single
129	**55**	1d. brown and carmine	40	35	10
130	**56**	2d. slate-blue and violet	40	50	10
131	**57**	3d. deep blue and blue	40	50	10
		a. Opt omitted (in vert pair with normal)		£4250	
129/31			*Set of* 3	1·10	1·25	25

No. 131a comes from a sheet on which the overprint was displaced downwards so that it is omitted from stamps in the top row and shown on the sheet margin at foot.

(Recess Waterlow)

1947 (17 Feb). *Royal Visit. T* **24a** *and similar designs. Wmk Mult Script CA. P* 12½.

132	1d. scarlet			10	10
133	2d. green			10	10
134	3d. ultramarine			10	10
135	1s. mauve			10	10
132/5			*Set of* 4	35	30
132/5 Perf "Specimen"		*Set of* 4	80·00		

Designs: *Vert*—1d. King George VI. *Horiz*—3d. Princess Elizabeth and Princess Margaret; 1s. The Royal Family.

1948 (1 Dec). *Royal Silver Wedding. As Nos.* 112/13 *of Antigua.*

136	1½d. ultramarine			30	10
137	10s. black			27·00	35·00

1949 (10 Oct). *75th Anniv of Universal Postal Union. As Nos.* 114/17 *of Antigua.*

138	1½d. blue			45	50
139	3d. deep blue			80	1·25
140	6d. magenta			90	80
141	1s. olive			95	80
138/41			*Set of* 4	2·75	3·00

POSTAGE DUE STAMPS

D 3	Normal	Large "d" (R. 9/6, 10/6)

Serif on "d" (R.1/6)

(Typo D.L.R.)

1932 (12 Dec)–**58.** *Wmk Mult Script CA. Ordinary paper. P* 14.

D4	**D 3**	½d. sage-green		6·00	27·00
D5		1d. carmine		5·50	8·00
		a. Chalk-surfaced paper (27.11.58)	75	9·50
D6		2d. violet		8·00	30·00
		a. Large "d"		60·00	
		b. Chalk-surfaced paper (27.11.58)	1·25	14·00
		ba. Large "d"		16·00	
		bb. Serif on "d"		5·00	
D4/6b			*Set of* 3	7·25	45·00
D4/6 Perf "Specimen"		*Set of* 3	60·00		

No. D6a first occurred on the 1947 printing.

Bermuda

12 pence (d) = 1 shilling; 20 shillings = 1 pound

CROWN COLONY

1937 (14 May). *Coronation. As Nos. 95/7 of Antigua, but printed by D.L.R. P* 14.

107	1d. scarlet	..	..	50	50
108	1½d. yellow-brown	..	..	60	1·40
109	2½d. bright blue	..	..	1·10	1·50
107/9	..	..	Set of 3	2·00	3·00
107/9 Perf "Specimen"	..	Set of 3	£110	

22 *Lucie* (yacht)

29 King George VI

26 Ships in Hamilton Harbour

27 St. David's Lighthouse

28 White-tailed Tropic Bird, Arms of Bermuda and Native Flower

(Des Miss Higginbotham (T **28**). Recess B.W.)

1938 (20 Jan)–**1952.** *T* **22**, *T* **23** (*but with portrait of King George VI*) *and T* **26** *to* **28**. *Wmk Mult Script CA. P* 12.

110	**26**	1d. black and red (*a*) (*b*)	65	20
111		1½d. deep blue and purple-brown (*a*) (*b*)	5·00	1·50
		a. Blue and brown (3.43) ..	5·50	2·50
		b. Lt blue & purple-brn (*a*) (*b*) (9.45)	2·25	35
		ba. "A" of "CA" missing from wmk ..		
112	**22**	2d. light blue and sepia (*a*) ..	40·00	8·00
112*a*		2d. ultramarine and scarlet (*a*) (*b*) (8.11.40) ..	1·50	80
113	**23**	2½d. light and deep blue (*a*) ..	11·00	1·25
113*a*		2½d. lt blue & sepia-black (*a*) (18.12.41)	3·00	1·50
		b. Pale blue & sepia-black (*a*) (3.43)	2·75	1·25
		c. Bright blue and deep sepia-black (*b*) (23.9.52)	4·00	2·50
114	**27**	3d. black and rose-red (*a*) ..	12·00	1·50
114*a*		3d. black & deep blue (*a*) (*b*) (16.7.41)	1·75	40
114*b*	**28**	7½d. black, blue & brt grn (*a*) (18.12.41)	6·50	2·00
		c. Black, blue & yellow-grn (*a*) (3.43)	4·50	2·25
115	**23**	1s. green (*a*) (*b*)	2·00	50
		a. Bluish green (*b*) (20.6.52) ..	6·50	4·75

Design:—2½d., 1s. Grape Bay, Paget Parish.

Perforations. Two different perforating machines were used on the various printings of these stamps: (*a*) the original 11.9 line perforation; (*b*) 11.9 × 11.75 comb perforation, introduced in July 1950. These perforations occur as indicated above.

Shading omitted from top right scroll (R. 1/1. March 1943 ptgs of 2s. and £1)

Lower right scroll with broken tail (R. 2/10. Line perforated printings only)

Broken top right scroll (R. 5/11. Line perforated ptgs only. A retouched state of the flaw is visible in later ptgs up to March 1943)

Broken lower right scroll (R. 5/12. Occurs on printings made between May 1941 and March 1943)

Gash in chin (R.2/5.
Ptgs between May
1941 and March 1943

Missing pearl
(R.5/1, Nov 1945
ptg of 5s. only)

(Typo D.L.R.)

1938 (20 Jan)–53. T **29**. *Wmk Mult Crown CA* (£1) *or Mult
Script CA* (others). *Chalk-surfaced paper. P* 14 (comb).

116	2s. deep purple and ultramarine/*grey-blue*	£110	10·00
	a. *Deep reddish purple and ultram/grey-blue* (10.40)	£200	15·00
	b. *Perf* 14¼ *line. Deep purple and ultram/grey-blue* (14.11.41)*	£300	85·00
	bc. Lower right scroll with broken tail	£850	£375
	bd. Broken top right scroll	£800	£325
	be. Broken lower right scroll	£800	£325
	bf. Gash in chin	£800	£325
	c. Ordinary paper. *Pur & bl /dp bl* (7.6.42)	7·00	1·50
	ce. Broken lower right scroll	£170	65·00
	cf. Gash in chin	£170	65·00
	d. Ordinary paper. *Purple and deep blue/pale blue* (5.3.43)	11·00	1·50
	db. Shading omitted from top right scroll	£700	£375
	de. Broken lower right scroll	£450	£250
	df. Gash in chin	£450	£250
	e. Perf 13. Ordinary paper. *Dull purple and blue/pale blue* (15.2.50)	16·00	14·00
	f. Perf 13. Ordinary paper. *Reddish purple and blue/pale blue* (10.10.50)	8·50	11·00
117	2s. 6d. black and red/*grey-blue*	70·00	8·00
	a. *Perf* 14¼ *line. Black and red/grey-blue* (21.2.42)*	£450	£110
	ac. Lower right scroll with broken tail	£1000	£425
	ad. Broken top right scroll	£950	£375
	ae. Broken lower right scroll	£950	£375
	af. Gash in chin	£950	£375
	b. Ordinary paper. *Black and red/pale blue* (5.3.43)	19·00	6·50
	be. Broken lower right scroll	£375	£170
	bf. Gash in chin	£375	£170
	c. Perf 13. Ordinary paper. *Black and orange-red/pale blue* (10.10.50)	19·00	11·00
	d. Perf 13. Ordinary paper. *Black and red/pale blue* (18.6.52)	16·00	12·00
118	5s. green and red/*yellow*	£140	25·00
	a. *Pale green and red/yellow* (14.3.39)*	£250	55·00
	b. *Perf* 14¼ *line. Dull yellow-green and red/yellow* (5.1.43)*	£200	28·00
	bc. Lower right scroll with broken tail	£600	£225
	bd. Broken top right scroll	£550	£180
	be. Broken lower right scroll	£550	£180
	bf. Gash in chin	£550	£180
	c. Ordinary paper. *Dull yellow-green and carmine-red/pale yellow* (5.42)	£350	90·00
	ce. Broken lower right scroll	£2000	£750
	cf. Gash in chin	£2000	£750
	d. Ordinary paper. *Pale bluish green and carmine-red/pale yellow* (5.3.43)	£100	50·00
	de. Broken lower right scroll	£550	£325
	df. Gash in chin	£550	£325
	e. Ordinary paper. *Green and red/pale yellow* (11.45)*	50·00	20·00
	ea. Missing pearl	£500	
	f. Perf 13. Ordinary paper. *Yellow-green and red/pale yellow* (15.2.50)	21·00	16·00
	g. Perf 13. *Green and scarlet/yellow* (*chalk-surfaced*) (10.10.50)	26·00	23·00

119	10s. green and deep lake/*pale emerald*	£450	£275
	a. *Bluish green and deep red/green* (8.39)*	£200	£130
	b. Perf 14¼ line. Ordinary paper. *Yellow-green and carmine/green* (1942)*	£400	£140
	bc. Lower right scroll with broken tail	£1000	£550
	bd. Broken top right scroll	£900	£475
	be. Broken lower right scroll	£900	£475
	bf. Gash in chin	£900	£475
	c. Ordinary paper. *Yellowish green and deep carmine-red/green* (5.3.43)	80·00	55·00
	ce. Broken lower right scroll	£1600	
	cf. Gash in chin	£1400	
	d. Ordinary paper. *Deep green and dull red/green* (*emerald back*) (11.12.46)	85·00	60·00
	e. Perf 13. Ordinary paper. *Green and vermilion/green* (19.9.51)	30·00	32·00
	f. Perf 13. Ordinary paper. *Green and dull red/green* (16.4.53)	30·00	40·00
120	12s. 6d. deep grey and brownish orange	£475	£400
	a. *Grey and brownish orange* (*shades*)	£170	60·00
	b. *Grey and pale orange* (9.11.40)*	85·00	50·00
	c. Ordinary paper (2.3.44)*	95·00	60·00
	ce. Broken lower right scroll	£1200	£1300
	cf. Gash in chin	£1200	
	d. Ordinary paper. *Grey & yell*† (7.9.47)*	£550	£450
	e. Perf 13. *Grey and pale orange* (*chalk-surfaced*) (10.10.50)	95·00	75·00
121	£1 purple and black/*red*	£275	£100
	a. *Pale purple & black/pale red* (13.3.43)*	80·00	60·00
	ab. Shading omitted from top right scroll	£1200	
	ae. Broken lower right scroll	£900	£650
	af. Gash in chin	£900	
	b. *Reddish purple and black/pale red* (29.3.45)*	70·00	45·00
	be. Broken lower right scroll	£950	
	bf. Gash in chin	£950	
	c. Perf 13. *Violet & black/scarlet* (7.12.51)	48·00	70·00
	d. Perf 13. *Brt violet & blk/scar* (10.12.52)	£160	£150
110/21c		*Set of* 16	£250 £140
110/21 Perf "Specimen"		*Set of* 16	£1500

Following extensive damage to their printing works on 29
December 1940 much of De La Rue's work was transferred to
other firms operating under their supervision. It is understood
that Williams Lea & Co produced those new printings ordered
for the Bermuda high value stamps during 1941. The first batch
of these printings showed the emergency use, by Williams Lea,
of a 14¼ line perforating machine (exact gauge 14.15) instead of
the comb perforation (exact gauge 13.9 × 13.8).

Dates marked * are those of earliest known use.

In No. 116c the coloured surfacing of the paper is mottled with
white specks sometimes accompanied by very close horizontal
lines. In Nos. 116d, 117b and 118c/d the surfacing is the same
colour as the back, sometimes applied in widely spaced
horizontal lines giving the appearance of laid paper.

†No. 120d is the so-called "lemon" shade.

HALF
PENNY

X   X

(30)   31 Postmaster Perot's Stamp

1940 (20 Dec). *No.* 110 *surch with T* **30**.

122	**26**	½d. on 1d. black and red (*shades*)	40	45

The spacing between "PENNY" and "X" varies from 12½ mm to
14 mm.

1946 (6 Nov). *Victory. As Nos.* 110/11 *of Antigua.*

123	1½d. brown	15	15
124	3d. blue	15	15
123/4 Perf "Specimen"	*Set of* 2	75·00	

1948 (1 Dec). *Royal Silver Wedding. As Nos.* 112/13 *of Antigua.*
125	1½d. red-brown	..	..	..	30	50
126	£1 carmine	..	..	..	..48·00	48·00

(Recess B.W.)

1949 (11 Apr). *Centenary of Postmaster Perot's Stamp. Wmk Mult Script CA. P* 13½.
127	**31**	2½d. blue and brown	..	..	..	15	15
128		3d. black and blue	..	..	..	15	15
129		6d. violet and green	..	..	..	15	15
127/9	..	..	..	..	*Set of* 3	40	40

1949 (10 Oct). *75th Anniv of Universal Postal Union. As Nos.* 114/17 *of Antigua.*
130	2½d. blue-black	..	..	..	75	75
131	3d. deep blue	..	..	..	1·25	75
132	6d. purple	..	..	..	80	75
133	1s. blue-green	..	..	..	80	75
130/3	..	..	..	..	*Set of* 4	3·25	2·75

STAMP BOOKLETS

1948 (5 Apr–10 May). *Pink (No.* SB1), *or light blue (No.* SB2) *covers. Stapled.*
SB1	5s. booklet containing six 1d., 1½d., 2d., 2½d. and 3d. (Nos. 110, 111*b*, 112*a*, 113*b*, 114*a*) in blocks of 6 (10 May)	£130
SB2	10s. 6d. booklet containing six 3d. and eighteen 6d. (Nos. 114*a*, 104) in blocks of 6 with twelve air mail labels	£150

POSTAL FISCAL

1937 (1 Feb). *As T* **15**, *but inscr* "REVENUE" *at each side. Wmk Mult Script CA. Chalk-surfaced paper. P* 14.
F1	12s. 6d. grey and orange £1000	£1100
	a. Break in scroll (R. 1/12) £2750	
	b. Broken crown and scroll (R. 2/12) .. £2750	
	c. Breaks in scrolls at right (R. 1/3) .. £2750	

No. F1 was issued for fiscal purposes towards the end of 1936. Its use as a postage stamp was authorised from 1 February to April 1937. The used price quoted above is for examples postmarked during this period. Later in the same year postmarks with other dates were obtained by favour.

For illustration of No. F1a/c see above Nos. 44 and 88.

British Forces in Egypt

1000 milliemes = 100 piastres = 1 Egyptian pound

British Guiana

100 cents = 1 British Guiana dollar

CROWN COLONY

1937 (12 May). *Coronation. As Nos. 95/7 of Antigua, but ptd by D.L.R. P* 14.

305	2 c. yellow-brown	15	10
306	4 c. grey-black	65	30
307	6 c. bright blue	85	1·00
305/7	Set of 3	1·50	1·25
305/7 Perf "Specimen"	Set of 3	50·00	

53 South America   54 Victoria Regia Lilies

(Recess Waterlow)

1938 (1 Feb)–**1952**. *As earlier types but with portrait of King George VI as in T* **53**/**4**. *Wmk Mult Script CA. P* 12½

308	**43**	1 c. yellow-green	11·00	55
		aa. Green (1944)	30	10
		a. Perf 14×13 (1949)	30	80
309	–	2 c. slate-violet	60	10
		a. Perf 13×14 (28.4.49)	30	10
310	**53**	4 c. scarlet and black	70	30
		a. Imperf horiz (vert pair) ..	£9500	£7500
		b. Perf 13×14 (1952)	45	15
311	**40**	6 c. deep ultramarine	40	10
		a. Perf 13×14 (24.10.49)	30	30
312	–	24 c. blue-green	26·00	10·00
		a. Wmk sideways	1·25	10
313	–	36 c. bright violet (7.3.38).. ..	2·00	20
		a. Perf 13×14 (13.12.51)	2·50	30
314	–	48 c. orange	60	40
		a. Perf 14×13 (8.5.51*)	1·50	1·25
315	–	60 c. red-brown	11·00	3·50
316	–	96 c. purple	2·50	2·75
		a. Perf 12½×13½ (1944)	4·25	4·75
		b. Perf 13×14 (8.2.51)	2·75	5·00
317	–	$1 bright violet	11·00	35
		a. Perf 14×13(1951)	£275	£375
318	–	$2 purple (11.6.45)	4·50	14·00
		a. Perf 14×13 (9.8.50)	8·50	14·00
319	**54**	$3 red-brown (2.7.45)	27·00	25·00
		a. Bright red-brown (12.46) ..	28·00	28·00
		b. Perf 14×13. *Red-brown* (29.10.52) ..	25·00	45·00
308a/19		*Set of 12*	55·00	40·00
308/19 Perf "Specimen"		*Set of 12*	£200	

Designs: *Vert*—2 c., 36 c. Kaieteur Falls; 6 c. Indian shooting fish; 96 c. Sir Walter Raleigh and his son. *Horiz*—1 c. Ploughing a rice field; 24 c. Sugar cane in punts; 48 c. Forest road; 60 c. Shooting logs over falls; $1 Botanical Gardens; $2 Mount Roraima.

*Earliest known postmark date.

1946 (1 Oct). *Victory. As Nos. 110/11 of Antigua.*

320	3 c. carmine	10	10
321	6 c. blue	10	10
320/1 Perf "Specimen" ..	Set of 2	48·00	

1948 (20 Dec). *Royal Silver Wedding. As Nos. 112/13 of Antigua, but $3 in recess.*

322	3 c. scarlet	10	40
323	$3 red-brown	12·00	23·00

1949 (10 Oct). *75th Anniv of Universal Postal Union. As Nos. 114/17 of Antigua.*

324	4 c. carmine	30	20
325	6 c. deep blue	50	45
326	12 c. orange	30	45
327	24 c. blue-green	30	60
324/7	Set of 4	1·25	1·50

1951 (16 Feb). *University College of B.W.I. As Nos. 118/19 of Antigua.*

328	3 c. black and carmine	30	15
329	6 c. black and blue	30	50

STAMP BOOKLETS

1938. *Black on orange cover. Stitched.*

SB7	36 c. booklet containing four 1 c., eight 2 c. and four 4 c. (Nos. 308/10) in blocks of 4 ..	£150

1944. *Black on orange cover. Stitched.*

SB8	24 c. booklet containing eight 1 c. and eight 2 c. (Nos. 308/9) in blocks of 4	£120

1945–49. *Black on red cover. Stapled.*

SB9	24 c. booklet containing 1 c., 2 c. and 3 c. (Nos. 290, 308, 309), each in block of 4	65·00
	a. Containing 1 c., 2 c and 3 c.(Nos. 290, 308aa, 309)	65·00
	b. Containing 1 c., 2 c and 3 c. (Nos. 290a, 308aa, 309)	65·00
	c. Containing 1 c., 2 c and 3 c. (Nos. 290b, 308aa, 309)	65·00
	d. Containing 1 c., 2 c. and 3 c. (Nos. 290b, 308aa, 309a)	65·00
	e. Containing 1 c., 2 c. and 3 c. (Nos. 290b, 308a, 309a)	65·00

POSTAGE DUE STAMPS

D 1

(Typo D.L.R.)

1940 (Mar)–**55**. *Wmk Mult Script CA. Chalk-surfaced paper (4 c.). P* 14.

D1	D 1	1 c. green	3·25	6·50
		a. Chalk-surfaced paper. *Deep green,* (30.4.52)	1·25	7·00
		ab. W9a (Crown missing)	£160	
		ac. W9b (St. Edward's Crown) ..	75·00	
D2		2 c. black	12·00	2·50
		a. Chalk-surfaced paper (30.4.52) ..	1·50	3·50
		ab. W9a (Crown missing)	£140	
		ac. W9b (St. Edward's Crown) ..	65·00	
D3		4 c. bright blue (1.5.52)	30	7·00
		a. W9a (Crown missing)	£120	
		b. W9b (St. Edward's Crown) ..	65·00	
D4		12 c. scarlet	25·00	7·00
		a. Chalk-surfaced paper (19.7.55) ..	10·00	20·00
D1a/4a		*Set of 4*	11·50	35·00
D1, D2 and D4 Perf "Specimen" ..		*Set of 3*	50·00	

British Honduras

100 cents = 1 British Honduras dollar

CROWN COLONY

1937 (12 May). *Coronation. As Nos. 95/7 of Antigua, but printed by D.L.R. P 14.*

147	3 c. orange	..	..	..	30	25
148	4 c. grey-black			..	1·10	25
149	5 c. bright blue			..	1·10	60
147/9 ..		..	..	Set of 3	2·25	1·00
147/9 Perf "Specimen"		..	..	Set of 3	50·00	

24 Maya Figures   **25** Chicle Tapping

(Recess B.W.)

1938 (10 Jan)–**47**. *T* **24/5** *and similar designs. Wmk Mult Script CA (sideways on horizontal stamps). P* 11½ × 11 *(horiz designs) or* 11 × 11½ *(vert designs).*

150	1 c. bright magenta and green (14.2.38)	..	10	90
151	2 c. black and scarlet (14.2.38)	..	20	90
	a. Perf 12 (1947)	..	..	1·90	90
152	3 c. purple and brown	..	..	30	55
153	4 c. black and green	..	..	30	70
154	5 c. mauve and dull blue	..	..	65	50
155	10 c. green and reddish brown (14.2.38)	..	65	60
156	15 c. brown and light blue (14.2.38)	..	1·50	70
157	25 c. blue and green (14.2.38) ..	..	1·75	1·00
158	50 c. black and purple (14.2.38)	..	11·00	3·00
159	$1 scarlet and olive (28.2.38)	..	20·00	7·00
160	$2 deep blue and maroon (28.2.38) ..	..	22·00	16·00
161	$5 scarlet and brown (28.2.38)	..	21·00	23·00
150/61	..	..	..	Set of 12	70·00 50·00
150/61 Perf "Specimen"		..	Set of 12	£160	

Designs: *Vert*—3 c. Cohune palm; $1 Court House, Belize. $2 Mahogany felling; $5 Arms of Colony. *Horiz*—4 c. Local products; 5 c. Grapefruit; 10 c. Mahogany logs in river; 15 c. Sergeant's Cay; 25 c. Dorey; 50 c. Chicle industry.

1946 (9 Sept). *Victory. As Nos. 110/11 of Antigua.*

162	3 c. brown	..	..	..	10	10
163	5 c. blue	..	..	..	10	10
162/3 Perf "Specimen"		..	Set of 2	50·00	

1948 (1 Oct). *Royal Silver Wedding. As Nos. 112/13 of Antigua.*

164	4 c. green	..	..	..	15	50
165	$5 brown	..	..	..	15·00	35·00

36 Island of St George's Cay   **37** H.M.S. *Merlin*

(Recess Waterlow)

1949 (10 Jan). *150th Anniv of Battle of St. George's Cay. Wmk Mult Script CA. P* 12½.

166	**36**	1 c. ultramarine and green	..	..	10	40
167		3 c. blue and yellow-brown	..	..	10	50
168		4 c. olive and violet	..	..	10	50
169	**37**	5 c. brown and deep blue	..	..	50	50
170		10 c. green and red-brown	..	..	50	30
171		15 c. emerald and ultramarine	..	..	50	20
166/71		..	..	Set of 6	1·50	1·90

1949 (10 Oct). *75th Anniv of U.P.U. As Nos. 114/17 of Antigua.*

172	4 c. blue-green	..	..	..	40	30
173	5 c. deep blue ..	..	..	..	55	20
174	10 c. red-brown	..	..	..	70	1·25
175	25 c. blue	..	..	..	85	50
172/5 ..	..	..	..	Set of 4	2·25	2·00

1951 (16 Feb). *Inauguration of B.W.I. University College. As Nos. 118/19 of Antigua.*

176	3 c. reddish violet and brown	..	..	65	70
177	10 c. green and brown ..	..	..	45	30

POSTAGE DUE STAMPS

D 1

(Typo D.L.R.)

1923–64. *Wmk Mult Script CA. Ordinary paper. P* 14.

D1	**D 1**	1 c. black	..	..	1·50	10·00
		a. Chalk-surfaced paper (25.9.56)	..	50	14·00
		b. White uncoated paper (9.4.64)	..	14·00	26·00
D2		2 c. black		..	1·25	5·50
		a. Chalk-surfaced paper (25.9.56)	..	50	14·00
D3		4 c. black		..	1·25	6·00
		a. Missing top serif on "C" (R. 6/6)	..	6·00	
		b. Chalk-surfaced paper (25.9.56)	..	90	9·50
		ba. Missing top serif on "C" (R. 6/6)		4·50	
D1/3		..	..	..	Set of 3	3·50 19·00
D1a/3b		..	..	..	Set of 3	1·75 35·00
D1/3 Optd "Specimen"	..	..	Set of 3	48·00	

The early ordinary paper printings were yellowish and quite distinct from No. D1b.

British Occupation of Italian Colonies

MIDDLE EAST FORCES

For use in territory occupied by British Forces in Eritrea (1942), Italian Somaliland (from 13 April 1942), Cyrenaica (1943), Tripolitania (1943), and some of the Dodecanese Islands (1945).

PRICES. Our prices for used stamps with "M.E.F." overprints are for specimens with identifiable postmarks of the territories in which they were issued. These stamps were also used in the United Kingdom with official sanction, from the summer of 1950 onwards, and with U.K. postmarks are worth about 25 per cent less.

PRINTERS. Considerable research has been undertaken to discover the origins of Nos. M1/10. It is now suggested that Nos. M1/5, previously assigned to Harrison and Sons, were produced by the Army Printing Services, Cairo, and that the smaller printing, Nos. M6/10, previously identified as the work of the Army Printing Services, Cairo, was from an unidentified printer within the Middle East Forces area.

M.E.F. M.E.F.
(M 1)   (M 2)

Opt. 14 mm long. Regular lettering and upright oblong stops.   Opt. 13½ mm long. Regular lettering and square stops.

M.E.F.
(M 2a)

Opt. 13½ mm long. Rough lettering and round stops.

(Illustrations twice actual size)

M.E.F.

Sliced "M"
(R.6/10)

1942 (2 Mar). *Stamps of Great Britain optd.* W **127**. *P* 15 × 14.

(a) With Type M 1

M 1	128	1d. scarlet (No. 463)		35	80
		a. Sliced "M"		30·00	
M 2		2d. orange (No. 465)		20	1·75
		a. Sliced "M"		20·00	
M 3		2½d. ultramarine (No. 466)		20	20
		a. Sliced "M"		20·00	
M 4		3d. violet (No. 467)		20	10
		a. Opt double		— £1900	
M 5	129	5d. brown		20	15
		a. Sliced "M"		20·00	

(b) With Type M 2

M 6	128	1d. scarlet (No. 463)		40·00	9·00
		a. Optd. with Type M 2a		32·00	8·50
		b. Nos. M6/a se-tenant vert		£140	60·00
M 7		2d. orange (No. 465)		50·00	60·00
		a. Optd with Type M 2a		45·00	50·00
		b. Nos. M7/a se-tenant vert		£200	£140
M 8		2½d. ultramarine (No. 466)		26·00	6·50
		a. Optd with Type M 2a		24·00	5·00
		b. Nos. M8/a se-tenant vert		£110	45·00
M 9		3d. violet (No. 467)		75·00	23·00
		a. Optd with Type M 2a		65·00	20·00
		b. Nos. M9/a se-tenant vert		£275	£100
M10	129	5d. brown		£250	65·00
		a. Optd with Type M 2a		£250	65·00
		b. Nos. M10/a se-tenant vert		£800	£425

See note after No. M21.
Nos. M6/10 were issued in panes of 60 (6 × 10), rows 2, 3, and 7 being overprinted with Type M **2** and the other seven rows with Type M 2a.

M.E.F.
(M 3)

Optd 13½ mm long. Regular lettering and upright oblong stops.

(Illustration twice actual size)

1943 (1 Jan)–*1947*. *Stamps of Great Britain optd with Type* M **3** *by Harrison & Sons.* W **127**, *P* 15 × 14 (1d. to 1s.); W **133**, *P* 14 (*others*).

M11	128	1d. pale scarlet (No. 486)		1·50	10
M12		2d. pale orange (No. 488)		1·50	55
M13		2½d. light ultramarine (No. 489)		45	10
M14		3d. pale violet (No. 490)		1·50	10
M15	129	5d. brown		2·25	10
M16		6d. purple		40	10
M17	130	9d. deep olive-green		85	10
M18		1s. bistre-brown		50	10
M19	131	2s. 6d. yellow-green		7·00	30
M20		5s. red (1947)		11·00	17·00
M21	132	10s. ultramarine (1947)		14·00	10·00
M11/21			*Set of 11*	35·00	25·00
M18/21 Optd "Specimen"			*Set of 4*	£500	

The overprint on No. M15 should not be confused with the other overprints on the 5d. value. It can be distinguished from No. M5 by the ½ mm difference in length; and from No. M10 by the more intense colour, thicker lettering and larger stops.

POSTAGE DUE STAMPS

M.E.F.
(MD 1)

1942. *Postage Due Stamps of Great Britain optd with Type* MD 1, *in blue-black.* W **127** (*sideways*). *P* 14 × 15.

MD1	D 1	½d. emerald				30	4·25
MD2		1d. carmine				30	1·50
MD3		2d. agate				1·25	1·00
MD4		3d. violet				50	4·25
MD5		1s. deep blue (Optd S. £150)				3·25	8·00
MD1/5					*Set of 5*	5·00	17·00

CYRENAICA

In June 1949 the British authorities recognised the leader of the Senussi, Amir Mohammed Idris Al-Senussi, as Amir of Cyrenaica with autonomy in internal affairs.

(Currency. 10 millièmes = 1 piastre, 100 piastres = 1 Egyptian pound)

24   Mounted Warrior   25

(Recess Waterlow)

1950 (16 Jan). *P* 12½.

136	24	1 m. brown	..	..	40	90
137		2 m. carmine	..	..	60	70
138		3 m. orange-yellow	..	..	60	70
139		4 m. blue-green	..	..	1·25	2·50
140		5 m. grey-black	..	..	60	70
141		8 m. orange	..	..	75	55
142		10 m. violet	..	..	75	60
143		12 m. scarlet	..	..	75	55
144		20 m. blue	..	..	75	60
145	25	50 m. ultramarine and purple-brown	..	2·25	3·00
146		100 m. carmine and black	..	6·00	9·00
147		200 m. violet and deep blue	..	11·00	25·00
148		500 m. orange-yellow and green	..	42·00	65·00
136/148		.. .. ..	*Set of* 13	60·00	£100

POSTAGE DUE STAMPS

D 26

(Recess Waterlow)

1950 (16 Jan). *P* 12½.

D149	D 26	2 m. brown	..	..	45·00	75·00
D150		4 m. blue-green	..	..	45·00	75·00
D151		8 m. scarlet	..	..	45·00	75·00
D152		10 m. orange	..	..	45·00	75·00
D153		20 m. orange-yellow	..	..	45·00	75·00
D154		40 m. blue	..	..	45·00	75·00
D155		100 m. grey-brown	..	..	45·00	75·00
D149/155		.. ..	*Set of* 7	£275	£475

On 24 December 1951 Cyrenaica united with Tripolitania, Fezzan and Ghadames to form the independent Kingdom of Libya, whose issues are listed in Part 13 (*Africa since Independence F—M*) of this catalogue.

ERITREA

From early 1950 examples of Nos. E1/32 exist precancelled in manuscript by a black or blue horizontal line for use by British troops on concession rate mail.

BRITISH MILITARY ADMINISTRATION

(Currency. 100 cents = 1 shilling)

B. M. A.
ERITREA

B. M. A.
ERITREA

10
CENTS

5 SHILLINGS

(E 1)

(E 2)

SH. 50 SH .50

Normal	Misplaced Stop

1948–9. *Stamps of Great Britain surch as Types* E 1 *or* E 2.

E 1	128	5 c. on ½d. pale green	..	..	50	65
E 2		10 c. on 1d. pale scarlet	..	..	65	2·00
E 3		20 c. on 2d. pale orange	..	..	45	2·25
E 4		25 c. on 2½d. light ultramarine	..	..	40	60
E 5		30 c. on 3d. pale violet	..	..	1·25	4·00
E 6	129	40 c. on 5d. brown	..	..	30	4·00
E 7		50 c. on 6d. purple	..	..	30	60

E 7a	130	65 c. on 8d. bright carmine (1.2.49)	..	7·00	2·00
E 8		75 c. on 9d. deep olive-green	..	50	75
E 9		1 s. on 1s. bistre-brown	..	..	50	50
E10	131	2 s. 50 c. on 2s. 6d. yellow-green	..	6·50	10·00
		a. Misplaced stop (R. 4/7)	..	80·00	£110
E11		5 s. on 5s. red	..	..	6·50	16·00
E12	132	10 s. on 10s. ultramarine	..	15·00	21·00
E1/12	..	.. .. ..	*Set of* 12	35·00	55·00

BRITISH ADMINISTRATION

1950 (6 Feb). *As Nos.* E1/12, *but surch* "B.A. ERITREA" *and new values instead of* 'B.M.A.' *etc.*

E13	128	5 c. on ½d. pale green	..	..	50	6·00
E14		10 c. on 1d. pale scarlet	..	..	30	2·75
E15		20 c. on 2d. pale orange	..	..	30	70
E16		25 c. on 2½d. light ultramarine	..	30	60
E17		30 c. on 3d. pale violet	..	..	30	1·00
E18	129	40 c. on 5d. brown	..	..	40	90
E19		50 c. on 6d. purple	..	..	30	20
E20	130	65 c. on 8d. bright carmine	..	40	1·00
E21		75 c. on 9d. deep olive-green	..	30	25
E22		1 s. on 1s. bistre-brown	..	..	30	15
E23	131	2 s. 50 c. on 2s. 6d. yellow-green	..	3·50	4·50
E24		5 s. on 5s. red	..	..	6·00	9·00
E25	132	10 s. on 10s. ultramarine	..	42·00	42·00
E13/25		.. .. ..	*Set of* 13	48·00	60·00

1951 (28 May*). *Nos.* 503/4, 506/7 *and* 509/11 *of Great Britain surch* "B.A. ERITREA" *and new values.*

E26	128	5 c. on ½d. pale orange	..	..	30	60
E27		10 c. on 1d. light ultramarine	..	30	60
E28		20 c. on 2d. pale red-brown	..	30	30
E29		25 c. on 2½d. pale scarlet	..	30	30
E30	147	2 s. 50 c. on 2s. 6d. yellow-green	..	5·50	18·00
E31	148	5 s. on 5s. red	..	..	17·00	17·00
E32		10 s. on 10s. ultramarine	..	18·00	17·00
E26/32		.. ..	*Set of* 7	38·00	45·00

*This is the local release date. The stamps were placed on sale in London on 3 May.

POSTAGE DUE STAMPS

B. M. A.
ERITREA

10 CENTS

(ED 1)

1948. *Postage Due stamps of Great Britain surch as Type* ED 1.

ED1	D 1	5 c. on ½d. emerald	..	..	9·00	18·00
ED2		10 c. on 1d. carmine	..	..	7·50	18·00
		a. No stop after "B"	..	85·00	
ED3		20 c. on 2d. agate	..	..	7·00	13·00
		a. No stop after "A"	..	60·00	
		b. No stop after "B" (R. 1/9)	..	90·00	
ED4		30 c. on 3d. violet	..	..	8·00	12·00
ED5		1 s. on 1s. deep blue	..	..	15·00	22·00
ED1/5.		.. .. ..	*Set of* 5	42·00	75·00

1950 (6 Feb). *As Nos.* ED1/5, *but surch* "B.A. ERITREA" *and new values instead of* 'B.M.A.' *etc.*

ED6	D 1	5 c. on ½d. emerald	..	11·00	28·00
ED7		10 c. on 1d. carmine	..	8·00	14·00
		a. "C" of "CENTS" omitted	..	£1300	
		ab. "C" omitted and vertical oblong for "E" of "CENTS"	..	£2000	
ED8		20 c. on 2d. agate	..	..	9·50	13·00
ED9		30 c. on 3d. violet	..	..	9·50	13·00
ED10		1 s. on 1s. deep blue	..	..	15·00	22·00
		a. Stop after "A" omitted (R. 2/13)	..	£225	
ED6/10		.. .. ..	*Set of* 5	48·00	80·00

No. ED7a, and probably No. ED7ab, occurred on R.7/20, but the error was quickly corrected.

Stamps of Ethiopia were used in Eritrea after 15 September 1952 following federation with Ethiopia.

SOMALIA
BRITISH OCCUPATION

E.A.F.

(S 1. "East Africa Forces")

1943 (15 Jan)–**46**. *Stamps of Great Britain optd with Type* S 1, *in blue.*

S1	128	1d. pale scarlet ..	..	..	60	40
S2		2d. pale orange ..	..	..	1·50	1·25
S3		2½d. light ultramarine ..	..	..	30	3·50
S4		3d. pale violet ..	..	..	50	15
S5	129	5d. brown	..	..	50	40
S6		6d. purple	..	..	30	90
S7	130	9d. deep olive-green	..	..	60	2·25
S8		1s. bistre-brown	..	..	1·50	15
S9	131	2s. 6d. yellow-green (1946)	..	6·00	6·00
S1/9		..	..	*Set of* 9	10·50	13·50
S8/9 Optd "Specimen"		..		*Set of* 2	£250	

The note *re* used prices above Type M 1 of Middle East Forces also applies to the above issue.

BRITISH MILITARY ADMINISTRATION

(Currency. 100 cents = 1 shilling)

1948 (27 May). *Stamps of Great Britain surch* "B.M.A./ SOMALIA" *and new values, as Types* E 1 *and* E 2 *of Eritrea.*

S10	128	5 c. on ½d. pale green ..	..	..	40	1·25
S11		15 c. on 1½d. pale red-brown	..	..	65	10·00
S12		20 c. on 2d. pale orange	..	..	75	3·25
S13		25 c. on 2½d. light ultramarine ..	..	50	4·00
S14		30 c. on 3d. pale violet	..	..	2·00	9·00
S15	129	40 c. on 5d. brown	..	..	40	20
S16		50 c. on 6d. purple	..	..	40	2·00
S17	130	75 c. on 9d. deep olive-green	..	2·00	13·00
S18		1 s. on 1s. bistre-brown..	..	1·25	20
S19	131	2 s. 50 c. on 2s. 6d. yellow-green	..	3·25	17·00
		a. Misplaced stop (R. 4/7)	..	..	80·00	£180
S20		5 s. on 5s. red	..	..	7·00	25·00
S10/20		..	..	*Set of* 11	17·00	75·00

For illustration of No. S19a, see previous column above No. E1 of Eritrea.

BRITISH ADMINISTRATION

1950 (2 Jan). *As Nos.* S10/20, *but surch* "B.A./SOMALIA" *and new values, instead of* "B.M.A." *etc.*

S21	128	5 c. on ½d. pale green ..	..	..	20	2·00
S22		15 c. on 1½d. pale red-brown	..	..	60	12·00
S23		20 c. on 2d. pale orange ..	..	60	3·50
S24		25 c. on 2½d. light ultramarine..	..	40	4·50
S25		30 c. on 3d. pale violet	..	..	1·00	3·00
S26	129	40 c. on 5d. brown	..	..	55	85
S27		50 c. on 6d. purple	..	..	40	1·00
S28	130	75 c. on 9d. deep olive-green	..	1·00	4·75
S29		1 s. on 1s. bistre-brown..	..	60	1·50
S30	131	2 s. 50 c. on 2s. 6d. yellow-green	..	4·00	18·00
S31		5 s. on 5s. red	..	..	7·50	26·00
S21/31		..	..	*Set of* 11	15·00	70·00

Somalia reverted to Italian Administration on 1 April 1950 later becoming independent. Later issues will be found listed in Part 8 (*Italy and Switzerland*) of this catalogue.

TRIPOLITANIA
BRITISH MILITARY ADMINISTRATION

(Currency. 100 centesimi = 1 Military Administration lira)

Normal	Misaligned surcharge (R.8/8, 18/8)

1948 (1 July). *Stamps of Great Britain surch* "B.M.A./TRIPOLI-TANIA" *and new values, as Types* E 1 *and* E 2 *of Eritrea, but expressed in M(ilitary) A(dministration) L(ire).*

T 1	128	1 l. on ½d. pale green		..	30	80
T 2		2 l. on 1d. pale scarlet		..	20	25
T 3		3 l. on 1½d. pale red-brown		..	20	50
		a. Misaligned surch	..	..	17·00	
T 4		4 l. on 2d. pale orange		..	25	50
		a. Misaligned surch		..	20·00	
T 5		5 l. on 2½d. light ultramarine		..	30	20
T 6		6 l. on 3d. pale violet		..	20	40
T 7	129	10 l. on 5d. brown	..	..	20	25
T 8		12 l. on 6d. purple	..	..	30	20
T 9	130	18 l. on 9d. deep olive-green		..	50	65
T10		24 l. on 1s. bistre-brown ..		..	50	65
T11	131	60 l. on 2s. 6d. yellow-green		..	2·00	5·00
T12		120 l. on 5s. red	..	..	8·00	14·00
T13	132	240 l. on 10s. ultramarine		..	18·00	75·00
T1/13		..	..	*Set of* 13	28·00	90·00

BRITISH ADMINISTRATION

1950 (6 Feb). *As Nos.* T1/13, *but surch.* "B.A. TRIPOLITANIA" *and new values, instead of* "B.M.A." *etc.*

T14	128	1 l. on ½d. pale green		..	90	7·00
T15		2 l. on 1d. pale scarlet		..	1·00	40
T16		3 l. on 1½d. pale red-brown		..	35	6·50
		a. Misaligned surch		..	27·00	
T17		4 l. on 2d. pale orange		..	25	4·50
		a. Misaligned surch		..	20·00	
T18		5 l. on 2½d. light ultramarine		..	25	70
T19		6 l. on 3d. pale violet		..	90	1·75
T20	129	10 l. on 5d. brown	..	..	30	2·50
T21		12 l. on 6d. purple	..	..	60	50
T22	130	18 l. on 9d. deep olive-green		..	65	1·60
T23		24 l. on 1s. bistre-brown ..		..	65	3·50
T24	131	60 l. on 2s. 6d. yellow-green		..	3·75	10·00
T25		120 l. on 5s. red	..	..	14·00	21·00
T26	132	240 l. on 10s. ultramarine		..	19·00	38·00
T14/26		..	..	*Set of* 13	38·00	85·00

1951 (3 May). *Nos.* 503/7 *and* 509/11 *of Great Britain surch* "B.A. TRIPOLITANIA" *and new values.*

T27	128	1 l. on ½d. pale orange..		..	20	3·00
T28		2 l. on 1d. light ultramarine		..	20	90
T29		3 l. on 1½d. pale green..		..	30	6·50
T30		4 l. on 2d. pale red-brown		..	20	1·25
T31		5 l. on 2½d. pale scarlet		..	30	6·50
T32	147	60 l. on 2s. 6d. yellow-green		..	3·50	14·00
T33	148	120 l. on 5s. red	..	..	7·50	18·00
T34	149	240 l. on 10s. ultramarine		..	22·00	28·00
T27/34		..	..	*Set of* 8	30·00	70·00

POSTAGE DUE STAMPS

1948. *Postage Due stamps of Great Britain surch.* "B.M.A./ TRIPOLITANIA" *and new values, as Type* ED 1 *of Eritrea, but expressed in M(ilitary) A(dministration) L(ire).*

TD1	D 1	1 l. on ½d. emerald ..		..	4·00	30·00
		a. No stop after "A"		..	55·00	
TD2		2 l. on 1d. carmine		..	2·50	28·00
		a. No stop after "A"		..	42·00	
		b. No stop after "M" (R.1/17)		..	75·00	
TD3		4 l. on 2d. agate		..	6·50	20·00
		a. No stop after "A"		..	£100	
		b. No stop after "M"				
TD4		6 l. on 3d. violet		..	7·50	20·00
TD5		24 l. on 1s. deep blue ..		..	26·00	80·00
TD1/5		..	..	*Set of* 5	42·00	£160

1950 (6 Feb). *As Nos.* TD1/5, *but surch* "B.A. TRIPOLITANIA" *and new values, instead of* "B.M.A." *etc.*

TD 6	D 1	1 l. on ½d. emerald ..		..	7·50	48·00
		a. No stop after "B"		..	90·00	
TD 7		2 l. on 1d. carmine		..	2·50	23·00
		a. No stop after "B"		..	60·00	
TD 8		4 l. on 2d. agate		..	2·75	25·00
		a. No stop after "B"		..	65·00	
TD 9		6 l. on 3d. violet		..	15·00	60·00
		a. No stop after "B"		..	£130	
TD10		24 l. on 1s. deep blue ..		..	32·00	£100
		a. No stop after "A"		..	£250	
		b. No stop after "B"		..	£250	
TD6/10		..	..	*Set of* 5	55·00	£225

Tripolitania became part of the independent kingdom of Libya on 24 December 1951.

British Postal Agencies in Eastern Arabia

12 pies = 1 anna; 16 annas = 1 rupee

Certain Arab States in Eastern Arabia, whilst remaining independent, had British postal administrations.

Bahrain and Kuwait (from 1948) and Qatar (from 1957) used British stamps overprinted and surcharged in local currency. Abu Dhabi (from 1964) and Trucial States (from 1961 and used only in Dubai) had definitive issues made under the auspices of the British Agencies.

In addition, British stamps were surcharged with value only for use in Muscat and certain other states. They were formerly listed under Muscat as they were first put on sale there, but in view of their more extended use, the list has been transferred here, retaining the same numbering.

The stamps were used in Muscat from 1 April 1948 to 29 April 1966; in Dubai from 1 April 1948 to 6 January 1961; in Qatar: Doha from August 1950, Umm Said from February 1956, to 31 March 1957; and in Abu Dhabi from 30 March 1963 (Das Island from December 1960) to 29 March 1964.

Nos. 21/2 were placed on sale in Kuwait Post Offices in April and May 1951 and from February to November 1953 due to shortages of stamps with "KUWAIT" overprint. Isolated examples of other values can be found commercially used from Bahrain or Kuwait.

Stamps of Great Britain surcharged

I
ANNA
(3)

2 RUPEES
(4)

$1\frac{1}{2}$
I

$1\frac{1}{2}$
II

Two types of 1½ a. surcharge:
I. "1" 3¼ mm high and aligns with top of "2" in "½" (Rows 1 to 10).
II. "1" 3½ mm high with foot of figure below top of "2" (Rows 11 to 20).

1948 (1 Apr). *Surch with T 3 (½ a. to 1 r.) or 4 (2 r.).*

16	**128**	½ a. on ½d. pale green	..	1·50	3·25
17		1 a. on 1d. pale scarlet	..	1·50	20
18		1½ a. on 1½d. pale red-brown (I)	..	2·25	30
		a. Type II	..	2·25	30
		b. Vert pair. Nos. 18/a	..	18·00	
19		2 a. on 2d. pale orange	..	1·25	45
20		2½ a. on 2½d. light ultramarine	..	1·75	3·00
21		3 a. on 3d. pale violet ..	..	1·75	10
22	**129**	6 a. on 6d. purple	..	1·75	10

23	**130**	1 r. on 1s. bistre-brown	..	3·00	50
24	**131**	2 r. on 2s. 6d. yellow-green	..	7·00	24·00
16/24		.. .. ..	*Set of* 9	19·00	29·00

One example of No. 22 is known with the surcharge almost completely omitted from position R. 20/2 in the sheet.

$2\frac{1}{2}$
ANNAS
(5)

15
RUPEES
≡
(6)

1948 (26 Apr). *Royal Silver Wedding. Nos. 493/4 surch with T 5 or 6.*

25	**137**	2½ a. on 2½d. ultramarine	..	1·00	50
26	**138**	15 r. on £1 blue..	..	23·00	35·00

1948 (29 July). *Olympic Games. Nos. 495/8 surch with new values in "ANNAS" or "1 RUPEE", as T 5/6, but in one line on 2½ a. (vert) or 6 a. and 1 r. (horiz) and grills obliterating former values of all except 2½ a.*

27	**139**	2½ a. on 2½d. ultramarine	..	35	1·25
28	**140**	3 a. on 3d. violet	..	45	1·60
29	**141**	6 a. on 6d. bright purple	..	45	1·60
30	**142**	1 r. on 1s. brown	..	1·25	1·90
		a. Surch double	..	£600	
27/30		.. .. ..	*Set of* 4	2·25	5·75

1949 (10 Oct). *75th Anniv of Universal Postal Union. Nos. 499/502 surch with new values in "ANNAS" or "1 RUPEE" as T 3/4, but all in one line, with grills obliterating former values.*

31	**143**	2½ a. on 2½d. ultramarine	..	60	2·25
32	**144**	3 a. on 3d. violet	..	60	2·25
33	**145**	6 a. on 6d. bright purple	..	60	1·75
34	**146**	1 r. on 1s. brown	..	3·00	2·50
31/4		.. .. ..	*Set of* 4	4·25	8·00

≡ 2 RUPEES
(6a)

≡ 2 RUPEES
(6b)

Type 6a. "2" and "RUPEES" level and in line with lower of the two bars.
Type 6b. "2" raised in relation to "RUPEES" and whole surcharge below the lower bar.

1950 (2 Oct)–**55**. *Nos. 503/8 surch as T 3 and No. 509 with T 6a.*

35	**128**	½ a. on ½d. pale orange (3.5.51)	..	30	5·50
36		1 a. on 1d. light ultramarine (3.5.51) ..		30	2·75
37		1½ a. on 1½d. pale green (I) (3.5.51)	..	2·25	15·00
		a. Type II	..	2·25	15·00
		b. Vert pair. Nos. 37/a	..	25·00	
38		2 a. on 2d. pale red-brown (3.5.51)	..	30	5·50
39		2½ a. on 2½d. pale scarlet (3.5.51)	..	30	13·00
40	**129**	4 a. on 4d. light ultramarine	..	30	1·75
41	**147**	2 r. on 2s. 6d. yellow-green (3.5.51)	..	22·00	5·50
		a. Surch with Type 6b (1955)	..	95·00	65·00
35/41		.. .. ..	*Set of* 7	23·00	42·00

British Solomon Islands

12 pence (d) = 1 shilling; 20 shillings = 1 pound

PROTECTORATE

1937 (13 May). *Coronation. As Nos. 95/7 of Antigua.*
P 11×11½.

57	1d. violet		30	50
58	1½d. carmine		30	60
59	3d. blue		50	50
57/9		*Set of* 3	1·00	1·40
57/9 Perf "Specimen"		*Set of* 3	60·00	

5 Spears and Shield

6 Native Constable and Chief

7 Canoe House

8 Roviana Canoe

(Recess D.L.R. (2d., 3d., 2s. and 2s. 6d.), Waterlow (others))

1939 (1 Feb)–**1951**. *T* 5/8 *and similar designs. Wmk Mult Script
CA. P* 13½ (2d., 3d., 2s. and 2s. 6d.) *or* 12½ (others).

60	½d. blue and blue-green		15	80
61	1d. brown and deep violet		15	70
62	1½d. blue-green and carmine		50	1·25
63	2d. orange-brown and black		60	1·50
	a. Perf 12 (7.11.51)		30	1·50
64	2½d. magenta and sage-green		1·25	1·00
	a. Imperf horiz (vert pair)		£8000	
65	3d. black and ultramarine		80	1·00
	a. Perf 12 (29.11.51)		1·00	2·00
66	4½d. green and chocolate		6·50	13·00
67	6d. deep violet and reddish purple		50	1·00
68	1s. green and black		1·00	65
69	2s. black and orange		6·00	3·50
70	2s. 6d. black and violet		25·00	4·50
71	5s. emerald-green and scarlet		30·00	9·00
72	10s. sage-green and magenta (27.4.42)		7·00	8·50
60/72		*Set of* 13	70·00	42·00
60/72 Perf "Specimen"		*Set of* 13	£275	

Designs: *Horiz* (*as T* 8)—1½d. Artificial Island, Malaita; 1s.
Breadfruit; 5s. Malaita canoe. (*As T* 7)—3d. Roviana canoes; 2s.
Tinakula volcano; 2s. 6d. Common Scrub Hen. *Vert* (*as T* 6)—4½d.,
10s. Native house, Reef Islands; 6d. Coconut plantation.

1946 (15 Oct). *Victory. As Nos. 110/11 of Antigua.*

73	1½d. carmine		15	60
74	3d. blue		15	10
73/4 Perf "Specimen"		*Set of* 2	55·00	

Pocket handkerchief
flaw (R. 1/6)

1949 (14 Mar). *Royal Silver Wedding. As Nos. 112/13 of
Antigua.*

75	2d. black		50	40
	a. Pocket handkerchief flaw		17·00	
76	10s. magenta		13·00	10·00

1949 (10 Oct). *75th Anniv of U.P.U. As Nos. 114/17 of Antigua.*

77	2d. red-brown		1·00	1·00
78	3d. deep blue		1·75	1·00
79	5d. deep blue-green		1·25	1·40
80	1s. blue-black		1·25	1·00
77/80		*Set of* 4	4·75	4·00

POSTAGE DUE STAMPS

D 1

(Typo B.W.)

1940 (1 Sept). *Wmk Mult Script CA. P* 12.

D1	D 1	1d. emerald-green		5·50	6·50
D2		2d. scarlet		6·00	6·50
D3		3d. brown		6·00	10·00
D4		4d. blue		9·50	11·00
D5		5d. grey-green		10·00	17·00
D6		6d. purple		10·00	15·00
D7		1s. violet		14·00	26·00
D8		1s. 6d. turquoise-green		24·00	45·00
D1/8			*Set of* 8	75·00	£120
D1/8 Perf "Specimen"			*Set of* 8	£150	

Brunei

100 cents = 1 Malayan dollar

PROTECTED STATE

Sultan Ahmed Tajudin Akhazul Khairi Wadin, 1924–1950

PRINTERS. All Brunei stamps from Nos. 34 to 95 were recess-printed by De La Rue.

5 View on Brunei River   **7** Native houses, Water Village

Retouch   Normal

RETOUCHES. We list the very distinctive 5 c. Retouch (top left value tablet, 1st row, 8th stamp) but there are others of interest, notably in the clouds.

1924 (Feb)–**37.** *Printed from single plates as Type* II, *except* 30 c. *and* $1 *as Type* I. *Wmk Mult Script CA. P* 14.

60	5	1 c. black (9.26) ..	..	..	..	60	35
61		2 c. brown (3.24)				90	3·75
62		2 c. green (3.33) ..				60	30
63		3 c. green (3.24) ..				80	4·75
64		4 c. maroon (3.24)				1·50	75
65		4 c. orange (1929)				1·00	50
66		5 c. orange-yellow* (3.24)				2·75	90
		a. "5 c." retouch				£140	£110
67		5 c. grey (1931) ..				9·00	8·50
		a. "5 c." retouch				£325	£275
68		5 c. chocolate (1933)				5·50	15
		a. "5 c." retouch				£160	50·00
69	7	6 c. intense black** (3.24)				11·00	10·00
70		6 c. scarlet (1931)				3·75	11·00
71	5	8 c. ultramarine (9.27) ..				6·00	5·00
72		8 c. grey-black (1933)				5·50	55
73		10 c. purple/*yellow* (3.37)				11·00	23·00
74	7	12 c. blue ..				4·50	9·00
		a. Pale greenish blue (1927)				£130	£200
75	5	25 c. slate-purple (1931) ..				5·00	11·00
76		30 c. purple and orange-yellow (1931)				7·00	16·00
77		50 c. black/*emerald* (1931)				7·00	15·00
78		$1 black and red/*blue* (1931) ..				24·00	65·00
60/78		..			*Set of* 19	95·00	£160
60/72, 74/8 Optd/Perf "Specimen"					*Set of* 18	£350	

*For 5 c. orange, see No. 82. No. 66 is a "Wet" printing and No. 82 a "Dry".

**For 6 c. black, see No. 83. Apart from the difference in shade there is a variation in size, No. 69 being 37¾ mm long and No. 83 39 mm.

The 2 c. orange and 3 c. blue-green in Type **5**, and the 6 c. greenish grey, 8 c. red and 15 c. ultramarine in Type **7** were not issued without the Japanese Occupation overprint, although unoverprinted examples exist (*Price for set of* 5, £400 *un*).

During the life of this issue De La Rue changed the method of production from a "Wet" to a "Dry" process. Initially the stamps were printed on ungummed paper which was dampened before being put on the press. Once the paper had dried, and contracted in the process, the gum was then applied. "Dry" printings, introduced around 1934, were on pre-gummed paper. The contraction of the

"Wet" printings was considerable and usually involves a difference of between 0.5 mm and 1 mm when compared with the larger "Dry" printings. The following stamps occur from both "Wet" and "Dry" printings: 1 c., 2 c. green, 4 c. orange, 5 c. chocolate, 6 c. scarlet, 8 c. grey-black, 10 c. and 25 c.

Stamps of this issue can be found either line or comb perforated.

Brunei was occupied by the Japanese Army in January 1942 and remained under Japanese administration until liberated by the 9th Australian Division in June 1945.

After the cessation of hostilities with the Japanese postal services were re-introduced by the British Military Administration. Post offices under B.M.A. control were opened at Brunei Town and Kuala Belait on 17 December 1945 where B.M.A. overprints on the stamps of NORTH BORNEO and SARAWAK were used until the reappearance of Brunei issues on 2 January 1947.

Redrawn clouds (R. 1/1
of No. 80*ab* only)

1947 (2 Jan)–**51.** *Colours changed and new values. Wmk Mult Script CA. P* 14.

79	5	1 c. chocolate				50	1·25
		a. "A" of "CA" missing from wmk			£1100	
80		2 c. grey ..		..		90	1·25
		a. Perf 14½×13½ (25.9.50)				1·50	3·50
		ab. Black (27.6.51)				2·00	4·75
		ac. Redrawn clouds				60·00	
81	7	3 c. green				1·00	2·50
82	5	5 c. orange*				80	1·25
		a. "5 c." retouch				55·00	75·00
		b. Perf 14½×13½ (25.9.50)				4·00	10·00
		c. Ditto "5 c." retouch ..				£120	£170
83	7	6 c. black*				1·00	2·75
84	5	8 c. scarlet				40	70
		a. Perf 13 (25.1.51)				55	8·00
85		10 c. violet				70	20
		a. Perf 14½×13½ (25.9.50)				2·00	4·50
86		15 c. ultramarine ..				50	60
87		25 c. deep claret				1·00	6·00
		a. Perf 14½×13½ (25.1.51)				1·50	6·00
88		30 c. black and orange				1·00	1·00
		a. Perf 14½×13½ (25.1.51)				1·50	10·00
89		50 c. black				1·50	55
		a. Perf 13 (25.9.50)				1·75	12·00
90		$1 black and scarlet				3·00	15
91		$5 green and red-orange (2.2.48)				16·00	14·00
92		$10 black and purple (2.2.48)				38·00	30·00
79/92					*Set of* 14	60·00	50·00
79/92 Perf "Specimen"		..			*Set of* 14	£200	

*See also Nos. 66 and 69.

The 1, 2, 3, 5, 6, 10 and 25 c. values utilised the plates of the pre-war issue and were line perforated until the introduction of the 14½×13½ comb machine for some values in 1950–51. The 8, 15, 50 c., $1, $2 and $5 were from new plates with the sheets comb perforated. The 30 c. was initially a pre-war plate, but it is believed that a new plate was introduced in 1951.

8 Sultan Ahmed Tajudin and Water Village

1949 (22 Sept). *Sultan's Silver Jubilee. Wmk Mult Script CA. P* 13.

93	8	8 c. black and carmine	..	..	55	60
94		25 c. purple and red-orange	..	..	55	1·10
95		50 c. black and blue	..	..	70	80
93/5	..	..	..	*Set of 3*	1·60	2·25

1949 (10 Oct). *75th Anniv of Universal Postal Union. As Nos.* 114/17 *of Antigua.*

96		8 c. carmine	..	..	1·50	1·25
97		15 c. deep blue	..	..	2·00	1·50
98		25 c. magenta	..	..	1·50	1·50
99		50 c. blue-black	..	..	1·75	1·25
96/9	..	..	..	*Set of 4*	6·00	5·00

JAPANESE OCCUPATION OF BRUNEI

Japanese forces landed in Northern Borneo on 15 December 1941 and the whole of Brunei had been occupied by 6 January 1942.

Brunei, North Borneo, Sarawak and, after a short period, Labuan, were administered as a single territory by the Japanese. Until September–October 1942, previous stamp issues, without overprint, continued to be used in conjunction with existing postmarks. From the Autumn of 1942 onwards unoverprinted stamps of Japan were made available and examples can be found used from the area for much of the remainder of the War. Japanese Occupation issues for Brunei, North Borneo and Sarawak were equally valid throughout the combined territory but not, in practice, equally available.

大 日 本

參 弗

南政国本日大 . . . . . . 便 郵 国 帝
(1) (2)

("Imperial Japanese   ("Imperial Japanese
Government")   Postal Service $3")

1942 (Oct)–**44**. *Stamps of Brunei handstamped with T* 1 *in violet to blue. Wmk Mult Script CA (except Nos.* J18/19, *Mult Crown CA).P* 14.

J 1	5	1 c. black	..	..	..	6·00	23·00
		a. Red opt	..	..	..	40·00	55·00
J 2		2 c. green	..	..	..	45·00	£100
J 3		2 c. orange (1943)	..	..	..	2·50	9·00
J 4		3 c. green	..	..	..	28·00	75·00
J 5		4 c. orange	..	..	..	3·00	13·00
J 6		5 c. chocolate	..	..	..	3·00	13·00
		a. "5 c." retouch	..	..	..	£150	£375
J 7	7	6 c. greenish grey (*p* 14×11½) (1944)	..	50·00	£200
J 8		6 c. scarlet	..	..	..	£550	£550
J 9	5	8 c. grey-black	..	..	..	£650	£850
J10	7	8 c. red	..	..	..	3·75	12·00
J11	5	10 c. purple/*yellow*	..	..	..	8·50	26·00
J12	7	12 c. blue	..	..	..	19·00	26·00
		a. Red opt	..	..	..	£100	£150
J13		15 c. ultramarine (1944)	..	..	13·00	25·00
J14	5	25 c. slate-purple	..	..	..	23·00	48·00
		a. Red opt	..	..	..	£150	£225
J15		30 c. purple and orange-yellow	..	90·00	£180
J16		50 c. black/*emerald*	..	..	..	38·00	60·00
		a. Red opt	..	..	..	£150	
J17		$1 black and red/*blue* (1944)	..	55·00	70·00
J18		$5 carmine/*green* (1944)	..	..	£800	£1500
J19		$25 black/*red* (1944)	..	..	£850	£1500

The overprint varies in shade from violet to blue, and, being handstamped, exists double, double one inverted and treble.

Nos. J3, J7, J10 and J13 were not issued without the overprint.

1944 (11 May). *No.* J1 *surch with T* 2 *in orange-red.*

J20	5	$3 on 1 c. black	..	..	£5000	£4500
		a. Surch on No. 60 of Brunei	..		£6000

Three separate handstamps were used to apply Type **2**, one for the top line, one for the bottom and the third for the two central characters.

Burma

12 pies = 1 anna; 16 annas = 1 rupee

BRITISH ADMINISTRATION

From 1 January 1886 Burma was a province of the Indian Empire but was separated from India and came under direct British administration on 1 April 1937.

BURMA **BURMA**

(1) (1a)

1937 (1 April). *Stamps of India* (*King George V inscr* "INDIA POSTAGE") *optd with T* **1** *or* **1a** (*rupee values*). *W* **69**. *P* 14.

1	3 p. slate	..	..	..	..	..	30	10
2	½ a. green						30	10
3	9 p. deep green	..	..	..	..	65	10
4	1 a. chocolate ..				..	30	10
5	2 a. vermilion (*small die*)	..	..	40	10
6	2½ a. orange	..	..	..	..	30	10
7	3 a. carmine ..	..	..	..	..	75	30
8	3½ a. deep blue ..				..	65	10
	a. *Dull blue* ..	..	..	..	4·00	4·00
9	4 a. sage-green	..	..	..	..	70	10
10	6 a. bistre	..	..	..	..	60	35
11	8 a. reddish purple	..	..	..	1·50	10
12	12 a. claret	..	..	..	..	2·50	85
13	1 r. chocolate and green	..	..	15·00	1·75
14	2 r. carmine and orange	..	..	18·00	7·50
15	5 r. ultramarine and purple ..	..	35·00	12·00
16	10 r. green and scarlet..	..	..	60·00	45·00
17	15 r. blue and olive	..	..	..	£180	85·00
18	25 r. orange and blue ..	..	..	£350	£170
1/18	..	..	..	..	*Set of* 18	£600	£275

The opt is at top on all values except the 3 a.

2 King George VI
and "Chinthes"

3 King George VI
and "Nagas"

4 Royal Barge

8 King George VI
and Peacock

10 Elephants' Heads

Extra trees flaw (R. 11/8)

(Des Maung Kyi (2 a. 6 p.), Maung Hline (3 a.), Maung Ohn Pe (3 a. 6 p.) and N. K. D. Naigamwalla (8 a.). Litho Security Ptg Press, Nasik)

1938 (15 Nov)–**40**. *T* **2/4**, **8** *and similar designs. W* **10**. *P* 14 (*vert*) *or* 13½ × 13 (*horiz*).

18a	2	1 p. red-orange (1.8.40)	..	..	3·00	80
19		3 p. bright violet	..	..	20	30
20		6 p. bright blue	..	..	20	10
21		9 p. yellow-green	..	..	1·00	80
22	3	1 a. purple-brown	..	..	20	10
23		1½ a. turquoise-green	..	..	20	60
24		2 a. carmine	..	..	45	10
25	4	2 a. 6 p. claret ..	..	..	10·00	80
26	—	3 a. dull violet ..	..	..	12·00	1·00
27	—	3 a. 6 p. light blue and blue	..	1·25	3·75
		a. Extra trees flaw	..	..	35·00	
28	3	4 a. greenish blue	..	..	60	10
29	—	8 a. myrtle-green	..	..	4·50	30
30	8	1 r. purple and blue	..	..	9·00	20
31		2 r. brown and purple	..	..	14·00	1·75
32	—	5 r. violet and scarlet	..	..	48·00	20·00
33	—	10 r. brown and myrtle	..	..	60·00	38·00
18a/33		..	..	*Set of* 16	£150	60·00

Designs: *Horiz* (*as T* **4**)—3 a. Burma teak; 3 a. 6 p. Burma rice; 8 a. River Irrawaddy. *Vert* (*as T* **8**)—5 r., 10 r. King George VI and "Nats".

The 1 a. exists lithographed and typographed, the latter having a "Jubilee" line in the sheet margin.

COMMEMORATION POSTAGE STAMP 6ᵗʰ MAY 1840

(11)

1940 (6 May) *Centenary of First Adhesive Postage Stamps. No.* 2? *surch with T* **11**.

34	4	1 a. on 2 a. 6 p. claret	..	..	3·00	8?

For stamps issued in 1942–45 see under Japanese Occupation.

CHIN HILLS DISTRICT. This area, in the far north-west o[f] the country, remained in British hands when the Japanes[e] overran Burma in May 1942.

During the period July to December 1942 the local official[s] were authorised to produce provisional stamps and the letter[s] "OHMS" are known overprinted by typewriter on Nos. 3, 20[,] 22/4, 28/9 and 31 of Burma or handstamped, in violet, on [...]

25, 27 and 29. The two types can also occur together or in combination with a handstamped "SERVICE".

From early in 1943 ordinary postage stamps of India were used from the Chin Hills post offices of Falam, Haka, Fort White and Tiddim, this expedient continuing until the fall of Falam to the Japanese on 7 November 1943.

The provisional stamps should only be collected on Official cover where dates and the sender's handwriting can be authenticated.

BRITISH MILITARY ADMINISTRATION

MILY ADMN	MILY ADMN
(12)	(13)

1945 (from 16 June). *Nos. 18a to 33 optd with T* **12** (*small stamps*) *or* **13** (*others*) *by Security Printing Press, Nasik.*

35	2	1 p. red-orange	..	..	10	10
		a. Opt omitted (in pair with normal)	..	£1300		
36		3 p. bright violet	..	..	10	30
37		6 p. bright blue ..	..	..	10	30
38		9 p. yellow-green	..	..	30	30
39	3	1 a. purple-brown (16.6)	..	..	10	10
40		1½ a. turquoise-green (16.6)	..	..	10	15
41		2 a. carmine	..	..	10	15
42	4	2 a. 6 p. claret	..	..	1·00	60
43	–	3 a. dull violet	..	..	1·50	20
44	–	3 a. 6 p. light blue and blue	..	..	10	70
		a. Extra trees flaw	..	..	12·00	
45	3	4 a. greenish blue	..	..	10	25
46	–	8 a. myrtle-green	..	..	10	40
47	8	1 r. purple and blue	..	..	50	50
48		2 r. brown and purple	..	..	50	1·00
49	–	5 r. violet and scarlet	..	..	50	1·00
50	–	10 r. brown and myrtle	..	..	50	1·00
35/50		..	..	*Set of* 16	4·50	6·25

Only the typographed version of the 1 a., No. 22, received this overprint.

BRITISH CIVIL ADMINISTRATION

1946 (1 Jan). *As Nos. 19/33, but colours changed.*

51	2	3 p. brown	..	..	10	90
52		6 p. deep violet ..	..	..	10	30
53		9 p. green	..	..	15	1·60
54	3	1 a. blue	..	..	15	20
55		1½ a. orange	..	..	15	10
56		2 a. claret	..	..	15	40
57	4	2 a. 6 p. greenish blue ..	..	..	40	2·00
57a	–	3 a. blue-violet ..	..	..	6·50	2·50
57b	–	3 a. 6 p. black and ultramarine	..	30	1·00
		ba. Extra trees flaw	..	..	15·00	
58	3	4 a. purple	..	..	30	30
59	–	8 a. maroon	..	..	1·75	1·25
60	8	1 r. violet and maroon	..	..	1·00	30
61		2 r. brown and orange	..	..	6·00	1·75
62	–	5 r. green and brown ..	..	6·00	8·50
63	–	10 r. claret and violet	..	..	6·00	13·00
51/63		..	..	*Set of* 15	26·00	30·00

No. 54 was printed in typography only.

14 Burman

(Des A. G. I. McGeogh. Litho Nasik)

1946 (2 May). *Victory. T* **14** *and similar vert designs. W* **10** (*sideways*). *P* 13.

64		9 p. turquoise-green ..	..	..	20	20
65		1½ a. violet	..	..	20	10
66		2 a. carmine	..	..	20	10
67		3 a. 6 p. ultramarine ..	..	..	20	20
64/7		..	..	*Set of* 4	70	50

Designs:—1½ a. Burmese woman; 2 a. Chinthe; 3 a. 6 p. Elephant.

INTERIM BURMESE GOVERNMENT

ကြားဖြတ် အစိုးရ။	ားဖြတ်ကြ အစိုးရ။	တ်ကြားဖြ အစိုးရ။
(18 *Trans.* "Interim Government")	18a	18b

Type **18a** shows the first character transposed to the end of the top line (R. 6/15).

Type **18b** shows the last two characters transposed to the front of the top line (R. 14/14).

Some sheets of the 3 p. show both errors corrected by a handstamp as Type **18**.

1947 (1 Oct). *Stamps of 1946 optd with T* **18** (*small stamps*) *or larger opt* (*others*).

68	2	3 p. brown	..	..	70	70
		a. Opt Type 18a	..	..	15·00	
		ab. Corrected by handstamp as Type 18				
		b. Opt Type 18b	..	..	15·00	
		ba. Corrected by handstamp as Type 18				
69		6 p. deep violet ..	..	..	10	30
		a. Opt Type 18a	..	..	8·00	
70		9 p. green	..	..	10	30
		a. Opt inverted	..	..	18·00	20·00
71	3	1 a. blue	..	..	10	30
		a. Vert pair, one with opt omitted				
72		1½ a. orange	..	..	90	10
73		2 a. claret	..	..	30	15
		a. Horiz pair, one with opt omitted				
		b. Opt Type 18a	..	..	16·00	
74	4	2 a. 6 p. greenish blue	..	..	1·75	95
75	–	3 a. blue-violet	..	..	2·50	1·50
76	–	3 a. 6 p. black and ultramarine	..	45	1·25
		a. Extra trees flaw	..	..	18·00	
77	3	4 a. purple	..	..	1·75	30
78	–	8 a. maroon	..	..	1·75	90
79	8	1 r. violet and maroon	..	..	2·50	30
80		2 r. brown and orange	..	..	3·25	3·25
81	–	5 r. green and brown	..	..	3·25	3·25
82	–	10 r. claret and violet	..	..	3·25	3·25
68/82		..	..	*Set of* 15	20·00	14·00

The 3 p., 6 p., 2 a., 2 a. 6 p., 3 a. 6 p. and 1 r. are also known with overprint inverted.

OFFICIAL STAMPS

BURMA	**BURMA**
(O 1)	(O 1a)

SERVICE	**SERVICE**
(O 1)	(O 1a)

1937 (Apr–June). *Stamps of India (King George V inscr* "INDIA POSTAGE") *optd with Type* O **1** *or* O **1a** (*rupee values*). *W* **69**. *P* 14.

O 1		3 p. slate	..	..	70	10
O 2		½ a. green	..	..	3·50	10
O 3		9 p. deep green	..	..	2·50	30
O 4		1 a. chocolate ..	..	..	2·50	10
O 5		2 a. vermilion (*small die*)	..	..	3·50	35
O 6		2½ a. orange	..	..	3·50	1·50
O 7		4 a. sage-green	..	..	2·50	10
O 8		6 a. bistre	..	..	3·50	4·75
O 9		8 a. reddish purple (1.4.37)	..	..	2·25	80
O10		12 a. claret (1.4.37)	..	..	2·25	3·00
O11		1 r. chocolate and green (1.4.37)	..	18·00	3·75
O12		2 r. carmine and orange	..	..	32·00	24·00
O13		5 r. ultramarine and purple ..	..	75·00	38·00
O14		10 r. green and scarlet..	..	£225	95·00
O1/14		..	..	*Set of* 14	£325	£150

For the above issue the stamps were either overprinted "BURMA" and "SERVICE" at one operation or had the two words applied separately. Research has yet to establish if all values exist with both forms of overprinting.

<table>
<tr><td colspan="2">SERVICE</td><td colspan="2">SERVICE</td></tr>
</table>

SERVICE   **SERVICE**
(O 2)   (O 3)

1939. *Nos. 19/24 and 28 optd with Type O 2 (typo) and Nos. 25 and 29/33 optd with Type O 3 (litho).*

O15	2	3 p. bright violet	..	..	15	20
O16		6 p. bright blue	..	..	15	20
O17		9 p. yellow-green	..	..	5·00	1·40
O18	3	1 a. purple-brown	..	..	15	15
O19		1½ a. turquoise-green	..	..	4·50	70
O20		2 a. carmine	..	..	1·25	20
O21	4	2 a. 6 p. claret	..	..	24·00	7·00
O22	3	4 a. greenish blue	..	..	5·50	45
O23	–	8 a. myrtle-green	..	..	24·00	3·75
O24	8	1 r. purple and blue	..	..	38·00	4·50
O25		2 r. brown and purple	..	..	45·00	8·00
O26	–	5 r. violet and scarlet	..	..	42·00	28·00
O27	–	10 r. brown and myrtle	..		£120	38·00
O15/27				Set of 13	£275	80·00

Both versions of the 1 a. value exist with this overprint.

1946. *British Civil Administration. Nos. 51/6 and 58 optd with Type O 2 (typo) and Nos. 57 and 59/63 optd with Type O 3 (litho).*

O28	2	3 p. brown	..	..	50	1·75
O29		6 p. deep violet	..	..	50	1·25
O30		9 p. green	..	..	10	2·25
O31	3	1 a. blue	..	..	10	1·50
O32		1½ a. orange	..	..	10	20
O33		2 a. claret	..	..	10	1·50
O34	4	2 a. 6 p. greenish blue	..	..	75	3·00
O35	3	4 a. purple	..	..	10	70
O36	–	8 a. maroon	..	..	50	1·75
O37	8	1 r. violet and maroon	..	..	60	2·25
O38		2 r. brown and orange	..	..	6·50	25·00
O39	–	5 r. green and brown	..	..	9·00	30·00
O40	–	10 r. claret and violet	..	..	17·00	48·00
O28/40				Set of 13	32·00	£110

1947. *Interim Burmese Government. Nos. O28/40 optd with T 18 (small stamps) or larger opt (others).*

O41	2	3 p. brown	..	..	15	40
O42		6 p. deep violet	..	..	40	10
O43		9 p. green	..	..	60	90
O44	3	1 a. blue	..	..	1·50	80
O45		1½ a. orange	..	..	2·75	20
O46		2 a. claret	..	..	1·25	15
O47	4	2 a. 6 p. greenish blue	..	..	14·00	5·00
O48	3	4 a. purple	..	..	4·25	40
O49	–	8 a. maroon	..	..	4·25	2·50
O50	8	1 r. violet and maroon	..	..	11·00	2·25
O51		2 r. brown and orange	..	..	14·00	16·00
O52	–	5 r. green and brown	..	..	14·00	18·00
O53	–	10 r. claret and violet	..	..	14·00	25·00
O41/53				Set of 13	75·00	65·00

JAPANESE OCCUPATION OF BURMA

BURMA INDEPENDENCE ARMY ADMINISTRATION

The Burma Independence Army, formed by Aung San in 1941, took control of the Delta area of the Irrawaddy in May 1942. They reopened a postal service in the area and were authorised by the Japanese to overprint local stocks of stamps with the Burmese emblem of a peacock.

Postage and Official stamps with the peacock overprints or hand-stamps were used for ordinary postal purposes with the probable exception of No. J44.

DISTINGUISHING FEATURES. Type 1. Body and head of Peacock always clearly outlined by broad uncoloured band. There are four slightly different sub-types of overprint Type 1.

Type 2. Peacock with slender neck and more delicately detailed tail. Clear spur on leg at right. Heavy fist-shaped blob of ink below and parallel to beak and neck.

Type 4. No basic curve. Each feather separately outlined. Straight, short legs.

Type 5. Much fine detail in wings and tail in clearly printed overprints. Thin, long legs ending in claws which, with the basic arc, enclose clear white spaces in well-printed copies. Blob of colour below beak shows shaded detail and never has the heavy fist-like appearance of this portion in Type 2.

Two sub-types may be distinguished in Type 5, the basic arc of one having a chord of 14–15 mm and the other 12½–13 mm.

Type 6. Similar to Type 5, but with arc deeply curved and reaching nearly to the top of the wings. Single diagonal line parallel to neck below beak.

Collectors are warned against forgeries of these overprints, often in the wrong colours or on the wrong values.

(1)

(2)

(3)

1942 (May). *Stamps of Burma overprinted with the national device of a Peacock.*

I. *Overprinted at Myaungmya*

A. *With Type 1 in black*

On Postage Stamps of King George V

J 1		9 p. deep green (No. 3)	..	..	£100
J 2		3½ a. deep blue (No. 8)	..	..	42·00

On Official Stamp of King George V

J 3		6 a. bistre (No. O8)	..	..	70·00

On Postage Stamps of King George VI

J 4	2	9 p. yellow-green	..	..	£150
J 5	3	1 a. purple-brown	..	..	£450
J 6		4 a. greenish blue (opt black on red)	..	£160
		a. Triple opt, black on double red	..	£425

On Official Stamps of King George VI

J 7	2	3 p. bright violet	..	18·00	60·00
J 8		6 p. bright blue	..	13·00	42·00
J 9	3	1 a. purple-brown	..	12·00	35·00
J 9a		1½ a. turquoise-green	..	£650	
J10		2 a. carmine	..	18·00	60·00
J11		4 a. greenish blue	..	18·00	50·00

The overprint on No. J6 was apparently first done in red in error, and then corrected in black. Some stamps have the black overprint so accurately superimposed that the red hardly shows. These are rare.

Nos. J5 and J9 exist with the Peacock overprint on both the typographed and the litho printings of the original stamps.

B. *With Types 2 or 3 (rupee values), in black*

On Postage Stamps of King George VI

J12	2	3 p. bright violet	..	16·00	50·00
J13		6 p. bright blue	..	38·00	70·00
J14		9 p. yellow-green	..	15·00	48·00
J15	3	1 a. purple-brown	..	13·00	42·00
J16		2 a. carmine	..	14·00	48·00
J17		4 a. greenish blue	..	30·00	70·00
		a. Opt double	..	£500	
		b. Opt inverted	..	£500	
		c. Opt double, one inverted	..	£350	
		d. Opt double, both inverted	..	£500	
J18		1 r. purple and blue	..	£225	
J19		2 r. brown and purple	..	£140	

The Myaungmya overprints (including No. J44) are usuall[y] clearly printed.

(4)   (5)   (6)

Type **5** generally shows the details of the peacock much less clearly and, due to heavy inking, or careless impression, sometimes appears as almost solid colour.

Type **6** was officially applied only to postal stationery. However, the handstamp remained in the possession of a postal official who used it on postage stamps after the war. These stamps are no longer listed.

II. *Handstamped (at Pyapon?) with T* **4***, in black (so-called experimental type)*

On Postage Stamps of King George VI

J19a	2	6 p. bright blue	..			£250
J19b	3	1 a. purple-brown		..	..	95·00
J20		2 a. carmine	..	..	..	95·00
J21		4 a. greenish blue		..	..	£550

Unused specimens of these stamps are usually in poor condition.

III. *Overprinted at Henzada with T* **5** *in blue, or blue-black*

On Postage Stamps of King George V

J22	3 p. slate (No. 1)	..	..	3·00	17·00
	a. Opt double	..	..	10·00	45·00
J23	9 p. deep green (No. 3)	..	..	21·00	60·00
	a. Opt double	..		80·00	
J24	2 a. vermilion (No. 5)	..	..	£100	£180

On Postage Stamps of King George VI

J25	2	1 p. red-orange	..	..	£160	£225
J26		3 p. bright violet	..	..	26·00	65·00
J27		6 p. bright blue	..	..	24·00	48·00
		a. Opt double	..		£100	
		b. Clear opt, on back and front	..	£225		
J28		9 p. yellow-green	..	..	£550	
J29	3	1 a. purple-brown	..	..	8·50	32·00
		a. Opt inverted	..	..	£350	
J30		1½ a. turquoise-green	..	..	20·00	55·00
		a. Opt omitted (in pair with normal)	..	£1200		
J31		2 a. carmine	..	..	20·00	55·00
J32		4 a. greenish blue	..	..	42·00	90·00
		a. Opt double	..	..	£225	
		b. Opt inverted	..	..	£800	

On Official Stamps of King George VI

J33	2	3 p. bright violet	..	..	£100	£190
J34		6 p. bright blue	..	..	£130	£190
J35	3	1½ a. turquoise-green	..	..	£130	£190
J35a		2 a. carmine	..	..	£325	£350
J36		4 a. greenish blue	..	..	£800	

(6a)

("Yon Thon" = "Office use")

V. *Official Stamp of King George VI optd at Myaungmya with Type* **6a** *in black*

J44	7	8 a. myrtle-green	..	..	75·00

No. J44 was probably for official use.

There are two types of T **6a**, one with base of peacock 8 mm long and the other with base about 5 mm long. The neck and other details also vary. The two types are found *se-tenant* in the sheet.

Stocks of the peacock types were withdrawn when the Japanese Directorate-General took control of the postal services in the Delta in August 1942.

JAPANESE ARMY ADMINISTRATION

7   8 Farmer

1942 (1 June). *Impressed by hand. Thick yellowish paper. P* 12 × 11. *No gum.*

J45	7	(1 a.) red	..	..	..	38·00 65·00

This device was the personal seal of Yano Sitza, the Japanese official in charge of the Posts and Telegraphs department of the Japanese Army Administration. It was impressed on paper already perforated by a line machine. Some stamps show part of the papermaker's watermark, either "ABSORBO DUPLICATOR" or "ELEPHANT BRAND", each with an elephant.

Other impressions of this seal on different papers, and showing signs of wear, were not valid for postal purposes.

(Des T. Kato. Typo *Rangoon Gazette* Press)

1942 (15 June). *Value in annas. P* 11 *or* 11 × 11½. *Laid bâtonné paper. No gum.*

J46	8	1 a. scarlet	..	..	..	15·00 15·00

Some stamps show part of the papermaker's watermark, either "ELEPHANT BRAND" or "TITAGHUR SUPERFINE", each with an elephant.

½A.   **1R.**

(9)   (10)

1942 (22 Sept). (a) *Nos.* 314/17, 320/2, 325, 327 *and* 396 *of Japan surch as T* **9/10**.

J47	9	¼ a. on 1 s. chestnut (Rice harvesting)		20·00	25·00
		a. Surch inverted	..	90·00	90·00
		b. Surch double, one inverted		£130	
J48		½ a. on 2 s. bright scarlet (General Nogi)	20·00	25·00
		a. Surch inverted	..	80·00	85·00
		b. Surch double, one inverted	..	£120	
J49		¾ a. on 3 s. green (Power station)	..	42·00	45·00
		a. Surch inverted	..	£100	£100
		b. Surch double, one inverted		—	£150
J50		1 a. on 5 s. claret (Admiral Togo)	..	35·00	38·00
		a. Surch inverted	..	£120	£120
		b. Surch double, one inverted	..	£140	£140
		c. Surch omitted (in pair with normal)	—	£170	
J51		3 a. on 7 s. green (Diamond Mts)	..	70·00	80·00
		a. Surch inverted	..	£120	
J52		4 a. on 4 s. emerald (Togo)	..	35·00	40·00
		a. Surch inverted	..	£120	
J53		8 a. on 8 s. violet (Meiji Shrine)	..	£140	£140
		a. Surch inverted	..	£190	£200
		b. Surch double, one inverted	..	£300	
		c. Surch in red	..	£225	£250
		d. Red surch inverted	..	£325	
		e. Red surch double (black and red)	£450	
J54	10	1 r. on 10 s. deep carmine (Yomei Gate)	15·00	24·00
		a. Surch inverted	..	80·00	90·00
		b. Surch double	..	80·00	£100
		c. Surch double (black and red)	..	£325	
		d. Surch omitted (in pair with normal)	£160	£160
		e. Surch omitted (in pair with inverted surch)	..	£225	
J55		2 r. on 20 s. ultramarine (Mt Fuji)	..	42·00	42·00
		a. Surch inverted	..	£110	£110
		b. Surch double, one inverted	..	£120	
		c. Surch omitted (in pair with normal black surch)	..	£160	£160
		d. Surch in red	..	..	40·00 40·00
		e. Red surch inverted	..	£110	£110
		f. Red surch double	..	£110	£110
		g. Surch omitted (in pair with normal red surch)	..	£200	£200
		ga. Surch omitted (in pair with double red surch)	..		
		h. Surch double (black and red)	..	£250	

J56	9	5 r. on 30 s. turquoise (Torii Shrine)	12·00	27·00
		a. Surch inverted	£110	
		b. Surch double	£110	
		c. Surch double, one inverted	£150	
		d. Surch omitted (in pair with normal surch)	£160	£160
		e. Surch omitted (in pair with inverted black surch)	£225	
		f. Surch in red	23·00	32·00
		fa. Red surch inverted	90·00	90·00
		fb. J56a and J56fa *se-tenant*	£325	£325
		fc. Surch omitted (in pair with normal red surch)	£160	£160

(b) No. 386 *of Japan commemorating the fall of Singapore similarly surch*

J56g	9	4 a. on 4 + 2 s. green and red	£140	£150
		h. Surch omitted (in pair with normal)	£475	
		ha. Surch omitted (in pair with inverted surch)	£500	
		i. Surch inverted	£325	

(New Currency. 100 cents = 1 rupee)

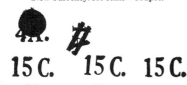

(11)	(12)	(13)

1942 (15 Oct). *Previous issues, with "anna" surcharges obliterated, handstamped with new value in cents, as T* **11** *and* **12** (*No. J57 handstamped with new value only*).

(a) On No. J46

J57		5 c. on 1 a. scarlet	11·00	15·00

(b) On Nos. J47/53

J58		1 c. on ¼ a. on 1 s. chestnut	38·00	38·00
		a. "1 c." omitted (in pair with normal)	£475	
J59		2 c. on ½ a. on 2 s. bright scarlet	38·00	38·00
J60		3 c. on ¾ a. on 3 s. green	40·00	40·00
		a. Surch in blue	£160	
J61		5 c. on 1 a. on 5 s. claret	60·00	65·00
J62		10 c. on 3 a. on 7 s. green	90·00	95·00
J63		15 c. on 4 a. on 4 s. emerald	28·00	30·00
J64		20 c. on 8 a. on 8 s. violet	£275	£225
		a. Surch on No. J53c (surch in red)	£200	£140

The "anna" surcharges were obliterated by any means available, in some cases by a bar or bars, and in others by the butt of a pencil dipped in ink. In the case of the fractional surcharges, the letter "A" and one figure of the fraction, were sometimes barred out, leaving the remainder of the fraction to represent the new value, e.g. the "1" of "½" deleted to create the 2 c. surcharge or the "4" of "¾" to create the 3 c. surcharge.

1942. *Nos. 314/17, 320/1 and 396 of Japan surcharged in cents only as T* **13**.

J65		1 c. on 1 s. chestnut (Rice harvesting)	17·00	20·00
		a. Surch inverted	£110	£110
J66		2 c. on 2 s. brt scarlet (General Nogi)	32·00	32·00
J67		3 c. on 3 s. green (Power station)	35·00	35·00
		a. Pair, with and without surch	—	£180
		b. Surch inverted	£120	
		c. Surch in blue	85·00	95·00
		d. Surch blue inverted	£200	£225
J68		5 c. on 5 s. claret (Admiral Togo)	38·00	38·00
		a. Pair, with and without surch	£250	
		b. Surch in violet	£130	£150
		ba. Surch inverted	—	£225
J69		10 c. on 7 s. green (Diamond Mts)	40·00	48·00
J70		15 c. on 4 s. emerald (Togo)	14·00	20·00
		a. Surch inverted	£120	£130
		b. Pair, with and without surch	—	£170
J71		20 c. on 8 s. violet (Meiji Shrine)	£110	85·00

Nos. J67c and J68b were issued for use in the Shan States.

BURMESE GOVERNMENT

On 1 November 1942 the Japanese Army Administration handed over the control of the postal department to the Burmese Government. On 1 August 1943 Burma was declared by the Japanese to be independent.

14 Burma State Crest	15 Farmer

(Des U Tun Tin and Maung Tin from drawing by U Ba Than. Typo Rangoon)

1943 (15 Feb). P 11. *No gum.*

J72	14	5 c. scarlet	12·00	16·00
		a. Imperf	13·00	17·00
		ab. Printed on both sides	80·00	

No. J72 was usually sold affixed to envelopes, particularly those with the embossed 1 a. King George VI stamp, which it covered. Unused specimens off cover are not often seen and blocks are rare.

1943. *Typo. No gum.* P 11½.

J73	15	1 c. orange (22 March)	1·00	2·50
		a. Brown-orange	70	2·75
J74		2 c. yellow-green (24 March)	60	1·00
		a. "3" for "2" in face value (R.2/10)		
		b. Blue-green	6·50	
J75		3 c. light blue (25 March)	70	85
		a. On laid paper	18·00	23·00
		b. Imperf between (horiz pair)		
J76		5 c. carmine (small "c") (17 March)	11·00	8·50
J77		5 c. carmine (large "C")	1·25	2·25
		a. Imperf (pair)	£160	
		b. "G" for "C" (R.2/6)	£170	
J78		10 c. grey-brown (25 March)	2·50	2·75
		a. Imperf (pair)	£225	
		b. Imperf between (horiz pair)		
J79		15 c. magenta (26 March)	30	90
		a. Imperf between (vert strip of 3)		
		b. On laid paper	6·00	14·00
		c. Inverted "C" in value (R.2/3)	£120	
J80		20 c. grey-lilac (29 March)	30	65
J81		30 c. deep blue-green (29 March)	30	70

The 1 c., 2 c. and 3 c. have large "C" in value as illustrated. The 10 c. and higher values have small "c". Nos. J73/81 had the face values inserted individually into the plate used for No. J46 with the original face value removed. There were a number of printings for each value, often showing differences such as missing stops, various founts of figures or "c", in the value tablets.

The face value error, No. J74a, was later corrected.

Some sheets of No. J75a show a sheet watermark of Britannia seated within a crowned oval spread across fifteen stamps in each sheet. Examples showing part of this sheet watermark are rare.

No. J79a shows the horizontal perforations omitted between rows 3/4 and 4/5.

There are marked varieties of shade in this issue.

16 Soldier carving word "Independence"	17 Rejoicing Peasant

18 Boy with National Flag

Normal   Skyline flaw (R. 5/6)

(Des Maung Ba Thit (**16**), Naung Ohn Maung (**17**), and Maung Soi Yi (**18**). Typo State Press, Rangoon)

1943 (1 Aug). *Independence Day.* (*a*) P 11.

J82	**16**	1 c. orange	..	..	..	6·00	10·00
J83	**17**	3 c. light blue	..	..	..	6·50	11·00
J84	**18**	5 c. carmine	..	..	..	12·00	7·50
		a. Skyline flaw	..	..	..	48·00	
J82/4		..	..	..	*Set of* 3	22·00	26·00

(b) Rouletted

J85	**16**	1 c. orange	..	..	..	1·00	1·50
		b. Perf×roul	..	..	..	80·00	
		c. Imperf (pair)	..	..	..	45·00	55·00
J86	**17**	3 c. light blue	..	..	..	1·00	1·50
		b. Perf×roul	..	..	..	80·00	85·00
		c. Imperf (pair)	..	..	..	45·00	55·00
J87	**18**	5 c. carmine	..	..	..	1·00	1·50
		a. Horiz roulette omitted (vert pair)			..		
		b. Perf×roul	..	..	..	50·00	55·00
		c. Imperf (pair)	..	..	..	45·00	55·00
		d. Skyline flaw	..	..	..	7·00	
J85/7		..	..	..	*Set of* 3	2·75	4·00

The stamps perf × rouletted may have one, two or three sides perforated.

The rouletted stamps often appear to be roughly perforated owing to failure to make clean cuts. These apparent perforations are very small and quite unlike the large, clean holes of the stamps perforated 11.

A few imperforate sets, mounted on a special card folder and cancelled with the commemorative postmark were presented to officials. These are rare.

19 Burmese   **20** Elephant carrying   **21** Watch Tower,
Woman   Log   Mandalay

(Litho G. Kolff & Co, Batavia)

1943 (1 Oct). P 12½.

J88	**19**	1 c. red-orange	..	..	..	14·00	15·00
J89		2 c. yellow-green	..	..	..	50	1·75
J90		3 c. deep violet	..	..	..	50	2·25
		a. *Bright violet*	..	..	..	70	2·25
J91	**20**	5 c. carmine	..	..	..	55	60
J92		10 c. blue	..	..	..	65	95
J93		15 c. red-orange	..	..	..	65	1·75
J94		20 c. yellow-green	..	..	..	65	1·75
J95		30 c. olive-brown	..	..	..	65	1·75
J96	**21**	1 r. red-orange	..	..	..	30	1·75
J97		2 r. bright violet	..	..	..	30	2·25
J88/97		..	..	..	*Set of* 10	17·00	27·00

ဗမာနိုင်ငံတော်

၂၀ ဆင့်။

22 Bullock Cart   **23** Shan Woman   (**24** "Burma State" and value)

(Litho G. Kolff & Co, Batavia)

1943 (1 Oct). *Issue for Shan States.* P 12½.

J 98	**22**	1 c. olive-brown	..	..	..	18·00	26·00
J 99		2 c. yellow-green	..	..	..	20·00	26·00
J100		3 c. bright violet	..	..	..	2·75	7·50
J101		5 c. ultramarine	..	..	..	2·00	5·50
J102	**23**	10 c. blue	..	..	..	8·00	17·00
J103		20 c. carmine	..	..	..	22·00	17·00
J104		30 c. olive-brown	..	..	..	13·00	25·00
J98/104		..	..	..	*Set of* 7	75·00	£110

The Shan States, except for the frontier area around Keng Tung which was ceded to Thailand, were placed under the administration of the Burmese Government on 24 December 1943, and these stamps were later overprinted as T **24** for use throughout Burma.

1944 (1 Nov). *Optd as T* **24** (*the lower characters differ for each value*).

J105	**22**	1 c. olive-brown	..	..	..	2·50	6·00
J106		2 c. yellow-green	..	..	..	40	1·25
		a. Opt inverted	..	..	..	£275	£475
J107		3 c. bright violet	..	..	..	1·50	7·00
J108		5 c. ultramarine	..	..	..	80	1·00
J109	**23**	10 c. blue	..	..	..	1·75	2·00
J110		20 c. carmine	..	..	..	40	1·50
J111		30 c. olive-brown	..	..	..	40	1·75
J105/11		..	..	..	*Set of* 7	7·00	18·00

The British 14th Army recaptured Mandalay on 20 March 1945 and Rangoon on 6 May.

Canada

100 cents = 1 Canadian dollar

100 King George VI and Queen Elizabeth

1937 (10 May). *Coronation. P* 12.
356 **100** 3 c. carmine 85 30
No. 356 exists imperforate (*Price per pair* £375, *un*).

101 King George VI   **102** Memorial Chamber
Parliament Buildings,
Ottawa

107 Fairchild 45-80 Sekani
Seaplane over *Distributor* on
River Mackenzie

(T **101**. Photograph by Bertram Park)

1937–38. *T* **101/2**, **107** *and similar designs. (a) Postage.*
(i) *P* 12.
357	**101**	1 c. green (1.4.37)	1·50	10
		a. Booklet pane of 4 + 2 labels (14.4.37)	28·00	
		b. Booklet pane of 6 (18.5.37) ..	3·50	
358		2 c. brown (1.4.37)	1·75	10
		a. Booklet pane of 4 + 2 labels (14.4.37)	40·00	
		b. Booklet pane of 6 (3.5.38) ..	11·00	
359		3 c. scarlet (1.4.37)	2·25	10
		a. Booklet pane of 4 + 2 labels (14.4.37)	4·25	
360		4 c. yellow (10.5.37)	3·75	1·50
361		5 c. blue (10.5.37)	4·00	10
362		8 c. orange (10.5.37)	3·75	1·50
363	**102**	10 c. rose-carmine (15.6.38) ..	5·00	10
		a. Red	5·00	10
364	–	13 c. blue (15.11.38)	14·00	70
365	–	20 c. red-brown (15.6.38) ..	22·00	50
366	–	50 c. green (15.6.38)	45·00	6·00
367	–	$1 violet (15.6.38)	65·00	7·50
		a. Imperf horiz (vert pair) ..	£2500	
357/67		*Set of* 11	£150	16·00

Nos. 357/67 exist imperforate (*Prices per pair* 1 c. to 50 c. *each* £150, $1 £250 *un*).

(ii) *Coil stamps. Imperf × perf* 8
368	**101**	1 c. green (15.6.37)	3·50	1·50
369		2 c. brown (18.6.37)	3·50	2·00
370		3 c. scarlet (15.4.37)	17·00	50
368/70		*Set of* 3	22·00	3·50

(b) *Air. P* 12
371	**107**	6 c. blue (15.6.38)	9·00	40

Designs: *Horiz* (*as T* **107**)—13 c. Entrance to Halifax Harbour; 20 c. Fort Garry Gate, Winnipeg; 50 c. Entrance, Vancouver Harbour; $1 Chateau de Ramezay, Montreal.
No. 371 exists imperforate (*Price per pair* £325, *un*).

108 Queen Elizabeth II when   **109** National War
Princess and Princess Margaret   Memorial, Ottawa

110 King George VI and Queen Elizabeth

1939 (15 May). *Royal Visit. P* 12.
372	**108**	1 c. black and green	1·50	10
373	**109**	2 c. black and brown	50	40
374	**110**	3 c. black and carmine	50	10
372/4		*Set of* 3	2·25	50

Nos. 372/4 exist imperforate (*Price* £225, *un, for each pair*).

111   **112**   **113**
King George VI   King George VI   King George VI in
in Naval uniform   in Military uniform   Air Force uniform

114 Grain Elevator   **116** Parliament
Buildings

117 Ram Tank   121 Air Training Camp

122 Ontario Farm Scene   129 Alexander Graham
Bell and "Fame"

1942 (1 July)–**48.** *War Effort. T* 111/14, 116/17, 121 *and similar designs.* (*a*) *Postage.* (i) *P* 12.

375	111	1 c. green			1·50	10
		a. Booklet pane of 4 + 2 labels (12.9.42)			20·00	
		b. Booklet pane of 6 (24.11.42)			2·50	
376	112	2 c. brown			1·75	10
		a. Booklet pane of 4 + 2 labels (12.9.42)			23·00	
		b. Booklet pane of 6 (6.10.42)			18·00	
377	113	3 c. carmine-lake			1·25	50
		a. Booklet pane of 4 + 2 labels (20.8.42)			4·25	
378		3 c. purple (30.6.43)			90	10
		a. Booklet pane of 4 + 2 labels (28.8.43)			5·00	
		b. Booklet pane of 6 (24.11.47)			11·00	
379	114	4 c. slate			5·50	80
380	112	4 c. carmine-lake (9.4.43)			70	10
		a. Booklet pane of 6 (3.5.43)			3·50	
381	111	5 c. blue			3·00	10
382	–	8 c. red-brown			5·50	65
383	116	10 c. brown			5·00	10
384	117	13 c. dull green			5·50	5·00
385		14 c. dull green (16.4.43)			13·00	55
386	–	20 c. chocolate			13·00	15
387	–	50 c. violet			24·00	2·00
388	–	$1 blue			48·00	4·50
375/88				*Set of* 14	£110	12·50

Nos. 375/88 exist imperforate (*Prices per pair* 1 c. to 8 c. *each* £180, 10 c. to 20 c. *each* £250, 50 c. and $1 *each* £325, *un*).

(ii) Coil stamps. Imperf × perf 8

389	111	1 c. green (9.2.43)			1·00	1·50
390	112	2 c. brown (24.11.42)			2·25	1·00
391	113	3 c. carmine-lake (23.9.42)			1·75	4·00
392		3 c. purple (19.8.43)			4·50	2·50
393	112	4 c. carmine-lake (13.5.43)			5·50	1·50
389/93				*Set of* 5	13·00	9·50

(iii) Booklet stamps. Imperf × perf 12 (1.9.43)

394	111	1 c. green			3·00	80
		a. Booklet pane of 3			9·00	
395	113	3 c. purple			3·00	90
		a. Booklet pane of 3			9·00	
396	112	4 c. carmine-lake			3·00	1·25
		a. Booklet pane of 3			9·00	
394/6				*Set of* 3	8·00	2·75

Nos. 394/6 are from booklets in which the stamps are in strips of three, imperforate at top and bottom and right-hand end.

(iv) Coil stamps. Imperf × perf 9½

397	111	1 c. green (13.7.48)			3·75	4·00
397a	112	2 c. brown (1.10.48)			8·50	19·00
398	113	3 c. purple (2.7.48)			5·50	6·00
398a	112	4 c. carmine-lake (22.7.48)			8·50	3·50
397/8a				*Set of* 4	23·00	29·00

(b) Air. P 12

399	121	6 c. blue (1.7.42)			11·00	3·50
400		7 c. blue (16.4.43)			2·00	10

Designs: *Horiz* (*as T* 114)—8 c. Farm scene. (*As T* 117)—20 c. Launching of corvette H.M.C.S. *La Malbaie*, Sorel; 50 c. Munitions factory; $1 H.M.S. *Cossack* (destroyer).
Nos. 399/400 exist imperforate (*Price* £400, *un, for each pair*).

OMNIBUS ISSUES

Details, together with prices for complete sets, of the various Omnibus issues from the 1937 Coronation series to the B.W.I. University College set are included in a special section at the end of the listings.

1946 (16 Sept)–**47.** *Peace Re-conversion. T* 122 *and similar horiz designs. P* 12. (*a*) *Postage.*

401		8 c. brown			1·25	1·25
402		10 c. olive-green			1·75	10
403		14 c. sepia			4·00	70
404		20 c. slate			3·00	10
405		50 c. green			17·00	2·00
406		$1 purple			32·00	2·00

(b) Air

407		7 c. blue			3·75	10
		a. Booklet pane of 4 (24.11.47)			9·00	
401/7				*Set of* 7	55·00	5·50

Designs:—7 c. Canada Geese in flight; 10 c. Great Bear Lake; 14 c. St. Maurice River Power Station; 20 c. Combine Harvester; 50 c. Lumbering in British Columbia; $1 *Abegweit* (train ferry), Prince Edward Is.

1947 (3 Mar). *Birth Centenary of Bell* (*inventor of telephone*). *P* 12.

408	129	4 c. blue			15	10

130 "Canadian   131 Queen Elizabeth II
Citizenship".   when Princess

1947 (1 July). *Advent of Canadian Citizenship and Eightieth Anniv of Confederation. P* 12.

409	130	4 c. blue			10	10

(From photograph by Dorothy Wilding)

1948 (16 Feb). *Princess Elizabeth's Marriage. P* 12.

410	131	4 c. blue			10	10

132 Queen Victoria, Parliament   133 Cabot's Ship *Matthew*
Building, Ottawa, and King
George VI

1948 (1 Oct). *One Hundred Years of Responsible Government. P* 12.

411	132	4 c. grey			10	10

1949 (1 Apr). *Entry of Newfoundland into Canadian Confederation. P* 12.

412	133	4 c. green			30	10

134 "Founding of Halifax, 1749" (C. W. Jefferys)

1949 (21 June). *Bicentenary of Halifax, Nova Scotia. P* 12.
413 134 4 c. violet 10 10

135   136   137

138 King George VI 139

(From photographs by Dorothy Wilding)
1949 (15 Nov)–**51.** (i) *P* 12.
414 135 1 c. green 10 10
415 136 2 c. sepia 15 20
415a   2 c. olive-green (25.7.51) 30 10
416 137 3 c. purple 30 10
           a. Booklet pane of 4 + 2 labels (12.4.50) 2·25
417 138 4 c. carmine-lake 20 10
           a. Booklet pane of 6 (5.5.50).. .. 27·00
417b   4 c. vermilion (2.6.51) 40 10
           ba. Booklet pane of 6 .. .. 6·00
418 139 5 c. blue .. .. 1·25 10
414/18 .. .. .. *Set of* 7 2·40 35

(ii) *Imperf* × *perf* 9½ (*coil stamps*)
419 135 1 c. green (18.5.50) .. .. 90 1·00
420 136 2 c. sepia (18.5.50) .. .. 4·50 4·00
420a   2 c. olive-green (9.10.51) .. .. 1·75 1·40
421 137 3 c. purple (18.5.50) .. .. 2·25 2·00
422 138 4 c. carmine-lake (20.4.50) .. 14·00 7·50
422a   4 c. vermilion (27.11.51) .. .. 1·50 2·00
419/22a .. .. .. *Set of* 6 22·00 16·00

(iii) *Imperf* × *perf* 12 (*booklets*)
422b 135 1 c. green (18.5.50) .. .. 50 1·60
           ba. Booklet pane of 3 .. .. .. 1·50
423 137 3 c. purple (18.5.50) .. .. 1·25 85
           a. Booklet pane of 3 .. .. .. 3·75
423b 138 4 c. carmine-lake (18.5.50) .. 15·00 7·00
           ba. Booklet pane of 3 .. .. 45·00
423c   4 c. vermilion (25.10.51) .. .. 7·00 7·00
           ca. Booklet pane of 3 .. .. 21·00
422b/3c .. .. .. *Set of* 4 21·00 14·50
These booklet panes are imperforate at top, bottom and
right-hand end.

140 King George VI   141 Oil Wells in Alberta

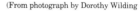
(From photograph by Dorothy Wilding

1950 (19 Jan). *As T* **135/9** *but without* "POSTES POSTAGE", *as*
T **140**. (i) *P* 12.
424 1 c. green 10 50
425 2 c. sepia 10 60
426 3 c. purple 10 90
427 4 c. carmine-lake 10 20
428 5 c. blue .. .. 30 1·25
424/8 .. .. *Set of* 5 60 3·00

(ii) *Imperf* × *perf* 9½ (*coil stamps*)
429 1 c. green 30 90
430 3 c. purple .. .. 80 1·50

1950 (1 Mar). *P* 12.
431 141 50 c. green .. .. .. 7·50 1·00

142 Drying Furs   143 Fisherman

1950 (2 Oct). *P* 12.
432 142 10 c. brown-purple 85 10

1951 (1 Feb). *P* 12.
433 143 $1 ultramarine .. .. .. 45·00 4·75

144 Sir R. L. Borden   145 W. L. Mackenzie
                              King

1951 (25 June). *Prime Ministers* (1*st issue*). *P* 12.
434 144 3 c. blue-green 10 50
435 145 4 c. rose-carmine 10 10
See also Nos. 444/5, 475/6 and 483/4.

146 Mail Trains, 1851 and   147 SS. *City of Toronto* and
      1951   SS. *Prince George*

148 Mail Coach and   149 Reproduction
DC-4M North Star   of 3d., 1851

1951 (24 Sept). *Canadian Stamp Centenary. P* 12.
436 146 4 c. black 35 1
437 147 5 c. violet .. .. 65 1·7
438 148 7 c. blue 35 1
439 149 15 c. scarlet 85 1
436/9 .. .. *Set of* 4 2·00 2·5

150 Queen Elizabeth II
when Princess and
Duke of Edinburgh

1951 (26 Oct).   *Royal Visit. P* 12.
440 **150** 4 c. violet   10   10

STAMP BOOKLETS

B 4

1937 (14 Apr)–**38**.   *Blue and white cover. Panes of four* 1 *c.,* 2 *c. and* 3 *c.* (*Nos.* 357a, 358a, 359a) *and 2 labels.*
SB28   25 c. booklet. Cover as Type B **3** with English text 80·00
  a. French text (4.1.38)   . .   . .   . .   90·00
SB29   25 c. booklet. Cover as Type B **4** with English text
    57 mm wide   . .   . .   . .   50·00
  a. English text 63 mm wide . .   . .   80·00
  b. French text 57 mm wide (4.1.38) . .   85·00
  ba. French text 63 mm wide £130

1937 (23–27 Apr).   *Red and white cover. Two panes of four* 3 *c.* (*No.* 359a) *and 2 labels.*
SB30   25 c. booklet. Cover as Type B **3** with English text
    (27 Apr)   . .   . .   . .   14·00
  a. French text (23 Apr)   . .   . .   20·00
SB31   25 c. booklet. Cover as Type B **4** with English text
    57 mm wide (27 Apr)   . .   . .   10·00
  a. English text 63 mm wide . .   . .   22·00
  b. French text 57 mm wide (23 Apr) . .   13·00
  ba. French text 63 mm wide £120

1937 (18 May)–**38**.   *Green and white cover. Four panes of six* 1 *c.* (*No.* 357b).
SB32   25 c. booklet. Cover as Type B **3** with English text 23·00
  a. French text (14.10.38)   . .   . .   30·00
SB33   25 c. booklet. Cover as Type B **4** with English text
    57 mm wide   . .   . .   . .   16·00
  a. English text 63 mm wide . .   . .   42·00
  b. French text 57 mm wide (14.10.38) . .   18·00
  ba. French text 63 mm wide £100

1938 (3 May)–**39**.   *Brown and white cover. Two panes of six* 2 *c.* (*No.* 358b).
SB34   25 c. booklet. Cover as Type B **3** with English text 28·00
  a. French text (3.3.39)   . .   . .   35·00
SB35   25 c. booklet. Cover as Type B **4** with English text
    57 mm wide   . .   . .   . .   23·00
  a. English text 63 mm wide . .   . .   50·00
  b. French text 57 mm wide . .   . .   32·00
  ba. French text 63 mm wide . .   . .   75·00

1942 (20–29 Aug)   *Red and white cover. Two panes of four* 3 *c.* (*No.* 377a) *and 2 labels.*
SB36   25 c. booklet. Cover as Type B **4** with English text 8·50
  a. French text (29 Aug)   . .   . .   12·00

1942 (12–14 Sept).   *Violet and white cover. Panes of four* 1 *c.,* 2 *c. and* 3 *c.* (*Nos.* 375a, 376a, 377a), *each with* 2 *labels.*
SB37   25 c. booklet. Cover as Type B **4** with English text
    (14 Sept)   . .   . .   . .   45·00
  a. French text (12 Sept)   . .   . .   90·00

1942 (6 Oct)–**43**.   *Brown and white cover. Two panes of six* 2 *c.* (*No.* 376b).
SB38   25 c. booklet. Cover as Type B **4** with English text 38·00
  a. French text (6.4.43)   . .   . .   60·00

1942 (24 Nov)–**46**.   *Green and white cover. Four panes of six* 1 *c.* (*No.* 375b).
SB39   25 c. booklet. Cover as Type B **4** with English text 11·00
  a. French text (16.2.43)   . .   . .   17·00
  b. Bilingual text (8.1.46)   . .   . .   17·00

1943 (3 May)–**46**.   *Orange and white cover. One pane of six* 4 *c.* (*No.* 380a).
SB40   25 c. booklet. Cover as Type B **4** with English text 3·75
  a. French text (12.5.43)   . .   . .   8·00
  b. Bilingual text (8.1.46)   . .   . .   12·00

1943 (28 Aug)–**46**.   *Purple and white cover. Two panes of four* 3 *c.* (*No.* 378a) *and* 2 *labels.*
SB41   25 c. booklet. Cover as Type B **4** with English text 10·00
  a. French text (7.9.43)   . .   . .   20·00
  b. Bilingual text (8.1.46)   . .   . .   15·00

B 5

1943 (1 Sept)–**46**.   *Black and white cover. Panes of three* 1 *c.,* 3 *c. and* 4 *c.* (*Nos.* 394a, 395a, 396a) (3×1).
SB42   25 c. booklet. Cover as Type B **5** with English text 25·00
  a. French text (18.9.43)   . .   . .   29·00
  c. Bilingual text (23.1.46)   . .   . .   27·00

B 6

1947 (24 Nov).   *Brown on orange cover. Panes of six* 3 *c. and* 4 *c.* (3×2) *and two panes of four* 7 *c.* (2×2) (*Nos.* 378b, 380a, 407a).
SB43 $1 booklet. Cover as Type B **6** with English text 25·00
  a. French text   . .   . .   . .   35·00

1950 (12 Apr–18 May).   *Purple and white cover. Two panes of four* 3 *c.* (*No.* 416a) *and* 2 *labels* (3×2).
SB44   25 c. booklet. Cover as Type B **4** with English text 5·00
  a. Bilingual text (18 May)   . .   . .   5·00

1950 (5–10 May).   *Orange and white cover. One pane of six* 4 *c.* (*No.* 417a) (3×2).
SB45   25 c. booklet. Cover as Type B **4** with English text 28·00
  a. Stitched   . .   . .   . .   60·00
  b. Bilingual text (10 May)   . .   . .   28·00

1950 (18 May).   *Black and white cover. Panes of three* 1 *c.,* 3 *c. and* 4 *c.* (*Nos.* 422ba, 423a, 423ba) (3×1).
SB46   25 c. booklet. Cover as Type B **5** with English text 50·00
  a. Bilingual text   . .   . .   . .   50·00

1951 (2 June).   *Orange and white cover. One pane of six* 4 *c.* (*No.* 417ba) (3×2).
SB47   25 c. booklet. Cover as Type B **4** with English text 6·00
  a. Stitched   . .   . .   . .   11·00
  b. Bilingual text   . .   . .   . .   7·50

1951 (25 Oct)–**52**.   *Black and white cover. Panes of three* 1 *c.,* 3 *c. and* 4 *c.* (*Nos.* 422ba, 423a, 423ca) (3×1).
SB48   25 c. booklet. Cover as Type B **5** with English text 26·00
  a. Bilingual text (9.7.52)   . .   . .   28·00

SPECIAL DELIVERY STAMPS

S 6 Canadian Coat of Arms

1938–39. *P* 12.
S 9 **S 6** 10 c. green (1.4.39) .. .. .. 18·00 2·75
S10 20 c. scarlet (15.6.38) .. .. .. 45·00 23·00
Nos. S9/10 exist imperforate (*Price* £350, *un, for each pair*).

(S 7)

1939 (1 Mar). *Surch with Type* **S 7.**
S11 **S 6** 10 c. on 20 c. scarlet .. .. .. 8·00 8·00

S 8 Coat of Arms and Flags

S 9 Lockheed L.18 Lodestar

1942 (1 July)–**1943.** *War Effort. P* 12. (*a*) *Postage.*
S12 **S 8** 10 c. green .. .. 3·50 30

(*b*) *Air*
S13 **S 9** 16 c. ultramarine .. .. .. 3·25 45
S14 17 c. ultramarine (1.4.43) .. .. 3·75 55
Nos. S12/14 exist imperforate (*Prices per un pair* 10 c. £325, 16 c. £375, 17 c. £375).

S 10 Arms of Canada and Peace Symbols

S 11 Canadair DC-4M North Star

1946 (16 Sept–5 Dec). *P* 12. (*a*) *Postage*
S15 **S 10** 10 c. green .. .. 2·00 30

(*b*) *Air*. (i) *Circumflex accent in* "EXPRES"
S16 **S 11** 17 c. ultramarine .. .. .. 4·00 3·25

(ii) *Grave accent in* "EXPRÈS"
S17 **S 11** 17 c. ultramarine (5.12.46) .. 5·00 3·75

POSTAGE DUE STAMPS

D 4

1935–65. *P* 12.
D18 **D 4** 1 c. violet (14.10.35) 40 10
D19 2 c. violet (9.9.35) 50 10
D20 3 c. violet (4.65) .. .. 2·75 5·00
D21 4 c. violet (2.7.35) .. .. .. 1·00 10
D22 5 c. violet (12.48) .. .. .. 2·50 35
D23 6 c. violet (1957) .. .. 1·50 3·00
D24 10 c. violet (16.9.35) 60 10
D18/24 .. .. *Set of* 7 8·50 8·00
The 1 c., 2 c., 4 c. and 10 c. exist imperforate (*Price* £140 *for each un pair*).

OFFICIAL STAMPS

Stamps perforated "O H M S" were introduced in May 1923 for use by the Receiver General's department in Ottawa and by the Assistant Receiver Generals' offices in provincial cities. From 1 July 1939 this use was extended to all departments of the federal government and such stamps continued to be produced until replaced by the "O.H.M.S." overprinted issue of 1949.

The perforated initials can appear either upright, inverted or sideways on individual stamps. The prices quoted are for the cheapest version. Stamps perforated with Type O **1** are only priced used. Only isolated examples are known mint and these are very rare.

A number of forged examples of the perforated "O.H.M.S." are known, in particular of Type O **2**. Many of these forged perforated initials were applied to stamps which had already been used and this can aid their detection. Genuine examples, postmarked after the perforated initials were applied, often show the cancellation ink bleeding into the holes.

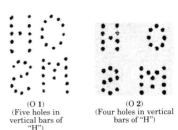

(O **1**)   (O **2**)
(Five holes in   (Four holes in vertical
vertical bars of   bars of "H")
"H")

1937 (10 May). *Coronation. No.* 356 *punctured as Type* O **1.**
O96 **100** 3 c. carmine .. .. — 40·00

1937–38. *Nos.* 357/67, 370 *and* 371 *punctured as Type* O **1.**
(*a*) *Postage*
O 97 **101** 1 c. green .. .. — 2·50
O 98 2 c. brown .. .. — 2·75
O 99 3 c. scarlet .. .. — 2·50
O100 4 c. yellow .. .. — 8·00
O101 5 c. blue .. .. — 6·50
O102 8 c. orange .. .. — 13·00
O103 **102** 10 c. rose-carmine .. .. — 20·00
a. Red .. .. — 23·00

O104 – 13 c. blue .. .. — 28·00
O105 – 20 c. red-brown .. .. .. — 28·00
O106 – 50 c. green .. .. .. — 65·00
O107 – $1 violet .. .. — 95·00
O97/107 .. .. *Set of* 11 — £250

(b) Coil stamp
O108 **101** 3 c. scarlet .. .. .. — 65·00

(c) Air
O109 **107** 6 c. blue .. .. .. — 28·00

1939 (15 May). *Royal Visit. Nos. 372/4 punctured as Type* O **1**.
O110 **108** 1 c. black and green .. — 32·00
O111 **109** 2 c. black and brown .. — 42·00
O112 **110** 3 c. black and carmine .. — 32·00
O110/12 .. .. .. *Set of* 3 — 95·00

1939 (1 July). *Air. No. 274 punctured as Type* O **2**.
O113 **59** 5 c. olive-brown .. .. 20·00 14·00

1939 (1 July). *Nos. 347/50 and 355 punctured as Type* O **2**.

(a) Postage
O114 **94** 10 c. carmine .. .. .. 50·00 38·00
O115 – 13 c. purple .. .. .. 50·00 38·00
O116 – 20 c. olive-green .. .. 70·00 48·00
O117 – 50 c. deep violet .. .. 50·00 38·00

(b) Air
O118 **99** 6 c. red-brown .. .. 50·00 42·00
O114/18 .. .. *Set of* 5 £250 £180

1939 (1 July). *Coronation. No. 356 punctured as Type* O **2**.
O119 **100** 3 c. carmine .. .. 70·00 45·00

1939 (1 July). *Nos. 357/67, 369/70 and 371 punctured as Type* O **2**. *(a) Postage*
O120 **101** 1 c. green .. .. .. 1·50 10
O121 2 c. brown .. .. .. 2·25 10
O122 3 c. scarlet .. .. .. 2·50 10
O123 4 c. yellow .. .. .. 5·00 2·25
O124 5 c. blue .. .. .. 3·50 20
O125 8 c. orange .. .. .. 10·00 3·75
O126 **102** 10 c. rose-carmine .. 48·00 3·25
a. Red .. 7·00 30
O127 – 13 c. blue .. .. .. 13·00 1·50
O128 – 20 c. red-brown .. .. 35·00 50
O129 – 50 c. green .. .. .. 40·00 8·00
O130 – $1 violet .. .. .. £110 30·00
O120/30 .. *Set of* 11 £200 42·00

(b) Coil stamps
O131 **101** 2 c. brown .. .. .. 70·00 40·00
O132 3 c. scarlet .. .. .. 70·00 40·00

(c) Air
O133 **107** 6 c. blue .. .. .. 3·00 80

1939 (1 July). *Royal Visit. Nos. 372/4 punctured as Type* O **2**.
O134 **108** 1 c. black and green .. 80·00 38·00
O135 **109** 2 c. black and brown .. 80·00 38·00
O136 **110** 3 c. black and carmine .. 80·00 38·00
O134/6 .. .. .. *Set of* 3 £225 £100

1942–43. *War Effort. Nos. 375/88 and 399/400 punctured as Type* O **2**. *(a) Postage*
O137 **111** 1 c. green 40 10
O138 **112** 2 c. brown 50 10
O139 **113** 3 c. carmine-lake .. 1·10 40
O140 3 c. purple 60 10
O141 **114** 4 c. slate .. .. .. 2·75 75
O142 **112** 4 c. carmine-lake .. 55 10
O143 **111** 5 c. blue .. .. .. 1·25 15
O144 – 8 c. red-brown .. .. 7·50 2·00
O145 **116** 10 c. brown .. .. .. 4·50 20
O146 **117** 13 c. dull green .. 5·50 5·50
O147 14 c. dull green .. 9·00 85
O148 – 20 c. chocolate .. 11·00 70
O149 – 50 c. violet .. .. .. 35·00 5·50
O150 – $1 blue .. .. .. 90·00 25·00

(b) Air
O151 **121** 6 c. blue .. .. .. 3·50 2·00
O152 7 c. blue .. .. .. 3·00 25
O137/52 .. .. *Set of* 16 £160 40·00

1946. *Peace Re-conversion. Nos. 401/7 punctured as Type* O **2**.

(a) Postage
O153 **122** 8 c. brown .. .. .. 7·00 3·50
O154 – 10 c. olive-green .. .. 3·00 15
O155 – 14 c. sepia .. .. .. 3·75 55
O156 – 20 c. slate .. .. .. 4·00 50
O157 – 50 c. green .. .. .. 22·00 5·00
O158 – $1 purple .. .. .. 60·00 15·00

(b) Air
O159 – 7 c. blue .. .. .. 2·50 40
O153/9 .. .. .. *Set of* 7 90·00 23·00

1949. *Nos. 415 and 416 punctured as Type* O **2**.
O160 **136** 2 c. sepia 75 75
O161 **137** 3 c. purple 75 75

O.H.M.S.

(O 3)

1949. *Nos. 375/6, 378, 380 and 402/7 optd as Type* O **3** *by typography.*

(a) Postage
O162 **111** 1 c. green .. .. .. 1·75 2·00
a. Missing stop after "S" .. £140 45·00
O163 **112** 2 c. brown .. .. .. 12·00 12·00
a. Missing stop after "S" .. £140 85·00
O164 **113** 3 c. purple .. .. .. 1·25 1·10
O165 **112** 4 c. carmine-lake .. 2·00 80
O166 – 10 c. olive-green .. .. 3·75 15
a. Missing stop after "S" .. 70·00 35·00
O167 – 14 c. sepia .. .. .. 4·50 1·75
a. Missing stop after "S" .. 90·00 45·00
O168 – 20 c. slate .. .. .. 12·00 60
a. Missing stop after "S" .. £130 50·00
O169 – 50 c. green £160 £110
a. Missing stop after "S" .. £800 £475
O170 – $1 purple .. .. .. 50·00 45·00
a. Missing stop after "S" .. £1300
O171 – 7 c. blue .. .. .. 24·00 7·00
a. Missing stop after "S" .. £120 60·00
O162/71 .. .. .. *Set of* 10 £225 £140

Forgeries exist of this overprint. Genuine examples are 2.3×15 mm and show the tops of all letters aligned, as are the stops.
Only a few sheets of the $1 showed the variety, No. O170a.

MISSING STOP VARIETIES. These occur on R. 6/2 of the lower left pane (Nos. O162a, O163a and O176a) and R. 10/2 of the lower left pane (O166a, O167a, O168a, O169a, O170a and O171a). No. O176a also occurs on R. 8/8 of the upper left pane in addition to R. 6/2 of the lower left pane.

1949–50. *Nos. 414/15, 416/17, 418 and 431 optd as Type* O **3** *by typography.*
O172 **135** 1 c. green 85 85
O173 **136** 2 c. sepia .. .. .. 1·75 1·50
O174 **137** 3 c. purple .. .. .. 1·00 70
O175 **138** 4 c. carmine-lake .. 1·50 15
O176 **139** 5 c. blue (1949) .. .. 2·50 2·00
a. Missing stop after "S" .. 80·00 38·00
O177 **141** 50 c. green (1950) .. 32·00 28·00
O172/7 .. .. *Set of* 6 35·00 30·00

G   G   G
(O 4) (O 5) (O 6)

Type O **6** differs from Type O **5** in having a thinner appearance and an upward sloping left serif to the lower arm. It results from a new plate introduced in 1961/62. Variations in thickness are known in Type O **4** but these are due to wear and subsequent cleaning of the plate. All are produced by typography. Examples showing the "G" applied by lithography are forgeries.

52   Canada

1950 (2 Oct)–**52**. *Nos.* 402/4, 406/7, 414/18 *and* 431 *optd with Type* O 4 (1 *to* 5 *c.*) *or* O 5 (7 *c. to* $1). (*a*) *Postage.*

O178	135	1 c. green		70	10
O179	136	2 c. sepia		1·50	1·60
O180		2 c. olive-green (11.51)		1·75	10
O181	137	3 c. purple		1·50	10
O182	138	4 c. carmine-lake		1·50	30
O183		4 c. vermilion (1.5.52)		1·60	10
O184	139	5 c. blue		2·50	30
O185	–	10 c. olive-green		3·00	10
O186	–	14 c. sepia		11·00	2·25
O187	–	20 c. slate		13·00	20
O188	141	50 c. green		10·00	7·50
O189	–	$1 purple		60·00	55·00

(*b*) *Air*

O190	–	7 c. blue		24·00	12·00
O178/90			Set of 13	£120	70·00

1950–51. *Nos.* 432/3 *optd with Type* O 5.

O191	142	10 c. brown-purple		2·25	10
		a. Opt omitted in pair with normal	£400	£350
O192	143	$1 ultramarine (1.2.51)		55·00	60·00

OFFICIAL SPECIAL DELIVERY STAMPS

1938–39. *Nos.* S9/10 *punctured as Type* O 1.

OS7	S 6	10 c. green		–	32·00
OS8		20 c. scarlet		–	60·00

1939 (1 Mar). *No.* S11 *punctured as Type* O 1.

OS9	S 6	10 c. on 20 c. scarlet		–	60·00

1939 (1 July). *Inscr* "CENTS" *at foot. No.* S7 *punctured as Type* O 2.

OS10	S 4	20 c. brown-red		£150	80·00

1939 (1 July). *No.* S8 *punctured as Type* O 2.

OS11	S 5	20 c. scarlet		80·00	38·00

1939 (1 July). *No.* S9 *punctured as Type* O 2.

OS12	S 6	10 c. green		6·00	4·50

1939 (1 July). *No.* S11 *punctured as Type* O 2.

OS13	S 6	10 c. on 20 c. scarlet		95·00	50·00

1942–43. *Nos.* S12/14 *punctured as Type* O 2. (*a*) *Postage*

OS14	S 8	10 c. green		8·00	6·50

(*b*) *Air*

OS15	S 9	16 c. ultramarine		15·00	11·00
OS16		17 c. ultramarine		8·50	6·50

1946–47. *Nos.* S15/17 *punctured as Type* O 2. (*a*) *Postage*

OS17	S 10	10 c. green		6·00	4·50

(*b*) *Air*

OS18	S 11	17 c. ultramarine (circumflex accent)	25·00	20·00
OS19		17 c. ultramarine (grave accent)		50·00	50·00

1950. *No.* S15 *optd as Type* O 3, *but larger.*

OS20	S 10	10 c. green		17·00	20·00

1950 (2 Oct). *No.* S15 *optd as Type* O 4, *but larger.*

OS21	S 10	10 c. green		26·00	26·00

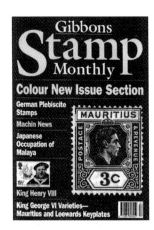

Cayman Islands

12 pence (d) = 1 shilling; 20 shillings = 1 pound

DEPENDENCY OF JAMAICA

1937 (13 May). *Coronation Issue. As Nos. 95/7 of Antigua.*
P 11×11½.

112	½d. green	..	..	..	30	20
113	1d. carmine	..	..	..	50	20
114	2½d. blue	..	..	..	95	40
112/14	..	..	..	Set of 3	1·60	70
112/14 Perf "Specimen"	..	..	Set of 3	75·00	

26 Beach View    **27** Dolphin fish
(*Coryphaena hippurus*)

(Recess D.L.R. (½d., 2d., 6d., 1s., 10s.), Waterlow (others))

1938 (5 May)–**48.** *T 26/7 and similar designs. Wmk Mult Script
CA (sideways on ¼d., 1d., 1½d., 2½d., 3d., 2s., 5s.). Various
perfs.*

115	26	¼d. red-orange (p 12½)		..	10	55
		a. Perf 13½×12½ (16.7.43)		10	55
116	27	½d. green (p 13×11½)		50	55
		a. Perf 14 (16.7.43)		..	1·25	1·40
		b. "A" of "CA" missing from wmk	..	£1000	
117	–	1d. scarlet (p 12½)	..	30	75
118	26	1½d. black (p 12½)	..	30	10
119	–	2d. violet (p 11½×13)	..	1·50	40
		a. Perf 14 (16.7.43)		60	30
120	–	2½d. bright blue (p 12½)	..	40	20
120a	–	2½d. orange (p 12½) (25.8.47)	..	1·50	50
121	–	3d. orange (p 12½)	..	40	15
121a	–	3d. bright blue (p 12½) (25.8.47)	1·50	30
122	–	6d. olive-green (p 11½×13)	..	6·50	4·00
		a. Perf 14 (16.7.43)		1·50	1·00
		b. Brownish olive (p 11½×13)		
		(8.7.47)		3·00	1·50
123	27	1s. red-brown (p 13×11½)	..	3·50	1·50
		a. Perf 14 (16.7.43)		3·50	2·00
124	26	2s. yellow-green (shades) (p 12½)	..	48·00	14·00
		a. Deep green (16.7.43)		25·00	9·00
125	–	5s. carmine-lake (p 12½)	..	32·00	15·00
		a. Crimson (1948)	..	45·00	19·00
126	–	10s. chocolate (p 11½×13)	..	23·00	9·00
		a. Perf 14 (16.7.43)		21·00	9·00
115/26a		..	..	Set of 14	80·00	35·00
115/26 Perf "Specimen"	..	..	Set of 14	£275	

Designs: *Horiz (as T 26)*—1d., 3d. Cayman Islands map; 2½d.,
5s. *Rembro* (schooner). *Vert (as T 27)*—2d., 6d., 10s. Hawksbill
Turtles.

Stop after "1946" (R.2/1)

1946 (26 Aug). *Victory. As Nos. 110/11 of Antigua.*

127	1½d. black	..	..	..	20	10
128	3d. orange-yellow	..	..	20	10
	a. Stop after "1946"	..	..	12·00	
127/8 Perf "Specimen"	..	Set of 2	65·00	

1948 (29 Nov). *Royal Silver Wedding. As Nos. 112/13 of
Antigua.*

129	½d. green	..	..	..	10	10
130	10s. violet-blue	..	..	12·00	10·00

1949 (10 Oct). *75th Anniv of Universal Postal Union. As Nos.
114/17 of Antigua.*

131	2½d. orange	..	..	..	20	30
132	3d. deep blue	..	..	1·00	70
133	6d. olive	..	..	..	75	80
134	1s. red-brown	..	..	..	75	30
131/4 ..	..	..	..	Set of 4	2·40	1·90

31 Cat Boat   **32** Coconut Grove, Cayman
Brac

(Recess B.W.)

1950 (2 Oct). *T 31/2 and similar horiz designs. Wmk Mult Script
CA. P 11½ × 11.*

135	¼d. bright blue and pale scarlet	..	15	60
136	½d. reddish violet and emerald-green	15	1·25
137	1d. olive-green and deep blue	..	60	75
138	1½d. green and brown	..	30	75
139	2d. reddish violet and rose-carmine	1·00	1·50
140	2½d. turquoise and black	..	50	60
141	3d. bright green and light blue	..	1·40	1·50
142	6d. red-brown and blue	..	2·00	1·25
143	9d. scarlet and grey-green	..	2·75	2·00
144	1s. brown and orange	..	3·25	2·75
145	2s. violet and reddish purple	..	7·50	8·00
146	5s. olive-green and violet	..	10·00	7·00
147	10s. black and scarlet	..	13·00	12·00
135/47			Set of 13	38·00	35·00

Designs:—1d. Green Turtle; 1½d. Thatch rope industry; 2d.
Cayman seamen; 2½d. Map of Cayman Islands; 3d. Parrot Fish;
6d. Bluff, Cayman Brac; 9d. Georgetown harbour; 1s. Turtle in
"crawl"; 2s. *Ziroma* (schooner); 5s. Boat-building; 10s. Government Offices, Grand Cayman.

PRICES OF SETS

Set prices are given for many issues, generally
those containing three stamps or more. Definitive
sets include one of each value or major colour
change, but do not cover different perforations,
die types or minor shades. Where a choice is
possible the set prices are based on the cheapest
versions of the stamps included in the listings.

Ceylon

100 cents = 1 rupee

CROWN COLONY

1937 (12 May). *Coronation. As Nos. 95/7 of Antigua.*
P 11×11½.

383	6 c. carmine	..	..	65	15
384	9 c. green	..	..	2·50	2·00
385	20 c. blue	..	..	3·50	3·75
383/5	..	..	*Set of 3*	6·00	5·50
383/5 Perf "Specimen"	..	..	*Set of 3*	60·00	

69 Tapping Rubber

70 Sigiriya (Lion Rock)

71 Ancient Guard-stone, Anuradhapura

72 King George VI

COCONUT PALMS

Apostrophe flaw (Frame Pl 1A R.6/6) (ptg of 1 Jan 1943 only)

(Recess B.W. (stamps perf 11 × 11½ or 11½ × 11), D.L.R. (all others) T **72** typo D.L.R.)

1938–49. *T* **69/72** *and designs as 1935–36, but with portrait of King George VI instead of King George V, "POSTAGE & REVENUE" omitted and some redrawn. Wmk Mult Script CA (sideways on 10, 15, 25, 30 c. and 1 r.). Chalk-surfaced paper (5 r.). Various perfs.*

386	69	2 c. blk & carm (*p* 11½×13) (25.4.38)		9·00	1·75
		a. Perf 13½×13 (1938)	..	£110	1·75
		b. Perf 13½ (25.4.38)	..	65	10
		c. Perf 11×11½ (17.2.44)	..	40	75
		cw. Wmk inverted	..	..	—	£350
		d. Perf 12 (22.4.49)	..	..	1·25	3·00

387	60	3 c. black & dp blue-green (*p* 13×11½) (21.3.38)	..	9·00	30
		a. Perf 13×13½ (1938)	..	£250	6·50
		b. Perf 13½ (21.3.38)	..	2·50	10
		c. Perf 14 (7.41)	..	£110	95
		d. Perf 11½×11 (14.5.42)	..	60	10
		da. "A" of "CA" missing from wmk	..	£750	£750
		e. Perf 12 (14.1.46)	..	40	40
387f	–	5 c. sage-grn & orge (*p* 13½) (1.1.43)	30	10
		fa. Apostrophe flaw	..	38·00	
		g. Perf 12 (1947)	..	1·25	30
388	–	6 c. black and blue (*p* 11×11½) (1.1.38)	30	10
389	70	10 c. blk & light bl (*p* 11½×11) (1.2.38)	1·25	10
		a. Wmk upright (1.6.44)	..	2·50	40
390	–	15 c. grn & red-brn (*p* 11½×11) (1.1.38)	1·25	10
		a. Wmk upright (23.7.45)	..	2·75	50
391	–	20 c. blk & grey-bl (*p* 11×11½) (15.1.38)	3·25	10
392	–	25 c. dp bl & choc (*p* 11½×11) (15.1.38)	3·50	30
		a. Wmk upright (1944)	..	3·50	10
393	–	30 c. carm & grn (*p* 11½×11) (1.2.38)	11·00	1·25
		a. Wmk upright (16.4.45)	..	10·00	15·00
394	–	50 c. blk & mve (*p* 13×11½) (25.4.38)	..	£160	42·00
		a. Perf 13×13½ (1938)	..	£350	2·75
		b. Perf 13½ (25.4.38)	..	13·00	30
		c. Perf 14 (4.42)	..	£100	27·00
		d. Perf 11½×11 (14.5.42)	..	3·50	30
		e. Perf 12 (14.1.46)	..	3·25	20
395	–	1 r. blue-violet & chocolate (*p* 11½×11) (1.2.38)	14·00	75
		a. Wmk upright (1944)	..	13·00	2·25
396	71	2 r. blk and carm (*p* 11×11½) (1.2.38)	12·00	1·75
396a		2 r. blk & vio (*p* 11×11½) (15.3.47)	..	1·50	1·10
397	72	5 r. green and purple (*p* 14) (1.7.38)	38·00	4·00
		a. Ordinary paper. *Green and pale purple* (19.2.43)	..	12·00	2·00
386/97a (*cheapest*)		*Set of 14*	55·00	6·50
386/97 Perf "Specimen"	..	*Set of 14*	£300	

Designs: *Vert*—5 c. Coconut Palms; 6 c. Colombo Harbour; 20 c. Plucking tea. *Horiz*—15 c. River scene; 25 c. Temple of the Tooth, Kandy; 30 c. Ancient irrigation tank; 50 c. Wild elephants; 1 r. Trincomalee.

3 CENTS

(73)

3 CENTS

(74)

1940–41. *Nos. 388 and 391 surch.*

398	73	3 c. on 6 c. (10.5.41)	..	..	10	10
399	73	3 c. on 20 c. (5.11.40)	..	..	2·00	1·00

1946 (10 Dec). *Victory. As Nos. 110/11 of Antigua.*

400	6 c. blue	..	..	..	10	10
401	15 c. brown	..	..	..	10	40
400/1 Perf "Specimen"		*Set of 2*	55·00	

OMNIBUS ISSUES

Details, together with prices for complete sets, of the various Omnibus issues from the 1937 Coronation series to the B.W.I. University College set are included in a special section at the end of the listings.

75 Parliament Building   76 Adam's Peak

(Des R. Tenison and M. S. V. Rodrigo. Recess B.W.)

1947 (25 Nov). *Inauguration of New Constitution.* T **75/6** *and similar designs. Wmk Mult Script CA.* P 11 × 12 (*horiz*) *or* 12 × 11 (*vert*).

402	6 c. black and blue	..	..	10	15
403	10 c. black, orange and carmine	..	..	10	20
404	15 c. green and purple..	..	..	10	30
405	25 c. ochre and emerald-green	..	..	10	15
402/5 ..	..	..	..	*Set of* 4	35	70
402/5 Perf "Specimen"	..	..	*Set of* 4	85·00	

Designs: *Horiz*—15 c. Temple of the Tooth. *Vert*—25 c. Anuradhapura.

DOMINION

79 Lion Flag of   80 D. S. Senanayake
Dominion

81 Lotus Flowers and Sinhalese Letters "Sri"

(Recess (flag typo) B.W.)

1949 (4 Feb–5 Apr). *First Anniv of Independence.* (*a*) *Wmk Mult Script CA* (*sideways on* 4 *c.*). P 12½×12 (4 *c.*) *or* 12×12½ (5 *c.*).

406	79	4 c. yellow, carmine and brown	..	10	20
407	80	5 c. brown and green	..	..	..	10	10

(*b*) W **81** (*sideways on* 15 *c.*). P 13 × 12½ (15 *c.*) *or* 12 × 12½ (25 *c.*) (5 April)

408	79	15 c. yellow, carmine and vermilion	..	25	15
409	80	25 c. brown and blue	..	..	15	40
406/9 ..	..	..	..	..	*Set of* 4	40	75

The 15 c. is larger, measuring 28 × 12 mm.

82 Globe and Forms of Transport

(Recess D.L.R.)

1949 (10 Oct). *75th Anniv of Universal Postal Union.* W **81**. P 13 (25 *c.*) *or* 12 (*others*).

410	**82**	5 c. brown and bluish green	..	..	75	10
411	**83**	15 c. black and carmine	..	..	1·40	1·10
412	**84**	25 c. black and ultramarine	..	1·40	1·10
410/12	..	..	..	..	*Set of* 3	3·25	2·00

85 Kandyan   88 Sigiriya
Dancer   (Lion Rock)

89 Octagon Library, Temple   90 Ruins at Madirigiriya
of the Tooth

(Recess B.W.)

1950 (4 Feb). T **85, 88/90** *and similar designs.* W **81**. P 11 × 11½ (75 *c.*), 11½ × 11 (1 *r.*), 12 × 12½ (*others*).

413	4 c. purple and scarlet	..	..	..	10	10
414	5 c. green	..	..	..	..	10	10
415	15 c. blue-green and violet	..	..	1·50	30
416	30 c. carmine and yellow	..	..	30	40
417	75 c. ultramarine and orange	..	..	1·75	10
418	1 r. deep blue and brown	..	..	1·75	30
413/18	..	..	..	..	*Set of* 6	4·75	95

Designs: *Vert* (*as* T **88**)—5 c. Kiri Vehera, Polonnaruwa; 15 c. Vesak Orchid.

For these values with redrawn inscriptions see Nos. 450/1, 454, 456, 460 and 462.

91 Sambars, Ruhuna   92 Ancient Guard-   96 Star Orchid
National Park   stone, Anuradhapura

97 Rubber Plantation   **99** Tea Plantation

I. No. 424   II. No. 424a (Dot added)

(Photo Courvoisier)

1951 (1 Aug)–54. *T* **91/2, 96/7, 99** *and similar designs. No wmk.*
P 11½.
419	2 c. brown and blue-green (15.5.54) ..	..	10	40
420	3 c. black and slate-violet (15.5.54) ..	..	10	50
421	6 c. brown-black & yellow-green (15.5.54) ..		10	20
422	10 c. green and blue-grey	..	75	65
423	25 c. orange-brown & bright blue (15.3.54) ..		10	20
424	35 c. red and deep green (I) (1.2.52) ..	..	1·50	1·50
	a. Type II (1954) ..	..	4·50	60
425	40 c. deep brown (15.5.54)	..	4·50	60
426	50 c. indigo and slate-grey (15.3.54) ..	..	30	10
427	85 c. black and deep blue-green (15.5.54)	..	50	10
428	2 r. blue and deep brown (15.5.54) ..	..	6·50	70
429	5 r. brown and orange (15.3.54)	..	4·75	80
430	10 r. red-brown and buff (15.3.54)	..	20·00	6·00
419/30	.. .. ..	*Set of* 12	35·00	10·00

Designs: *Vert* (*as T* **91**)—6 c. Harvesting rice; 10 c. Coconut trees; 25 c. Sigiriya fresco. (*As T* **99**)—5 r. Bas-relief, Anuradhapura; 10 r. Harvesting rice. *Horiz* (*as T* **97**)—50 c. Outrigger canoe; (*as T* **99**)—2 r. River Gal Dam.

STAMP BOOKLETS

1937 (Apr–June). *Coronation of King George VI. Black on blue* (*No.* SB15) *or olive-green* (*No.* SB16) *covers. Stapled.*
SB15 1 r. 80, booklet containing thirty 6 c. (No. 383) in blocks of 10 and pane of four airmail labels (June) £700
SB16 2 r. 70, booklet containing thirty 9 c. (No. 384) in blocks of 10 and pane of four airmail labels £750

1938. *Black on blue* (*No.* SB17) *or pale green* (*No.* SB18) *covers. Stapled.*
SB17 1 r. 80, booklet containing thirty 6 c. (No. 388) in blocks of 10 and pane of four airmail labels
SB18 3 r. booklet containing fifteen 20 c. (No. 391) in blocks of 5 or 10 and pane of four airmail labels .. .. ..

1941. *Black on pink cover, with contents amended in manuscript. Stapled.*
SB19 1 r. 80, booklet containing sixty 3 c. on 6 c. (No. 398) in blocks of 10 ..
   a. Black on blue cover .. .. ..

1951 (5 Dec). *Black on buff cover. Stitched.*
SB20 1 r. booklet containing twenty 5 c. (No. 414) in blocks of four and pane of airmail labels .. 12·00
   a. Containing two blocks of ten 5 c. stamps and no airmail labels .. .. ..

1952 (21 Jan). *Black on green cover. Stitched.*
SB21 6 r. booklet containing eight 75 c. (No. 417) in blocks of 4 and two panes of four airmail labels .. .. 18·00

Cyprus

180 piastres = 1 Cyprus pound

CROWN COLONY

1937 (12 May). *Coronation. As Nos. 95/7 of Antigua.*
P 11×11½.

148	¾ pi. grey	..	..	..	75	20
149	1½ pi. carmine	..	..	1·25	80
150	2½ pi. blue	..	..	2·50	1·25
148/50		..	..	*Set of* 3	4·00	2·00
148/50 Perf "Specimen"	..	..	*Set of* 3	£100

35 Vouni Palace

36 Map of Cyprus

37 Othello's Tower,
Famagusta

38 King George VI

(Recess Waterlow)

1938 (12 May)**–1951.** *T* **35** *to* **38** *and other designs as 1934, but with portrait of King George VI. Wmk Mult Script CA. P* 12½.

151	**35**	¼ pi. ultramarine and orange-brown	20	20
152	**25**	½ pi. green	30	10
152a	–	½ pi. violet (2.7.51)	1·75	20
153	–	¾ pi. black and violet	12·00	40
154	–	1 pi. orange	40	10
		a. Perf 13½ × 12½ (1944)	£375	26·00
155	–	1½ pi. carmine	5·00	1·50
155a	–	1½ pi. violet (15.3.43)	30	30
155ab	–	1½ pi. green (2.7.51)	2·25	40
155b	–	2 pi. black and carmine (2.2.42)	30	10
		c. Perf 12½ × 13½ (10.44)	1·75	4·00
156	–	2½ pi. ultramarine	..	..	15·00	3·00
156a	–	3 pi. ultramarine (2.2.42)	..	80	15
156b	–	4 pi. ultramarine (2.7.51)	..	3·00	30
157	**36**	4½ pi. grey	..	40	10
158	**31**	6 pi. black and blue	..	..	65	1·00
159	**37**	9 pi. black and purple	..	1·75	20
160	–	18 pi. black and olive-green	..	5·00	85
		a. Black and sage-green (19.8.47)	..	7·50	1·50
161	–	45 pi. green and black	..	..	13·00	2·50
162	**38**	90 pi. mauve and black	..	20·00	4·50
163		£1 scarlet and indigo	..	45·00	20·00
151/63		..	..	*Set of* 19	£110	32·00
151/63 Perf "Specimen"		..	*Set of* 16	£375

Designs: *Horiz*—½ pi. Small Marble Forum, Salamis; ¾ pi., 2 pi. Peristerona Church; 1 pi. Soli Theatre; 1½ pi. Kyrenia Harbour; 2½ pi., 3 pi., 4 pi. Kolossi Castle; 45 pi. Forest scene. *Vert*—6 pi. Bayraktar Mosque, Nicosia; 18 pi. Buyuk Khan, Nicosia.

1946 (21 Oct). *Victory. As Nos. 110/11 of Antigua.*

164	1½ pi. deep violet	..	..	..	15	10
165	3 pi. blue	..	..	..	15	15
164/5 Perf "Specimen"	..	..	*Set of* 2	90·00

Extra decoration
(R. 3/5)

1948 (20 Dec). *Royal Silver Wedding. As Nos. 112/13 of Antigua.*

166	1½ pi. violet	..	..	..	50	20
	a. Extra decoration	..	..	30·00
167	£1 indigo	..	..	42·00	48·00

1949 (10 Oct). *75th Anniv of Universal Postal Union. As Nos. 114/17 of Antigua but inscr* "CYPRUS" *(recess).*

168	1½ pi. violet	..	..	..	90	70
169	2 pi. carmine-red	..	..	1·25	1·25
170	3 pi. deep blue	..	..	1·25	1·00
171	9 pi. purple	..	..	..	1·75	1·10
168/71	..	..	..	*Set of* 4	4·75	3·50

Dominica

1937. 12 pence (d) = 1 shilling; 20 shillings = 1 pound
1949. 100 cents = 1 West Indian dollar

CROWN COLONY

1937 (12 May). *Coronation. As Nos. 95/7 of Antigua.*
P 11×11½.

96	1d. carmine					40	10
97	1½d. yellow-brown					40	10
98	2½d. blue					60	1·00
96/8				*Set of 3*		1·25	1·10
96/8 Perf "Specimen"				*Set of 3*		55·00	

17 Fresh Water Lake    **18** Layou River

(Recess Waterlow)

1938 (15 Aug)–**47**. *T* **17/18** *and similar horiz designs. Wmk Mult Script CA. P* 12½.

99	17	½d. brown and green			10	15
100	18	1d. grey and scarlet			20	20
101	–	1½d. green and purple			30	70
102	–	2d. carmine and grey-black			40	70
103	–	2½d. purple and bright blue			4·00	1·75
		a. Purple & bright ultramarine (8.42)			20	1·25
104	18	3d. olive-green and brown			30	40
104*a*	–	3½d. ultramarine and purple (15.10.47)			1·50	75
105	17	6d. emerald-green and violet			1·75	80
105*a*		7d. green and yellow-brown (15.10.47)			1·50	80
106	–	1s. violet and olive-green			2·25	65
106*a*	18	2s. slate and purple (15.10.47)			4·50	6·00
107	17	2s. 6d. black and vermilion			12·00	4·75
108	18	5s. light blue and sepia			7·50	6·00
108*a*	–	10s. black and brown-orange (15.10.47)			12·00	14·00
99/108*a*				*Set of 14*	40·00	32·00

Designs:–1½d., 2½d., 3½d. Picking limes; 2d., 1s., 10s. Boiling Lake.

21 King George VI

(Photo Harrison)

1940 (15 Apr)–**42**. *Wmk Mult Script CA. Chalk-surfaced paper. P* 15×14.

109	21	¼d. chocolate			60	15
		a. Ordinary paper (1942)			10	10
99/109 Perf "Specimen"				*Set of 15*	£225	

1946 (14 Oct). *Victory. As Nos. 110/11 of Antigua.*

110	1d. carmine				20	10
111	3½d. blue				20	10
110/11 Perf "Specimen"			*Set of 2*	48·00	

1948 (1 Dec). *Royal Silver Wedding. As Nos. 112/13 of Antigua.*

112	1d. scarlet				15	10
113	10s. red-brown				7·00	19·00

(New Currency. 100 cents = 1 B.W.I., later East Caribbean dollar)

1949 (10 Oct). *75th Anniv of Universal Postal Union. As Nos. 114/17 of Antigua.*

114	5 c. blue				15	15
115	6 c. brown				30	80
116	12 c. purple				30	50
117	24 c. olive				30	30
114/17				*Set of 4*	95	1·60

1951 (16 Feb). *Inauguration of B.W.I. University College. As Nos. 118/19 of Antigua.*

118	3 c. yellow-green and reddish violet			75	30
119	12 c. deep green and carmine			75	20

22 King George VI   **23** Drying Cocoa

(Photo Harrison (½ c.). Recess B.W. (others))

1951 (1 July). *T* **22** *and designs as T* **23**. *Wmk Mult Script CA. Chalk-surfaced paper* (½ c.). *P* 15×14 (½ c.), 13½×13 ($2.40), 13×13½ (*others*).

120	½ c. chocolate				10	15
121	1 c. black and vermilion				10	30
	b. "A" of "CA" missing from wmk			£500	
	c. "JA" for "CA" in wmk			£500	
122	2 c. red-brown and deep green				10	20
	a. "C" of "CA" missing from wmk			†	—
	b. "A" of "CA" missing from wmk			£600	
123	3 c. green and reddish violet				15	70
	a. "C" of "CA" missing from wmk				
	c. "JA" for "CA" in wmk			£500	
124	4 c. brown-orange and sepia				30	60
	a. "C" of "CA" missing from wmk			£600	
	b. "A" of "CA" missing from wmk			£600	
125	5 c. black and carmine				85	30
	a. "C" of "CA" missing from wmk			£800	
	b. "A" of "CA" missing from wmk			£800	
126	6 c. olive and chestnut				90	30
	b. "A" of "CA" missing from wmk			£1000	
127	8 c. blue-green and blue				60	60
128	12 c. black and bright green				45	1·25
	a. "C" of "CA" missing from wmk			£1200	
129	14 c. blue and violet				95	1·25
	a. "C" of "CA" missing from wmk			£1200	
	b. "A" of "CA" missing from wmk			£1200	
130	24 c. reddish violet and rose-carmine			75	30
	a. "C" of "CA" missing from wmk			†	—
131	48 c. bright green and red-orange			2·00	5·50
	a. "C" of "CA" missing from wmk			£1200	
	b. "A" of "CA" missing from wmk			£1200	
132	60 c. carmine and black				2·25	3·75
133	$1.20, emerald and black				4·00	3·75
	a. "C" of "CA" missing from wmk			£1400	
	b. "A" of "CA" missing from wmk			£1400	
134	$2.40, orange and black				22·00	27·00
120/34				*Set of 15*	30·00	42·00

Designs: *Horiz*—2 c., 60 c. Making Carib baskets; 3 c., 48 c. Lime plantation; 4 c. Picking oranges; 5 c. Bananas; 6 c. Botanical Gardens; 8 c. Drying vanilla beans; 12 c., $1.20, Fresh Water Lake; 14 c. Layou River; 24 c. Boiling Lake. *Vert*—$2.40, Picking oranges.

Examples of Nos. 121b, 122b, 124b, 125b, 126b, 129b, 131b and 133b show traces of the *right leg* of the "A", *as seen from the front of the stamp.*

Nos. 121c and 123c may represent an attempt to repair the missing "C" variety.

NEW
CONSTITUTION
1951

(34)

1951 (15 Oct).   *New Constitution. Nos.* 123, 125, 127 *and* 129 *optd with T* **34** *by B.W.*

135	3 c. green and reddish violet	..	..	15	70
136	5 c. black and carmine	..	..	..	15	70
137	8 c. blue-green and blue (R.)	..	..	15	15
	a. "JA" for "CA" in wmk	..	..		
138	14 c. blue and violet (R.)	..	..	..	15	20
	b. "A" of "CA" missing from wmk	..	£900	
135/8	..	..	..	..	*Set of* 4	55	1·60

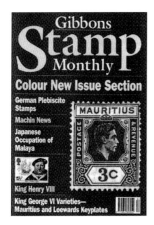

Falkland Islands

12 pence (d) = 1 shilling; 20 shillings = 1 pound

CROWN COLONY

1937 (12 May). *Coronation. As Nos. 95/7 of Antigua.*
P 11×11½.

143	½d. green	..	..	..	..	..	30	10
144	1d. carmine	..	..	..	..	..	40	45
145	2½d. blue	..	..	..	..	..	80	55
143/5	..	..	..	..	*Set of 3*	1·40	1·00
143/5 Perf "Specimen"				*Set of 3*	£160	

27 Whales' Jaw Bones

(Des G. Roberts (Nos. 146, 148/9, 158 and 160/3), K. Lellman (No. 159). Recess B.W.)

1938 (3 Jan)–**50.** *Horiz designs as T* **27.** *Wmk Mult Script CA.*
P 12.

146	½d. black and green (*shades*)	..	..	20	75
147	1d. black and carmine	..	..	25·00	1·25
	a. Black and scarlet..	..	..	3·00	75
148	1d. black and violet (14.7.41)	..	2·50	1·75
	a. Black and purple-violet (1.43)	..	4·75	1·75
149	2d. black and deep violet	..	..	1·00	50
150	2d. black and carmine-red (14.7.41)..	75	2·25
	a. Black and red (1.43)	..	..	1·00	60
151	2½d. black and bright blue	..	..	45	30
152	2½d. black and blue (15.6.49)..	..	3·50	4·50
153	3d. black and blue (14.7.41)..	..	4·50	1·75
	a. Black and deep blue (1.43)	..	5·50	1·75
154	4d. black and purple..	..	..	2·25	50
155	6d. black and brown ..	..	..	4·50	2·25
156	6d. black (15.6.49)	..	..	3·25	4·50
157	9d. black and grey-blue	..	..	11·00	65
158	1s. pale blue ..	..	..	65·00	18·00
	a. Deep blue (1941) ..	..	..	14·00	2·50
159	1s. 3d. black and carmine-red (11.12.46)	..	2·00	1·40
160	2s. 6d. slate ..	..	..	55·00	10·00
161	5s. bright blue and pale brown	..	£110	50·00
	b. Indigo and yellow-brown (1942)	£450	£130
	c. Blue and buff-brown (9.2.50)	£110	£130
162	10s. black and orange	..	..	55·00	27·00
163	£1 black and violet	..	..	£110	48·00
146/63				*Set of 18*	£325	£140
146/63 (*ex* 152, 156) Perf "Specimen"		*Set of 16*	£850	

Designs:—Nos. 147 and 150, Black-necked Swan; Nos. 148/9, Battle Memorial; Nos. 151 and 154, Magellan Goose; Nos. 152 and 154, Magellan Goose; Nos. 155/6, *Discovery II* (polar supply vessel); No. 157, *William Scoresby* (research ship); No. 158, Mount Sugar Top; No. 159; Turkey Vultures; No. 160 Gentoo Penguins; No. 161, Southern Sealion; No. 162, Deception Island; No. 163, Arms of Falkland Islands.

1946 (7 Oct). *Victory. As Nos. 110/11 of Antigua.*

164	1d. dull violet	..	..	..	..	30	15
165	3d. blue	..	..	..	..	45	15
164/5 Perf "Specimen"			*Set of 2*	£140	

1948 (1 Nov). *Royal Silver Wedding. As Nos.* 112/13 *of Antigua.*

166	2½d. ultramarine	..	..	..	2·00	70
167	£1 mauve	..	..	..	90·00	55·00

1949 (10 Oct). *75th Anniv of Universal Postal Union. As Nos.* 114/17 *of Antigua.*

168	1d. violet	..	..	..	..	1·50	75
169	3d. deep blue..	..	..	..	4·00	2·00
170	1s. 3d. deep blue-green	..	..	4·50	2·25
171	2s. blue	..	..	..	..	4·50	7·50
168/71	..	..	..	..	*Set of 4*	13·00	11·00

39 Sheep **43** Arms of the Colony

(Des from sketches by V. Spencer. Recess Waterlow)

1952 (2 Jan). *T* **39, 43** *and similar designs. Wmk Mult Script CA. P* 13×13½ (*vert*) *or* 13½×13 (*horiz*).

172	½d. green	..	..	..	..	70	70
173	1d. scarlet	..	..	..	..	80	40
174	2d. violet	..	..	..	3·25	2·00
175	2½d. black and light ultramarine	..	95	50
176	3d. deep ultramarine	..	..	1·00	1·00
177	4d. reddish purple	..	..	6·50	2·50
178	6d. bistre-brown	..	..	12·00	1·00
179	9d. orange-yellow	..	..	7·50	3·75
180	1s. black	..	..	..	15·00	80
181	1s. 3d. orange	..	..	..	12·00	7·00
182	2s. 6d. olive-green	..	..	16·00	8·00
183	5s. purple	..	..	..	8·50	6·00
184	10s. grey	..	..	..	18·00	24·00
185	£1 black	..	..	..	25·00	24·00
172/185				*Set of 14*	£110	70·00

Designs: *Horiz*—1d. *Fitzroy* (supply ship); 2d. Magellan Goose; 2½d. Map of Falkland Islands; 4d. Auster Autocrat aircraft; 9d. *John Biscoe I* (research ship); 9d. View of the Two Sisters; 1s. 3d. Kelp goose and gander; 10s. Southern Sealion and South American Fur Seal; £1 Hulk of *Great Britain*. *Vert*—1s. Gentoo Penguins; 2s. 6d. Sheep-shearing; 5s. Battle Memorial.

FALKLAND ISLANDS DEPENDENCIES

A. GRAHAM LAND

For use at Port Lockroy (established February 1944) and Hope Bay (established 12 February 1945) bases.
Falkland Islands definitive stamps with face values of 1s. 3d. and above were valid for use from Graham Land in conjunction with Nos. A1/8 and subsequently Nos. G1/16.

Stamps of FALKLAND ISLANDS *cancelled at Port Lockroy or Hope Bay with Graham Land circular datestamps between* 12 February 1944 *and* 31 January 1954.

1938–50. *King George VI* (Nos. 159/63).

Z2	2s. 6d. slate	..	..	..	..	30·00
Z3	5s. indigo and yellow-brown	..	..	£130
Z4	10s. black and orange	..	..	40·00
Z5	£1 black and violet	..	..	60·00

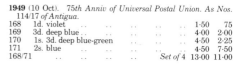

1952. *King George VI (Nos. 181/5)*
Z 6	1s. 3d. orange	..	..	..	..	..
Z 7	2s. 6d. olive-green	..	..	..	..	..
Z 8	5s. purple	..	..	..	..	..
Z 9	10s. grey	..	..	..	..	..
Z10	£1 black	..	..	..	..	..

GRAHAM LAND

DEPENDENCY OF

(A 1)

1944 (12 Feb)–**45.** *Falkland Islands Nos.* 146, 148, 150, 153/5, 157 *and* 158a *optd with Type* A **1**, *in red, by B.W.*
A1	½d. black and green	..	..	30	1·00
	a. *Blue-black and green*	..	..	£500	£375
A2	1d. black and violet	..	..	30	1·00
A3	2d. black and carmine-red	..	..	40	1·00
A4	3d. black and blue	..	..	30	1·00
A5	4d. black and purple	..	..	3·00	1·75
A6	6d. black and brown	..	..	12·00	2·25
	a. *Blue-black and brown* (24.9.45)	..	20·00	
A7	9d. black and grey-blue	..	..	1·00	1·25
A8	1s. deep blue	..	..	1·00	1·25
A1/8		..	*Set of* 8	16·00	9·50
A1/8 Perf "Specimen"	..	..	*Set of* 8	£325	

B. SOUTH GEORGIA

Stamps of FALKLAND ISLANDS *cancelled at Grytviken with South Georgia circular datestamps.*

1937. *Coronation (Nos. 143/5).*
Z70	½d. green	..	..	..	2·00
Z71	1d. carmine	..	..	..	2·00
Z72	2½d. blue	..	..	..	2·00

1938–50. *King George VI (Nos. 146/63).*
Z73	½d. black and green	..	..	..	3·00
Z74	1d. black and carmine	..	..	..	5·00
	a. *Black and scarlet*	..	..	..	2·00
Z75	1d. black and violet	..	..	..	4·00
Z76	2d. black and deep violet	..	..	..	6·00
Z77	2d. black and carmine-red	..	..	..	7·00
Z78	2½d. black and bright blue (No. 151)	..	..	2·00
Z79	3d. black and blue	..	..	..	6·00
Z80	4d. black and purple	..	..	..	6·00
Z81	6d. black and brown	..	..	..	8·00
Z82	9d. black and grey-blue	..	..	..	10·00
Z83	1s. pale blue	..	..	..	30·00
	a. *Deep blue*	..	..	..	30·00
Z84	1s. 3d. black and carmine-red	..	..	30·00
Z85	2s. 6d. slate	..	..	..	20·00
Z86	5s. bright blue and pale brown	..	..	£100
	a. *Indigo and yellow-brown*	..	..	£130
Z87	10s. black and orange	..	..	..	40·00
Z88	£1 black and violet	..	..	..	60·00

Falkland Islands definitive stamps with values of 1s. 3d. and above continued to be valid from South Georgia after the introduction of Nos. B1/8 and subsequently Nos. G1/16.

1952. *King George VI (Nos. 181/5).*
Z89	1s. 3d. orange	..	..	..	25·00
Z90	2s. 6d. olive-green	..	..	..	
Z91	5s. purple	..	..	..	
Z92	10s. grey	..	..	..	
Z93	£1 black	..	..	..	

1944 (3 Apr)–**45.** *Falkland Islands Nos.* 146, 148, 150, 153/5, 157 *and* 158a *optd* "SOUTH GEORGIA/DEPENDENCY OF", *in red, as Type* A **1** *of Graham Land.*
B1	½d. black and green	..	..	30	1·00
	a. Wmk sideways	..	..	£2500	
B2	1d. black and violet	..	..	30	1·00
B3	2d. black and carmine-red	..	..	40	1·00
B4	3d. black and blue	..	..	30	1·00
B5	4d. black and purple	..	..	3·00	1·75

B6	6d. black and brown	..	..	..	12·00	2·25
	a. *Blue-black and brown* (24.9.45)	..	20·00		
B7	9d. black and grey-blue	..	..	1·00	1·25
B8	1s. deep blue	..	..	1·00	1·25
B1/8			*Set of* 8	16·00	9·50
B1/8 Perf "Specimen"	..	..	*Set of* 8	£325	

For later issues, see after No. G44.

C. SOUTH ORKNEYS

Used from the *Fitzroy* in February 1944 and at Laurie Island (established January 1946).

Falkland Islands definitive stamps with face values of 1s. 3d. and above were valid for use from the South Orkneys in conjunction with Nos. C1/8 and subsequently Nos. G1/16.

Stamps of FALKLAND ISLANDS *cancelled on the* Fitzroy, *at Laurie Island or at Signy Island with South Orkneys circular datestamps between* 21 February 1944 *and* 31 January 1954.

1938–50. *King George VI (Nos. 160/3).*
Z95	2s. 6d. slate	..	..	..	30·00
Z96	5s. indigo and yellow-brown	..	..	£130
Z97	10s. black and orange	..	..	40·00
Z98	£1 black and violet	..	..	60·00

1952. *King George VI (Nos. 181/5).*
Z 99	1s. 3d. orange	..	..	..	
Z100	2s. 6d. olive-green	..	..	..	
Z101	5s. purple	..	..	..	
Z102	10s. grey	..	..	..	
Z103	£1 black	..	..	..	

1944 (21 Feb)–**45.** *Falkland Islands Nos.* 146, 148, 150, 153/5, 157 *and* 158a *optd* "SOUTH ORKNEYS/DEPENDENCY OF", *in red as Type* A **1** *of Graham Land.*
C1	½d. black and green	..	..	30	1·00
C2	1d. black and violet	..	..	30	1·00
	w. Wmk inverted	..	..		
C3	2d. black and carmine-red	..	..	40	1·00
C4	3d. black and blue	..	..	30	1·00
C5	4d. black and purple	..	..	3·00	1·75
C6	6d. black and brown	..	..	12·00	2·25
	a. *Blue-black and brown* (24.9.45)	..	20·00		
C7	9d. black and grey-blue	..	..	1·00	1·25
C8	1s. deep blue	..	..	1·00	1·25
C1/8		..	*Set of* 8	16·00	9·50
C1/8 Perf "Specimen"	..	..	*Set of* 8	£325	

D. SOUTH SHETLANDS

Stamps of FALKLAND ISLANDS *cancelled at Port Foster or Admiralty Bay with South Shetlands circular datestamps between* 5 February 1944 *and* 31 January 1954

1938–50. *King George VI (Nos. 160/3).*
Z159	2s. 6d. slate	..	..	..	30·00
Z160	5s. indigo and yellow-brown	..	..	£130
Z161	10s. black and orange	..	..	40·00
Z162	£1 black and violet	..	..	60·00

1952. *King George VI (Nos. 181/5).*
Z163	1s. 3d. orange	..	..	..	
Z164	2s. 6d. olive-green	..	..	..	
Z165	5s. purple	..	..	..	
Z166	10s. grey	..	..	..	
Z167	£1 black	..	..	..	

1944 (5 Feb)–**45.** *Falkland Islands Nos.* 146, 148, 150, 153/5, 157 *and* 158a *optd* "SOUTH SHETLANDS/DEPENDENCY OF", *in red, as Type* A **1** *of Graham Land.*
D1	½d. black and green	..	..	30	1·00
D2	1d. black and violet	..	..	30	1·00
D3	2d. black and carmine-red	..	..	40	1·00
D4	3d. black and blue	..	..	30	1·00
D5	4d. black and purple	..	..	3·00	1·75
D6	6d. black and brown	..	..	12·00	2·25
	a. *Blue-black and brown* (24.9.45)	..	20·00		

D7	9d. black and grey-blue	..	..	..	1·00	1·25
D8	1s. deep blue	..	..	..	1·00	1·25
D1/8	..	..	..	Set of 8	16·00	9·50
D1/8 Perf "Specimen"	..	..	Set of 8	£325	

E. FALKLAND ISLANDS DEPENDENCIES

G 1   Extra island (Plate 1
R. 3/9)

(Map litho, frame recess D.L.R.)

1946 (12 July*)–**49.** *Wmk Mult Script CA (sideways).* P 12.

(a) *Map thick and coarse*

G 1	G 1	½d. black and green	..	..	..	1·00	2·00
		a. Extra island..			..	42·00	
		b. Missing "I" ..	..	..	..	42·00	
G 2		1d. black and violet			..	1·25	1·75
		a. Extra island..			..	48·00	
		b. Missing "I" ..	..	..	..	48·00	
G 3		2d. black and carmine	..		..	1·25	2·50
		a. Extra island..			..	55·00	
		b. Missing "I" ..	..	..	..	55·00	
G 4		3d. black and blue	..		..	1·25	3·75
		a. Extra island..			..	60·00	
		b. Missing "I" ..	..	..	..	60·00	
G 5		4d. black and claret	..		..	2·25	4·50
G 6		6d. black and orange	..		..	3·25	4·50
		a. Extra island..			..	85·00	
		b. Missing "I" ..	..	..	..	85·00	
		c. *Black and ochre*	..		..	45·00	90·00
		ca. Extra island..			..	£200	
		cb. Missing "I" ..	..	..	..	£200	
G 7		9d. black and brown	..		..	2·00	2·75
G 8		1s. black and purple	..		..	2·00	4·00
G1/8	..	..	..	..	Set of 8	13·00	23·00
G1/8 Perf "Specimen"	..		Set of 8	£425	

(b) *Map thin and clear* (16.2.48)

G 9	G 1	½d. black and green	..		..	2·25	7·50
		a. Recess frame printed double, one					
		albino and inverted	..		..	£800	
G10		1d. black and violet	..		..	1·50	11·00
G11		2d. black and carmine	..		..	6·50	16·00
G11a		2½d. black and deep blue (6.3.49)	..	9·50	7·00
G12		3d. black and blue ..	..		..	2·75	4·50
G13		4d. black and claret	..		..	16·00	16·00
G14		6d. black and orange	..		..	19·00	11·00
G15		9d. black and brown	..		..	19·00	10·00
G16		1s. black and purple	..		..	20·00	10·00
G9/16	..	..	..	..	Set of 9	85·00	85·00

*This is the date of issue for South Georgia. Nos. G1/8 were released in London on 11 February.

In Nos. G1/8 a variety with a gap in the 80th parallel occurs six times in each sheet of all values in positions R. 1/4, 1/9, 3/4, 3/9, 5/4 and 5/9 (*Price for set of 8 £40 mint, in pairs with normal*).

A constant variety, dot on "I" of "SOUTH", occurs on R. 5/2, 5/4, 5/6, 5/8 and 5/10 of all values of the "thin map" set with the exception of the 2½d.

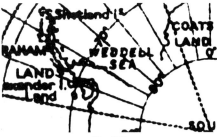

Nos. G1/8

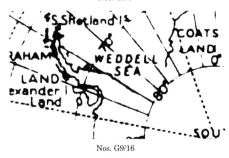

Nos. G9/16

On Nos. G9 to G16 the map is redrawn; the "o°" meridian does not pass through the "S" of "COATS", the "n" of "Alexander" is not joined to the "L" of "Land" below, and the loops of letters "s" and "t" are generally more open.

1946 (4 Oct*).   *Victory. As Nos.* 110/11 *of Antigua.*

G17	1d. deep violet	..	..	..	..	50	15
G18	3d. blue	..	..	..	..	75	15
G17/18 Perf "Specimen"	..	..	Set of 2	£120	

*This is the date of issue for South Georgia. The stamps were placed on sale from the South Orkneys on 17 January 1947, from the South Shetlands on 30 January 1947 and from Graham Land on 10 February 1947.

1948 (6 Dec). *Royal Silver Wedding. As Nos.* 112/13 *of Antigua, but* 1s. *in recess.*

| G19 | 2½d. ultramarine | .. | .. | .. | .. | 1·00 | 75 |
| G20 | 1s. violet-blue | .. | .. | .. | .. | 3·00 | 1·75 |

1949 (10 Oct). *75th Anniv of U.P.U. As Nos.* 114/17 *of Antigua.*

G21	1d. violet	..	..	..	..	1·50	1·50
G22	2d. carmine-red	..	..	..	..	4·00	2·50
G23	3d. deep blue ..	..	..	..	..	4·00	1·25
G24	6d. red-orange	..	..	..	..	7·00	3·00
G21/4	..	..	..	..	Set of 4	15·00	7·50

PRICES OF SETS

Set prices are given for many issues, generally those containing three stamps or more. Definitive sets include one of each value or major colour change, but do not cover different perforations, die types or minor shades. Where a choice is possible the set prices are based on the cheapest versions of the stamps included in the listings.

Missing "I" in "S. Shetland Is." (Plate 1 R. 1/2)

Fiji

12 pence (d) = 1 shilling; 20 shillings = 1 pound

CROWN COLONY

1937 (12 May). *Coronation. As Nos. 95/7 of Antigua.*
P 11×11½.

246	1d. purple	..	..	70	45
247	2d. grey-black	..	..	80	80
248	3d. Prussian blue	..	..	80	95
246/8 ..			*Set of* 3	2·10	2·00
246/8 Perf "Specimen"			*Set of* 3	55·00	

28 Native sailing Canoe

29 Native Village

30 Camakua (canoe)

31 Map of Fiji Islands

Two Dies of Type 3C:

Die I	Die II
Empty Canoe	Native in Canoe

Two Dies of Type 31:

Die I	Die II
Without "180°"	With "180°"

Extra palm frond
(R. 5/8)

Spur on arms medallion (Pl 2
R. 4/2) (ptg of 26 Nov 1945)

(Des V. E. Ousey (½d., 1s., 2s. 6d.), Miss C. D. Lovejoy (1d., 1½d., 5d.), Miss I. Stinson (3d., 5s.) and A. V. Guy (2d. (Nos. 253/4), 2½d., 6d., 2s.). Recess De La Rue (½d., 1½d., 2d., (Nos. 253/5a)) 2½d., 6d., 8d., 1s. 5d., 1s. 6d.), Waterlow (others))

1938 (5 Apr)–**1955.** *T* 28/31 *and similar designs. Wmk Mult Script CA. Various perfs.*

249	28	½d. green (*p* 13½)	..	10	40
		a. Perf 14 (5.41)		20·00	3·50
		b. Perf 12 (8.48)		40	2·00
		ba. Extra palm frond	..	24·00	
250	29	1d. brown and blue (*p* 12½)	..	30	20
251	30	1½d. carmine (Die I) (*p* 13½)	..	15·00	35
252		1½d. carmine (Die II) (*p* 13½) (1.10.40)		1·40	2·50
		a. Deep carmine (10.42)		3·25	1·25
		b. Perf 14 (6.42)		18·00	16·00
		c. Perf 12 (21.7.49)	..	90	1·25
253	31	2d. brown and green (Die I) (*p* 13½)		38·00	40
254		2d. brn & grn (Die II) (*p* 13½) (1.10.40)		16·00	16·00
255	–	2d. green & magenta (*p* 13½) (19.5.42)		40	60
		a. Perf 12 (27.5.16)	..	55	70
256	31	2½d. brown & grn (Die II) (*p* 14) (6.1.42)		60	60
		a. Perf 13½ (1.44)	..	60	60
		b. Perf 12 (19.1.48)	..	70	50
257	–	3d. blue (*p* 12½)	..	85	30
		a. Spur on arms medallion	..	£120	
258	–	5d. blue and scarlet (*p* 12½)	..	42·00	10·00
259	–	5d. yellow-grn & scar (*p* 12½) (1.10.40)		20	30
260	31	6d. black (Die I) (*p* 13×12)		60·00	10·00
261		6d. black (Die II) (*p* 13½) (1.10.40)		3·00	1·75
		a. Violet-black (1.44)	..	25·00	24·00
		b. Perf 12. *Black* (5.6.47)		1·50	1·00
261*c*		8d. carmine (*p* 14) (15.11.48)	..	1·00	70
		d. Perf 13 (7.6.50)	..	70	2·25
262	–	1s. black and yellow (*p* 12½)	..	75	50
263	–	1s. black & carmine (*p* 14) (13.6.40)		20	10
263*a*	–	1s. 6d. ultramarine (*p* 14) (1.8.50)		4·50	2·25
		b. Perf 13 (16.2.55)	..	1·25	15·00
264	–	2s. violet and orange (*p* 12½)		2·50	40
265	–	2s. 6d. green and brown (*p* 12½)		2·50	1·25
266	–	2s. green and purple (*p* 12½)		2·50	1·25
266*a*	–	10s. orange & emer (*p* 12½) (13.3.50)		32·00	40·00
266*b*	–	£1 ultram & carm (*p* 12½) (13.3.50)		48·00	50·00
249/66*b*			*Set of* 22	£250	£120
249/66 excl 261*c* and 263*a* Perf					
"Specimen"	..	..	*Set of* 18	£450	

Designs: *Horiz* (*as T* 30)—2d. (Nos. 255/a) Government Offices. (*As T* 29)—3d. Canoe and arms of Fiji; 8d., 1s. 5d., 1s. 6d. Arms of Fiji; 2s. Suva Harbour; 2s. 6d. River scene; 5s. Chief's hut. *Vert* (*as T* 29)—5d. Sugar cane; 1s. Spearing fish by torchlight; 10s. Pawpaw Tree; £1 Police bugler.

2½d.

1941 (10 Feb).   *No. 254 surch with T* **42** *by Govt Printer, Suva.*
267   31   2½d. on 2d. brown and green   40   20

1946 (17 Aug).   *Victory. As Nos.* 110/11 *of Antigua.*
268   2½d. green   10   50
    a. Printed double, one albino   ..   £225
269   3d. blue   10   10
268/9 Perf "Specimen"   ..   *Set of 2* 60·00

1948 (17 Dec).   *Royal Silver Wedding. As Nos.* 112/13 *of Antigua.*
270   2½d. green   40   75
271   5s. violet-blue   ..   ..   ..   14·00   6·50

1949 (10 Oct).   *75th Anniv of U.P.U. As Nos.* 114/17 *of Antigua.*
272   2d. bright reddish purple   65   30
273   3d. deep blue ..   ..   1·75   1·50
274   8d. carmine-red   70   1·25
275   1s. 6d. blue   80   1·00
272/5 ..   ..   *Set of 4*   3·50   3·50

43 Children Bathing   **44** Rugby Football

(Recess B.W.)

1951 (17 Sept).   *Health Stamps. Wmk Mult Script CA. P* 13½.
276   **43**   1d. + 1d. brown   10   40
277   **44**   2d. + 1d. green   30   40

STAMP BOOKLETS

1939 (10 Mar).   *Black on green (No.* SB3) *or black on pink (No.* SB4) *covers. Stapled.*
SB3   3s. booklet containing eight ½d. and eight 1d.
    (Nos. 249/50) in blocks of 8 and twelve 2d. (No.
    253) in blocks of 6   ..   ..   ..   £550
SB4   5s. 9d. booklet containing ten ½d. and ten 1d.
    (Nos. 249/50) in blocks of 10 and twenty-seven
    2d. (No. 253) in blocks of 9   ..   ..   £1600

POSTAGE DUE STAMPS

D **4**

(Typo Waterlow)
1940 (3 July).   *Wmk Mult Script CA. P* 12½.
D11   D **4**   1d. emerald-green   ..   ..   ..   5·50   45·00
D12   2d. emerald-green   ..   ..   ..   7·00   45·00
D13   3d. emerald-green   ..   ..   ..   9·00   50·00
D14   4d. emerald-green   ..   ..   ..   12·00   55·00
D15   5d. emerald-green   ..   ..   ..   13·00   55·00
D16   6d. emerald-green   ..   ..   ..   15·00   60·00
D17   1s. carmine-lake   ..   ..   ..   20·00   90·00
D18   1s. 6d. carmine-lake   ..   ..   ..   21·00   £130
D11/18   ..   ..   ..   *Set of 8*   90·00   £475
D11/18 Perf "Specimen"   ..   ..   *Set of 8*   £180

All values are known with forged postmarks, including one of Levuka dated "8 APR 41" and others of Suva dated "12 AUG 42", "14 AU 42" or "20 MR 45".

The use of postage due stamps was discontinued on 30 April 1946.

Gambia

12 pence (d) = 1 shilling; 20 shillings = 1 pound

CROWN COLONY

1937 (12 May). *Coronation. As Nos. 95/7 of Antigua.*
P 11×11½
147	1d. yellow-brown	..	..	30	15
148	1½d. carmine ..	..	..	30	30
149	3d. blue	..	..	80	45
147/9 ..			*Set of* 3	1·25	80
147/9 Perf "Specimen"			*Set of* 3	60·00	

11 Elephant (from Colony Badge)

(Recess B.W.)

1938 (1 Apr)–**46.** *Wmk Mult Script CA. P* 12.
150	**11**	½d. black and emerald-green	..	15	50
151		1d. purple and brown	..	20	40
152		1½d. brown-lake and bright carmine	..	£140	12·00
		a. Brown-lake and scarlet ..	..	1·75	1·50
		b. Brown-lake and vermilion	..	30	1·25
152c		1½d. blue and black (2.1.45)	..	30	1·25
153		2d. blue and black	..	1·50	2·00
153a		2d. lake and scarlet (1.10.43)	..	60	1·50

154	**11**	3d. light blue and grey-blue	..	30	10
154a		5d. sage-green & purple-brn (13.3.41)	45	45
155		6d. olive-green and claret	..	..	1·00	35
156		1s. slate-blue and violet	..	..	1·75	10
156a		1s. 3d. chocolate & lt blue (28.11.46)	1·75	1·75
157		2s. carmine and blue	..	..	4·50	3·25
158		2s. 6d. sepia and dull green ..	..	12·00	2·00
159		4s. vermilion and purple	..	19·00	2·50
160		5s. blue and vermilion	..	18·00	4·00
161		10s. orange and black	..	17·00	8·00
150/61		..	..	*Set of* 16	70·00	26·00
150/61 Perf "Specimen" ..		..	*Set of* 16	£225	

1946 (6 Aug). *Victory. As Nos. 110/11 of Antigua.*
162	1½d. black	..	..	..	10	10
163	3d. blue	..	..	..	10	10
162/3 Perf "Specimen"	..		*Set of* 2	55·00	

1948 (24 Dec). *Royal Silver Wedding. As Nos. 112/13 of Antigua.*
164	1½d. black	..	..	..	25	10
165	£1 mauve	..	..	..	12·00	13·00

1949 (10 Oct). *75th Anniv of Universal Postal Union. As Nos. 114/17 of Antigua.*
166	1½d. blue-black	..	..	..	40	30
167	3d. deep blue	..	..	1·25	30
168	6d. magenta ..	..	..	..	60	30
169	1s. violet	..	..	..	60	30
166/9 ..	..	..	..	*Set of* 4	2·50	1·10

Gibraltar

12 pence (d) = 1 shilling; 20 shillings = 1 pound

CROWN COLONY

1937 (12 May). *Coronation. As Nos. 95/7 of Antigua.*
P 11×11½.

118	½d. green ..	.. ..		25	10
119	2d. grey-black	.. ..		80	1·50
120	3d. blue ..	.. .. ..		2·00	1·60
118/20	.. .. ..	*Set of* 3	2·75	2·75
118/20 Perf "Specimen" ..		*Set of* 3	75·00	

14 King George VI   **15** Rock of Gibraltar

16 The Rock (North Side)

Broken second "R" in "GIBRALTAR"
(Frame Pl.2 R.9/4)

(Des Captain H. St. C. Garrood. Recess D.L.R.)

1938 (25 Feb)–**51.** *Designs as T* **14/16**. *Wmk Mult Script CA.*

121	½d. deep green (*p* 13½×14)	..	..	10	40
122	1d. yellow-brown (*p* 14)		..	23·00	2·25
	a. Perf 13½ ..	..	..	26·00	2·00
	ab. Perf 13½. Wmk sideways (1940)	..	4·75	6·50
	b. Perf 13. Wmk sideways. *Red-brown*			
	(1942)	..	..	50	55
	c. Perf 13. Wmk sideways. *Deep brown*			
	(1944)	..	..	30	3·00
	d. Perf 13. *Red-brown* (1949) ..		1·50	1·25
123	1½d. carmine (*p* 14)	..	..	35·00	75
	a. Perf 13½ ..	..	..	£250	32·00
123*b*	1½d. slate-violet (*p* 13) (1.1.43) ..		30	85
124	2d. grey (*p* 14)	..	..	25·00	40
	a. Perf 13½ ..	..	..	30	35
	ab. Perf 13½. Wmk sideways (1939)	..	£600	42·00
	b. Perf 13. Wmk sideways (1943)		30	85
	ba. "A" of "CA" missing from wmk	..	£1000	
124*c*	2d. carm (*p* 13) (*wmk sideways*) (15.7.44)	40	60
125	3d. light blue (*p* 13½) ..	..	15·00	80
	a. Perf 14	..	..	£120	5·00
	b. Perf 13 (1942)	..	..	30	30
	ba. Greenish blue (2.51)	..	..	3·50	2·50
125*c*	5d. red-orange (*p* 13) (1.10.47) ..		70	1·25

126	6d. carm & grey-violet (*p* 13½) (16.3.38)	48·00	3·00
	a. Perf 14	..	..	£120	1·25
	b. Perf 13 (1942)	..	..	2·00	1·25
	c. Perf 13. *Scarlet and grey-violet* (1945)	4·25	2·75
127	1s. black and green (*p* 14) (16.3.38)	..	38·00	18·00
	a. Perf 13½	..	..	55·00	6·50
	b. Perf 13 (1942)	..	..	3·00	3·75
	ba. Broken "R" ..	..	..	90·00	
128	2s. black and brown (*p* 14) (16.3.38)	..	65·00	25·00
	a. Perf 13½ ..	..	..	£110	32·00
	b. Perf 13 (1942)	..	..	3·25	5·00
	ba. Broken "R" ..	..	..	£100	
129	5s. black and carmine (*p* 14) (16.3.38)	90·00	£140
	a. Perf 13½	..	..	38·00	17·00
	b. Perf 13 (1944)	..	..	12·00	17·00
	ba. Broken "R" ..	..	..	£150	
130	10s. black and blue (*p* 14) (16.3.38)	..	65·00	£110
	a. Perf 13 (1943)	..	..	35·00	25·00
	ab. Broken "R" ..	..	..	£225	
131	£1 orange (*p* 13½×14) (16.3.38)	..	35·00	45·00
121/31	.. .. ..	*Set of* 14	£110	85·00
121/31 Perf "Specimen" ..		*Set of* 14	£450	

Designs:—½d., £1, Type **14**. *Horiz as T* **15/16**—1d., 1½d. (*both*), Type **15**; 2d. (*both*), Type **16**; 3d., 5d. Europa Point; 6d. Moorish Castle; 1s. Southport Gate; 2s. Eliott Memorial; 5s. Government House; 10s. Catalan Bay.

The ½d., 1d. and both colours of the 2d. exist in coils constructed from normal sheets. These were originally joined vertically, but, because of technical problems, the 1d. and 2d. grey were subsequently issued in horizontal coils. The 2d. carmine only exists in the horizontal version.

1946 (12 Oct). *Victory. As Nos. 110/11 of Antigua.*

132	½d. green	..	..	10	10
133	3d. ultramarine	..	..	30	20
132/3 Perf "Specimen"	..	*Set of* 2	60·00	

1948 (1 Dec). *Royal Silver Wedding. As Nos. 112/13 of Antigua.*

134	½d. green	..	..	..	70	60
135	£1 brown-orange	..	..	..	50·00	60·00

1949 (10 Oct). *75th Anniv of Universal Postal Union. As Nos. 114/17 of Antigua.*

136	2d. carmine ..		..	1·25	85
137	3d. deep blue ..		..	2·00	85
138	6d. purple	..	..	2·00	85
139	1s. blue-green	..	..	2·00	2·00
136/9 ..	..	..	*Set of* 4	6·50	4·00

NEW CONSTITUTION
1950
(23)

1950 (1 Aug). *Inauguration of Legislative Council. Nos. 124c, 125b, 126b and 127b optd as T* **23**.

140	**16**	2d. carmine	..	..	30	1·00
141	–	3d. light blue	..	..	30	1·00
142	–	6d. carmine and grey-violet	..	..	40	1·00
		a. Opt double	..	..	£500	£600
143	–	1s. black and green (R.)	..	..	40	1·40
		a. Broken "R" ..	..	..	38·00	
140/3	..	..	..	*Set of* 4	1·25	4·00

On stamps from the lower part of the sheet of No. 142a the two impressions are almost coincident.

Gilbert and Ellice Islands

12 pence (d) = 1 shilling; 20 shillings = 1 pound

CROWN COLONY

1937 (12 May). *Coronation. As Nos. 95/7 of Antigua, but ptd by D.L.R. P 14.*

40	1d. violet ..	..	..	..	35	55
41	1½d. scarlet	..	..	..	45	55
42	3d. bright blue	..	..	..	60	60
40/2			*Set of 3*	1·25	1·50
40/2 Perf "Specimen"		..	*Set of 3*	65·00

6 Great Frigate Bird   7 Pandanus Pine

8 Canoe crossing Reef

(Recess B.W. (½d., 2d., 2s. 6d.), Waterlow (1d., 5d., 6d., 2s., 5s.), D.L.R. (1½d., 2½d., 3d., 1s.))

1939 (14 Jan)–**55**. *T **6**/8 and similar horiz designs. Wmk Mult Script CA (sideways on ½d., 2d. and 2s. 6d.). P 11½×11 (½d., 2d., 2s. 6d.), 12½ (1d., 5d., 6d., 2s., 5s.) or 13½ (1½d., 2½d., 3d., 1s.).*

43	½d. indigo and deep bluish green ..	..	30	75
	a. "A" of "CA" missing from wmk	..		
44	1d. emerald and plum	..	..	30	1·50
45	1½d. brownish black and bright carmine	..	30	90
46	2d. red-brown and grey-black	..	..	20	1·00
47	2½d. brownish black and deep olive	..	40	70
	a. *Brownish black & olive-green* (12.5.43)	3·00	3·25
48	3d. brownish black and ultramarine	..	45	1·00
	a. *Perf 12. Black and bright blue* (24.8.55)	50	2·25
49	5d. deep ultramarine and sepia	..	4·25	1·25
	a. *Ultramarine and sepia* (12.5.43)	..	4·75	5·00
	b. *Ultramarine & blackish brn* (20.10.44)	4·25	4·25
50	6d. olive-green and deep violet	..	40	50
51	1s. brownish black and turquoise-green	..	6·50	1·75
	a. *Brownish black & turquoise-bl* (12.5.43)	4·50	2·00
	ab. *Perf 12* (8.5.51)	..	4·50	13·00
52	2s. deep ultramarine and orange-red	..	16·00	8·50

53	2s. 6d. deep blue and emerald	..	..	17·00	14·00
54	5s. deep rose-red and royal blue	..	..	18·00	16·00
43/54			*Set of 12*	55·00	42·00
43/54 Perf "Specimen"	..	..	*Set of 12*	£250

Designs: *As T **6**—2d.* Canoe and boat-house; *2s. 6d.* Gilbert Islands canoe. *As T **7**—5d.* Ellice Islands canoe; *6d.* Coconut palms; *2s.* H.M.C.S. *Nimanoa*; *5s.* Coat of arms. *As T **8**—2½d.* Native house; *3d.* Seascape; *1s.* Cantilever jetty, Ocean Island.

1946 (16 Dec). *Victory. As Nos. 110/11 of Antigua.*

55	1d. purple	..	..	..	15	20
56	3d. blue	..	..	..	15	20
55/6 Perf "Specimen"		..	*Set of 2*	55·00

1949 (29 Aug). *Royal Silver Wedding. As Nos. 112/13 of Antigua.*

57	1d. violet	..	..	..	40	50
58	£1 scarlet	..	..	..	15·00	18·00

1949 (10 Oct). *75th Anniv of U.P.U. As Nos. 114/17 of Antigua.*

59	1d. purple	..	..	..	55	90
60	2d. grey-black	..	..	..	1·75	1·75
61	3d. deep blue	..	..	..	1·50	1·75
62	1s. blue	..	..	..	1·75	2·00
59/62 ..	..	..	*Set of 4*	5·00	5·75

POSTAGE DUE STAMPS

D 1

(Typo B.W.)

1940 (Aug). *Wmk Mult Script CA. P 12.*

D1	D 1	1d. emerald-green	..	..	7·50	17·00
D2		2d. scarlet	..	..	8·50	17·00
D3		3d. brown	..	..	12·00	18·00
D4		4d. blue ..	..	..	14·00	25·00
D5		5d. grey-green	..	..	19·00	25·00
D6		6d. purple	..	..	19·00	25·00
D7		1s. violet	..	..	21·00	35·00
D8		1s. 6d. turquoise-green..	..	40·00	70·00
D1/8			*Set of 8*	£130	£200
D1/8 Perf "Specimen"	..	..	*Set of 8*	£160

Examples of all values are known showing a forged Post Office Ocean Island postmark dated "16 DE 46".

Gold Coast

12 pence (d) = 1 shilling; 20 shillings = 1 pound

CROWN COLONY

1937 (12 May). *Coronation. As Nos. 95/7 of Antigua.* P 11×11½.

117	1d. buff	..	..	..	..	1·25	1·00
118	2d. slate			..	..	1·40	2·75
119	3d. blue	..	..	..	..	1·40	1·25
117/19		..	..	*Set of 3*		3·50	4·50
117/19 Perf "Specimen"				*Set of 3*		50·00	

14

15 King George VI and Christiansborg Castle, Accra

(Recess B.W.)

1938 (1 Apr)–41. *Wmk Mult Script CA. P* 12×11½ (*T* **14**) *or* 11½×12 (*T* **15**)*.

120	**14**	½d. green	..	..	..	..	30	40
121		1d. red-brown	..	..	..	..	30	10
122		1½d. scarlet	..	..	..	..	35	50
123		2d. slate	..	..	..	..	35	25
124		3d. blue ..	..	..	..	..	35	20
125		4d. magenta	..	..	..	..	50	90
126		6d. purple	..	..	..	..	50	10
127		9d. orange	..	..	..	..	70	40
128	**15**	1s. black and olive-green	..	..	70	40
129		1s. 3d. brown & turquoise-bl (12.4.41)	2·00	40
130		2s. blue and violet	..	..	..	4·00	6·50
131		5s. olive-green and carmine	..	..	7·00	8·50
132		10s. black and violet (7.40)	..	..	7·00	15·00
120/32		..	..	..	*Set of 13*	22·00	30·00
120/32 Perf "Specimen"				*Set of 13*	£160	

*Nos. 120 to 132, except 1s. 3d. and 10s., exist in two perforations: (a) Line-perf 12, from early printings; (b) Comb-perf 12×11.8 (vertical design) or 11.8×12 (horiz design) from later printings. The 1s. 3d. and 10s. exist only comb-perf 11.8×12.

1946 (14 Oct). *Victory. As Nos. 110/11 of Antigua. P* 13½×14.

133	2d. slate-violet	..	..	..	..	9·50	2·25
	a. Perf 13½ ..	..	..	..	..	10	10
134	4d. claret	..	..	..	..	1·50	2·50
	a. Perf 13½ ..	..	..	..	..	60	1·75
133/4 Perf "Specimen"		..	..	*Set of 2*	50·00	

16 Northern Territories Mounted Constabulary

17 Christiansborg Castle

(Des B. A. Johnston (1½d.), M. Ziorkley and B. A. Abban (2d.), P.O. draughtsman (2½d.), C. Gomez (1s.), M. Ziorkley (10s.); others from photographs. Recess B.W.)

1948 (1 July). *T* **16/17** *and similar designs. Wmk Mult Script CA. P* 12 × 11½ (*vert*) *or* 11½ × 12 (*horiz*).

135	½d. emerald-green	..	..	..	20	30
136	1d. blue	..	..	..	15	15
137	1½d. scarlet	..	..	..	1·25	70
138	2d. purple-brown	..	..	..	55	10
139	2½d. yellow-brown and scarlet	..	..	2·00	2·50
140	3d. light blue ..	..	..	..	4·00	45
141	4d. magenta ..	..	..	..	3·50	1·25
142	6d. black and orange..	..	..	30	30
143	1s. black and vermilion	..	..	60	30
144	2s. sage-green and magenta..	..	..	3·00	2·00
145	5s. purple and black ..	..	..	20·00	4·00
146	10s. black and sage-green	..	..	8·00	4·50
135/46	..	..	..	*Set of 12*	40·00	14·50
135/46 Perf "Specimen"			*Set of 12*	£225	

Designs: *Horiz*—1½d. Emblem of Joint Provincial Council; 2½d. Map showing position of Gold Coast; 3d. Manganese mine; 4d. Lake Bosumtwi; 1s. Breaking cocoa pods; 2s. Trooping the Colour; 5s. Surfboats. *Vert*—2d. Talking drums; 6d. Cocoa farmer; 10s. Forest.

1948 (20 Dec). *Royal Silver Wedding. As Nos. 112/13 of Antigua.*

147	1½d. scarlet	..	..	..	..	30	30
148	10s. grey-olive	..	..	..	11·00	14·00

1949 (10 Oct). *75th Anniv of U.P.U. As Nos. 114/17 of Antigua.*

149	2d. red-brown	..	..	..	..	30	30
150	2½d. orange	..	..	..	..	1·50	1·75
151	3d. deep blue ..	..	..	..	50	70
152	1s. blue-green	..	..	..	50	50
149/52	..	..	..	..	*Set of 4*	2·50	3·00

POSTAGE DUE STAMPS

D 1

Normal

Lower serif at left of "3" missing (R. 9/1)

1951–52. *Chalk-surfaced paper. Wmk Mult Script CA. P* 14.

D5	D 1	2d. black (13.12.51)	..	..	2·50	16·00
		a. Error. Crown missing, W **9**a	..	£400	
		b. Error. St. Edward's Crown, W **9**b	..	£225	
		c. Large "d" (R. 9/6, 10/6)	..	14·00	
D6		3d. black (13.12.51)	..	..	1·50	14·00
		a. Error. Crown missing, W **9**a	..	£400	
		b. Error. St. Edward's Crown, W **9**b	..	£225	
		c. Missing serif	..	..	14·00	
D7		6d. black (1.10.52)	..	..	1·75	8·00
		a. Error. Crown missing, W **9**a	..	£550	
		b. Error. St. Edward's Crown, W **9**b	..	£375	
D8		1s. black (1.10.52)	..	..	2·25	48·00
		b. Error. St. Edward's Crown, W **9**b	..	£500	
D5/8			..	..	*Set of 4*	7·25	75·00

For illustration of No. D5c see above Nos. D4/6 of Bechuanaland Protectorate.

Grenada

1937. 12 pence (d) = 1 shilling; 20 shillings = 1 pound
1949. 100 cents = 1 West Indian dollar

CROWN COLONY

1937 (12 May). *Coronation. As Nos.* 95/7 *of Antigua. P* 11x11½.

149	1d. violet	40	20
150	1½d. carmine	40	20
151	2½d. blue	80	30
149/51	*Set of* 3	1·40	65
149/51 Perf "Specimen"	*Set of* 3	50·00	

35 King George VI

(Photo Harrison)

1937 (12 July)–**50**. *Wmk Mult Script CA. Chalk-surfaced paper. P* 15×14.

152	**35**	¼d. brown	1·40	10
		a. Ordinary paper (11.42)	30	50
		b. Ordinary paper. *Chocolate* (1.45)	20	60
		c. Chalk-surfaced paper. *Chocolate* (8.50)	50	1·50

The ordinary paper is thick, smooth and opaque.

36 Grand Anse Beach

40 Badge of the Colony

Colon flaw
(R. 5/8. Corrected on
ptg of Nov 1950)

(Recess D.L.R. (10s.), Waterlow (others))

1938 (16 Mar)–**50**. *As T* **31/4** (*but portrait of King George VI as in T* **36**) *and T* **40**. *Wmk Mult Script CA* (*sideways on T* **32**). *P* 12½ *or* 12 × 13 (10s.).

153	**36**	½d. yellow-green	4·50	90
		a. Perf 12½ × 13½ (1938)	5·00	80
		b. Perf 12½. *Blue-green*	30	1·00
		ba. Perf 12½ × 13½. *Blue-green*	4·00	4·00
154	**32**	1d. black and sepia	75	20
		a. Perf 13½ × 12½ (1938)	30	50
155	**33**	1½d. black and scarlet	40	40
		a. Perf 12½ × 13½ (1938)	2·25	30
156	**32**	2d. black and orange	30	50
		a. Perf 13½ × 12½ (1938)	2·00	40
157	**34**	2½d. bright blue	30	30
		a. Perf 12½ × 13½ (?March 1950)	£4000	£200
158	**32**	3d. black and olive-green	9·00	1·40
		a. Perf 13½ × 12½ (16.3.38)	5·50	80
		ab. Perf 13½ × 12½. *Black and brown-olive* (1942)	30	80
		b. Perf 12½. *Black and brown-olive* (16.8.50)	30	1·60
		ba. Colon flaw	35·00	
159		6d. black and purple	85	40
		a. Perf 13½ × 12½ (1942)	1·75	50
160		1s. black and brown	1·50	30
		a. Perf 13½ × 12½ (1941)	2·75	1·25
161	**32**	2s. black and ultramarine	13·00	1·25
		a. Perf 13½ × 12½ (1941)	17·00	1·50
162		5s. black and violet	3·25	1·50
		a. Perf 13½ × 12½ (1947)	2·75	5·50
163	**40**	10s. steel blue and carmine (*narrow*) (*p* 12 × 13)	55·00	9·00
		a. Perf 14. *Steel blue and bright carmine* (*narrow*)	£180	45·00
		b. Perf 14. *Slate-blue and bright carmine* (*narrow*) (1943)	£180	£110
		c. Perf 12. *Slate-blue and bright carmine* (*narrow*) (1943)	£425	£650
		d. Perf 14. *Slate-blue and carmine-lake* (*wide*) (1944)	80·00	7·50
		e. Perf 14. *Blue-black and carmine* (*narrow*) (1943)	27·00	8·00
		f. Perf 14. *Blue-black and bright carmine* (*wide*) (1947)	25·00	25·00
152/63e		*Set of* 12	40·00	12·00
152/63 Perf "Specimen"		*Set of* 12	£225	

Designs: *Horiz*—1d., 2d., 3d., 6d., 1s., 2s., 5s. Badge of Colony. *Vert*—1½d. Grand Etang; 2½d. St. George's.

In the earlier printings of the 10s. the paper was dampened before printing and the subsequent shrinkage produced narrow frames 23½ to 23¾ mm wide. Later printings were made on dry paper producing wide frames 24¼ mm wide.

No. 163a is one of the earlier printings line perf 13.8 × 14.1.

No. 163b is line-perf 14.1.

Nos. 163b/c show a blurred centre caused by the use of a worn plate.

Nos. 163a and 163b may be found with gum more or less yellow due to local climatic conditions.

Examples of No. 163c are known showing forged St. George's postmarks dated "21 AU 42", "21 AU 43" or "2 OC 43".

1946 (25 Sept). *Victory. As Nos.* 110/11 *of Antigua.*

164	1½d. carmine	10	10
165	3½d. blue	10	10
164/5 Perf "Specimen"	*Set of* 2	50·00	

1948 (27 Oct). *Royal Silver Wedding. As Nos.* 112/13 *of Antigua.*

166	1½d. scarlet	15	10
167	10s. slate-green	7·00	16·00

(New Currency. 100 cents = 1 West Indian, later Eastern Caribbean, dollar)

1949 (10 Oct). *75th Anniv of Universal Postal Union. As Nos.* 114/17 *of Antigua.*

168	5 c. ultramarine	20	10
169	6 c. olive	50	50
170	12 c. magenta	35	30
171	24 c. red-brown	35	30
168/71	*Set of* 4	1·25	1·10

41 King
George VI

42 Badge of the
Colony

43 Badge of the
Colony

(Recess B.W. (T **41**), D.L.R. (others))

1951 (8 Jan). *Wmk Mult Script CA. P* 11½ (*T* **41**), 11½ × 12½
(*T* **42**), *and* 11½ × 13 (*T* **43**).

172	**41**	½ c. black and red-brown	..	..	15	1·00
173		1 c. black and emerald-green	..	..	15	25
174		2 c. black and brown	..	..	15	30
175		3 c. black and rose-carmine	..	..	15	10
176		4 c. black and orange	..	..	35	40
177		5 c. black and violet	..	..	20	10
178		6 c. black and olive	..	..	30	60
179		7 c. black and light blue	..	..	1·75	10
180		12 c. black and purple	..	..	2·25	30
181	**42**	25 c. black and sepia	..	..	2·25	50
182		50 c. black and blue	..	..	5·50	40
183		$1.50, black and yellow-orange	..	7·50	4·75
184	**43**	$2.50, slate-blue and carmine	..	5·50	5·00
172/184		..	..	..	*Set of* 13	24·00	12·00

1951 (16 Feb). *Inauguration of B.W.I. University College. As Nos.*
118/19 *of Antigua.*

185		3 c. black and carmine	..	..	45	20
186		6 c. black and olive	..	..	45	20

NEW CONSTITUTION

1951

(44)

1951 (21 Sept). *New Constitution. Nos.* 175/7 *and* 180 *optd
with T* **44** *by B.W.*

187	**41**	3 c. black and rose-carmine	..	..	10	10
188		4 c. black and orange	..	..	10	10
189		5 c. black and violet (R.)	..	..	10	10
190		12 c. black and purple	..	..	10	15
187/90		..	..	..	*Set of* 4	30	40

POSTAGE DUE STAMPS

D **1**

1952 (1 Mar). *As Type* D **1**, *but inscr* "POSTAGE DUE". *Value in
cents. Chalk-surfaced paper. Wmk Mult Script CA. P* 14.

D15	2 c. black	..	..	..	..	30	3·75
	a. Error. Crown missing. W **9a**	..	75·00	
	b. Error. St. Edward Crown. W **9b**	..	38·00	
D16	4 c. black	..	..	..	..	30	10·00
	a. Error. Crown missing. W **9a**	..	75·00	
	b. Error. St. Edward Crown. W **9b**	..	38·00	
D17	6 c. black	..	..	..	..	45	10·00
	a. Error. Crown missing. W **9a**	..	95·00	
	b. Error. St. Edward Crown. W **9b**	..	65·00	
D18	8 c. black	..	..	..	..	75	10·00
	a. Error. Crown missing. W **9a**	..	£170	
	b. Error. St. Edward Crown. W **9b**	..	£110	
D15/18	..	..	..	..	*Set of* 4	1·60	30·00

Hong Kong

100 cents = 1 Hong Kong dollar

CROWN COLONY

1937 (12 May). *Coronation. As Nos. 95/7 of Antigua. P* 11×11½.

137	4 c. green			6·00	2·50
138	15 c. carmine			12·00	3·25
139	25 c. blue			15·00	2·50
137/9			*Set of 3*	30·00	7·50
137/9 Perf "Specimen"			*Set of 3*	£180	

29 King George VI

1938–52. *Wmk Mult Script CA. Chalk-surfaced paper* (80 c., $1 (*No.* 155), $2 (*No.* 157), $5 (*No.* 159), $10 (*No.* 161)). *P.* 14.

140	**29**	1 c. brown (24.5.38)		1·75	80
		a. Pale brown (4.2.52)		2·00	4·50
141		2 c. grey (5.4.38)		1·75	30
		a. Perf 14½×14 (28.9.45)		1·75	4·50
142		4 c. orange (5.4.38)		2·75	1·25
		a. Perf 14½×14 (28.9.45)		4·50	3·25
143		5 c. green (24.5.38)		1·00	20
		a. Perf 14½×14 (28.9.45)		2·50	5·00
144		8 c. red-brown (1.11.41)		1·75	2·25
		a. Imperf (pair)		£22000	
145		10 c. bright violet (13.4.38)		42·00	75
		a. Perf 14½×14. *Dull violet* (28.9.45)		6·50	20
		b. Dull reddish violet (9.4.46)		50·00	70
		c. Reddish lilac (9.4.47)		15·00	20
146		15 c. scarlet (13.4.38)		1·25	30
147		20 c. black (1.2.46)		1·25	30
148		20 c. scarlet-vermilion (1.4.48)		6·50	40
		a. Rose-red (25.4.51)		14·00	5·50
149		25 c. bright blue (5.4.38)		23·00	80
150		25 c. pale yellow-olive (9.4.46)		4·75	1·25
151		30 c. yellow-olive (13.4.38)		£150	1·40
		a. Perf 14½×14. *Yellowish olive* (28.9.45)		15·00	8·00
152		30 c. blue (9.4.46)		6·00	20
153		50 c. reddish purple (13.4.38)		38·00	70
		a. Perf 14½×14. *Deep magenta* (28.9.45)		24·00	1·10
		b. Chalk-surfaced paper. *Brt purple* (9.4.47)		8·00	20
154		80 c. carmine (2.2.48)		4·50	95
155		$1 dull lilac and blue (*chalk-surfaced paper*) (27.4.38)		8·00	2·50
		a. Ordinary paper. *Pale reddish lilac and blue* (28.9.45)		9·50	4·75
156		$1 red-orange and green (9.4.46)		11·00	30
		a. Chalk-surfaced paper (21.6.48)		40·00	3·25
		b. Chalk-surfaced paper. *Yellow-orge and green* (6.11.52)		65·00	14·00
157		$2 red-orange and green (24.5.38)		70·00	14·00
158		$2 reddish violet and scarlet (9.4.46)		18·00	1·25
		a. Chalk-surfaced paper (9.4.47)		28·00	75
159		$5 dull lilac and scarlet (2.6.38)		55·00	48·00
160		$5 green and violet (9.4.46)		75·00	5·00
		a. Yellowish green and violet (9.4.46)		£150	16·00
		ab. Chalk-surfaced paper (9.4.46)		90·00	2·75
161		$10 green and violet (2.6.38)		£375	75·00
162		$10 bright lilac and blue (9.4.46)		£130	22·00
		a. Chalk-surfaced paper. *Reddish violet and blue* (9.4.47)		£150	18·00
140/62			*Set of 23*	£750	£150
140/62 Perf "Specimen"			*Set of 23*	£1600	

The varieties perf 14½×14 with the exception of the 4 c. were printed and perforated by Bradbury, Wilkinson & Co, Ltd, from De La Rue plates and are on rough-surfaced paper. The date quoted for these are the eventual local release dates. Stamps from these printings were on sale in London from late 1941.

Nos. 142a and 144 were printed by Harrison & Sons in 1941 and issued in sheets of 120 (12×10) instead of two panes of 60 (6×10).

Also in 1941 Williams, Lea & Co printed the $1 and $2 perf 14 from De La Rue plates.

Nos. 160/a were separate printings released in Hong Kong on the same day.

No. 144a. One imperforate sheet was found and most of the stamps were sold singly to the public at a branch P.O. and used for postage.

30 Street Scene

31 *Empress of Japan* (liner) and Junk

(Des W. E. Jones. Recess B.W.)

1941 (26 Feb). *Centenary of British Occupation. T* **30**/1 *and similar designs. Wmk Mult Script CA* (*sideways on horiz designs*). *P* 13½ × 13 (2 c. *and* 25 c.) *or* 13 × 13½ (*others*).

163	2 c. orange and chocolate			4·00	1·75
164	4 c. bright purple and carmine			5·50	1·75
165	5 c. black and green			2·00	50
166	15 c. black and scarlet			5·50	1·00
167	25 c. chocolate and blue			14·00	3·25
168	$1 blue and orange			55·00	7·00
163/168			*Set of 6*	75·00	14·00
163/8 Perf "Specimen"			*Set of 6*	£325	

Designs: *Horiz*—5 c. The University; 15 c. The Harbour; $1 *Falcon* (clipper) and Short S.23 Empire "C" Class flying boat. *Vert*—25 c. The Hong Kong Bank.

Hong Kong was under Japanese occupation from 25 December 1941 until 30 August 1945. The Japanese post offices in the colony were closed from 31 August and mail was carried free, marked with cachets reading "HONG KONG/1945/POSTAGE PAID". Military administration lasted until 1 May 1946. Hong Kong stamps were re-introduced on 28 September 1945.

36 King George VI and Phoenix

Extra stroke (R. 1/2)

(Des W. E. Jones. Recess D.L.R.)

1946 (29 Aug). *Victory. Wmk Mult Script CA. P* 13.
169	**36**	30 c. blue and red (*shades*)	..	..	1·75	1·00
		a. Extra stroke		..	42·00	
170		$1 brown and red	..	..	3·50	75
		a. Extra stroke		..	75·00	
169/70 Perf "Specimen"	..		*Set of* 2	£160		

Spur on "N" of "KONG" (R. 2/9)

1948 (22 Dec). *Royal Silver Wedding. As Nos.* 112/13 *of Antigua.*
171	10 c. violet ..	..	..	..	2·50	80
	a. Spur on "N"	..	..	..	50·00	
172	$10 carmine	..	..	..	£325	70·00

1949 (10 Oct). *75th Anniv of Universal Postal Union. As Nos.* 114/17 *of Antigua.*
173	10 c. violet	..	..	..	3·75	50
174	20 c. carmine-red	..	..	..	15·00	3·00
175	30 c. deep blue	..	..	..	12·00	1·75
176	80 c. bright reddish purple	..	..	35·00	9·50
173/6 ..	..	..	..	*Set of* 4	60·00	13·00

POSTAGE DUE STAMPS

D **1** Post-office Scales

(Typo D.L.R.)

1938 (Feb)–**63**. *Wmk Mult Script CA* (*sideways*). *Ordinary paper. P* 14.
D 6	D **1**	2 c. grey	..	..	..	13·00	9·00
		a. Chalk-surfaced paper (21.3.56)	..	1·10	10·00	
D 7		4 c. orange	..	..	..	14·00	6·50
		a. Chalk-surfaced paper. *Orange-yellow* (23.5.61)	..		2·50	8·50
D 8		6 c. scarlet	..	..	..	9·50	5·50
D 9		8 c. chestnut (26.2.46)	..	..	5·50	32·00
D10		10 c. violet	..	..	..	25·00	45
		a. Chalk-surfaced paper (17.9.63)	..	14·00	6·00	
D11		20 c. black (26.2.46)	..	..	9·00	3·00
D12		50 c. blue (7.47)	..	..	..	35·00	15·00
D6a/12				*Set of* 7	70·00	65·00	
D6/12 Perf "Specimen"	..	..	*Set of* 7	£300		

JAPANESE OCCUPATION OF HONG KONG

Hong Kong surrendered to the Japanese on 25 December 1941. The postal service was not resumed until 22 January 1942 when the G.P.O. and Kowloon Central Office re-opened.

Initially six values (1, 2, 3, 4, 10 and 30 s.) of the current Japanese definitive set were on sale, but the range was gradually expanded to cover all values between ½ s. and 10 y. Supply of these Japanese stamps was often interrupted and, during the period between 28 July 1942 and 21 April 1943, circular "Postage Paid" handstamps were sometimes used. A substantial increase in postage rates on 16 April 1945 led to the issue of the local surcharges, Nos. J1/3.

      (1)   (2)

1945 (16 Apr). *Stamps of Japan surch with T* 1 (*No.* J1) *or as T* **2**.
J1	1.50 yen on 1 s. brown	..	..	25·00	21·00
J2	3 yen on 2 s. scarlet	..	..	12·00	17·00
J3	5 yen on 5 s. claret..	..	..	£850	£130

Designs (18½ × 22 *mm*):—1 s. Girl Worker; 2 s. Gen. Nogi; 5 s. Admiral Togo.

No. J3 has four characters of value similarly arranged but differing from T **2**.

India

12 pies = 1 anna; 16 annas = 1 rupee

91 King George VI

92 Dak Runner

93 King George VI

1937 (23 Aug–15 Dec). *Typo.* W **69**. *P* 13½ × 14 *or* 14 × 13½ (*T* 93).

247	**91**	3 p. slate	..	..	50	10
248		½ a. red-brown	..	..	75	10
249		9 p. green (23.8.37)	..	..	3·75	20
250		1 a. carmine (23.8.37)	..	..	30	10
		a. *Tête-bêche* (vert pair)	..		65	1·75
		w. Wmk inverted (from booklets)		..	30	40
251	**92**	2 a. vermilion	..	..	2·00	30
252	–	2½ a. bright violet	..	..	75	20
253	–	3 a. yellow-green	..	..	4·50	30
254	–	3½ a. bright blue	..	..	3·25	50
255	–	4 a. brown	..	..	13·00	20
256	–	6 a. turquoise-green	..	..	14·00	80
257	–	8 a. slate-violet	..	..	7·50	50
258	–	12 a. lake	..	..	18·00	1·10
259	**93**	1 r. grey and red-brown	..	..	1·00	15
260		2 r. purple and brown	..	..	3·75	30
261		5 r. green and blue	..	..	15·00	50
		w. Wmk inverted	..		30·00	
262		10 r. purple and claret	..	..	15·00	70
263		15 r. brown and green	..	..	65·00	55·00
		w. Wmk inverted	..		65·00	55·00
264		25 r. slate-violet and purple		..	85·00	17·00
247/64		..	..	*Set of* 18	£225	70·00

Designs: *Horiz as T* **92**—2½ a. Dak bullock cart; 3 a. Dak tonga; 3½ a. Dak camel; 4 a. Mail train; 6 a. *Strathnaver* (liner); 8 a. Mail lorry; 12 a. Armstrong Whitworth A.W.27 Ensign 1 mail plane (small head).

100*a* King George VI

101   King George VI   **102**

103 Armstrong Whitworth
A.W.27 Ensign I Mail Plane
(large head)

(*T* **100***a*/**102** des T. I. Archer. Typo)

1940–43. W **69**. *P* 13½ × 14.

265	**100***a*	3 p. slate	..	..	25	10
266		½ a. purple (1.10.42)	..	..	40	10
267		9 p. green	..	..	40	10
268		1 a. carmine (1.4.43)	..	..	40	10
269	**101**	1 a. 3 p. yellow-brown	..	..	90	10
269*a*		1½ a. dull violet (9.42)	..	..	50	10
270		2 a. vermilion	..	..	85	10
271		3 a. bright violet (1942)	..	..	1·75	10
272		3½ a. bright blue	..	..	70	10
273	**102**	4 a. brown	..	..	45	10
274		6 a. turquoise-green	..	..	2·00	10
275		8 a. slate-violet	..	..	1·50	10
276		12 a. lake	..	..	2·75	50
277	**103**	14 a. purple (15.10.40)	..	..	18·00	1·25
265/277		..	..	*Set of* 14	28·00	2·25

The 1½ a. and 3 a. were at first printed by lithography and were of finer execution and without Jubilee lines in the sheet margins.

105 "Victory" and King
George VI

= =

3 PIES

(**106**)

1946 (2 Jan). *Victory. Litho.* W **69**. *P* 13.

278	**105**	9 p. yellow-green (8.2.46)	..	..	30	30
279		1½ a. dull violet	..	..	30	30
280		3½ a. bright blue	..	..	75	60
281		12 a. claret (8.2.46)	..	..	1·50	55
278/81		..	..	*Set of* 4	2·50	1·60

1946 (8 Aug). *Surch with T* **106**.

282	**101**	3 p. on 1 a. 3 p. yellow-brown	..	..	10	15

DOMINION

301 Asokan Capital
(Inscr reads
"Long Live India")

302 Indian National Flag

74 India

303 Douglas DC-4

(Des T. I. Archer. Litho)

1947 (21 Nov–15 Dec). *Independence. W 69. P* 14 × 13½ (1½ a.) *or* 13½ × 14 (*others*).

301	301	1½ a. grey-green (15 Dec)	..	..	15	10
302	302	3½ a. orange-red, blue and green	..	30	60
		w. Wmk inverted ..	..	..	5·00	5·00
303	303	12 a. ultramarine (15 Dec)	..	..	1·25	1·50
301/3		..	..	..	*Set of* 3	1·50	2·00

304 Lockheed Constellation

(Des T. I. Archer. Litho)

1948 (29 May). *Air. Inauguration of India-U.K. Air Service. W* 69. *P* 13½ × 14.

304	304	12 a. black and ultramarine	..	..	1·00	1·75

305 Mahatma Gandhi 306

(Photo Courvoisier)

1948 (15 Aug). *First Anniv of Independence. P* 11½.

305	305	1½ a. brown	..	..	..	..	1·75	30
306		3½ a. violet	..	..	..	..	4·25	1·50
307		12 a. grey-green	..	..	..	..	6·00	60
308	306	10 r. purple-brown and lake	..	..	55·00	40·00
305/8	..	..	..	..	..	*Set of* 4	60·00	40·00

307 Ajanta Panel   308 Konarak Horse   309 Trimurti

310 Bodhisattva   311 Nataraja   312 Sanchi Stupa, East Gate

313 Bodh Gaya Temple   314 Bhuvanesvara   315 Gol Gumbad, Bijapur

316 Kandarya Mahadeva Temple   317 Golden Temple, Amritsar

318 Victory Tower, Chittorgarh   319 Red Fort, Delhi

320 Taj Mahal, Agra   321 Qutb Minar, Delhi

322 Satrunjaya Temple, Palitana

(Des T. I. Archer and I. M. Das. Typo (low values), litho (rupee values))

1949 (15 Aug). *W* 69 (*sideways** *on* 6 *p.,* 1 *r. and* 10 *r.*). *P* 14 (3 *p. to* 2 *a.*), 13½ (3 *a. to* 12 *a.*), 14×13½ (1 *r. and* 10 *r.*) 13½×14 (2 *r. and* 5 *r.*), 13 (15 *r.*).

309	307	3 p. slate-violet	..	..	..	15	10
		w. Wmk inverted ..	..	..		
310	308	6 p. purple-brown	..	..	25	10
		w. Wmk star pointing right	..	2·75	90
311	309	9 p. yellow-green	..	..	40	10
312	310	1 a. turquoise	..	..	..	60	10
313	311	2 a. carmine	..	..	..	80	10
		w. Wmk inverted ..	..	..	8·00	90

314	312	3 a. brown-orange	..	..	1·50	10
315	313	3½ a. bright blue	..	..	2·00	2·75
316	314	4 a. lake	..	..	5·00	10
		w. Wmk inverted ..	..		11·00	1·00
317	315	6 a. violet ..	..	..	1·50	10
		w. Wmk inverted ..	..		3·00	45
318	316	8 a. turquoise-green	..	..	1·50	10
		w. Wmk inverted ..	..			
319	317	12 a. dull blue	..	..	1·50	10
		w. Wmk inverted ..	..		4·00	60
320	318	1 r. dull violet and green	..		9·00	10
		w. Wmk star pointing left	..		17·00	60
321	319	2 r. claret and violet	..	..	10·00	15
		w. Wmk inverted ..	..		20·00	80
322	320	5 r. blue-green and red-brown	..		28·00	80
		w. Wmk inverted ..	..		40·00	1·25
323	321	10 r. purple-brown and deep blue	..		45·00	4·25
		a. Purple-brown and blue	..		85·00	3·75
		aw. Wmk star pointing left				
324	322	15 r. brown and claret	..	..	14·00	17·00
309/24		..	..	Set of 16	£110	22·00

*The normal sideways watermark has the star pointing to the left on the 6 p. value and to the right on the 1 r. and 10 r. (323a) *when seen from the back of the stamp.*
For T 310 with statue reversed see No. 333.

323 Globe and Asokan Capital

1949 (10 Oct). *75th Anniv of U.P.U. Litho. W* **69**. *P* 13.

325	323	9 p. green	..	..	1·00	1·25
326		2 a. rose		..	1·25	1·75
327		3½ a. bright blue	..	..	2·00	2·25
328		12 a. brown-purple	..	..	3·50	2·50
325/8 ..		..	..	Set of 4	7·00	7·00

REPUBLIC
REPUBLIC OF INDIA

324 Rejoicing Crowds    328 As T 310, but statue reversed

(Des D. J. Keymer & Co. Litho)

1950 (26 Jan). *Inauguration of Republic. T* **324** *and similar designs. W* **69** *(sideways on* 3½ *a.). P* 13.

329	2 a. scarlet	..	..	1·00	30
	w. Wmk inverted	..	..	10·00	1·60
330	3½ a. ultramarine ..		..	1·75	2·75
331	4 a. violet	..	..	1·75	50
332	12 a. maroon	..	..	3·75	2·25
	w. Wmk inverted	..	..	12·00	4·00
329/32	..	..	Set of 4	7·50	5·25

Designs: *Vert*—3½ a. Quill, ink-well and verse. *Horiz*—4 a. Ear corn and plough; 12 a. Spinning-wheel and cloth.

1950 (15 July)–**51.** *Typo. W* **69**. *P* 14 (1 a.), 13½ (*others*).

333	328	1 a. turquoise ..	..	2·50	10
333a	313	2½ a. lake (30.4.51)	..	2·50	2·50
333b	314	4 a. bright blue (30.4.51)	..	6·00	10
333/b ..		..	Set of 3	10·00	2·50

NEW INFORMATION

The editor is always interested to correspond with people who have new information that will improve or correct the Catalogue.

329 *Stegodon ganesa*   330 Torch

1951 (13 Jan). *Centenary of Geological Survey of India. Litho. W* **69**. *P* 13.

334	329	2 a. black and claret	..	..	1·75	15

1951 (4 Mar). *First Asian Games, New Delhi. Litho. W* **69** *(sideways). P* 14.

335	330	2 a. reddish purple and brown-orange ..	1·00	30
336		12 a. chocolate and light blue ..	..	5·00	90

STAMP BOOKLETS

1937. *Black on red cover. Stamps with wmk upright or inverted. Stitched.*

SB22   1 r. booklet containing sixteen 1 a. (No. 250) in blocks of 4   ..   ..   £130

OFFICIAL STAMPS

SERVICE   **SERVICE**
(O **17**)(13½ mm)   (O **18**) (19½ mm)

1937–39. *Stamps of King George VI optd as Types O* **17** *or O* **18** *(rupee values).*

O135	91	½ a. red-brown (1938)	..	15·00	15
O136		9 p. green (1937)	..	15·00	20
O137		1 a. carmine (1937)	..	2·00	10
O138	93	1 r. grey and red-brown (5.38) ..	..	50	50
O139		2 r. purple and brown (5.38)	..	1·50	2·50
O140		5 r. green and blue (10.38)	..	2·50	4·25
O141		10 r. purple and claret (1939)	..	14·00	4·75
O135/41		..	Set of 7	45·00	11·00

SERVICE 1A   INDIA POSTAGE / SERVICE
(O **19**)   (O **20**)

1939 (May). *Stamp of King George V, surch with Type O* **19**.

O142	82	1 a. on 1¼ a. mauve ..	..	..	9·00	20

(Des T. I. Archer)

1939 (1 June)–**42.** *Typo. W* **69**. *P* 14.

O143	O 20	3 p. slate ..	..	..	40	10
O144		½ a. red-brown	..	..	2·75	10
O144a		½ a. purple (1942)	..	..	30	10
O145		9 p. green	..	..	30	10
O146		1 a. carmine	..	..	30	10
O146a		1 a. 3 p. yellow-brown (1941)	..	3·75	70
O146b		1½ a. dull violet (1942)	..	65	10
O147		2 a. vermilion	..	..	60	10
O148		2½ a. bright violet	..	..	60	40
O149		4 a. brown	..	..	60	10
O150		8 a. slate-violet	..	..	90	20
O143/50		..	..	Set of 11	10·00	1·50

1948 (15 Aug). *First Anniv of Independence. Nos. 305/8 optd as Type O 17.*

O150a	305	1½ a. brown	..	..	..	42·00	30·00
O150b		3½ a. violet	..	..	..	£700	£450
O150c		12 a. grey-green				£1900	£1600
O150d	306	10 r. purple-brown and lake		£10000	

Nos. O150a/d were only issued to the Governor-General's Secretariat.

O 21 Asokan Capital

O 22

(Des T. I. Archer)

1950 (2 Jan)–**51.** *Typo (O 21) or litho (O 22). W 69. P 14.*

O151	O 21	3 p. slate-violet (1.7.50)	..	..	10	10
O152		6 p. purple-brown (1.7.50)	..	..	10	10
O153		9 p. green (1.7.50)	..	..	30	10
O154		1 a. turquoise (1.7.50)	..	..	70	10
O155		2 a. carmine (1.7.50)	..	..	1·25	10
		w. Wmk inverted	..			
O156		3 a. red-orange (1.7.50)	..	4·25	1·75
O157		4 a. lake (1.7.50)	..	..	11·00	10
O158		4 a. ultramarine (1.10.51)	..	50	10
O159		6 a. bright violet (1.7.50)	..	4·00	40
O160		8 a. red-brown (1.7.50)	..	2·25	10
		w. Wmk inverted	..		8·00	
O161	O 22	1 r. violet	..	..	2·75	10
		w. Wmk inverted	..			
O162		2 r. rose-carmine	..	..	1·00	50
O163		5 r. bluish green	..	..	2·00	1·50
O164		10 r. reddish brown	..	4·00	15·00
O151/64	..	..	..	..	*Set of 14*	30·00	18·00

INDIAN NATIONAL ARMY

The following are stated to have been used in the Japanese occupied areas of India during the drive on Imphal. Issued by the Indian National Army.

Genuine examples are inscribed "PROVISIONAL GOVERNMENT OF FREE INDIA". Forgeries also exist inscribed "PROVISIONAL GOVT. OF FREE INDIA".

Typo in Rangoon. No gum. Perf 11½ or imperf. 1 p. violet, 1 p. maroon, 1 a. green   *Price from* £50 *each unused*

JAPANESE OCCUPATION OF THE ANDAMAN AND NICOBAR ISLANDS

The Andaman Islands in the Bay of Bengal were occupied on the 23 March 1942 and the Nicobar Islands in July 1942. Civil administration was resumed in October 1945.

The following Indian stamps were surcharged with large figures preceded by a decimal point:—

Postage stamps—.3 on ½ a. (No. 248), .5 on 1 a. (No. 250), .10 on 2 a. (No. 236b), .30 on 6 a. (No. 274).

Official stamps—.10 on 1 a. 3 p. (No. O146a), .20 on 3 p. (No. O143), .20 in red on 3 p. (No. O143).

Prices from £300 *each unused*

INDIAN CONVENTION STATES

Stamps of India overprinted

CHAMBA

Raja Lakshman Singh, 1935–1971

CHAMBA STATE	**CHAMBA STATE**
(3)	(4)

CHAMBA STATE	CHAMBA	CHAMBA
(5)	(6)	(7)

1938. *King George VI. Nos. 247/64 optd with T 3 (3 p. to 1 a.), T 5 (2 a. to 12 a.) or T 4 (rupee values).*

82	91	3 p. slate		..	..	3·00	6·50
83		½ a. red-brown	..	..		90	3·75
84		9 p. green	..	..	..	3·50	18·00
85		1 a. carmine	..	..		90	1·10
86	92	2 a. vermilion	..	..		2·25	5·50
87	–	2½ a. bright violet	..	..	2·75	12·00
88	–	3 a. yellow-green	..	..	4·00	13·00
89	–	3½ a. bright blue	..	..	3·50	15·00
90	–	4 a. brown	..	..	11·00	8·00
91	–	6 a. turquoise-green	..	10·00	30·00
92	–	8 a. slate-violet	..	11·00	26·00
93	–	12 a. lake	..	..	4·75	30·00
94	93	1 r. grey and red-brown	..	25·00	38·00
95		2 r. purple and brown	..	40·00	£160
96		5 r. green and blue	..	65·00	£250
97		10 r. purple and claret	..	£120	£400
98		15 r. brown and green	..	£225	£550
99		25 r. slate-violet and purple	£250	£650
82/99	..	..	..	..	*Set of 18*	£700	£2000

1942–47. *Optd with T 6 (to 12 a.), "CHAMBA" only, as in T 5 (14 a.) or T 7 (rupee values). (a) Stamps of 1937. W 69 (inverted on 15 r.).*

100	91	½ a. red-brown	..	..	18·00	14·00
101		1 a. carmine	..	..	22·00	14·00
102	93	1 r. grey and red-brown	..	21·00	38·00
103		2 r. purple and brown	..	28·00	£140
104		5 r. green and blue	..	60·00	£150
105		10 r. purple and claret	..	95·00	£300
106		15 r. brown and green	..	£200	£475
107		25 r. slate-violet and purple	£225	£550
100/107	..				*Set of 8*	£600	£1500

(b) Stamps of 1940–43

108	100a	3 p. slate	..	..	60	2·75
109		½ a. purple (1943)	..	..	70	1·75
110		9 p. green	..	..	70	7·00
111		1 a. carmine (1943)	..	..	90	1·75
112	101	1½ a. dull violet (1943)	..	90	5·00
113		2 a. vermilion (1943)	..	1·75	5·50
114		3 a. bright violet	..	..	5·50	13·00
115		3½ a. bright blue	..	..	3·50	21·00
116	102	4 a. brown	..	..	4·25	6·50
117		6 a. turquoise-green	..	13·00	30·00
118		8 a. slate-violet	..	13·00	35·00
119		12 a. lake	..	..	26·00	45·00
120	103	14 a. purple (1947)	..	5·00	3·00
108/120		..	..	..	*Set of 13*	70·00	£16

The 3 a. exists printed by lithography or typography.

OFFICIAL STAMPS

CHAMBA STATE	**CHAMBA STATE**
SERVICE	**SERVICE**
(O 2)	(O 3)

1938–40. *King George VI. Optd with Type O 2 or O 3 (rupee values).*

O66	91	9 p. green	..	..	6·00	27·0
O67		1 a. carmine	..	..	4·75	1·5
O68	93	1 r. grey and red-brown (1940?)	..	£600	£85
O69		2 r. purple and brown (1939)	..	50·00	£22
O70		5 r. green and blue (1939)	..	80·00	£30
O71		10 r. purple and claret (1939)	..	£120	£47
O66/71		..	..	..	*Set of 6*	£800	£17C

CHAMBA
SERVICE
(O 4)

1940–43. (a) Official stamps optd with T **6**.

O72	O 20	3 p. slate	..	..	60	50
O73		½ a. red-brown	..	..	11·00	1·25
O74		½ a. purple (1943) ..		..	60	1·10
O75		9 p. green ..	..	..	2·50	4·00
		w. Wmk inverted	..	..	10·00	
O76		1 a. carmine (1941)	..	..	60	90
O77		1 a. 3 p. yellow-brown (1941)	..	35·00	12·00
O78		1½ a. dull violet (1943)	..	3·75	3·50
O79		2 a. vermilion	..	..	2·75	2·75
O80		2½ a. bright violet (1941)	..	1·75	13·00
O81		4 a. brown ..	..	..	3·25	5·50
O82		8 a. slate-violet	..	..	8·00	32·00
		w. Wmk inverted	..	..	7·00	32·00

(b) Postage stamps optd with Type O **4**.

O83	93	1 r. grey and red-brown (1942)	..	32·00	£120
O84		2 r. purple and brown (1942)	..	50·00	£180
O85		5 r. green and blue (1942)	..	80·00	£275
O86		10 r. purple and claret (1942)	..	£120	£475
O72/86	..	..	..	Set of 15	£325	£1000

Chamba became part of Himachal Pradesh on 15 April 1948.

GWALIOR
Maharaja George Jivaji Rao Sindhia, 1925–1961

GWALIOR
गवालियर
(4)

GWALIOR
गवालियर
(5)

1938–48. King George VI. Nos. 247/50, 253, 255/6, and 259/64 optd with T **4** or **5** (rupee values).

105	91	3 p. slate	..	..	3·25	10
106		½ a. red-brown	..	..	3·25	10
107		9 p. green (1939)	..	..	32·00	2·50
108		1 a. carmine	..	..	3·25	15
109	—	3 a. yellow-green (1939)	..	7·00	2·50
110	—	4 a. brown	..	..	35·00	1·50
111		6 a. turquoise-green (1939)	..	2·50	5·50
112	93	1 r. grey and red-brown (1942)..	4·00	1·50
113		2 r. purple and brown (1948)	..	22·00	6·00
114		5 r. green and blue (1948)	..	40·00	25·00
115		10 r. purple and claret (1948)	..	38·00	35·00
116		15 r. brown and green (1948)	..	£120	£150
117		25 r. slate-violet and purple (1948)	..	£110	£120
105/117		..	..	Set of 13	£375	£300

1942–5. King George VI. Optd with T **4**.

118	100a	3 p. slate	..	..	45	10
		w. Wmk inverted	..	..	—	10·00
119		½ a. purple (1943)	..	..	45	10
120		9 p. green	..	..	45	10
121		1 a. carmine (1943)	..	..	40	10
		a. Optd double	..	..	—	£120
122	101	1½ a. dull violet	..	..	3·25	20
123		2 a. vermilion	..	..	55	20
124		3 a. bright violet	..	..	4·25	30
		a. Opt double	..	..	—	£120
125	102	4 a. brown	..	..	1·00	20
126		6 a. turquoise-green (1945) ..	20·00	14·00
127		8 a. slate-violet (1944)	..	2·75	2·75
128		12 a. lake (1943)	..	..	35·00	14·00
118/28		..	..	Set of 11	35·00	28·00

The 1½ a. and 3 a. exist printed by lithography or typography.

GWALIOR
गवालियर
(6)

1949 (Apr). King George VI. Optd with T **6** at the Alizah Printing Press, Gwalior.

129	100a	3 p. slate	..	..	60	50
130		½ a. purple	..	..	60	50
131		1 a. carmine	..	..	75	60
132	101	2 a. vermilion ..	..	..	12·00	1·50
133		3 a. bright violet	..	..	30·00	18·00
134	102	4 a. brown	..	..	2·00	2·50
135		6 a. turquoise-green	..	32·00	40·00
136		8 a. slate-violet	..	75·00	42·00
137		12 a. lake ..	..	..	£275	£110
129/137		..	..	Set of 9	£375	£190

OFFICIAL STAMPS

गवालियर

गवालियर

सरविस
(O 1)

सरविस
(O 2)

1938. King George VI. Optd as Type O **1** (13 mm).

O78	91	½ a. red-brown	..	..	7·50	30
O79		1 a. carmine	..	..	1·10	20

गवालियर
(O 3)

1ᴬ_____1ᴬ
(O 4)

1940–42. Official stamps optd with Type O **3**.

O80	O 20	3 p. slate	..	..	50	10
O81		½ a. red-brown	..	..	4·00	25
O82		½ a. purple (1942) ..		..	50	10
O83		9 p. green (1942)	..	..	70	50
O84		1 a. carmine	..	..	3·25	10
O85		1 a. 3 p. yellow-brown (1942)	..	25·00	1·60
		w. Wmk inverted	..	—	10·00
O86		1½ a. dull violet (1942)	..	1·00	30
O87		2 a. vermilion	..	..	1·00	30
O88		4 a. brown (1942)	..	..	1·25	1·40
O89		8 a. slate-violet (1942)	..	2·50	5·50
O80/9		..	..	Set of 10	35·00	9·00

1941. Stamp of 1932 (King George V) optd with Type O **1** and surch with Type O **4**.

O90	82	1 a. on 1¼ a. mauve	..	..	16·00	2·50
		a. Wmk inverted	..	..	18·00	3·00

1942–47. King George VI. Optd with Type O **2**.

O91	93	1 r. grey and red-brown	..	10·00	11·00
O92		2 r. purple and brown	..	22·00	55·00
O93		5 r. green and blue (1943)	..	45·00	£300
O94		10 r. purple and claret (1947)	..	£120	£600
O91/4 ..		..	..	Set of 4	£180	£850

Gwalior became part of Madhya Bharat by 1 July 1948.

JIND
Maharaja Ranbir Singh, 1887–1959

JIND STATE
(5)

JIND STATE
(6)

1937–38. King George VI. Nos. 247/64 optd with T **5** or T **6** (rupee values).

109	91	3 p. slate	..	..	4·25	1·00
110		½ a. red-brown ..	..	..	60	2·25
111		9 p. green (1937)	..	..	60	1·75
112		1 a. carmine (1937)	..	..	60	35
113	92	2 a. vermilion ..	..	..	1·50	10·00
114	—	2½ a. bright violet	..	1·00	10·00
115	—	3 a. yellow-green	..	3·75	9·00
116	—	3½ a. bright blue ..	..	1·10	10·00
117	—	4 a. brown	..	..	4·50	9·50

118	–	6 a. turquoise-green	.. .. ..	2·00	13·00
119	–	8 a. slate-violet ..	.. .. ..	2·00	14·00
120	–	12 a. lake ..	.. .. ..	1·75	14·00
121	93	1 r. grey and red-brown	.. ..	13·00	24·00
122		2 r. purple and brown	.. ..	16·00	65·00
123		5 r. green and blue	.. ..	30·00	50·00
124		10 r. purple and claret	.. ..	55·00	60·00
125		15 r. brown and green	.. ..	£150	£500
126		25 r. slate-violet and purple	.. ..	£325	£550
109/126		.. .. ..	*Set of* 18	£550	£1200

JIND
(7)

1941–43. *King George VI. Optd with T* 7. (*a*) *Stamps of* 1937. W 69 (*inverted on* 15 *r.*).

127	91	3 p. slate	.. .. ..	8·50	12·00
128		½ a. red-brown ..	.. ..	1·00	30
129		9 p. green	.. ..	8·00	9·50
130		1 a. carmine ..	.. ..	1·00	2·75
131	93	1 r. grey and red-brown	..	7·50	16·00
132		2 r. purple and brown..	..	15·00	20·00
133		5 r. green and blue	..	38·00	55·00
134		10 r. purple and claret ..	..	55·00	55·00
135		15 r. brown and green ..	..	£120	£120
136		25 r. slate-violet and purple	..	£110	£325
127/136		.. ..	*Set of* 10	£325	£550

(*b*) *Stamps of* 1940–43

137	100a	3 p. slate (1942)	.. ..	50	50
138		½ a. purple (1943)	.. ..	50	75
139		9 p. green (1942)	.. ..	50	2·00
140		1 a. carmine (1942) ..	..	65	60
141	101	1 a. 3 p. yellow-brown	..	1·00	2·25
142		1½ a. dull violet (1942) ..	..	5·00	3·25
143		2 a. vermilion ..	..	1·60	2·00
144		3 a. bright violet (1942)	..	10·00	2·00
145		3½ a. bright blue	..	4·00	4·00
146	102	4 a. brown	..	2·75	2·00
147		6 a. turquoise-green	..	3·50	7·50
148		8 a. slate-violet	..	2·50	7·50
149		12 a. lake	..	9·50	7·50
137/149		.. ..	*Set of* 13	38·00	38·00

The 1½ a. and 3 a. exist printed by lithography or typography.

OFFICIAL STAMPS

JIND STATE
SERVICE
(O 17)

**JIND STATE
SERVICE**
(O 18)

JIND
SERVICE
(O 19)

1937–40. *King George VI. Optd with Types* O 17 *or* O 18 (*rupee values*).

O66	91	½ a. red-brown (1938)	.. ..	48·00	30
O67		9 p. green	.. ..	85	5·00
O68		1 a. carmine	.. ..	55	30
O69	93	1 r. grey and red-brown (1940)..	..	23·00	40·00
O70		2 r. purple and brown (1940)	..	40·00	£160
O71		5 r. green and blue (1940)	..	85·00	£275
O72		10 r. purple and claret (1940)	..	£160	£600
O66/72		.. ..	*Set of* 7	£325	£900

1939–43. (*a*) *Official stamps optd with T* 7.

O73	O 20	3 p. slate	.. ..	50	50
O74		½ a. red-brown	.. ..	2·00	50
O75		½ a. purple (1943) ..	..	60	30
O76		9 p. green	.. ..	1·50	6·00
O77		1 a. carmine	.. ..	1·50	15
O78		1½ a. dull violet (1942)	..	4·25	1·00
O79		2 a. vermilion	.. ..	1·50	30
		w. Wmk inverted ..		—	2·00
O80		2½ a. bright violet	.. ..	1·00	4·75
O81		4 a. brown ..	.. ..	2·25	1·00
O82		8 a. slate-violet	.. ..	2·50	2·50

(*b*) *Postage stamps optd with Type* O 19

O83	93	1 r. grey and red-brown (1942)..	..	18·00	38·00
O84		2 r. purple and brown (1942)	..	40·00	£110
O85		5 r. green and blue (1942)	..	90·00	£250
O86		10 r. purple and claret (1942)	..	£160	£325
O73/86		.. ..	*Set of* 14	£300	£650

Jind was absorbed into the Patiala and East Punjab States Union by 20 August 1948.

NABHA
Maharaja Partab Singh, 1928–1971

NABHA STATE
(3)

NABHA STATE
(4)

NABHA STATE
(5)

NABHA
(6)

1938. *King George VI. Nos.* 247/64 *optd as T* 3 (3 *p. to* 1 *a.*), T 5 (2 *a. to* 12 *a.*) *or T* 4 (*rupee values*). W 69 (*inverted on* 15 *r.*).

77	91	3 p. slate	.. .. ..	4·75	30
78		½ a. red-brown	.. ..	2·50	45
79		9 p. green	.. .. ..	15·00	3·00
80		1 a. carmine ..	.. ..	1·10	30
81	92	2 a. vermilion ..	.. ..	1·00	3·25
82	–	2½ a. bright violet	.. ..	1·00	5·50
83	–	3 a. yellow-green	.. ..	1·10	3·25
84	–	3½ a. bright blue	.. ..	1·10	11·00
85	–	4 a. brown	.. ..	3·75	4·75
86	–	6 a. turquoise-green	.. ..	1·60	11·00
87	–	8 a. slate-violet	.. ..	1·90	11·00
88	–	12 a. lake	.. ..	2·25	13·00
89	93	1 r. grey and red-brown	..	10·00	18·00
90		2 r. purple and brown	..	19·00	65·00
91		5 r. green and blue	..	48·00	£140
92		10 r. purple and claret ..	..	80·00	£275
93		15 r. brown and green	..	£200	£500
94		25 r. slate-violet and purple	..	£200	£500
		w. Wmk inverted	..	£300	£600
77/94		.. ..	*Set of* 18	£550	£1400

1941–45. *King George VI. Optd with T* 6. (*a*) *Stamps of* 1937.

95	91	3 p. slate (1942)..	.. ..	27·00	2·00
96		½ a. red-brown (1942)	..	65·00	3·25
97		9 p. green (1942)	.. ..	10·00	9·50
98		1 a. carmine (1942)	..	10·00	2·00
95/8	..	.. ..	*Set of* 4	£100	15·00

(*b*) *Stamps of* 1940-43

105	100a	3 p. slate (1942)	.. ..	80	45
106		½ a. purple (1943)	.. ..	3·25	45
107		9 p. green (1942)	.. ..	2·50	45
108		1 a. carmine (1945) ..	..	80	1·90
109	101	1 a. 3 p. yellow-brown	..	80	1·00
110		1½ a. dull violet (1942) ..	..	1·00	75
111		2 a. vermilion (1943) ..	..	80	2·25
112		3 a. bright violet (1943)	..	1·75	2·25
113		3½ a. bright blue (1944)	..	7·50	26·00
114	102	4 a. brown ..	.. ..	1·60	75
115		6 a. turquoise-green (1943)	..	6·50	29·00
116		8 a. slate-violet (1943)	..	4·75	22·00
117		12 a. lake (1943)	.. ..	4·50	29·00
105/117		.. ..	*Set of* 13	32·00	£100

The 1½ a. exists printed by lithography or typography.

OFFICIAL STAMPS

NABHA STATE
SERVICE
(O 10)

**NABHA
SERVICE**
(O 11)

1938. *King George VI. Optd as Type* O 10.

O53	91	9 p. green	.. .. ..	1·25	2·0●
O54		1 a. carmine	.. ..	6·50	3●

1940–43. (*a*) *Official stamps optd with T* 6.

O55	O 20	3 p. slate (1942)	.. ..	55	6●
O56		½ a. red-brown (1942)	..	70	3●
O57		½ a. purple (1943) ..	..	1·50	4●
O58		9 p. green ..	.. ..	2·00	2●
O59		1 a. carmine (1942)	..	50	2●
O61		1½ a. dull violet (1942)	..	60	4●
O62		2 a. vermilion (1942)	..	80	5●
		w. Wmk inverted		2·00	1·0●
O64		4 a. brown (1942) ..	..	3·50	1·7●
O65		8 a. slate-violet (1942)	..	5·50	10·0●

(b) *Postage stamps optd with Type* O 11.

O66	93	1 r. grey and red-brown (1942)	..	8·50	25·00
O67		2 r. purple and brown (1942)	..	23·00	£120
O68		5 r. green and blue (1942)	..	£200	£400
O55/68		*Set of* 12		£225	£500

Nabha was absorbed into the Patiala and East Punjab States Union by 20 August 1948.

PATIALA
Maharaja Bhupindra Singh, 1900–1938

PATIALA STATE	**PATIALA STATE**
(4)	(5)

PATIALA STATE	**PATIALA**	**PATIALA**
(6)	(7)	(8)

1937–8. *King George VI. Nos. 247/64 optd with T* **4** (3 *p. to* 1 *a.*), *T* **6** (2 *a. to* 12 *a.*), *or T* **5** (*rupee values*).

80	91	3 p. slate	..	..	..	24·00	30
81		½ a. red-brown	..	..	..	5·50	20
82		9 p. green (1937)	..	..	..	1·90	45
83		1 a. carmine (1937)	..	..	..	1·25	20
84	92	2 a. vermilion	..	..	..	1·50	4·50
85	–	2½ a. bright violet	..	..	..	1·90	10·00
86	–	3 a. yellow-green	..	..	..	2·00	4·00
87	–	3½ a. bright blue	..	..	..	2·50	13·00
88	–	4 a. brown	..	..	..	13·00	8·50
89	–	6 a. turquoise-green	..	..	..	15·00	25·00
90	–	8 a. slate-violet	..	..	..	16·00	30·00
91	–	12 a. lake	..	..	..	16·00	28·00
92	93	1 r. grey and red-brown	..	..	..	17·00	32·00
93		2 r. purple and brown	..	..	..	26·00	70·00
94		5 r. green and blue	..	..	..	42·00	£130
95		10 r. purple and claret	..	..	..	65·00	£200
96		15 r. brown and green	..	..	..	£120	£350
97		25 r. slate-violet and purple	..	..	..	£150	£425
80/97		*Set of* 18				£450	£1200

Maharaja Yadavindra Singh, 1938–1971

1941–6. *King George VI. Optd with T* **7** *or* 8 (*rupee value*).

(a) *Stamps of* 1937

98	91	3 p. slate	..	..	..	7·50	50
99		½ a. red-brown	..	..	..	6·50	20
100		9 p. green	..	..	..	£130	2·50
		w. Wmk inverted					
101		1 a. carmine	..	..	..	17·00	60
102	93	1 r. grey and red-brown (1946)	..	..	7·00	55·00
98/102		*Set of* 5				£150	55·00

(b) *Stamps of* 1940–43

103	100a	3 p. slate (1942)	..	..	..	1·25	15
104		½ a. purple (1943)	..	..	..	1·40	15
		a. Pair, one without opt			..	£3250	
105		9 p. green (1942)	..	..	..	1·00	15
		a. Vert pair, one without opt			..	£2250	
106		1 a. carmine (1944)	..	..	..	80	10
107	101	1 a. 3 p. yellow-brown	..	..	..	1·60	1·50
108		1½ a. violet (1942)	..	..	..	5·00	1·50
109		2 a. vermilion (1944)	..	..	..	5·00	25
110		3 a. bright violet (1944)	..	..	..	3·50	75
111		3½ a. bright blue (1944)	..	..	..	12·00	19·00
112	102	4 a. brown (1944)	..	..	..	3·75	90
113		6 a. turquoise-green (1944)	..	..	..	2·50	12·00
114		8 a. slate-violet (1944)	..	..	..	3·00	6·00
115		12 a. lake (1945)	..	..	..	8·00	38·00
103/15		*Set of* 13				42·00	70·00

The 1½ a. exists printed by lithography or typography.

OFFICIAL STAMPS

PATIALA STATE SERVICE	**PATIALA STATE SERVICE**
(O 5)	(O 6)

1937–39. *King George VI. Optd with Types* O **5** *or* O **6** (*rupee values*).

O63	91	½ a. red-brown (1938)	..	..	75	20
O64		9 p. green (1938)	..	..	13·00	50·00
O65		1 a. carmine	..	..	75	20
O66	93	1 r. grey and red-brown (1939)	..	1·00	3·50
O67		2 r. purple and brown (1939)	..	6·00	5·00
O68		5 r. green and blue (1939)	..	15·00	50·00
O63/8		*Set of* 6			32·00	£100

1A ____ 1A   **1A SERVICE 1A**   PATIALA SERVICE

(O 7)   (O 8)   (O 9)

1939–40. *Stamp of* 1932 (*King George V*).

(a) *Optd with Types* O **5** *and* O **7**

O69	82	1 a. on 1¼ a. mauve	..	..	5·50	1·40
		w. Wmk inverted	..	..	5·50	1·40

(b) *Optd with T* **4** *and* O **8**

O70	82	1 a. on 1¼ a. mauve (1940)	..	..	4·00	1·60
		w. Wmk inverted	..	..	4·00	1·60

"SERVICE" measures 9¼ mm on No. O69 but only 8¾ mm on O70.

1939–44. (a) *Official stamps optd with T* **7**.

O71	O 20	3 p. slate (1940)	..	..	45	10
O72		½ a. red-brown	..	..	3·00	10
O73		½ a. purple (1942)	..	..	45	10
O74		9 p. green	..	..	45	20
		w. Wmk inverted				
O75		1 a. carmine	..	..	75	10
O76		1 a. 3 p. yellow-brown (1941)	..	85	25
O77		1½ a. dull violet (1944)	..	2·75	20
O78		2 a. vermilion (1940)	..	..	4·25	15
		w. Wmk inverted				
O79		2½ a. bright violet (1940)	..	85	65
O80		4 a. brown (1943)	..	..	85	1·00
O81		8 a. slate-violet (1940)	..	1·40	3·50

(b) *Postage stamps optd with Type* O **9**.

O82	93	1 r. grey and red-brown (1943)	..	8·50	5·00
O83		2 r. purple and brown (1944)	..	15·00	40·00
O84		5 r. green and blue (1944)	..	21·00	60·00
O71/84		*Set of* 14			55·00	£100

Patiala became part of the Patiala and East Punjab States Union by 20 August 1948.

INDIAN FEUDATORY STATES

BARWANI
Rana Devi Singh, 1930–1971

1    2    3

4   Rana Devi Singh   5

1932 (Oct)–**47**. *Medium to thick wove paper.*

A. *Close setting* (2½–4½ *mm*). *P* 11, 12 *or compound* (1932–41)
B. *Wide setting* (6–7 *mm*). *P* 11 (1945–47)

					A		B	
32	**4**	¼ a. slate	..	..	..	1·00	12·00	3·00	17·00
33		½ a. blue-green			..	1·75	12·00	2·75	12·00
34		1 a. brown	..		..	1·75	11·00	7·00	12·00
		a. Imperf between (horiz							
		pair)	..	..	.. £1100	—	†	
		b. *Chocolate.* Perf 8½							
		(1947) ..			†	12·50	30·00	
35		2 a. purple (*shades*)		..	3·25	18·00	†	
		a. *Rose-carmine* (1945)	..	†	£140	£250	
36		4 a. olive-green	..	..	6·00	23·00	20·00	28·00
32A/6A		..	*Set of* 5	12·00	60·00		

The measurements given in the heading indicate the vertical spacing between impressions. There are eight settings of this interesting issue: four "Close" where the over-all stamp dimensions from centre to centre of perfs vary in width from 21½ to 23 mm and in height from 25 to 27½ mm; three "Wide", width 23–23½ mm and height 29–30 mm and one "Medium" (26½ × 31 mm) (No. 34*b* only).

1933–47. *P* 11.

A. *Close setting* (3–4½ *mm*). *Thick, cream-surfaced wove paper* (1933 *and* 1941 (*No*. 38*a*A)
B *Wide setting* (7–10 *mm*). *Medium to thick wove paper* (1939–47)

					A		B	
37	**1**	¼ a. black	..	..	..	2·25	35·00	2·75	21·00
38		½ a. blue-green	..	..	10·00	20·00	†	
		a. *Yellowish green* (1941)		7·00	17·00	3·75	23·00
39	**2**	1 a. brown (*shades*)	..	12·00	18·00	10·00	17·00
		a. Perf 8½ (5 mm) (1947)		†	10·00	30·00	
40		2 a. bright purple (1939)	..	†	60·00	£140	
41		2 a. rose-carmine (1945)	..	†	22·00	75·00	
42	**3**	4 a. sage-green	..	..	24·00	48·00	21·00	38·00
		a. *Pale sage-green* (1939)		†	10·00	27·00	

There were two "Close" settings (over-all stamp size 25 × 29 mm) and five "Wide" settings with over-all sizes 26½–31½ × 31–36½ mm. There was also one "Medium" setting (26½ × 31 mm) but this was confined to the 1 a. perf 8½, No. 39a.

1938. *P* 11.
43 **5** 1 a. brown .. .. 23·00 45·00
Stamps printed in red with designs similar to Types **3** and **5** were intended for fiscal use.

STAMP BOOKLETS

Nos. 32/47, produced by the *Times of India* Press in a series of nine printings between 1932 and 1947, were only issued in booklet form. Booklets from the 1932, 1933, 1937 and 1939 printings had plain card or paper covers in various colours, usually containing eight blocks of 4, except for the 1933 printing, which contained twenty blocks of 4. Booklets from the 1945 printing had plain white tissue covers from the same stock as the interleaving. All these booklets were stapled at left.
The following booklets, from a printing in 1941 and a series of three printings in 1947, had printed covers, produced by a handstamp in the case of Nos. SB14/15.

1941. *Buff, green* (*No. SB3*) *or blue* (*No. SB7*) *card covers inscribed* "BARWANI STATE POSTAGE STAMPS", *booklet value in brackets and number and value of stamps thus* "(Rs 4) 32 2 Annas". *Panes of* 4 *with margin at left only. Stapled.*

(*a*) *Booklets* 59×55 *mm*

SB1	8 a. booklet containing thirty-two ¼ a. (No. 32A)	£200
SB2	1 r. booklet containing thirty-two ½ a. (No. 33A)	£350
SB3	2 r. booklet containing thirty-two 1 a. (No. 34A)	£400
SB4	4 r. booklet containing thirty-two 2 a. (No. 35A)	£250
SB5	8 r. booklet containing thirty-two 4 a. (No. 36A)	£350

(*b*) *Booklets* 63×60 *mm* (*No. SB6*) *or* 73×72 *mm* (*No. SB7*)

SB6	1 r. booklet containing thirty-two ½ a. (No. 38aA)	£450
SB7	8 r. booklet containing thirty-two 4 a. (No. 42B)	£650

1947. *Grey tissue covers inscribed* "32 STAMPS VALUE....' *Panes of* 4 *with margins all round. Stapled at left.*

(*a*) *Booklets* 70×95 *mm*.

SB 8	1 r. booklet containing thirty-two ½ a. (No. 33B)	£450
SB 9	2 r. booklet containing thirty-two 1 a. (No. 34B)	£600
SB10	8 r. booklet containing thirty-two 4 a. (No. 36B)	£750

(*b*) *Booklets* 76×95 *mm*

SB11	8 a. booklet containing thirty-two ¼ a. (No. 37B)	£500
SB12	4 r. booklet containing thirty-two 2 a. (No. 41B)	£600
SB13	8 r. booklet containing thirty-two 4 a. (No. 42aB)	£350

1947. *Buff paper covers with violet handstamp inscribed* "32 STAMPS VALUE Rs 2/-". *Panes of* 4 *with margins all round, Sewn with twine at left.*

SB14	2 r. booklets (71×69 *mm*) containing thirty-two 1 a. (No. 34*b*B)	.. ..	£450
SB15	2 r. booklet (71×73 *mm*) containing thirty-two 1 a. (No. 39aB)	.. ..	£350

1947. *Grey tissue covers inscribed* "32 STAMPS VALUE As 8". *Panes of* 4 *with margins all round. Stapled at left.*

SB16	8 a. booklet (70×75 *mm*) containing thirty-two ¼ a. (No. 32B)	..	£120
SB17	8 a. booklet (85×75 *mm*) containing thirty-two ¼ a. (No. 37B)	.. .. ..	£140

Barwani became part of Madhya Bharat by 1 July 1948

BHOPAL
Nawab Mohammad Hamidullah Khan, 1926–1949

OFFICIAL STAMPS

PRINTERS. From No. O333 all issues were printed by the Bhopal Govt Ptg Wks in typography.

O 8

O 9   O 10 The Moti Mahal

1936 (July)–**38.** *Optd* "SERVICE". *P* 12.

O333	O 9	¼ a. orange (Br.)	..	..		90	2
		a. Imperf between (vert pair)		£110		
		ab. Imperf between (horiz pair)	..	†	£15
		b. Opt inverted	..	..	£170	£14
		c. Black opt	..	..	7·00	7
		ca. Opt inverted	..	..	†	£18
		cb. Opt double	..	..	†	£18
O334		¼ a. yellow (Br.) (1938)	..	1·50	
O335		1 a. scarlet ..	..	..	1·25	1
		a. Imperf between (horiz pair)	70·00	70·0
		b. Imperf between (vert pair)	..	†	£12
		c. Imperf between (block of four)	£180	£18

1936–49. *As Type* O **10** (*various palaces*). *P* 12.

(*a*) *Optd* "SERVICE" (13½ *mm*)

O336	½ a. purple-brown and yellow-green	..	70	
	a. Imperf between (vert pair)	..	†	£10
	ab. Imperf between (horiz pair)	..	†	£10
	b. Opt double	..	..	£160	£10
	c. Frame double ..	..	..	80·00	15·
	d. *Purple-brown and green* (1938)	..	70	

(b) Optd "SERVICE" (11 *mm*)

O337	2 a. brown and blue (1937)		90	25
	a. Imperf between (vert pair) ..	..	†	£150
	ab. Imperf between (horiz pair) ..	..	†	£110
	b. Opt inverted ..	..	£150	£150
	c. Pair, one without opt ..		£300	
	d. As c. but opt inverted ..		£450	
O338	2 a. green and violet (1938)		4·50	25
	a. Imperf between (vert pair) ..		†	£110
	b. Imperf between (vert strip of 3)	..	80·00	85·00
	c. Frame double ..	..	†	£110
	d. Centre double ..		†	£110
O339	4 a. blue and brown (1937)		2·25	50
	a. Imperf between (horiz pair) ..	..	†	£300
	b. Opt omitted ..	..	†	£160
	c. Opt double ..	..	†	£120
	d. Centre double	..	†	£160
	e. Blue and reddish brown (1938)		2·25	55
	ea. Frame double	..	†	£120
O340	8 a. bright purple and blue (1938)		3·00	65
	a. Imperf between (vert pair) ..		†	£180
	b. Opt omitted ..	..	†	90·00
	c. Opt double ..	..	†	£110
	d. Imperf vert (horiz pair) and opt			
	omitted	..	†	£150
	e. Imperf (pair) and opt omitted		†	£150
O341	1 r. blue and reddish purple (Br.) (1938) ..		9·00	4·00
	a. Imperf horiz (vert pair)	..	†	£700
	b. Opt in black (1942)	..	10·00	4·00
	ba. Light blue and bright purple		32·00	27·00
	bb. Laid paper	..	£350	£375
O336/41	..	*Set of 6*	18·00	5·25

(c) Optd "SERVICE" (11½ *mm*) *with serifs*

O342	1 r. dull blue and bright purple (Blk.)			
	(1949) ..	..	38·00	60·00
	a. "SREVICE" for "SERVICE" (R. 6/6)		£120	£160
	b. "SERVICE" omitted ..		£425	

(d) Optd "SERVICE" (13½ *mm*) *with serifs*

O343	8 a. bright purple and blue (1949) ..		48·00	70·00
	a. "SERAICE" for "SERVICE" (R. 6/5)		£190	£275
	b. Fig "1" for "I" in "SERVICE" (R. 7/1)		£190	£275

The ½ a. is inscr "BHOPAL GOVT" below the arms, other values have "BHOPAL STATE".
Designs:—(37½ × 22½ *mm*) 2 a. The Moti Masjid; 4 a. Taj Mahal and Be-Nazir Palaces. (39 × 24 *mm*)—8 a. Ahmadabad Palace. (45½ × 27½ *mm*)—1 r. Rait Ghat.

O 11 Tiger　　　O 13 The Moti Mahal

1940. *As Type* O 11 *(animals). P* 12.

O344	¼ a. bright blue ..	..	2·25	55
O345	1 a. bright purple (Spotted Deer)..	..	13·00	65

1941. *As Type* O 8 *but coloured centre inscr* "SERVICE"; *bottom frame inscr* "BHOPAL STATE POSTAGE". *P* 12.

O346	1 a. 3 p. emerald-green ..	..	70	60
	a. Imperf between (pair)..	..	£250	£250

1944–47. *As Type* O 13 *(various palaces). P* 12.

O347	½ a. green ..	..	85	35
	a. Imperf (pair) ..	..	†	50·00
	b. Imperf between (vert pair) ..		†	95·00
	c. Doubly printed	..	†	85·00
O348	2 a. violet ..	..	4·75	1·90
	a. Imperf (pair) ..	..	†	50·00
	c. Bright purple (1945) ..		1·60	1·90
	d. Mauve (1947) ..		10·00	8·50
	e. Error. Chocolate (imperf)		95·00	95·00
O349	4 a. chocolate	..	2·75	90
	a. Imperf (pair) ..		†	65·00
	b. Imperf vert (horiz pair) ..		†	£120
	c. Doubly printed	..	†	95·00
O347/9	..	*Set of 3*	4·75	2·75

Design inscr "BHOPAL STATE":—2 a. The Moti Masjid; 4 a. Be-azir Palaces.

O 14 Arms of Bhopal　(O 15)　(O 16)

1944–49. *P* 12.

O350	O 14	3 p. bright blue ..	65	20
	a. Imperf between (vert pair) ..		65·00	70·00
	b. Imperf between (horiz pair) ..		†	£120
	c. Stamp doubly printed	..	38·00	
O351	9 p. chestnut (*shades*) (1945) ..		5·50	1·50
	a. Imperf (pair) ..	..	†	£110
	b. Orange-brown	..	2·00	2·00
O352	1 a. purple (1945) ..		3·00	60
	a. Imperf horiz (vert pair) ..		†	£180
	b. Violet (1946) ..		4·75	1·50
O353	1½ a. claret (1945) ..		1·25	35
	a. Imperf between (horiz pair) ..		†	£170
O354	3 a. yellow ..		6·00	5·50
	a. Imperf (pair) ..	..	†	£110
	b. Imperf horiz (vert pair) ..		†	£140
	c. Imperf vert (horiz pair) ..		†	£140
	d. Orange-brown (1949) ..		55·00	50·00
O355	6 a. carmine (1945) ..		9·00	26·00
	a. Imperf (pair) ..	..	†	£120
	b. Imperf horiz (vert pair) ..		†	£140
	c. Imperf vert (horiz pair) ..		†	£140
O350/5	..	*Set of 6*	20·00	30·00

1949 (July). *Surch with Type* O 15. *P* 12.

O356	O 14	2 a. on 1½ a. claret ..	2·25	4·50
	a. Stop omitted ..	..	11·00	18·00
	b. Imperf (pair) ..	..	£150	£160
	ba. Stop omitted (pair) ..		£400	£425
	c. "2" omitted (in pair with normal)		£400	

The "stop omitted" variety occurs on positions 60 and 69 in the sheet of 81.

1949. *Surch with Type* O 16. *Imperf.*

O357	O 14	2 a. on 1½ a. claret ..	£400	£425
	a. Perf 12 ..	..	£450	£450

Three different types of "2" occur in the setting of Type O 16.

BIJAWAR
Maharaja Sarwant Singh, 1899–1941

1　　　　2

(Typo Lakshmi Art Ptg Works, Bombay)

1935 (1 July)**–36**. *(a) P* 11.

1	1	3 p. brown ..	3·25	2·50
	a. Imperf (pair) ..	..	5·50	
	b. Imperf between (vert pair) ..		80·00	
	c. Imperf horiz (vert pair) ..		50·00	
2	6 p. carmine ..	..	3·50	2·50
	a. Imperf (pair) ..	..	85·00	
	b. Imperf between (vert pair) ..		80·00	
	c. Imperf between (horiz pair) ..		80·00	
	d. Imperf horiz (vert pair) ..		80·00	
3	9 p. violet..	..	3·50	3·25
	a. Imperf (pair) ..	..	£140	
	b. Imperf between (vert pair) ..		80·00	
	c. Imperf between (horiz pair) ..		80·00	
	d. Imperf horiz (vert pair) ..		80·00	

4	1	1 a. blue	..	..	..	4·25	3·75
		a. Imperf (pair)	..	..	..	85·00	
		b. Imperf between (vert pair)	..	..	85·00	
		c. Imperf between (horiz pair)	..	..	£100	
		d. Imperf horiz (vert pair)	..	..	85·00	
		e. Imperf vert (horiz strip of 3)	..	£130	
5		2 a. deep green	..	..	..	4·25	4·75
		a. Imperf (pair)	..	..	..	£100	
		b. Imperf horiz (vert pair)	..	..	11·00	
		c. Imperf between (vert pair)	..	..	35·00	
		d. Imperf between (horiz pair)	..	50·00	75·00
1/5		..	..	..	..	*Set of 5* 17·00	15·00

(b) Roul 7 (1936)

6	1	3 p. brown	..	..	..	1·75	1·90
		a. Printed on gummed side	..	..	£375	
7		6 p. carmine	..	..	..	3·50	12·00
8		9 p. violet	..	..	..	5·50	60·00
9		1 a. blue	..	..	..	5·50	65·00
10		2 a. deep green	..	..	..	6·00	70·00
6/10		..	..	..	*Set of 5* 20·00	£190

1937 (May). *Typo. P 9.*

11	2	4 a. orange	..	..	..	7·00	55·00
		a. Imperf between (vert pair)	..	..	£140	
		b. Imperf (pair)	..	..	..	£225	
12		6 a. lemon	..	..	..	7·00	55·00
		a. Imperf between (vert pair)	..	..	£140	
		b. Imperf (pair)	..	..	..	£225	
13		8 a. emerald-green	..	..	..	7·00	70·00
		a. Imperf (pair)	..	..	..	£250	
14		12 a. greenish blue	..	..	..	7·00	70·00
		a. Imperf (pair)	..	..	..	£300	
15		1 r. bright violet	..	..	..	28·00	£110
		a. "1 Rs" for "1 R" (R. 1/2)	..	48·00	£300
		b. Imperf (pair)	..	..	..	£375	
		ba. "1 Rs" for "1 R" (R. 1/2)	..	£850	
11/15		..	..	..	*Set of 5* 50·00	£325

The stamps of Bijawar were withdrawn in 1941.

BUNDI

Maharao Raja Ishwari Singh, 1927–1945

20

1941–44. *Typo. P 11.*

79	20	3 p. bright blue	..	..	..	75	3·00
80		6 p. deep blue	..	..	..	1·90	3·75
81		1 a. orange-red	..	..	..	2·25	4·50
82		2 a. chestnut	..	..	..	4·00	10·00
		a. Deep brown (no gum) (1944)	..	13·00	14·00
83		4 a. bright green	..	..	..	7·00	30·00
84		8 a. dull green	..	..	..	7·00	70·00
85		1 r. deep blue	..	..	..	26·00	£140
79/85		..	..	..	*Set of 7* 45·00	£250

The first printing only of Nos. 79/85 is usual with gum; all further printings, including No. 82a, are without gum.

Maharao Raja Bahadur Singh, 1945–1971

21 Maharao Raja   22 Bundi
    Bahadur Singh

(Typo *Times of India* Press, Bombay)

1947. *P* 11.

86	21	¼ a. blue-green	..	..	..	90	21·00
87		½ a. violet	..	..	..	90	21·00
88		1 a. yellow-green	..	..	..	80	21·00
89	–	2 a. vermilion	..	..	..	1·10	38·00
90	–	4 a. orange	..	..	..	1·25	50·00
91	22	8 a. ultramarine	..	..	..	2·25	
92		1 r. chocolate	..	..	..	12·00	
86/92		..	..	..	*Set of 7*	17·00	

On the 2 and 4 a. the Maharao is in Indian dress.

OFFICIAL STAMPS

1941. *Nos. 79 to 85 optd* "SERVICE".

O53	20	3 p. bright blue (R.)	..	..	2·50	7·00
O54		6 p. deep blue (R.)	..	..	9·50	6·50
O55		1 a. orange-red	..	..	..	8·00	7·00
O56		2 a. brown	..	..	..	7·00	8·50
O57		4 a. bright green	..	..	..	24·00	70·00
O58		8 a. dull green	..	..	..	85·00	£250
O59		1 r. deep blue (R.)	..	..	£100	£275
O53/9		..	..	..	*Set of 7*	£200	£550

Two different types of "R" occur in the "SERVICE" overprint. On five positions in the sheet of 12 the "R" shows a larger loop and a pointed diagonal leg.

Bundi became part of the Rajasthan Union by 15 April 1948.

CHARKHARI

Maharaja Arimardan Singh, 1920–1942

$\frac{1}{2}$ **As.**

(8)

1939 (Dec)–**40.** *Nos. 21/2 surch as T* 8.

54	2	½ a. on 8 a. brown-red (1940)	..	26·00	95·00
		a. No space between "¹/²" and "As"	..	32·00	95·00
		b. Surch inverted	..	..	..	£225	
		c. "1" of "¹/²" inverted	..	..	£200	
55		1 a. on 1 r. chestnut (1940)	..	70·00	£200
		a. Surch inverted	..	..	..	£250	
56		"1 ANNA" on 1 r. chestnut	..	..	£475	£500

Maharaja Jaiendra Singh, 1942–1971

Charkhari became part of Vindhya Pradesh by 1 May 1948

COCHIN

Maharaja Rama Varma III, 1932–1941

18 Maharaja Rama Varma III

"DOUBLE PRINTS". The errors previously listed under thi description are now identified as blanket offsets, a type of variet outside the scope of this catalogue. Examples occur on issues from 1938 onwards.

SPACING OF OVERPRINTS AND SURCHARGES. Th typeset overprints and surcharges issued from 1939 onwards sho considerable differences in spacing. Except for specialists, howeve these differences have little significance as they occur within th same settings and do not represent separate printings.

(Litho The Associated Printers, Madras)

1938. *W 8a* (A) *P* 11 *or* (B) *P* 13 × 13½.

					A		B	
67	18	2 p. brown	..	..	1·00	30	5·50	60
68		4 p. green	..	..	85	10	8·00	10·00
69		6 p. red-brown	..	..	2·25	10	† £1900	
70		1 a. brown-orange	..	..	50·00	60·00	60·00	65·00
71		2¼ a. sage-green	..	..	6·00	15	12·00	2·75
67/71		..	..	*Set of* 5	55·00	60·00	†	

Most examples of Nos. 70A/B were used fiscally. Collectors are warned against examples which have been cleaned and regummed or provided with forged postmarks.

ANCHAL **ANCHAL** **THREE PIES**
(19) (19a) (20)

SURCHARGED **ANCHAL**

ONE ANNA
THREE PIES **NINE PIES**
(21) (22)

ANCHAL **ANCHAL**

NINE PIES **SURCHARGED**
NINE PIES
(23) (24)

1939 (Jan). *Nos.* 57 *and* 70 *optd with T* **19**/a. A. *P* 11. B. *P* 13×13½.

					A		B	
72	18	1 a. brn-orge (*recess*) (T **19**)		†	1·50	30		
73		1 a. brn-orge (*litho*) (T **19**)	..	£225	45	—	£200	
74		1 a. brn-orge (*litho*) (T **19**a)		75	1·60	10·00	50	

In 1939 it was decided that there would be separate 1 a. stamps for revenue and postal purposes. The "ANCHAL" overprints were applied to stamps intended for postal purposes.

1943–44. *T* **18** *variously optd or surch.*

I. *Recess-printed stamp. No.* 58

				A		B	
75	3 p. on 1 a. 8 p. carmine (T **20**)	..	..	£160	70·00		
76	3 p. on 1 a. 8 p. carmine (T **21**)	..	..	2·00	6·00		
77	6 p. on 1 a. 8 p. carmine (T **20**)	..	..	2·50	16·00		
78	1 a. 3 p. on 1 a. 8 p. carmine (T **21**)	..	..	1·00	30		

II. *Lithographed stamps. Nos.* 68 *and* 70.
A. *P* 11. B. *P* 13×13½

				A		B	
79	3 p. on 4 p. (T **21**)	..	..	5·00	2·50	13·00	2·00
80	6 p. on 1 a. (T **22**)	..	..	£250	£170	†	
	a. "SIX PIES" double	..	..	†	£550	†	
81	6 p. on 1 a. (T **23**)	..	..	£225	£150	80·00	38·00
82	9 p. on 1 a. (T **22**)	..	..	90·00	95·00	†	
83	9 p. on 1 a. (T **23**)	..	..	†	†	£140	24·00
84	9 p. on 1 a. (T **24**)	..	..	†	13·00	3·50	

Maharaja Kerala Varma II, 1941–1943

26 Maharaja Kerala Varma II

27 (*The actual measurement of this wmk is* 6¼ × 3⅝ *in.*)

(Litho The Associated Printers, Madras)

1943. *Frame of* 1 *a. inscr* "ANCHAL & REVENUE". A. *P* 11. B. *P* 13 × 13½. (*a*) *W 8a.*

				A	B	
85	26	2 p. grey-brown	..	† £1400	1·00	1·25
85a		4 p. green	..	†	£375	£225
85b		1 a. brown-orange	..	†	70·00	85·00
85/b		..	*Set of* 3	†	£400	£275

(*b*) *W* **27**

				A	B	
86	26	2 p. grey-brown	..	† £1700	25·00	1·25
87		4 p. green	..	3·00	2·50	7·00	13·00
88		6 p. red-brown	..	8·00	1·10	1·25	10
89		9 p. ultramarine	..	19·00	1·00	†	
		a. Imperf between (horiz pair)	..	£1200	—	†	
90		1 a. brown-orange	..	20·00	35·00	£190	£140
91		2¼ a. yellow-green	..	24·00	6·00	15·00	90

Part of W **27** appears on many stamps in each sheet, while others are entirely without wmk.

Although inscribed "ANCHAL (=Postage) & REVENUE" most examples of Nos. 85b and 90A/B were used fiscally. Collectors are warned against examples which have been cleaned and regummed or provided with forged postmarks.

Maharaja Ravi Varma 1943–1946

1943. *T* **26** *variously opt or surch.* A. *P* 11. B. *P* 13×13½

(*a*) *W 8a.*

			A	B	
92	3 p. on 4 p. (T **21**)	..	..	†	48·00	13·00
92a	9 p. on 1 a. (T **23**)	..	..	†	4·25	19·00
92b	9 p. on 1 a. (T **24**)	..	..	†	2·25	1·75
92c	1 a. 3 p. on 1 a. (T **21**)	..	..	†	—	£2750

(*b*) *W* **27**

			A	B	
93	2 p. on 6 p. (T **20**)	..	..	85	1·90	75	1·75
94	3 p. on 4 p. (T **20**)	..	..	1·90	10	†	
95	3 p. on 4 p. (T **21**)	..	..	†	2·50	10	
96	3 p. on 6 p. (T **20**)	..	..	85	30	85	20
97	4 p. on 6 p. (T **20**)	..	..	†	2·25	7·00	

No. 92c is believed to be an error; a sheet of No. 85b having been included in a stock of No. O52 intended to become No. O66.

MINIMUM PRICE

The minimum price quote is 10p which represents a handling charge rather than a basis for valuing common stamps. For further notes about prices see introductory pages.

28 Maharaja Ravi Varma 29

I   II

(Litho The Associated Printers, Madras)

1944–48. W **27**. _No gum._ (a) _Type_ I. _P_ 11.
98   **28**   9 p. ultramarine (1944) ..   ..   8·00   1·40

(b) _Type_ II. _P_ 13
98a **28**   9 p. ultramarine (1946) ..   ..   4·00   8·50
  ab. Perf 13 × 13½   ..   ..   24·00   1·50
99   1 a. 3 p. magenta (1948)   ..   6·00   6·50
  a. Perf 13 × 13½   ..   ..   £130 25·00
100   1 a. 9 p. ultramarine (_shades_) (1948) .. 10·00   8·00
98a/100   ..   ..   ..   _Set of_ 3 18·00 14·50
Nos. 98a/100 are line-perforated, Nos. 98ab and 99a comb-perforated.

Maharaja Kerala Varma III, 1946–48

(Litho The Associated Printers, Madras)

1946–48. _Frame of 1 a. inscr_ "ANCHAL & REVENUE". W **27**. _No gum (except for stamps perf_ 11). _P_ 13.
101 **29**   2 p. chocolate   80   10
  a. Imperf horiz (vert pair)   .. £1000 £1000
  c. Perf 11   ..   ..   8·00   60
  d. Perf 11 × 13   ..   .. £350 £140
102   3 p. carmine   50   10
103   4 p. grey-green ..   .. £1400 80·00
104   6 p. red-brown (1947)   ..   20·00   8·50
  a. Perf 11   ..   ..   £140   2·00
105   9 p. ultramarine   50   10
  a. Imperf between (horiz pair)   .. † £1100
106   1 a. orange (1948)   ..   5·50 24·00
  a. Perf 11   ..   ..   £425
107   2 a. black   ..   ..   80·00   5·00
  a. Perf 11   ..   ..   £110   5·00
108   3 a. vermilion   ..   ..   50·00   50
101/8 ..   ..   _Set of_ 8 £1500 £100
Although inscribed "ANCHAL (=Postage) & REVENUE" most examples of No. 106 were used fiscally.
The 1 a. 3 p. magenta, 1 a. 9p. ultramarine and 2¼ a. yellow-green in Type **29** subsequently appeared surcharged or overprinted for official use. Examples of the 1 a. 3 p. magenta exist without overprint, but may have not have been issued in this state (_Price £325 unused_).

30 Maharaja Kerala Varma III

NEW INFORMATION
The editor is always interested to correspond with people who have new information that will improve or correct the Catalogue.

Tail to turban flaw (R. 1/7)

(Litho The Associated Printers, Madras)

1948–50. W **27**. _P_ 11.
109 **30**   2 p. grey-brown   75   15
  a. Imperf vert (horiz pair)   ..   † £950
110   3 p. carmine   75   15
  a. Imperf between (vert pair)   ..   † £900
111   4 p. green   ..   ..   7·00   60
  a. Imperf vert (horiz pair)   .. £250 £275
112   6 p. chestnut   ..   ..   10·00   20
  a. Imperf vert (horiz pair)   ..   £700
113   9 p. ultramarine   ..   ..   1·75   15
114   2 a. black   ..   ..   38·00   40
115   3 a. orange-red   ..   ..   48·00   50
  a. Imperf vert (horiz pair)   .. £1300
116   3 a. 4 p. violet (1950)   ..   90·00 £350
  a. Tail to turban flaw   ..   £225
109/16   ..   ..   ..   _Set of_ 8 £180 £350

Maharaja Rama Varma IV, 1948–1964

31 Chinese Nets   32 Dutch Palace

(Litho The Associated Printers, Madras)

1949   W **27**. _P_ 11.
117 **31**   2 a. black   ..   ..   2·25   4·00
  a. Imperf vert (horiz pair)   ..   £425
118 **32**   2¼ a. green   ..   ..   1·50   3·50
  a. Imperf vert (horiz pair)   ..   £425

SIX PIES

ആറു പൈ

(33)

ൈവ   Normal

ൈവ   Error

Due to similarities between two Malayalam characters some values of the 1948 provisional issue exist with an error in the second word of the Malayalam surcharge. On Nos. 119, 122 and O103 this occurs twice in the setting of 48. No. 125 shows four examples and No. O104b one. Most instances are as illustrated above, but in two instances on the setting for No. 125 the error occurs on the second character.

1949. *Surch as T* 33. (i) *On* 1944–48 *issue. P* 13.

119	28	6 p. on 1 a. 3 p. magenta	.. ..	2·00	2·25
		a. Incorrect character ..	..	19·00	19·00
120		1 a. on 1 a. 9 p. ultramarine (R.)	..	75	75

(ii) *On* 1946–48 *issue*

121	29	3 p. on 9 p. ultramarine..	..	6·00	13·00
122		6 p. on 1 a. 3 p. magenta	..	8·00	9·00
		a. Surch double	..	†	£375
		b. Incorrect character ..	..	55·00	55·00
123		1 a. on 1 a. 9 p. ultramarine (R.)	..	3·00	1·00
		a. Surch in black	..	†	£1400
		b. Black surch with smaller native characters 7½ mm instead of 10 mm long ..	..	†	£1800

(iii) *On* 1948–50 *issue*

124	30	3 p. on 9 p. ultramarine	..	1·75	1·75
		a. Larger native characters 20 mm instead of 16½ mm long ..		1·90	50
		ab. Imperf between (vert pair)..		†	£950
		b. Surch double	..	£350	
125		3 p. on 9 p. ultramarine (R.)	..	2·75	1·75
		a. Incorrect character..	..	13·00	8·50
126		6 p. on 9 p. ultramarine (R.)	..	75	40
119/26		*Set of* 8		22·00	26·00

1949. *Surch as T* 20. *W* 27. *P* 13.

127	29	6 p. on 1 a. orange	..	55·00	£110
128		9 p. on 1 a. orange	..	55·00	£110

OFFICIAL STAMPS

ON   **ON**

C   **G**   **C**   **G**

S   **S**

(O 7 Curved back to "c")   (O 8)

ON   **ON**   **ON**

C   **G**   **C**   **G**   **C**   **G**

S   **S**   **S**

(O 9 Circular "O"; N with serifs)   (O 10 Oval "O")   (O 11)

1938–44. *Lithographed stamps of* 1938. *W* 8*a*, *optd.*

(*a*) *With Type* O 7 *or* O 8 (1 *a*). I. *P* 11. II. *P* 13 × 13½.

				I		II	
O47	18	4 p. green ..	..	16·00	1·10	17·00	1·50
		a. Inverted "S" ..	..	19·00	1·10	†	
O48		6 p. red-brown ..	..	14·00	30	†	
		a. Inverted "S" ..	..	17·00	40	†	
O49		1 a. brown-orange	..	£250	2·50	†	
O50		2 a. grey-black ..	..	10·00	50	†	
		a. Inverted "S" ..	..	11·00	50	†	

(*b*) *With Type* O 9 (*litho*) *or* O 10 (6 *p.*)

					I	II
O51	18	6 p. red-brown	..	†	5·00	1·60
O52		1 a. brown-orange	..	1·00	10	†
O53		3 a. vermilion	..	2·75	50	†

(*c*) *With Type* O 11

O53*a*	18	6 p. red-brown	..	£700	£300	†

The inverted "S" varieties, Nos. O47a, O48a and O50a, occur 21 times in the setting of 48.

1942–43. *Unissued stamps optd with Type* O 10. *Litho. W* 27. I. *P* 11. II. *P* 13 × 13½.

				I		II	
O54	18	4 p. green	..	60·00	11·00	1·10	60
O55		6 p. red-brown ..	..	90·00	11·00	17·00	90
		a. Optd both sides	..	†		†	85·00
O56		1 a. brown-orange	..	16·00	5·00	1·25	3·25
		a. Optd both sides	..	†		—	—
O56*b*		2 a. grey-black (1943)	..	48·00	60	†	
		ba. Opt omitted	..		† £1000		†
O56*c*		2¼ a. sage-green (1943)	..	£800	3·25	†	
O56*d*		3 a. vermilion (1943)	..	10·00	3·25	†	

1943. *Official stamps variously surch with T* 20 *or* 21.

(i) *On* 1½ *a. purple, of* 1919–33

O57	10	9 p. on 1½ a. (b) (*T* 20)	..	..	£325	18·00

(ii) *On recess-printed* 1 *a.* 8 *p. carmine of* 1933–44 (*Type* O 5 *opt*)

O58	3 p. on 1 a. 8 p. (T 21)..	..	..	3·00	40
O59	9 p. on 1 a. 8 p. (T 20)..	..	..	£110	26·00
O60	1 a. 9 p. on 1 a. 8 p. (T 20)	..	..	1·10	1·60
O61	1 a. 9 p. on 1 a. 8 p. (T 21)	..	..	80	30

(iii) *On lithographed stamps of* 1938–44. *T* 18. I. *P* 11. II. *P* 13 × 13½

(*a*) *W* 8*a*

		I		II	
O62	3 p. on 4 p. (Types O 7 and 20)	†		15·00	3·25
	a. Surch double	†		£250	£140
O63	3 p. on 4 p. (Types O 7 and 21)	†		75·00	40·00
O64	3 p. on 1 a. (Types O 9 and 20)	1·75	1·60	†	
O65	9 p. on 1 a. (Types O 9 and 20)	£180	45·00	†	
O66	1 a. 3 p. on 1 a. (Types O 9 and 21) ..	£225	90·00	†	

(*b*) *W* 27

		I		II	
O67	3 p. on 4 p. (Types O 10 and 20)	†		70·00	42·00
O67*a*	3 p. on 4 p. (Types O 10 and 21)	†		£375	—
O67*b*	3 p. on 1 a. (Types O 10 and 20)	£110	60·00	80·00	60·00

1944. *Optd with Type* O 10. *W* 27. *P* 13 × 13½.

					I	II
O68	26	4 p. green	..	..	13·00	1·40
		a. Perf 11	..	..	95·00	3·50
		b. Perf 13	..	..	£200	60·00
O69		6 p. red-brown	..	..	80	10
		a. Opt double..	..	..	—	55·00
		b. Perf 11	..	..	70	10
		c. Perf 13	..	..	7·00	2·00
O70		1 a. brown-orange	..	..	£1300	45·00
O71		2 a. black	..	..	2·50	35
O72		2¼ a. yellow-green	..	..	1·60	35
		a. Optd both sides	..	..	†	95·00
O73		3 a. vermilion	..	..	4·00	40
		a. Perf 11	..	..	3·75	40

Stamps perforated 13 × 13½ are from a comb machine; those perforated 13 from a line perforator.

1944. *Optd with Type* O 10 *and variously surch as Types* 20 *and* 21. *W* 27.

				I		II	
O74	26	3 p. on 4 p. (T 20)	..	5·00	45	1·00	10
		b. Optd Type O 10 on both sides	..	†	£100	†	
O75		3 p. on 4 p. (T 21)	..	£375	£160	3·00	30
O76		3 p. on 1 a. (T 20)	..	†		11·00	2·25
O77		9 p. on 6 p. (T 20)	..	†		4·50	80
		a. Stamp printed both sides ..	..	†		—	—
O78		9 p. on 6 p. (T 21)	..	†		2·25	20
O79		1 a. 3 p. on 1 a. (T 20)	..	†		3·75	50
O80		1 a. 3 p. on 1 a. (T 21)	..	†		2·50	10
O74/80..		..	*Set of* 7	†		25·00	3·75

1946–47. *Stamps of* 1944-48 *optd with Type* O **10.** *Type* II. *P* 13.
O81	28	9 p. ultramarine		1·50	10
		a. Stamp printed both sides		†	£275
		b. Perf 13 × 13½		2·50	10
O82		1 a. 3 p. magenta (1947)		65	20
		a. Opt double		17·00	12·00
		b. Optd both sides, opt double on reverse		40·00	
O83		1 a. 9 p. ultramarine (1947)		40	40
		a. Opt double			
O81b/83		*Set of* 3		2·25	60

1948. *Stamps of* 1946-48 *and unissued values optd with Type* O **2.** *P* 13.
O84	29	3 p. carmine		35	10
		a. Stamp printed both sides		†	
O85		4 p. grey-green		20·00	4·50
O86		6 p. red-brown		4·00	40
O87		9 p. ultramarine		75	10
O88		1 a. 3 p. magenta		1·40	20
O89		1 a. 9 p. ultramarine		1·40	40
O90		2 a. black		12·00	1·75
O91		2¼ a. yellow-green		13·00	1·60
O84/91		*Set of* 8		48·00	8·00

1949. *Stamps of* 1948-50 *and unissued values optd with Type* O **7.**
O92	30	3 p. carmine		35	10
		a. "C" for "G" in opt		6·00	2·50
O93		4 p. green		65	15
		a. Imperf between (pair)		†	£850
		b. Optd on reverse		55·00	55·00
		c. "C" for "G" in opt		8·50	3·25
O94		6 p. chestnut		1·50	10
		a. Imperf between (vert pair)		†	£950
		b. "C" for "G" in opt		13·00	2·50
O95		9 p. ultramarine		1·25	10
		a. "C" for "G" in opt		10·00	3·00
O96		2 a. black		65	15
		a. "C" for "G" in opt		9·50	3·50
O97		2¼ a. yellow-green		1·75	3·50
		a. "C" for "G" in opt		16·00	25·00
O98		3 a. orange-red		1·10	30
		a. "C" for "G" in opt		13·00	6·00
O99		3 a. 4 p. violet		22·00	20·00
		a. "C" for "G" in opt		£190	£190
O92/9		*Set of* 8		26·00	22·00

The "C" for "G" variety occurs on R. 1/4. Nos. O92/9, O103/4 and O104b also exist with a flat back to "G" which occurs twice in each sheet on R. 1/5 and R. 2/8.

1949. *Official stamps surch as T* **33.** (i) *On* 1944 *issue.*
O100	28	1 a. on 1 a. 9 p. ultramarine (R.)		60	35

(ii) *On* 1948 *issue*
O101	29	1 a. on 1 a. 9 p. ultramarine (R.)		12·00	9·00

(iii) *On* 1949 *issue*
O103	30	6 p. on 3 p. carmine		35	45
		a. Imperf between (vert pair)		†	£700
		b. Surch double		†	£275
		c. "C" for "G" in opt		6·50	7·00
		d. Incorrect character		6·50	7·00
O104		9 p. on 4 p. green (18 *mm long*)		55	1·10
		a. Imperf between (horiz pair)		£600	
		b. Larger native characters, 22 mm long		75	60
		ba. Ditto. Imperf between (horiz pair)		£600	£600
		bb. Incorrect character		11·00	9·00
		c. "C" for "G" in opt		9·00	12·00
		ca. Ditto. Larger native characters, 22 mm long		11·00	9·00
O100/4		*Set of* 4		12·00	9·50

1949. *No.* 124a, *but with lines of surch* 17½ *mm apart, optd* "SERVICE".
O105	30	3 p. on 9 p. ultramarine		60	65

From 1 July 1949 Cochin formed part of the new state of Travancore-Cochin. Existing stocks of Cochin issues continued to be used in conjunction with stamps of Travancore surcharged in Indian currency.

DUNGARPUR

Maharawal Lakshman Singh, 1918–1971

1 State Arms

(Litho Shri Lakshman Bijaya Printing Press, Dungarpur)

1933–47. *P* 11.
1	**1**	¼ a. bistre-yellow			—	95·00
2		¼ a. rose (1935)			—	£275
3		¼ a. red-brown (1937)			—	£180
4		1 a. pale turquoise-blue			—	85·00
5		1 a. rose (1938)			—	£900
6		1 a. 3 p. deep reddish violet (1935)			—	£130
7		2 a. deep dull green (1947)			—	£160
8		4 a. rose-red (1934)			—	£300

Nos. 2 and 5 are known in a *se-tenant* strip of 3, the centre stamp being the 1 a. value.

2   **3**   **4**

Maharawal Lakshman Singh

Three dies of ½ a. (*shown actual size*):

Die I.   Size 21×25½ mm. Large portrait (head 5 mm and turban 7 mm wide), correctly aligned (sheets of 12 and left-hand stamps in subsequent blocks of four *se-tenant* horizontally with Die II)

Die II.   Size 20×24½ mm. Large portrait (head 4¾ mm and turban 7 mm wide), but with less detail at foot and with distinct tilt to left (right-hand stamps in sheets of four horizontally *se-tenant* with Die I)

Die III. Size 21×25½ mm. Small portrait (head 4½ mm and turban 6½ mm wide) (sheets of 4)

(Typo L.V. Indap & Co, Bombay)

1939–46. T **2** (*various frames*) *and* 3/4. *Various perfs.*

9	2	¼ a. orange (*p* 12, 11, 10½ *or* 10)	£300	42·00
10		½ a. verm (Die I) (*p* 12, 11 *or* 10½) (1940)	£150	32·00
		a. Die II (*p* 10½) (1944)	£150	42·00
		ab. Horiz pair. Die I and Die II	£325	£100
		b. Die III (*p* 10) (1945)	£200	32·00
		c. Imperf between (vert pair)	†	£1400
11		1 a. deep blue (*p* 12, 11, 10½ *or* 10)	£140	24·00
12	3	1 a. 3 p. brt mauve (*p* 10½ *or* 10) (1944)	£350	£120
13	4	1½ a. deep violet (*p* 10) (1946)	£375	£120
14	2	2 a. brt green (*p* 12, *pin perf* 11½) (1943)	£425	£200
15		4 a. brown (*p* 12, 10½ *or* 10) (1940)	£350	90·00

Stamps perforated 12, 11 and 10½ were printed in sheets of 12 (4×3) which were imperforate along the top, bottom and, sometimes, at right so that examples exist with one or two adjacent sides imperforate. Stamps perforated 10 were printed in sheets of 4 either imperforate at top, bottom and right-hand side or fully perforated.

Dungarpur became part of Rajasthan by 15 April 1948.

HYDERABAD
Nawab Mir Osman Ali Khan Asaf Jah VII, 1911–1967

12 Symbols   13 The Char Minar

14 Bidar College

(Plates by De La Rue. Recess Stamps Office, Hyderabad)

1931 (12 Nov)**–47.** T **12** *to* **14** (*and similar types*). W **7**. *Wove paper.* P 13½.

41	12	4 p. black	30	10
		a. Laid paper (1947)	2·25	4·25
		b. Imperf (pair)	48·00	70·00
42		8 p. green	30	10
		a. Imperf between (vert pair)	—	£550
		b. Imperf (pair)	60·00	85·00
		c. Laid paper (1947)	3·00	4·00
43	13	1 a. brown (*shades*)	30	10
		a. Imperf between (horiz pair)	—	£550
44	–	2 a. violet (*shades*)	1·50	10
		a. Imperf (pair)	£130	£180
45	–	4 a. ultramarine	1·25	15
		a. Imperf (pair)	£160	£225
46	–	8 a. orange	3·00	1·75
		a. Yellow-orange (1944)	55·00	30·00

47	14	12 a. scarlet	3·75	7·50
48	–	1 r. yellow	3·25	2·75
41/8		*Set of* 8	12·50	11·50

Designs (*as* T **14**): *Horiz*—2 a. High Court of Justice; 4 a. Osman Sagar Reservoir. *Vert*—8 a. Entrance to Ajanta Caves; 1 r. Victory Tower, Daulatabad.

Nos. 41a and 42c have a large sheet watermark "THE NIZAM's GOVERNMENT HYDERABAD DECCAN" and arms within a circle, but this does not appear on all stamps.

15 Unani General Hospital   16 Family Reunion

(Litho Indian Security Printing Press, Nasik)

1937 (13 Feb). *Various horiz designs as* T **15**, *inscr* "H.E.H. THE NIZAM'S SILVER JUBILEE". P 14.

49		4 p. slate and violet	30	60
50		8 p. slate and brown	45	80
51		1 a. slate and orange-yellow	60	40
52		2 a. slate and green	80	2·25
49/52		*Set of* 4	1·90	3·50

Designs:—8 p. Osmania General Hospital; 1 a. Osmania University; 2 a. Osmania Jubilee Hall.

(Des T. I. Archer. Typo)

1945 (6 Dec). *Victory.* W **7** (*very faint*). *Wove paper.* P 13½.

53	16	1 a. blue	10	10
		a. Imperf between (vert pair)	£500	
		b. Laid paper	45	55

No. 53b shows the sheet watermark described beneath Nos. 41/8

17 Town Hall   18 Power House, Hyderabad

(Des. T. I. Archer. Litho Government Press)

1947 (17 Feb). *Reformed Legislature.* P 13½.

54	17	1 a. black	50	75
		a. Imperf between (pair)	—	£700

(Des T. I. Archer. Typo)

1947–49. *As* T **18** (*inscr* "H. E. H. THE NIZAM'S GOVT. POSTAGE"). W **7**. P 13½.

55		1 a. 4 p. green	55	1·00
56		3 a. greenish blue	65	1·50
		a. Bluish green	1·25	1·75
57		6 a. sepia	3·00	8·50
		a. Red-brown (1949)	18·00	24·00
		ab. Imperf (pair)	90·00	
55/7		*Set of* 3	3·75	10·00

Designs:—3 a. Kaktyai Arch, Warangal Fort; 6 a. Golkunda Fort.

1947. *As* 1915 *issue but colour changed.* P 13½.

58	8	½ a. claret	80	50
		a. Imperf between (horizontal pair)	—	£275
		b. Imperf between (vert pair)	—	£350

An Independence commemorative set of four, 4 p., 8 p., 1 a. and 2 a., was prepared in 1948, but not issued.

1948. *As T* **12** ("POSTAGE" *at foot*). *Recess. W* **7**. *P* 13½.
59   6 p. claret   ..   ..   5·00   4·00
  Following intervention by the forces of the Dominion of India during September 1948 the Hyderabad postal system was taken over by the Dominion authorities, operating as an agency of the India Post Office.

1949. *T* **12** ("POSTAGE" *at top*). *Litho. W* **7**. *P* 13½.
60   **12**   2 p. bistre-brown   ..   ..   1·00   1·50
  a. Imperf between (horizontal pair)   ..   †   £500
  b. Imperf (pair) £475   £475
  No. 60 was produced from a transfer taken from a plate of the 4 p., No. 41, with each impression amended individually.

OFFICIAL STAMPS

1934–44. *Nos.* 41/8 *optd with Type* O **2**.
O46   4 p. black   85   10
  a. Imperf (pair)   ..   ..   60·00
  b. Imperf between (vert pair)   ..   £500   £500
  c. Imperf between (horiz pair)   ..   —   £500
O47   8 p. green   35   10
  a. Opt inverted   ..   ..   †   £150
  b. Imperf between (horiz pair)   ..   —   £500
  c. Opt double   ..   ..   ..   †   £120
  d. Imperf (pair) £110   £140
O48   1 a. brown   45   10
  a. Imperf between (vert pair)   ..   £400   £400
  b. Imperf between (horiz pair)   ..   —   £400
  c. Imperf (pair) £150   £180
  d. Opt double   ..   ..   —   £160
O49   2 a. violet   ..   ..   ..   3·00   10
  a. Imperf between (horiz pair)   ..   †   £750
O50   4 a. ultramarine   ..   ..   1·60   20
  a. Opt double   ..   ..   †   £350
  b. Imperf between (vert pair)   ..   †   £800
O51   8 a. orange (1935)   ..   ..   7·50   50
  a. *Yellow-orange* (1944)   ..   —   38·00
O52   12 a. scarlet (1935)   ..   ..   5·50   1·25
O53   1 r. yellow (1935)   ..   ..   10·00   2·00
O46/53   ..   ..   ..   *Set of* 8   26·00   3·75

1947. *No.* 58 *optd with Type* O **2**.
O54   **8**   ½ a. claret   ..   ..   9·00   4·75
  a. Pair, one without opt   ..

1949. *No.* 60 *optd with Type* O **2**.
O55   **12**   2 p. bistre-brown   ..   ..   7·00   5·00

1950. *No.* 59 *optd with Type* O **2**.
O56   6 p. claret   ..   ..   ..   8·50   15·00

IDAR

Maharaja Himmat Singh, 1931–1960

1 Maharaja Himmat Singh **2**

(Typo M. N. Kothari & Sons, Bombay)

1932 (1 Oct)–**39.** *P* 11. (*a*) *White panels.*
1   **1**   ½ a. emerald   ..   ..   ..   9·00   14·00
  a. Imperf between (pair)   ..   £800
  b. *Yellow-green*   ..   ..   8·00   14·00
  ba. Imperf between (horiz pair)   ..   £750
  c. *Pale yellow-green* (thick paper)   ..   10·00   16·00

(*b*) *Coloured panels*
2   **1**   ½ a. emerald (1939)   ..   ..   12·00   16·00
  a. *Yellow-green*   ..   ..   7·00   16·00
  b. *Pale yellow-green* (thick paper)   ..   18·00   18·00
  In No. 2 the whole design is composed of half-tone dots. In No. 1 the dots are confined to the oval portrait.

(Typo P. G. Mehta & Co, Hitmatnagar)

1944 (21 Oct). *P* 12.
3   **2**   ½ a. blue-green   ..   ..   1·60   38·00
  a. Imperf between (vert pair)..   £200
  b. *Yellow-green*   ..   ..   1·10   42·00
  ba. Imperf between (vert pair)..   12·00
4   1 a. violet   ..   ..   ..   1·60   38·00
  a. Imperf (pair) £200
  b. Imperf vert (horiz pair)   ..   £225
5   2 a. blue   ..   ..   ..   2·00   55·00
  a. Imperf between (vert pair)   ..   70·00
  b. Imperf between (horiz pair)   ..   £150
6   4 a. vermilion   ..   ..   2·50   60·00
  a. Doubly printed £450
3/6   ..   ..   *Set of* 4   6·50   £170
  Nos. 1 to 6 are from booklet panes of 4 stamps, producing single stamps with one or two adjacent sides imperf.
  The 4 a. violet is believed to be a colour trial.

POSTAL FISCAL STAMPS

F **1**

1940 (?)–**45.** *Typo. P* 11 (*No.* F1) *or* 12 *on two or three sides.*
F1   –   1 a. violet   ..   ..   50·00   85·00
F2   F **1**   1 a. violet (1943)   ..   —   85·00
F3   1¼ a. on 1 a. violet   ..   80·00   £170
F4   1¼ a. yellow-green (1945)   ..   12·00
  a. Imperf between (vert pair)   ..   29·00
  b. *Blue-green* (1945)   ..   38·00   85·00
  No. F1 shows the portrait as Type 1. Used prices are for examples with postal cancellations. No. F3 shows a handstamped surcharge in Gujerati.

Idar became part of Bombay Province on 10 June 1948.

INDORE
Maharaja Yeshwant Rao Holkar II, 1926–1961

(**8**)   **9**

1940 (1 Aug). *Surch in words as T* **8** *by* Times of India *Press, Bombay.*
33   **7**   ¼ a. on 5 r. black and brown-orange (*b*)   5·00   55
  a. Surch double (Blk. + G.)   ..   †   £400
34   ½ a. on 2 r. black and carmine (*b*)   ..   9·00   1·40
35   1 a. on 1¼ a. green (*c*) (*d*) (*e*)   ..   9·00   40
  b. Surch inverted (*d*)   ..   ..   90·00
  c. Surch double (*c*) £325
33/5   ..   ..   ..   *Set of* 3   21·00   2·10

(Typo "*Times of India*" Press, Bombay)

1941–46. *P* 11.
36   **9**   ¼ a. red-orange   ..   ..   1·75   10
37   ½ a. claret   ..   ..   ..   1·10   10
38   1 a. green   ..   ..   ..   7·00   10
39   1¼ a. yellow-green   ..   ..   12·00   30
  a. Imperf (pair) £190
40   2 a. turquoise-blue   ..   ..   11·00   1·00
41   4 a. yellow-brown (1946)   ..   12·00   9·00

Larger size (23 × 28 *mm*)
42   2 r. black and carmine (1943)   ..   9·00   90·00
43   5 r. black and yellow-orange (1943)   ..   9·00   £120
36/43   ..   ..   *Set of* 8   55·00   £200

JAIPUR

Maharaja Sawai Man Singh II, 1922–1970

7 Maharaja Sawai   10 Maharaja Sawai
Man Singh II   Man Singh II

(Des T. I. Archer. Litho Indian Security Printing Press, Nasik)

1932–46. *P* 14. (*a*) *Inscr* "POSTAGE & REVENUE".

52	10	1 a. black and blue	..	..	35	45
53		2 a. black and buff	..	..	75	75
54		4 a. black and grey-green	..	3·00	4·00
55		8 a. black and chocolate..	..	4·50	7·00
56		1 r. black and yellow-bistre	..	14·00	65·00
57		2 r. black and yellow-green	..	65·00	£250
52/7	..	..	..	*Set of* 6	80·00	£300

(*b*) *Inscr* "POSTAGE"

58	7	¼ a. black and brown-lake	..	30	15
59		¾ a. black and brown-red (1943?)	4·00	2·00
60		1 a. black and blue (1943?)	..	4·75	1·50
61		2 a. black and buff (1943?)	..	4·75	2·00
62		2½ a. black and carmine ..	..	1·25	1·00
63		3 a. black and green	..	90	40
64		4 a. black and grey-green (1943?)	..	12·00	60·00
65		6 a. black and deep blue	..	1·90	15·00
		a. Black and pale blue (1946)..	5·50	40·00
66		8 a. black and chocolate (1946)..	..	11·00	60·00
67		1 r. black and yellow-bistre (1946)	..	19·00	85·00
58/67	..	..	..	..	*Set of* 10	55·00	£200

One Rupee

(11)

1936. *Nos.* 57 *and* 51 *surch with T* 11.

68	10	1 r. on 2 r. black and yellow-green (R.)	4·50	50·00
69	–	1 r. on 5 r. black and purple	..	4·50	40·00

पाव आना

(12)   13 Maharaja and Amber Palace

1938 (Dec). *No.* 41 *surch* "QUARTER ANNA" *in Devanagari,*
T 12.

70	7	¼ a. on ½ a. black and violet (R.)	..	8·00	11·00

(Recess D.L.R.)

1947 (Dec)**–48.** *Silver Jubilee of Maharaja's Accession to Throne.*
Various designs as T 13. *P* 13½ × 14.

71		¼ a. red-brown and green (5.48)	..	..	50	2·00
72		½ a. green and violet ..	..	..	20	1·75
73		¾ a. black and lake (5.48)	..	..	55	2·50
74		1 a. red-brown and ultramarine	..	35	1·75
75		2 a. violet and scarlet..	..	..	25	2·00
76		3 a. green and black (5.48)	..	..	65	3·00
77		4 a. ultramarine and brown ..	..	45	1·75
78		8 a. vermilion and brown	..	..	..	60	2·75
79		1 r. purple and green (5.48) ..	..	1·10	13·00
71/9	..	..		*Set of* 9	4·25	28·00

Designs:—¼ a. Palace Gate; ¾ a. Map of Jaipur; 1 a. Observatory; 2 a. Wind Palace; 3 a. Coat of Arms; 4 a. Amber Fort Gate; 8 a. Chariot of the Sun; 1 r. Maharaja's portrait between State flags.

3 PIES

(14)

1947 (Dec). *No.* 41 *surch with T* 14.

80	7	3 p. on ½ a. black and violet (R.)	..	14·00	22·00
		a. "PIE" for "PIES" ..	..	..	40·00	70·00
		b. Bars at left vertical..	..	48·00	80·00
		c. Surch inverted	..	..	35·00	32·00
		d. Surch inverted and "PIE" for "PIES"	£140	£130
		e. Surch double, one inverted..	..	48·00	45·00
		f. As variety e, but inverted surch showing "PIE" for "PIES"	£275	£250

There were three settings of Type **14**, each applied to quarter sheets of 30 (6×5). No. 80a occurs in two of these settings on R.5/5 and one of these settings also shows No. 80b on R.6/1.

OFFICIAL STAMPS

1936–46. *Stamps of 1932–46, inscr* "POSTAGE".

(*a*) *Optd at Nasik with Type* O **3**, *in red*

O23	7	¼ a. black and brown-lake (1936)	..	40	10
O24		¾ a. black and brown-red (1944)	..	1·50	35
O25		1 a. black and blue (1941?)	..	7·50	30
O26		2 a. black and buff (date?)	..	6·50	90
O27		2½ a. black and carmine (1946)	..	9·00	55·00
O28		4 a. black and grey-green (1942)	..	5·00	2·00
O29		8 a. black and chocolate (1943)	..	5·00	3·50
O30		1 r. black and yellow-bistre (date?)	..	£140	
O23/9		..		*Set of* 7	32·00	55·00

(*b*) *Optd locally as Type* O **2** (16 *mm long*), *in black*

O31	7	¼ a. black and red-brown (1936)	..	65·00	55·00

9 PIES

(O 5)

1947. *No.* O25 *surch with Type* O **5**, *in red.*

O32	7	9 p. on 1 a. black and blue	..	1·90	1·90

1947 (Dec). *No.* O13 *surch as T* 14, *but* "3 PIES" *placed higher.*

O33	7	3 p. on ½ a. black and violet (R.)	..	2·50	8·00
		a. Surch double, one inverted..	..	35·00	35·00
		ab. "PIE" for "PIES" in inverted surcharge	..	..	..	£190	£190
		c. Surch inverted	..	..	£950	£950

1949. *No.* O13 *surch* "THREE-QUARTER ANNA" *in Devanagari, as T* 12, *but with two bars on each side.*

O34	7	¾ a. on ½ a. black and violet (R.)	..	11·00	12·00
		a. Surch double	..	..	£950	£950

There are three different types of surcharge in the setting of 30, which vary in one or other of the Devanagari characters.

Jaipur became part of Rajasthan by 7 April 1949.

KISHANGARH

Maharaja Sumar Singh, 1939–1971

16 Maharaja Yagyanarayan Singh 17

1943–47. *Thick, soft, unsurfaced paper. Poor impression. Typo. Pin-perf.*

81	**16**	¼ a. pale dull blue (1945)	..	..	3·00	6·50
		a. Imperf (pair)	..	..	30·00	
82		¼ a. greenish blue (1947)	..	..	1·60	5·50
		a. Imperf (pair)	..	..	28·00	
83		½ a. deep green (1944) ..	..	..	90	1·40
		a. Imperf (pair)	..	..	25·00	25·00
		b. Imperf between (vert or horiz pair)		42·00	
84		½ a. yellow-green (1946)	..	..	4·50	6·00
		a. Imperf (pair)	..	..	25·00	25·00
		b. Imperf between (vert or horiz pair)		42·00	
85	**17**	1 a. carmine-red (1944)	..	..	5·00	2·50
		a. Double print	..	..		
		b. Imperf (pair)	..	..	25·00	25·00
		c. Imperf between (vert or horiz pair)		42·00	
		d. *Red-orange* (1947) ..	..	..	48·00	20·00
		da. Imperf (pair)	..	..	80·00	60·00
86		2 a. bright magenta	..	..	6·00	12·00
		a. Imperf (pair)	..	..	48·00	50·00
87		2 a. maroon (1947)	..	..	60·00	16·00
		a. Imperf (pair)	..	..	42·00	42·00
		b. Imperf between (vert or horiz pair)		75·00	
88	**16**	4 a. brown (1944)	..	..	21·00	16·00
		a. Imperf (pair)	..	..		
89		8 a. violet (1945)	..	..	42·00	£100
90		1 r. green (1945)	..	..	48·00	£120
		a. Imperf (pair)	..	..	£150	£250
90b		2 r. yellow (date?)	..	..		
		ba. Imperf (pair)	..	..	£325	
91		5 r. claret (1945)	..	..	£375	£400
		a. Imperf (pair)	..	..	£275	

MORVI

Maharaja Lakhdirji, 1922–1948

3

1935–48. *Typo. Morvi Press ptg. Rough perf 11.*

16	**3**	3 p. scarlet (*shades*)	..	..	60	1·90
		a. Imperf between (horiz pair)	..	£1200	
17		6 p. grey-green ..	..	..	75	2·00
		a. Emerald-green	..	..	4·50	20·00
18		1 a. brown	..	..	12·00	14·00
		a. Pale yellow-brown ..	..	..	16·00	24·00
		b. Chocolate	..	..	22·00	30·00
19		2 a. dull violet (*to* deep) ..	..	..	2·50	14·00
16/19				*Set of* 4	14·00	29·00

Nos. 17a, 18a and 18b were issued between 1944 and 1948.

Maharaja Mahendra Singh, 1948–1957

Morvi was merged with the United State of Kathiawar (later Saurashtra) by 15 April 1948.

ORCHHA

Maharaja Vir Singh II, 1930–1956

5 Maharaja Vir Singh II 6

(Litho Indian Security Printing Press, Nasik)

1939–42? *P* 13½ × 14 (*T* 5) *or* 14 × 13½ (*T* 6).

31	**5**	¼ a. chocolate	..	..	..	1·75	38·00
32		½ a. yellow-green	..	..	..	1·90	30·00
33		¾ a. bright blue	..	..	..	1·90	50·00
34		1 a. scarlet ..	..	..	..	1·90	10·00
35		1¼ a. blue	..	..	..	1·90	50·00
36		1½ a. mauve	..	..	..	2·25	65·00
37		2 a. vermilion	..	..	..	1·90	38·00
38		2½ a. turquoise-green	..	..	2·00	£110
39		3 a. slate-violet	..	..	..	3·25	60·00
40		4 a. slate	..	..	..	4·25	17·00
41		8 a. magenta	..	..	..	7·00	£110
42	**6**	1 r. grey-green	..	..	..	12·00	
43		2 r. bright violet	..	..	..	27·00	£325
44		5 r. yellow-orange ..	..	..	80·00	
45		10 r. turquoise-green (1942)	..	..	£300	
46		15 r. slate-lilac (date ?)	..	..	£2000	
47		25 r. claret (date ?) ..	..	..	£2000	

Orchha became part of Vindhya Pradesh by 1 May 1948.

RAJASTHAN

Rajasthan was formed in 1948–49 from a number of States in Rajputana; these included Bundi, Jaipur and Kishangarh, whose posts continued to function more or less separately until ordered by the Indian Government to close on 1 April 1950.

BUNDI

(1)

1949. *Nos. 86/92 of Bundi.* (a) *Handstamped with T* 1.

A. *In black.* B. *In violet.* C. *In blue*

					A	B	C
1	¼ a. blue-green	..	..		3·75	3·25	20·00
	a. Pair, one without opt	..		£130	†	†
2	½ a. violet	..	..		2·25	2·50	21·00
	a. Pair, one without opt	..		†	£140	†
3	1 a. yellow-green	..	..		3·25	9·50	24·00
	a. Pair, one without opt	..		†	£140	†
4	2 a. vermilion ..	..	..		6·00	20·00	—
5	4 a. orange	..	..		27·00	18·00	45·00
6	8 a. ultramarine	..	..		3·25	4·50	35·00
7	1 r. chocolate ..	..	..		—	£140	55·00

The above prices are for unused, used stamps being worth about six times the unused prices. Most of these handstamps are known, sideways, inverted or double.

(b) *Machine-printed as T* 1 *in black*

8	¼ a. blue-green	..	..	..		
9	½ a. violet	..	..	..		
10	1 a. yellow-green	..	..	..		
11	2 a. vermilion..	..	..	..	3·25	45·00
	a. Opt inverted	..	..	..	£250	

12	4 a. orange	..	..	..	..	2·00	45·00
	a. Opt double	..	..	..		£190	
13	8 a. ultramarine	..	..			40·00	
	a. Opt inverted	..	..			£375	
14	1 r. chocolate ..					7·50	

JAIPUR

राजस्थान

RAJASTHAN
(2)

1950 (26 Jan). *T* **7** *of Jaipur optd with T* **2**.

15	¼ a. black and brown-lake (No. 58) (B.)	..	3·25	12·00
16	½ a. black and violet (No. 41) (R.)	..	3·25	12·00
17	¾ a. black and brown-red (No. 59) (Blue-blk.)	4·50	14·00
	a. Opt in pale blue	..	12·00	29·00
18	1 a. black and blue (No. 60) (R.)	..	4·00	24·00
19	2 a. black and buff (No. 61) (R.)	..	4·50	28·00
20	2½ a. black and carmine (No. 62) (B.)	..	6·50	16·00
21	3 a. black and green (No. 63) (R.)	..	7·00	38·00
22	4 a. black and grey-green (No. 64) (R.)	..	7·00	42·00
23	6 a. black and pale blue (No. 65a) (R.)	..	8·00	60·00
24	8 a. black and chocolate (No. 66) (R.)	..	11·00	80·00
25	1 r. black and yellow-bistre (No. 67) (R.)	..	12·00	£120
15/25 ..	..	..	..	*Set of* 11	65·00	£400

KISHANGARH

1948–49. *Various stamps of Kishangarh handstamped with T* **1** *in red.*

(a) On stamps of 1899–1901

26	¼ a. rose-pink (No. 5a) (B.)	..	..	£120	
26a	¼ a. rose-pink (No. 22a)	..	..	—	£110
27	½ a. deep blue (No. 26)	..	..	£180	
29	1 a. brown-lilac (No. 29)	..	..	14·00	35·00
	b. Imperf (pair) ..	..	..	40·00	75·00
	c. Violet handstamp	..	..	—	£170
	d. Black handstamp	..	..	—	£200
30	4 a. chocolate (No. 31)	..	..	45·00	65·00
	a. Violet handstamp	..	..	—	£250
31	1 r. dull green (No. 32)	..	..	£140	£150
31a	2 r. brown-red (No. 34)	..	..	£170	
32	5 r. mauve (No. 35)	..	..	£160	£160

(b) On stamps of 1904–10

33	13	½ a. chestnut	..	..	..	—	80·00
33a		1 a. blue ..	..	..		—	£100
34		4 a. brown	..	..		13·00	
		a. Blue handstamp	..			£130	
35	12a	8 a. grey ..	..	..		60·00	95·00
36	13	8 a. violet	..	..		11·00	
37		1 r. green	..	..		11·00	
38		2 r. olive-yellow ..	..			18·00	
39		5 r. purple-brown	..			22·00	
		a. Blue handstamp	..			£200	

(c) On stamps of 1912–16

40	14	½ a. green (No. 64)	..	..		—	90·00
41		1 a. red ..	..	..		—	90·00
42		2 a. deep violet (No. 51) ..				£180	
43		2 a. purple (No. 66)	..	..		2·00	5·00
44		4 a. bright blue ..	..			—	£250
45		8 a. brown	..	..		5·00	
46		1 r. mauve	..	..		10·00	
47		2 r. deep green	..	..		10·00	
48		5 r. brown	..	..		£180	

(d) On stamps of 1928–36

49	16	½ a. yellow-green	..	..		70·00	
49a		2 a. magenta	..	..	..	—	£170
50		4 a. chestnut ..	..	..		£110	
51		8 a. violet	..	..		6·00	50·00
		a. Pair, one without handstamp			£275	
52		1 r. light green	..	..		20·00	
53		2 r. lemon-yellow	..	..		14·00	
54		5 r. claret	..	..		15·00	

(e) On stamps of 1943–47

55	16	¼ a. pale dull blue	..	..		50·00	50·00
56		¼ a. greenish blue	..	..		38·00	35·00
		a. Imperf (pair)	..	..		£130	
57		½ a. deep green	..	..		21·00	23·00
		a. Violet handstamp	..	..		—	£110
57b		½ a. yellow-green	..	..		28·00	30·00
		ba. Imperf (pair)	..			£130	
		bb. Blue handstamp	..			—	£110
58	17	1 a. carmine-red ..	..			30·00	30·00
		a. Violet handstamp	..	..		—	£120
58b		1 a. orange-red (*imperf*) ..				80·00	
		ba. Blue handstamp	..			90·00	
59		2 a. bright magenta	..	..		80·00	80·00
60		2 a. maroon (*imperf*)	..			90·00	
61	16	4 a. brown	..	..		1·75	5·50
62		8 a. violet	..	..		15·00	42·00
63		1 r. green	..	..		6·00	
64		2 r. yellow	..	..		£120	
65		5 r. claret	..	..		50·00	

A 1 a. value in deep violet-blue was issued for revenue purposes, but is known postally used (*Price* £60 *used*).

SHAHPURA

Rajadhiraj Umaid Singh, 1932–1947

Rajadhiraj Sudarshan Deo, 1947–1971

POSTAL FISCAL

F 1

1932–47. *Typo. P* 11, 11½ *or* 12.

F1	F 1	1 a. red (*shades*)	..	..	30·00	£100
		a. Pin-perf 7 (1947)	..	..		

Nos. F1/a were used for both fiscal and postal purposes. Manuscript cancellations must be assumed to be fiscal, unless on cover showing other evidence of postal use. The design was first issued for fiscal purposes in 1898.

Shahpura became part of Rajasthan by 15 April 1948.

SORUTH

JUNAGADH

Nawab Mahabat Khan III, 1911–1959

OFFICIAL STAMPS

SARKARI
(O 1)

1938. *No.* 57 *optd with Type* O **1**, *in vermilion.*

O13	17	1 a. black and carmine ..	..	..	9·00	1·50
		a. Brown-red opt	..	..	7·00	1·25

The state was occupied by Indian troops on 9 November 1947 following the flight of the Nawab to Pakistan.

UNITED STATE OF SAURASHTRA

The administration of Junagadh state was assumed by the Government of India on 7 November 1947. An Executive Council took office on 1 June 1948.

Under the new Constitution of India the United State of Saurashtra was formed on 15 February 1948, comprising 221 former states and estates of Kathiawar, including Jasdan, Morvi, Nawanagar and Wadhwan, but excluding Junagadh. A referendum was held by the Executive Council of Junagadh which then joined the United State on 20 January 1949. It is believed that the following issues were only used in Junagadh. The following issues were surcharged at the Junagadh State Press.

POSTAGE & REVENUE

ONE ANNA
(19)

Postage & Revenue

ONE ANNA
(20)

1949. *Stamps of* 1929 *surch.* (*a*) *With T* **19** *in red.*
58   **16**   1 a. on ½ a. black and deep blue (6.49)   7·00   3·50
　　　a. Surch double　　　　　　　　　† £300
　　　b. "AFNA" for "ANNA" and inverted
　　　　 "N" in "REVENUE"　　　　　.. £1300
　　　c. Larger first "A" in "ANNA"　　.. 80·00 60·00

　　　　　　(*b*) *With T* **20** *in green*
59   **18**   1 a. on 2 a. grey and dull yellow (2.49)   8·00 17·00
　　　a. "evenue" omitted　　　　　　— £325
No. 58c occurs on position 10.
A number of other varieties occur on No. 58, including: small "V"
in "REVENUE" (No. 8); small "N" in "REVENUE" (Nos. 9, 13 and
14); small "E" in "POSTAGE" (No. 12); thick "A" in "POSTAGE"
(No. 19); inverted "N" in "REVENUE" and small second "A" in
"ANNA" (No. 25); small "O" in "ONE" (No. 26); small "V" and "U"
in "REVENUE" (No. 28); small "N" in "ONE" (No. 37).
In No. 59 no stop after "ANNA" is known on Nos. 4, 17, 25, 34 and
38 and small "N" in "ONE" on Nos. 9, 11, 26 and 31.

21

(Typo Waterlow)

1949 (Sept). *Court Fee stamps of Bhavnagar state optd*
"SAURASHTRA" *and further optd* "U.S.S. REVENUE &
POSTAGE" *as in T* **21**, *in black. Typo. P* 11.
60   **21**   1 a. purple　　　　　　..　　6·50   7·00
　　　a. "POSTAGE" omitted　　..　　£200 £180
　　　b. Opt double ..　　　　　..　　£225 £275
Minor varieties include small "S" in "POSTAGE" (Nos. 9 and 49);
small "N" in "REVENUE" (Nos. 15 and 55); small "U" in
"REVENUE" (Nos. 18 and 58); small "V" in "REVENUE" (Nos. 24,
37, 64 and 77); and small "O" in "POSTAGE" (Nos. 31 and 71).
Various missing stop varieties also occur.

POSTAGE & REVENUE
ONE ANNA
(22)

1950 (Mar). *Stamp of* 1929 *surch with T* **22**.
61   **15**   1 a. on 3 p. black and blackish green   .. 45·00 48·00
　　　a. "P" of "POSTAGE" omitted　.. £375 £375
　　　b. "O" of "ONE" omitted　　..　　　£450
Other minor varieties include small "S" in "POSTAGE" with
small "V" in "REVENUE" (Nos. 14 and 26) and small "V" in
"REVENUE" (No. 11).

OFFICIAL STAMPS

1948 (July–Dec). *Nos. O4/O7 surch* "ONE ANNA" (2¼ *mm
high*) *by Junagadh State Press.*
O14   **18**   1 a. on 2 a. grey & dull yellow (B.)　.. £3500 19·00
O15   **15**   1 a. on 3 a. black and carmine (Aug)　.. £1700 42·00
　　　a. Surch double　　　　　　..　　† £1300
O16   **16**   1 a. on 4 a. black and purple (Dec)　.. £250 35·00
　　　a. "ANNE" for "ANNA" (R. 5/4)　.. £1900 £350
　　　b. "ANNN" for "ANNA" (R. 7/5)　.. £1900 £350
O17   **18**   1 a. on 8 a. black & yellow-green (Dec)　£250 28·00
　　　a. "ANNE" for "ANNA" (R. 5/4)　.. £2000 £275
　　　b. "ANNN" for "ANNA" (R. 7/5)　.. £2000 £275
Numerous minor varieties of fount occur in this surcharge.

1948 (Nov). *Handstamped* "ONE ANNA" (4 *mm high*).
O18   **17**   1 a. on 1 r. (No. O8)　　..　　..　£750 27·00
O19　　　1 a. on 1 r. (No. O12a) ..　　..　　£250 32·00
　　　a. Optd on No. O12　　..　　..　　— 50·00
A used copy of No. O12a is known surcharged in black as on
Nos. O14/17. This may have come from a proof sheet.

1949 (Jan). *Postage stamps optd with Type O* 3, *in red.*
O20   **15**   3 p. black and blackish green ..　　.. £225   9·50
O21   **16**   ½ a. black and deep blue　　..　　.. £500   8·50
O22   **18**   1 a. on 2 a. grey and dull yellow (No. 59) 55·00 17·00
Various wrong fount letters occur in the above surcharges.

MANUSCRIPT OVERPRINTS. Nos. 49, 50, 57, 58, 59 and 60
are known with manuscript overprints reading "Service" or
"SARKARI" (in English or Gujerati script), usually in red. Such
provisionals were used at Gadhda and Una between June and
December 1949 (*Price from* £75 *each, used on piece*).

The United State of Saurashtra postal service was
incorporated into that of India on 31 March 1950. The use of
Soruth stamps was permitted until the end of April.

TRAVANCORE
Maharaja Bala Rama Varma XI, 1924–1971

16 Maharaja Bala Rama
Varma XI and Subramania
Shrine

(Plates by Indian Security Printing Press, Nasik. Typo Stamp
Manufactory, Trivandrum)

1937 (29 Mar). *Temple Entry Proclamation. T* **16** *and similar
horiz designs. Wmk C. P* 12.
60　　　6 ca. carmine　　..　　..　　..　　40　　60
　　　a. Imperf between (horiz strip of 3)　.. £325
　　　b. Perf 12½　　..　　　　..　　1·10   1·50
　　　c. Compound perf　　..　　.. 21·00 21·00
61　　　12 ca. bright blue　..　　..　　1·10　20
　　　a. Perf 12½　　..　　..　　1·50　60
　　　ab. Imperf between (vert pair) ..　£300
　　　b. Compound perf　　..　　.. 32·00
62　　　1½ ch. yellow-green ..　　..　　65　　45
　　　a. Imperf between (vert pair) ..　£225
　　　b. Perf 12½　　..　　.. 16·00   4·00
　　　c. Compound perf
63　　　3 ch. violet ..　　..　　..　　.. 2·00   1·00
　　　a. Perf 12½　　..　　..　　.. 2·75   1·75
60/3 ..　　..　　..　　..　　*Set of* 4 3·75   2·00
Designs:—Maharaja's portrait and temples—12 ca. Sri Padmanabha; 1½ ch. Mahadeva; 3 ch. Kanyakumari.

COMPOUND PERFS. This term covers stamps perf compound of
12½ and 11, 12 and 11 or 12 or 12½, and where two or more
combinations exist the prices are for the commonest. Such
compounds can occur on values which do not exist perf 12 all round.

17 Lake Ashtamudi   18 Maharaja Bala
Rama Varma XI

(Des Nilakantha Pellai. Plates by Indian Security Printing
Press, Nasik. Typo Stamp Manufactory, Trivandrum)
1939 (9 Nov). *Maharaja's 27th Birthday. T* **17/18** *and similar
designs. Wmk C. P 12½.*

64	1 ch. yellow-green ..	..	..	.. 2·25	10
	a. Imperf between (horiz pair) ..		.. 20·00	
	b. Perf 11	..	..	.. 5·50	10
	ba. Imperf between (vert pair)	..	20·00	26·00
	bb. Imperf between (vert strip of 3)		20·00	28·00
	c. Perf 12	..	..	.. 10·00	75
	ca. Imperf between (horiz pair) ..		.. 20·00	
	cb. Imperf between (vert pair)	..	.. 21·00	
	d. Compound perf	..	..	.. 13·00	1·50
	da. Imperf between (vert pair) ..		.. 70·00	
65	1½ ch. scarlet	..	..	.. 1·00	1·25
	a. Doubly printed	..	..	.. £150	
	b. Imperf between (horiz pair) ..		.. 25·00	
	c. Imperf between (vert pair)	..	.. 20·00	
	d. Perf 11	..	..	.. 3·00	14·00
	da. Imperf horiz (vert pair)	..	.. 8·00	
	e. Perf 12	..	..	.. 18·00	2·50
	f. Perf 13½	..	..	.. 12·00	40·00
	g. Compound perf	..	..	.. 25·00	3·75
	h. Imperf (pair) ..	..	..	.. 28·00	
66	2 ch. orange	..	..	.. 2·75	50
	a. Perf 11	..	..	.. 11·00	30
	b. Perf 12	..	..	.. 50·00	3·75
	c. Compound perf	..	..	.. 50·00	4·00
67	3 ch. brown..	..	..	.. 3·75	10
	a. Doubly printed	..	..	— 80·00	
	b. Imperf between (horiz pair) ..		30·00	38·00
	c. Perf 11	..	..	.. 12·00	30
	ca. Doubly printed	..	..	35·00	40·00
	d. Perf 12	..	..	.. 24·00	1·90
	da. Imperf between (vert pair) ..		85·00	85·00
	e. Compound perf	..	..	.. 15·00	1·00
68	4 ch. red	..	..	.. 3·00	40
	a. Perf 11	..	..	.. 17·00	50
	b. Perf 12	..	..	.. 17·00	4·00
	c. Compound perf	..	..	75·00	70·00
69	7 ch. pale blue	..	..	.. 5·00	9·00
	a. Perf 11	..	..	.. 42·00	18·00
	ab. Blue ..	..	..	.. 42·00	14·00
	b. Compound perf	..	..	50·00	21·00
70	14 ch. turquoise-green	..	..	.. 4·75	30·00
	a. Perf 11	..	..	.. 5·50	45·00
64/70 ..	..	..	*Set of 7*	20·00	38·00

Designs: *Vert as T* **18**—1½ ch., 3 ch. Portraits of Maharaja in
different frames. *Horiz as T* **17**—4 ch. Sri Padmanabha Shrine;
7 ch. Cape Comorin; 14 ch. Pachipari Reservoir.

19 Maharaja and Aruvikara Falls   **2 CASH**
(20)

NEW INFORMATION

The editor is always interested to correspond with
people who have new information that will
improve or correct the Catalogue.

(Des Nilakantha Pellai. Plates by Indian Security Printing Press,
Nasik. Typo Stamp Manufactory, Trivandrum)
1941 (20 Oct). *Maharaja's 29th Birthday. T* **19** *and similar horiz
design. Wmk C. P 12½.*

71	6 ca. blackish violet	..	..	.. 3·25	10
	a. Perf 11	..	..	.. 3·50	10
	ab. Imperf between (vert pair)	..	.. 20·00	
	ac. Imperf horiz (vert pair) ..	..	27·00	38·00
	b. Perf 12	..	..	.. 12·00	1·00
	ba. Imperf between (horiz pair)	..	.. 20·00	
	bb. Imperf between (vert pair)	..	.. 28·00	
	bc. Imperf between (vert strip of 3) ..		.. 21·00	
	c. Compound perf	..	..	.. 3·50	80
72	¾ ch. brown	..	..	.. 3·50	15
	a. Perf 11	..	..	.. 5·00	15
	ab. Imperf between (horiz pair)	..	.. 80·00	
	ac. Imperf between (vert pair)	..	20·00	28·00
	ad. Imperf between (vert strip of 3) ..		.. 20·00	
	ae. Block of four imperf between (horiz and vert)	..	.. £100	
	b. Perf 12	..	..	.. 26·00	5·00
	c. Compound perf	..	..	.. 7·00	1·10

Design:—¾ ch. Maharaja and Marthanda Varma Bridge,
Alwaye.

1943 (17 Sept). *Nos.* 65, 71 *(colour changed) and* 72 *surch as T* **20**.
P 12½.

73	2 ca. on 1½ ch. scarlet..	..	..	75	30
	a. Imperf between (vert pair)	..	.. 28·00	
	b. "2" omitted	..	..	.. £150	£150
	c. "CA" omitted	..	..	.. £200	
	d. "ASH" omitted	..	..	.. £200	
	e. Perf 11	..	..	.. 30	20
	ea. "CA" omitted	..	..	.. £200	
	f. Compound perf	..	..	55	75
	fa. Imperf between (vert pair)	..	.. 80·00	
	fb. "2" omitted	..	..	.. £150	
74	4 ca. on ¾ ch. brown ..	..	..	2·25	80
	a. Perf 11	..	..	.. 2·00	20
	b. Perf 12	..	..	—	75·00
	c. Compound perf	..	..	3·00	1·00
75	8 ca. on 6 ca. scarlet	..	..	2·50	10
	a. Perf 11	..	..	.. 1·40	10
	ab. Imperf between (horiz pair)	..	26·00	
	b. Perf 12	..	..	..	— 50·00
	c. Compound perf	..	..	8·50	4·50
73/5	..	..	..	*Set of 3*	3·25	45

21 Maharaja Bala   (22)
Rama Varma XI

(Des Nilakantha Pellai. Plates by Indian Security Printing Press,
Nasik. Typo Stamp Manufactory, Trivandrum)
1946 (24 Oct). *Maharaja's 34th Birthday. Wmk C. P* 12½.

76	**21**	8 ca. carmine	..	..	.. 12·00	2·50
		a. Perf 11	..	..	65	65
		b. Perf 12	..	..	.. 20·00	3·00
		ba. Imperf between (horiz pair)	..	30·00	38·00
		bb. Imperf between (horiz strip of 3)	45·00	
		c. Compound perf .	..	..	

1946. *No.* O103 *revalidated for ordinary postage with opt T* **22**, *in
orange. P* 12½.

77	**19**	6 ca. blackish violet	..	..	.. 6·00	1·75
		a. Perf 11	..	..	.. 24·00	4·25
		b. Compound perf	..	..	6·00	3·75

OFFICIAL STAMPS

SPECIAL

SERVICE   SERVICE   SERVICE
                                8 CASH
(O 10)   (O 11)   (O 12)
13 mm   13½ mm

1939–41. *Nos. 35 and 40 with type-set opt, Type* O **10**. *P* 12½.

O85	**1**	6 ca. brown-red (1941) ..		..	70	20
		a. Perf 11	..	..	1·10	65
		b. Perf 12	..	..	70	30
		c. Compound perf		..	70	1·10
O86	**5**	¾ ch. reddish violet		.. 75·00	42·00
		a. Perf 12	..	.. 18·00	1·25
		b. Compound perf	.. 70·00	42·00

1939 (9 Nov). *Maharaja's 27th Birthday. Nos. 64/70 with type-set opt, Type* O **10**. *P* 12½.

O87		1 ch. yellow-green ..		..	2·75	25
O88		1½ ch. scarlet	..	..	3·00	75
		a. "SESVICE"	..	.. 65·00	26·00
		b. Perf 12	..	.. 21·00	4·25
		ba. "SESVICE"	..	—	80·00
		bb. Imperf between (horiz pair)	..	†	£100
		c. Compound perf		..	7·50	1·75
O89		2 ch. orange	..	..	2·75	3·25
		a. "SESVICE"	..	.. 95·00	£100
		b. Compound perf	.. 55·00	55·00
O90		3 ch. brown ..		..	2·50	20
		a. "SESVICE"	..	.. 48·00	21·00
		b. Perf 12	..	.. 10·00	45
		ba. "SESVICE"	..	.. £100	38·00
		c. Compound perf		..	5·50	2·50
O91		4 ch. red	..	..	5·00	2·00
O92		7 ch. pale blue	..	..	7·00	1·75
O93		14 ch. turquoise-green	..	..	8·00	5·00
O87/93		.. ..	..	*Set of* 7 28·00	9·00

1940 (?)**–45.** *Nos. 40a and 42b optd with Type* O **11**. *P* 12½.

O94	**5**	¾ ch. reddish violet		..	8·00	20
		a. Imperf between (horiz pair)		85·00	
		b. Perf 11	..	.. 40·00	1·10
		c. Perf 12	..	.. 10·00	20
		d. Compound perf	..	.. 35·00	75
O95	**1**	1½ ch. rose (1945)	..	.. 13·00	8·00
		a. Perf 12	..	..	3·75	1·00
		b. Compound perf	..	.. 16·00	11·00

1942 (?). *Nos. 64/70 optd with Type* O **11**. *P* 12½.

O 96		1 ch. yellow-green		..	60	10
		a. Imperf between (vert pair) ..		40·00	40·00
		b. Opt inverted	..	..	† 30·00	
		c. Opt double ..	..	.. 20·00	
		d. Perf 11	..	..	60	10
		da. Imperf between (vert pair)	..	23·00	
		db. Opt double ..	..	.. 70·00	70·00
		e. Perf 12	..	..	2·50	50
		ea. Imperf between (vert pair)	.. 65·00	65·00
		eb. Stamp doubly printed	..	90·00	
		ec. Opt inverted	..	..	† 70·00
		ed. Opt double ..	..	.. 20·00	
		f. Compound perf	..	..	4·00	1·00
		fa. Imperf between (vert pair)	..	† 90·00
		g. "S" inverted	..	..	— 28·00
O 97		1½ ch. scarlet	..	..	2·25	10
		a. Imperf between (horiz pair)	.. 45·00	
		b. Perf 11	..	..	1·00	15
		ba. Imperf between (vert pair) ..	.. 70·00	70·00
		bb. Imperf between (vert strip of 3)	50·00	
		bc. Imperf between (horiz pair)	..	† 75·00
		c. Perf 12	..	..	3·25	50
		ca. Imperf between (vert strip of 3)	.. 90·00	
		d. Compound perf	..	..	1·75	30
		e. Imperf (pair)	..	.. 25·00	
O 98		2 ch. orange	..	..	1·00	30
		a. Perf 11	..	..	4·50	80
		ab. Imperf between (vert pair)	..	
		b. Perf 12	..	.. 55·00	55·00
		ba. Imperf between (vert pair) ..	.. £200	£200
		c. Compound perf	.. 55·00	55·00
O 99		3 ch. brown	..	..	60	10
		a. Imperf between (vert pair)	..	
		b. Perf 11	..	..	1·50	10
		c. Perf 12	..	..	3·25	1·50
		ca. Imperf between (vert pair) ..	.. £170	£170
		d. Compound perf	..	.. 11·00	75
O100		4 ch. red	..	..	1·25	55
		a. Perf 11	..	..	2·25	45
		b. Perf 12	..	.. 10·00	2·75
		c. Compound perf	..	.. 42·00	19·00

O101		7 ch. pale blue	..	..	4·50	35
		a. Perf 11	..	..	4·00	2·75
		b. Perf 12	..	.. 12·00	5·00
		c. Compound perf	..	.. 13·00	4·00
		d. Blue (p 11) ..	..	..	6·50	3·25
		da. Perf 12	..	..	5·50	3·25
		db. Compound perf	..	.. 18·00	11·00
O102		14 ch. turquoise-green	..	..	7·50	70
		a. Perf 11	..	..	7·50	1·50
		b. Perf 12	..	..	7·00	2·40
		c. Compound perf	..	.. 40·00	5·50
O96/102		..	..	*Set of* 7 14·00	1·90

1942. *Maharaja's 29th Birthday. Nos* 71/2 *optd with Type* O **11**. *P* 12½.

O103		6 ca. blackish violet	..	..	40	30
		a. Perf 11	..	..	70	70
		b. Perf 12	..	.. 32·00	3·75
		c. Compound perf	..	..	1·50	1·00
O104		¾ ch. brown	..	..	2·25	10
		a. Imperf between (vert pair) ..	..	† £180
		b. Perf 11	..	..	4·50	10
		c. Perf 12	..	.. 32·00	1·50
		d. Compound perf	..	..	4·75	85

1943. *Surch with Type* O **12**. *P* 12½.

O105	**19**	8 ca. on 6 ca. scarlet	..	..	1·60	20
		a. Perf 11	..	..	1·25	10
		ab. Surch inverted	..	..	† £550
		b. Compound perf	..	..	4·50	1·25

1945. *Nos.* 73/4 *optd with Type* O **11**. *P* 12½.

O106		2 ca. on 1½ ch. scarlet	..	..	45	50
		a. Perf 11	..	..	45	15
		ab. Pair, one without surch	..	£180	
		b. Compound perf	..	..	70	1·00
		ba. "2" omitted ..	..	.. £160	£160
		c. Perf 12	..	..	
O107		4 ca. on ¾ ch. brown	..	..	1·50	30
		a. Perf 11	..	..	85	20
		b. Compound perf	..	..	1·25	1·00

1947. *Maharaja's 34th Birthday. Optd with Type* O **11**. *P* 11.

O108	**21**	8 ca. carmine	..	..	1·50	70
		a. Imperf between (horiz pair)	.. 35·00	
		ab. Imperf between (vert pair)	..	† 95·00
		b. Opt double..	..	..	† £140
		c. Perf 12½ ..	..	..	3·50	1·10
		ca. Stamp doubly printed	..	30·00	
		d. Perf 12	..	..	3·50	1·40
		da. Stamp doubly printed	..	32·00	

From 1 July 1949 Travancore formed part of the new State of Travancore-Cochin and stamps of Travancore surcharged in Indian currency were used.

TRAVANCORE-COCHIN

On 1 July 1949 the United State of Travancore and Cochin was formed ("U.S.T.C.") and the name was changed to State of Travancore-Cochin ("T.C.") by the new constitution of India on 26 January 1950.

NO WATERMARK VARIETIES. These were formerly listed but we have now decided to omit them as they do not occur in full sheets. They are best collected in pairs, with and without watermarks.

COMPOUND PERFS. The notes above Type **17** of Travancore also apply here.

VALIDITY OF STAMPS. From 6 June 1950 the stamps of Travancore-Cochin were valid on mail from both Indian and state post offices to destinations in India and abroad.

ONE ANNA

ഒരണ

(1)

2 p. on 6 ca.

രണ്ട ൨െപ്പൂസ	രണ്ട ൨െപ്പൂസ
Normal	1st character of 2nd group as 1st character of 1st group (Rt pane R.14/2)

1949 (1 July). *Stamps of Travancore surch in* "PIES" *or* "ANNAS" *as T* **1**. *P* 12½.

1	**19**	2 p. on 6 ca. blackish violet (R.)	..	..	1·40	75
		a. Surch inverted	..	..	27·00	
		b. Character error	..	..	80·00	55·00
		c. "O" inverted ..	..	..	20·00	12·00
		d. Perf 11	..	..	90	20
		da. Imperf between (vert pair)	..	..	85·00	85·00
		db. Pair, one without surch	..	..	75·00	
		dc. Character error	..	..	75·00	50·00
		dd. "O" inverted ..	..	..	21·00	12·00
		e. Perf 12	..	..	40	20
		ea. Imperf between (horiz pair)	..	..	35·00	
		eb. Imperf between (vert pair)	..	..	5·00	10·00
		ec. Surch inverted	..	..	60·00	
		ed. Character error	..	..	80·00	50·00
		ee. Imperf between (vert strip of 3)	..		28·00	
		ef. Block of four imperf between (horiz and vert)	..	..	35·00	
		eg. "O" inverted ..	..	..	21·00	12·00
		f. Perf 14	..	..	†	£325
		g. Imperf (pair)	..	..	8·50	
		h. Compound perf	..	..	—	25·00
2	**21**	4 p. on 8 ca. carmine	..	..	1·10	30
		a. Surch inverted	..	..	30·00	
		b. "S" inverted ..	..	..	65·00	35·00
		c. Perf 11	..	..	1·40	30
		ca. Imperf between (vert pair)	..	..	95·00	95·00
		cb. Surch inverted	..	..	60·00	
		cc. Pair, one without surch	..	..	75·00	
		cd. "FOUP" for "FOUR"	..	..	90·00	70·00
		ce. "S" inverted ..	..	..	60·00	35·00
		d. Perf 12	..	..	45	30
		da. Imperf between (vert pair)	..	..	16·00	
		db. Pair, one without surch	..	..	70·00	
		dc. "FOUP" for "FOUR"	..	..	85·00	65·00
		dd. "S" inverted ..	..	..	70·00	40·00
		de. Surch inverted	..	..	80·00	
		e. Imperf (pair) ..	..	..	60·00	
		f. Compound perf	..	..	—	25·00
		g. Perf 13½	..	..	†	£350
3	**17**	½ a. on 1 ch. yellow-green	..	..	1·75	30
		a. "NANA" for "ANNA" (Lt pane R.3/3)	..		95·00	70·00
		b. Inverted "H" in "HALF"	..	..	—	60·00
		c. Imperf between (vert pair)	..	..	†	85·00
		d. Perf 11	..	..	1·10	20
		da. Imperf between (vert pair)	..	..	23·00	
		db. Surch inverted	..	..	†	£110
		dc. "NANA" for "ANNA" (Lt pane R.3/3)	..		£110	80·00
		dd. Inverted "H" in "HALF"	..	..	—	65·00
		e. Perf 12	..	..	65	40
		ea. Imperf between (horiz pair)	..	..	27·00	32·00
		eb. Imperf between (vert pair)	..	..	4·50	9·50
		ec. Surch inverted	..	..	5·00	
		ed. "NANA" for "ANNA" (Lt pane R.3/3)	..		£130	85·00
		ee. Block of four imperf between (horiz and vert) ..	..	..	35·00	
		f. Perf 14	..	..	†	£300
		g. Imperf (pair) ..	..	..	8·50	17·00
		h. Compound perf	..	..	—	24·00
4	**18**	1 a. on 2 ch. orange	..	..	1·90	30
		a. Perf 11	..	..	55	20
		ab. Surch double	..	..	48·00	
		b. Perf 12	..	..	2·25	50
		ba. Imperf between (horiz pair)	..	..	5·00	
		bb. Imperf between (vert pair)	..	..	4·25	9·50
		bc. Block of four imperf between (horiz and vert) ..	..	..	35·00	
		c. Perf 13½	..	..	£110	2·00
		d. Imperf (pair)	..	..	8·50	
		e. Compound perf	..	..	26·00	18·00

5	**–**	2 a. on 4 ch. red (68)	..	..	1·90	60
		a. Surch inverted	..	..	†	£170
		b. "O" inverted ..	..	..	24·00	14·00
		c. Perf 11	..	..	1·90	60
		ca. "O" inverted ..	..	..	—	17·00
		d. Perf 12	..	..	1·60	55
		da. "O" inverted ..	..	..	29·00	18·00
		e. Compound perf	..	..	27·00	23·00
6	**18**	3 a. on 7 ch. pale blue (69)	..	..	7·00	3·50
		a. Perf 11	..	..	4·50	2·00
		ab. *Blue* ..	..	..	38·00	4·50
		ac. "3" omitted ..	..	..	†	£275
		b. Perf 12	..	..	7·00	2·75
		c. Compound perf	..	..	—	35·00
		ca. *Blue* ..	..	..	—	45·00
7	**–**	6 a. on 14 ch. turquoise-green (70)	..		8·50	15·00
		a. Accent omitted from native surch (Rt pane R.13/4) ..	..	..	£150	£160
		b. Perf 11	..	..	6·00	12·00
		ba. Accent omitted from native surch (Rt pane R.13/4) ..	..	..	£150	£160
		c. Perf 12	..	..	8·00	14·00
		ca. Accent omitted from native surch (Rt pane R. 13/4) ..	..	..	£160	£170
		d. Compound perf	..	..	19·00	19·00
		da. Accent omitted from native surch (Rt pane R.13/4) ..	..		£200	
		e. Imperf (pair) ..	..	..		

1/7   *Set of 7* 12·50 14·00
There are two settings of the ½ a. surcharge. In one the first native character is under the second downstroke of the "H" and in the other it is under the first downstroke of the "A" of "HALF". They occur on stamps perf 12½, 11 and 12 equally commonly and also on the Official stamps.

U. S. T. C. (2)

T.-C. (3)

SIX PIES (4)

1949. *No. 106 of Cochin optd with T* **2**.

8	**29**	1 a. orange	..	..	4·50	50·00
		a. No stop after "S" (R. 1/6)	..	..	55·00	
		b. Raised stop after "T" (R. 4/1) ..	..		55·00	

1950 (1 Apr). *No. 106 of Cochin optd with T* **3**.

9	**29**	1 a. orange	..	..	5·50	48·00
		a. No stop after "T"	..	..	45·00	
		b. Opt inverted	..	..	£160	
		ba. No stop after "T"	..	..	£1500	

The no stop variety occurs on No. 5 in the sheet and again on No. 8 in conjunction with a short hyphen.

1950 (1 Apr). *No. 9 surch as T* **4**.

10	**29**	6 p. on 1 a. orange	..	..	1·75	25·00
		a. No stop after "T" (R. 1/5)	..	..	17·00	
		b. Error. Surch on No. 8	..	..	25·00	
		ba. No stop after "S"	..	..	£200	
		bb. Raised stop after "I" ..	..	..	£200	
11		9 p. on 1 a. orange	..	..	1·40	25·00
		a. No stop after "T" (R. 1/5)	..	..	17·00	
		b. Error. Surch on No. 8	..	..	£150	
		ba. No stop after "S"	..	..	£500	
		bb. Raised stop after "T" ..	..	..	£500	

5 Conch or Chank Shell   **6** Palm Trees

(Litho Indian Security Printing Press, Nasik)

1950 (24 Oct).   *W* **69** *of India. P* 14.

12	**5**	2 p. rose-carmine	..	..	90	1·10
13	**6**	4 p. ultramarine	..	..	1·50	8·50

The ordinary issues of Travancore-Cochin became obsolete on 1 July 1951.

OFFICIAL STAMPS

VALIDITY. Travancore-Cochin official stamps were valid for use throughout India from 30 September 1950.

SERVICE   SERVICE
(O 1)   (O 2)

1949–51. *Stamps of Travancore surch with value as* **T 1** *and optd* "SERVICE". *No gum. P* 12½. (*a*) *With Type* O 1.

(i) Wmk C of Travancore

O 1	**19**	2 p. on 6 ca. blackish violet (R.)	..		70	20
		a. Imperf between (vert pair)	..		95·00	95·00
		b. Character error (Rt pane R. 14/2)			32·00	24·00
		c. "O" inverted	..	..	18·00	10·00
		d. Pair, one without surch	..		90·00	
		e. Perf 11	..	..	70	20
		ea. Imperf between (vert pair)	..		95·00	95·00
		eb. Character error (Rt pane R. 14/2)			42·00	32·00
		ec. "O" inverted		..	19·00	10·00
		f. Perf 12	..		35	20
		fa. Imperf between (horiz pair)	..		7·00	14·00
		fb. Imperf between (vert pair)	..		6·00	
		fc. Character error (Rt pane R.14/2)			35·00	28·00
		fd. "O" inverted	..		18·00	
		fe. Block of four imperf between (horiz and vert)	..	..	24·00	
		g. Imperf (pair)	..		8·00	15·00
		ga. Character error (Rt pane R. 14/2)			£150	
O 2	**21**	4 p. on 8 ca. carmine	..	..	1·75	55
		a. "FOUB" for "FOUR" (Lt pane R.2/3)		£120	80·00
		b. Perf 11	..		1·60	30
		ba. "FOUB" for "FOUR" (Lt pane R.2/3)		75·00	32·00
		c. Perf 12	..	..	1·75	55
		ca. "FOUB" for "FOUR" (Lt pane R.2/3)		75·00	50·00
		d. Compound perf	..	..	15·00	15·00
O 3	**17**	½ a. on 1 ch. yellow-green	..		50	25
		a. Pair, one without surch	..		55·00	
		b. Surch inverted	..	..	22·00	
		c. "NANA" for "ANNA" (Lt pane R.3/3)	..	..	£140	50·00
		d. Perf 11	..	..	1·00	25
		da. Pair, one without surch	..		85·00	
		db. Surch inverted	..		55·00	
		dc. "NANA" for "ANNA" (Lt pane R.3/3)	..	..	£130	60·00
		e. Perf 12	..	..	6·00	1·90
		ea. "NANA" for "ANNA" (Lt pane R.3/3)	..	..	£200	£110
		eb. Pair, one without surch	..		75·00	
		ec. Surch inverted on back only	..		£140	
		f. Compound perf	..	..	—	18·00
O 4	**18**	1 a. on 2 ch. orange	..	..	15·00	5·00
		a. Surch inverted	..		75·00	
		b. Pair, one without surch	..		£400	
		c. Perf 11	..		13·00	7·50
O 5	–	2 a. on 4 ch. red (68)	..		90	60
		b. Perf 11	..	..	3·75	60
		ba. Surch inverted	..		£375	
		c. Perf 12	..	..	4·25	3·25
		ca. O inverted	..		—	45·00
		cb. Pair, one without surch	..		£160	
		d. Compound perf	..		—	25·00
		e. Imperf (pair)	..		12·00	
O 6	–	3 a. on 7 ch. pale blue (69)	..	..	3·75	1·40
		a. Imperf between (vert pair)	..		16·00	
		b. Blue	..	..	22·00	5·00
		c. Perf 11	..	..	2·40	90
		ca. Blue	..	..	22·00	5·00
		d. Perf 12	..	..	2·25	2·75
		da. Imperf between (horiz pair)	..		12·00	
		db. Imperf between (vert pair)	..		8·00	
		dc. Block of four imperf between (horiz and vert)	..	..	28·00	
		dd. Blue	..	..	21·00	5·00
		e. Imperf (pair)	..	..	11·00	

O 7	–	6 a. on 14 ch. turquoise-green (70)	..	8·00	4·25
		a. Imperf between (vert pair)	..	25·00	
		b. Perf 11	..	..	6·50	3·25
		c. Perf 12	..	..	28·00	6·00
		ca. Imperf between (horiz pair)	..	22·00	
		cb. Imperf between (vert pair)	..	27·00	
		cc. Block of four imperf between (horiz and vert)	..	50·00	
		d. Imperf (pair)	..	..	14·00	
O1/7		..	..	..	*Set of* 7	22·00	9·25

(ii) W **27** *of Cochin*

O 8	**19**	2 p. on 6 ca. blackish violet (R.)	..	30	1·00
		a. Type O 1 double	..	..	17·00	
		b. Perf 11	..	..	65	1·10
		c. Perf 12	..	..	45	1·10
O 9	–	2 a. on 4 ch. red (68)	..	..	1·00	75
		a. Perf 11	..	..	60	65
		ab. Imperf between (vert pair)	..	£160	£160
		b. Compound perf	..	..	—	28·00

(b) With Type O 2

(i) Wmk C of Travancore

O10	**21**	4 p. on 8 ca. carmine	..	..	30	20
		a. "FOUB" for "FOUR" (Lt pane R.2/3)	80·00	32·00
		b. 2nd "E" of "SERVICE" in wrong fount	..	..	—	45·00
		c. "S" in "PIES" inverted	..		—	48·00
		d. Imperf between (vert pair)	..	†	85·00
		e. Perf 11	..	..	30	20
		ea. Imperf between (horiz pair)	..	4·50	
		eb. Imperf between (vert pair)	..	21·00	
		ec. "FOUB" for "FOUR" (Lt pane R.2/3)	85·00	32·00
		ed. 2nd "E" of "SERVICE" in wrong fount	..	..	85·00	45·00
		ee. "S" in "PIES" inverted	..		—	48·00
		ef. Block of four imperf between (horiz and vert)	..	30·00	
		f. Perf 12	..	..	30	20
		fa. Imperf between (horiz pair)	..	3·00	
		fb. Imperf between (vert pair)	..	2·00	
		fc. Block of four imperf between (horiz and vert)	..	10·00	18·00
		fd. "FOUB" for "FOUR" (Lt pane R.2/3)	90·00	32·00
		ff. 2nd "E" of "SERVICE" in wrong fount	..	..	80·00	45·00
		fg. "FOUK" for "FOUR"	..		†	£300
		g. Perf 13½	..	..	3·00	1·25
		h. Compound perf	..	..	8·00	8·00
		i. Imperf (pair)	..	..	6·00	
		ia. 2nd "E" of "SERVICE" in wrong fount	..	£100	
O11	**17**	½ a. on 1 ch. yellow-green	..	50	20
		a. "AANA" for "ANNA" (Rt pane R.13/1)	..	..	£110	60·00
		b. Perf 11	..	..	30	20
		ba. Imperf between (horiz pair)	..	45·00	45·00
		bb. Imperf between (vert pair)	..	6·00	
		bc. Block of four imperf between (horiz and vert)	..	40·00	
		bd. "AANA" for "ANNA" (Rt pane R.13/1)	..	..	65·00	40·00
		c. Perf 12	..	..	50	15
		ca. Imperf between (horiz pair)	..	3·50	
		cb. Imperf between (vert pair)	..	3·50	7·00
		cc. "AANA" for "ANNA" (Rt pane R.13/1)	..	..	80·00	48·00
		cd. Block of four imperf between (horiz and vert)	..	20·00	
		d. Compound perf	..	..	16·00	12·00
		da. "AANA" for "ANNA" (Rt pane R.13/1)	..	..	—	£13
		e. Imperf (pair)	..	..	6·00	12·00
O12	**18**	1 a. on 2 ch. orange	..	40	15
		a. Imperf between (vert pair)	..	†	90·00
		ab. Imperf between (horiz pair)	..	†	90·00
		b. Perf 11	..	..	1·90	20
		ba. Imperf between (horiz pair)	..	6·00	12·00
		bb. Imperf between (vert pair)	..	45·00	45·00
		c. Perf 12	..	..	40	15
		ca. Imperf between (horiz pair)	..	4·50	
		cb. Imperf between (vert pair)	..	3·50	7·5
		cc. Block of four imperf between (horiz and vert)	..	18·00	
		d. Compound perf	..	..	19·00	14·00
		e. Imperf (pair)	..	..	14·00	

O13	–	2 a. on 4 ch. red (68)	2·25	80
		a. "O" inverted	48·00	32·00
		b. Perf 11	1·50	1·10
		ba. "O" inverted ..	42·00	32·00
		c. Perf 12	7·00	1·10
		ca. Imperf between (vert pair)	£100	£120
		cb. "O" inverted ..	80·00	32·00
		d. Compound perf ..	21·00	13·00
O14	–	3 a. on 7 ch. pale blue (69) ..	5·00	1·10
		a. "S" inverted in "SERVICE" (Lt pane R.6/3)	65·00	32·00
		b. First "E" inverted (Lt pane R.7/4)	£140	£100
		c. "C" inverted (Lt pane R.4/1 and 5/1)	85·00	70·00
		d. Second "E" inverted (Lt pane R.3/2)	£130	95·00
		e. Perf 11	1·50	1·10
		ea. "S" inverted in "SERVICE" (Lt pane R.6/3)	50·00	32·00
		f. Perf 12	3·75	1·60
		fa. "S" inverted in "SERVICE" (Lt pane R.6/3)	£100	65·00
		g. Compound perf	—	32·00
		h. Imperf (pair)	32·00	
O15	–	6 a. on 14 ch. turquoise-green (70)	1·50	3·25
		a. Accent omitted from native surch	16·00	13·00
		b. "S" inverted in "SERVICE" (Lt pane R.6/3)	65·00	42·00
		c. Perf 11	11·00	3·25
		ca. Accent omitted from native surch	55·00	22·00
		cb. "S" inverted in "SERVICE" (Lt pane R.6/3)	£120	50·00
		d. Perf 12	35·00	4·50
		da. Accent omitted from native surch	£110	30·00
		db. "S" inverted in "SERVICE" (Lt pane R.6/3)	£200	65·00
		e. Compound perf	45·00	45·00
O10/15		.. .. .. *Set of* 6	5·00	5·00

(ii) *W* **27** *of Cochin*

O16	**17**	½ a. on 1 ch. yellow-green ..	1·00	65
		a. Perf 11	40	35
		b. Perf 12	16·00	8·00
		c. Compound perf.	9·00	3·50
O17	**18**	1 a. on 2 ch. orange	50	65
		a. Perf 11	50	40
		b. Perf 12	11·00	4·00
		c. Perf 13½	2·50	1·50
		d. Compound perf	4·50	3·75

Nos. O2, O10, O12 and O17 have the value at top in English and at bottom in native characters with "SERVICE" in between. All others have "SERVICE" below the surcharge.

Type O **2** was overprinted at one operation with the surcharges.

Nos. O10b, O10ed, O10ff and O10ia, show the second "E" of "SERVICE" with serifs matching those on the surcharge.

The "accent omitted" varieties on No. O15 occur on Left pane R. 5/1, 11/4 and Right pane R. 1/4, 12/4, 14/1 and 13/4.

The Official stamps became obsolete in September 1951.

Ireland

12 pence (d) = 1 shilling; 20 shillings = 1 pound

IRISH FREE STATE

6 "Sword of Light"

7 Map of Ireland

8 Arms of Ireland

21 George Washington, American Eagle and Irish Harp

22

(Des G. Atkinson. Typo)

1939 (1 Mar). *150th Anniv of U.S. Constitution and Installation of First U.S. President.* W **10**. P 15 × 14.

109	**21**	2d. scarlet	..	..	..	1·75	60
110		3d. blue ..	..	..	..	3·25	4·00

SIZE OF WATERMARK. T 22 can be found in various sizes from about 8 to 10 mm high. This is due to the use of two different dandy rolls supplied by different firms and to the effects of paper shrinkage and other factors such as pressure and machine speed.

9 Celtic Cross

10

18 St. Patrick

19 Ireland and New Constitution

White line above left value tablet joining horizontal line to ornament (R. 3/7)

1937 (8 Sept). W **10**. P 14×15.

102	**18**	2s. 6d. emerald-green	..	..	£140	65·00
		w. Wmk inverted	..	..	£500	£180
103		5s. maroon	..	..	£180	£110
		w. Wmk inverted	..	..	£450	£200
104		10s. deep blue ..	..	..	£140	50·00
102/4		..	..	*Set of 3*	£425	£200

See also Nos. 123/5.

EIRE

29 December 1937—17 April 1949

1937 (29 Dec). *Constitution Day.* W **10**. P 15×14.

105	**19**	2d. claret	..	..	..	1·00	20
		w. Wmk inverted	..	..	..	—	£180
106		3d. blue	..	..	..	4·00	3·50

For similar stamps see Nos. 176/7.

20 Father Mathew

(Des S. Keating. Typo)

1938 (1 July). *Centenary of Temperance Crusade.* W **10**. P 15 × 14.

107	**20**	2d. black	..	..	..	1·50	30
108		3d. blue ..	..	..	..	8·50	6·00

1940–68. *Typo.* W **22**. P 15×14 *or* 14×15 (2s. 6d. *to* 10s.).

111	**6**	½d. bright green (24.11.40)	..	..	2·00	40
		w. Wmk inverted	..	..	40·00	5·50
112	**7**	1d. carmine (26.10.40)	..	..	30	10
		aw. Wmk inverted	..	..	1·25	25
		b. From coils. Perf 14×imperf (9.40)		65·00	65·00
		c. From coils. Perf 15×imperf (20.3.46) ..	..	40·00	15·00
		cw. Wmk inverted	..	..	40·00	15·00
		d. Booklet pane. Three stamps plus three printed labels	..	..	£1500
113		1½d. claret (1.40)	..	..	12·00	30
		w. Wmk inverted	..	..	25·00	6·50
114		2d. grey-green (1.40)	..	..	30	10
		w. Wmk inverted	..	..	2·00	40
115	**8**	2½d. red-brown (3.41) ..	..	..	8·50	15
		w. Wmk inverted	..	..	13·00	1·75
116	**9**	3d. blue (12.40)	..	..	40	10
		w. Wmk inverted	..	..	3·50	35
117	**8**	4d. slate-blue (12.40)	..	..	55	10
		w. Wmk inverted	..	..	10·00	90
118	**6**	5d. deep violet (7.40)	..	..	65	10
		w. Wmk inverted	..	..	22·00	1·00
119		6d. claret (3.42)	..	..	1·75	50
		aw. Wmk inverted	..	..	12·00	1·40
		b. Chalky paper (1967)	..	..	1·25	20
119c		8d. scarlet (12.9.49) ..	..	..	80	65
		cw. Wmk inverted	..	..	25·00	3·75
120	**8**	9d. deep violet (7.40)	..	..	1·50	60
		w. Wmk inverted	..	..	8·50	2·00
121	**9**	10d. brown (7.40)	..	..	60	60
		aw. Wmk inverted	..	..	10·00	2·25
121b		11d. rose (12.9.49)	..	..	1·50	2·25

122	6	1s. light blue (6.40) ..	..	.. 80·00	17·00
		w. Wmk inverted	..	.. £550	95·00
123	18	2s. 6d. emerald-green (10.2.43)		.. 40·00	1·25
		aw. Wmk inverted	..	.. 28·00	3·00
		b. Chalk-surfaced paper (1968?)		.. 1·50	2·25
124		5s. maroon (15.12.42)	..	.. 40·00	2·75
		a. Line flaw	..		
		bw. Wmk inverted	..	.. 25·00	6·00
		c. Chalk-surfaced paper (1968?)		.. 13·00	3·50
		ca. Purple ..	..	.. 6·00	6·50
		cb. Line flaw	..	.. 60·00	
125		10s. deep blue (7.45) ..	..	.. 60·00	6·00
		aw. Wmk inverted	..	.. 90·00	22·00
		b. Chalk-surfaced paper (1968)		.. 19·00	8·50
		ba. Blue ..	..	.. 12·00	15·00
111/25			Set of 17	£110	29·00

There is a wide range of shades and also variation in paper used in this issue.
See also Nos. 227/8.

1941
J ȚCUIṁne
ÀISÉIRȚE
1916

(**23** *Trans* "In memory of the rising of 1916")   **24** Volunteer and G.P.O., Dublin

1941 (12 Apr). *25th Anniv of Easter Rising* (1916). *Provisional issue. T* **7** *and* **9** (2d. in new colour), optd with T **23**.

126	7	2d. orange (G.) ..	..	.. 2·00	50
127	9	3d. blue (V.) ..	..	.. 32·00	9·50

(Des V. Brown. Typo)

1941 (27 Oct). *25th Anniv of Easter Rising* (1916). *Definitive issue. W* **22**. *P* 15 × 14.

128	24	2½d. blue-black	..	.. 70	50

25 Dr. Douglas Hyde   **26** Sir William Rowan Hamilton   **27** Bro. Michael O'Clery

(Des S. O'Sullivan. Typo)

1943 (31 July). *50th Anniv of Founding of Gaelic League. W* **22**. *P* 15 × 14.

129	25	½d. green	..	.. 40	30
130		2½d. claret	..	.. 1·25	10

(Des S. O'Sullivan from a bust by Hogan. Typo)

1943 (13 Nov). *Centenary of Announcement of Discovery of Quaternions. W* 15 × 14.

131	26	½d. green	..	.. 40	40
132		2½d. brown	..	.. 1·75	10

(Des R. J. King. Typo)

1944 (30 June). *Tercentenary of Death of Michael O'Clery.* (*Commemorating the "Annals of the Four Masters"*). *W* **22** (*sideways**).

133	27	½d. emerald-green	..	.. 10	10
		w. Wmk facing left ..		.. 55	20
134		1s. red-brown ..	..	.. 70	10
		w. Wmk facing left ..	..	.. 2·00	50

*The normal sideways watermark shows the top of the e facing right, *as seen from the back of the stamp.*
Although issued as commemoratives these two stamps were kept in use as part of the current issue, replacing Nos. 111 and 122.

28 Edmund Ignatius Rice   **29** "Youth Sowing Seeds of Freedom"

(Des S. O'Sullivan. Typo)

1944 (29 Aug). *Death Centenary of Edmund Rice (founder of Irish Christian Brothers). W* **22**. *P* 15 × 14.

135	28	2½d. slate	..	.. 60	45
		a. Wmk inverted	..	..	

(Des R. J. King. Typo)

1945 (15 Sept). *Centenary of Death of Thomas Davis (founder of Young Ireland Movement). W* **22**. *P* 15 × 14.

136	29	2½d. blue	..	.. 1·00	25
		a. Wmk inverted	..	..	
137		6d. claret	..	.. 7·00	3·75

30 "Country and Homestead"

(Des R. J. King. Typo)

1946 (16 Sept). *Birth Centenaries of Davitt and Parnell (land reformers). W* **22**. *P* 15 × 14.

138	30	2½d. scarlet	..	.. 1·50	15
139		3d. blue ..	..	.. 3·50	3·00

31 Angel Victor over Rock of Cashel

(Des R. J. King. Recess Waterlow (1d. to 1s. 3d. until 1961), D.L.R. (8d., 1s. 3d. from 1961 and 1s. 5d.))

1948 (7 Apr)–**65**. *Air. T* **31** *and similar horiz designs. W* **22**. *P* 15 (*1s. 5d.*) *or* 15 × 14 (*others*).

140	31	1d. chocolate (4.4.49)	..	.. 2·00	3·25
141	–	3d. blue	..	.. 4·00	2·25
142	–	6d. magenta ..	..	.. 1·00	1·50
		aw. Wmk inverted	..	..	
142b	–	8d. lake-brown (13.12.54)		.. 6·00	5·00
143	–	1s. green (4.4.49)	..	.. 1·75	1·25
143a	31	1s. 3d. red-orange (13.12.54)		.. 6·00	1·25
		aw. Wmk inverted	..	.. £550	£225
143b		1s. 5d. deep ultramarine (1.4.65)		.. 3·50	1·00
140/3b			Set of 7	22·00	14·00

Designs:—3d., 8d. Lough Derg; 6d. Croagh Patrick; 1s. Glendalough.

PRICES OF SETS

Set prices are given for many issues, generally those containing three stamps or more. Definitive sets include one of each value or major colour change, but do not cover different perforations, die types or minor shades. Where a choice is possible the set prices are based on the cheapest versions of the stamps included in the listings.

35 Theobald Wolfe Tone

(Des K. Uhlemann. Typo)

1948 (19 Nov). *150th Anniv of Insurrection.* W **22**. P 15×14.
144	**35**	2½d. reddish purple			..	1·00	10
		w. Wmk inverted	..				
145		3d. violet	..	..	..	3·25	3·25

REPUBLIC OF IRELAND
18 April 1949

36 Leinster House and Arms   **37** J. C. Mangan
of Provinces

(Des Muriel Brandt. Typo)

1949 (21 Nov). *International Recognition of Republic.* W **22**.
P 15 × 14.
| 146 | **36** | 2½d. reddish brown | .. | .. | .. | 1·50 | 10 |
| 147 | | 3d. bright blue .. | .. | .. | .. | 5·50 | 3·75 |

(Des R. J. King. Typo)

1949 (5 Dec). *Death Centenary of James Clarence Mangan (poet).*
W **22**. P 15 × 14.
| 148 | **37** | 1d. green | .. | .. | .. | 1·50 | 20 |
| | | w. Wmk inverted | .. | .. | .. | | |

38 Statue of
St. Peter, Rome

(Recess Waterlow & Sons)

1950 (11 Sept). *Holy Year.* W **22**. P 12½.
149	**38**	2½d. violet	..	..	..	1·00	40
150		3d. blue	..	..	..	8·00	8·50
151		9d. brown	..	..	..	8·00	10·00
149/51		..	..	..	*Set of 3*	15·00	17·00

STAMP BOOKLETS

B 2 Harp and "EIRE"

1940. *Black on red cover as Type B* **2**.
SB2 2s. booklet containing six ½d., six 2d. (Nos. 71, 74), each in block of 6, and nine 1d. (No. 72) in block of 6 and pane of 3 stamps and 3 labels (No. 112d) £6500
Edition No.:—22–40

1940. *Black on red cover as Type B* **2**.
SB3 2s. booklet containing six ½d., six 2d. (Nos. 111, 114), each in block of 6, and nine 1d. (No. 112) in block of 6 and pane of 3 stamps and 3 labels (No. 112d) £6500
Edition No.:—23–40

1941–44. *Black on red cover as Type B* **2**.
SB4 2s. booklet containing twelve ½d., six 1d. and six 2d. (Nos. 111/12, 114) in blocks of 6 .. .. £750
Edition Nos.:—24–41, 25–42, 26–44

B 3

1945. *Black on red cover as Type B* **3**.
SB5 2s. booklet containing twelve ½d., six 1d. and six 2d. (Nos. 111/12, 114) in blocks of 6 .. .. £650
Edition No.:—27–45

1946. *Black on buff cover as Type B* **2**.
SB6 2s. booklet containing twelve ½d., six 1d. and six 2d. (Nos. 111/12, 114) in blocks of 6 .. .. £475
Edition No.:—28–46

1946–47. *Black on buff cover as Type B* **2**.
SB7 2s. booklet containing twelve ½d., six 1d. and six 2d. (Nos. 133, 112, 114) in blocks of 6 .. *From* £225
Edition Nos.:—29–46, 30–47

B 4 Harp only

1948–50. *Black on red cover as Type B* **4**.
SB8 2s. 6d. booklet containing six ½d., twelve 1d. and six 2½d. (Nos. 133, 112, 115) in blocks of 6 .. £120
Edition Nos.:—31–48, 32–49, 33–50

1951–53. *Black on buff cover as Type B* **4**.
SB9 2s. 6d. booklet containing six ½d., twelve 1d. and six 2½d. (Nos. 133, 112, 115) in blocks of 6 .. 55·00
Edition Nos.:—34–51, 35–52, 36–53

POSTAGE DUE STAMPS

D 1

1940–70.		W 22. P 14×15.			
D 5	D 1	½d. emerald-green (1942)	..	.. 35·00	22·00
		w. Wmk inverted	..	.. 75·00	40·00
D 6		1d. carmine (1941) ..	..	.. 1·00	70
		w. Wmk inverted	..	.. 45·00	5·50

D 7	D 1	1½d. vermilion (1953)	..	.. 1·75	6·50
		w. Wmk inverted ..	..	.. 15·00	21·00
D 8		2d. deep green (1940)	..	.. 2·75	70
		w. Wmk inverted ..	..	.. 14·00	4·25
D 9		3d. blue (10.11.52) ..	..	.. 2·25	2·25
		w. Wmk inverted ..	..	.. 6·00	4·50
D10		5d. blue-violet (3.3.43)	..	.. 4·25	3·00
		w. Wmk inverted ..	..	.. 5·50	7·00
D11		6d. plum (21.3.60) ..	..	.. 3·00	2·00
		a. Wmk sideways (1968) ..	..	70	85
D12		8d. orange (30.10.62)	..	.. 8·50	7·50
		w. Wmk inverted ..	..	.. 17·00	18·00
D13		10d. bright purple (27.1.65) ..	..	8·50	7·50
D14		1s. apple-green (10.2.69) ..	..	6·00	9·00
		a. Wmk sideways (1970) ..	..	60·00	8·50
D5/14	..	.. .. ..	*Set of* 10	65·00	55·00

Quality British & Commonwealth Stamps Direct to Your Door

Irresistibly simple, exceptionally quick and reassuringly reliable. Stanley Gibbons Mail Order service enables you to build your collection economically from the comfort of your own home.

We Provide:

- ■ Free advice from our team of international specialists.
- ■ Large stocks of guaranteed quality material.
- ■ Fast 48 hour order despatch.
- ■ Regular well produced, illustrated brochures and lists.
- ■ Exclusive special offers mailed regularly.
- ■ Wants lists service available.

Telephone 0171 836 8444 for free copies of our latest Great Britain, Channel Islands, Australia, Canada, New Zealand and Falkland Islands brochures.

Or send your wants list to:
Stanley Gibbons Mail Order
399 Strand, London
WC2R 0LX
and we'll do our best to help.

STANLEY GIBBONS
Mail Order

● **OUR NAME IS YOUR GUARANTEE OF QUALITY** ●

Jamaica

12 pence (d) = 1 shilling; 20 shillings = 1 pound

CROWN COLONY

47 King George VI and
Queen Elizabeth

55 King George VI

56 Tobacco Growing and
Cigar Making

(Des and recess D.L.R.)

1937 (12 May). *Coronation. Wmk Mult Script CA. P* 14.

118	**47**	1d. scarlet	..	..	30	15
119		1½d. grey-black	..	..	50	30
120		2½d. bright blue	..	..	1·25	70
118/20		..	..	*Set of* 3	1·90	1·00
118/20 Perf "Specimen" ..			..	*Set of* 3	55·00	

48 King
George VI

49 Coco Palms at
Don Christopher's
Cove

50 Bananas

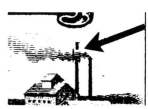

Repaired chimney (Centre plate 1 R. 11/1)

(Recess D.L.R. (T **48**, 5s. and 10s.), Waterlow (others))

1938 (10 Oct)–52. *T* **48/56** *and as Nos.* 88, 112/13, *but with inset portrait of King George VI, as in T* **49**. *Wmk Mult Script CA. P* 13½×14 (½d., 1d., 1½d.), 14 (5s., 10s.) *or* 12½ (*others*).

121	**48**	½d. blue-green (10.10.38)	..	70	10
		a. Wmk sideways ..	..	† £3000	
121b		½d. orange (25.10.51)	..	20	30
122		1d. scarlet ..	..	70	10
122a		1d. blue-green (25.10.51)	..	30	10
123		1½d. brown ..	..	60	10
124	**49**	2d. grey and green (10.12.38)	..	30	60
		a. Perf 13×13½ (1939)	..	1·00	30
		b. Perf 12½×13 (1951)	..	75	20
125	**44**	2½d. greenish blue & ultram (10.12.38)	3·00	1·50
126	**50**	3d. ultramarine and green (10.12.38)	70	1·00
		a. "A" of "CA" missing from wmk	..	£700	
126b		3d. greenish blue and ultram (15.8.49)	1·75	1·40
126c		3d. green and scarlet (1.7.52)	..	1·50	30
127	**51**	4d. brown and green (10.12.38)	..	40	10
128	**45**	6d. grey and purple (10.12.38)	..	1·75	30
		a. Perf 13½×13 (10.10.50)	..	1·75	10
129	**52**	9d. lake (10.12.38) ..	..	40	40
130	**53**	1s. green and purple-brown (10.12.38)	4·75	20
		a. Repaired chimney	..	£325	95·00
131	**54**	2s. blue and chocolate (10.12.38)	..	20·00	90
132	–	5s. slate-blue & yellow-orge (10.12.38)	13·00	3·50
		a. Perf 14, line (1941)	..	£2750	£190
		b. Perf 13 (24.10.49)	..	6·50	3·00
		ba. *Blue and orange* (10.10.50)	..	6·50	3·00
133	**55**	10s. myrtle-green (10.12.38)	..	11·00	7·50
		aa. Perf 13 (10.10.50)	..	9·00	5·00
133a	**56**	£1 chocolate and violet (15.8.49)	..	27·00	26·00
121/33a		..	..	*Set of* 18	70·00	35·00
121/33 Perf "Specimen" ..			..	*Set of* 13	£200	

Designs: *Vert* (*as T* **49**)—2½d. Wag Water River, St. Andrew; 5s. Jamaican scenery. *Horiz* (*as T* **55**)—6d. Priestman's River, Portland.

No. 130a occurred in conjunction with Frame plate 2 on printings between 1943 and 1951.

No. 132a shows the emergency use of a line perforation machine, giving an irregular gauge of 14–14.15, after the De La Rue works were damaged in December 1940. The normal comb measures 13.8×13.7.

51 Citrus Grove

52 Kingston Harbour

53 Sugar Industry

54 Bamboo Walk

SELF-GOVERNMENT

57 Courthouse, Falmouth

58 King Charles II and King George VI

59 Institute of Jamaica

(Recess Waterlow)

1945 (20 Aug)–46. *New Constitution. T* **57/9** *and similar designs. Wmk Mult Script CA. P* 12½.

134	**57**	1½d. sepia	..	..	20	30
		a. Perf 12½×13 (1946)	..	..	2·50	50
135	**58**	2d. green	..	..	6·00	90
		a. Perf 12½×13 (1945)	..	..	20	50
136	**59**	3d. ultramarine	..	..	20	50
		a. Perf 13 (1946)	..	..	70	2·25
137	–	4½d. slate	..	..	30	30
		a. Perf 13 (1946)	..	..	70	1·50
138	–	2s. red-brown	..	..	30	50
139	–	5s. indigo	..	..	1·00	1·00
140	**59**	10s. green	..	..	85	2·25
134/40		..	..	*Set of* 7	2·75	4·75
134/40 Perf "Specimen"		..	*Set of* 7	£140		

Designs: *Vert* (*as T* **57**)—2s. "Labour and Learning". *Horiz* (*as T* **59**)—4½d. House of Assembly; 5s. Scroll, flag and King George VI.

60 Houses of Parliament, London

(Des and recess D.L.R.)

1946 (14 Oct). *Victory. Wmk Mult Script CA. P* 13½×14.

141	**60**	1½d. purple-brown	..	..	1·75	10
		a. Perf 13½	..	..	30	45
142		3d. blue	..	..	1·75	1·75
		a. Perf 13½	..	..	30	4·00
141/2 Perf "Specimen"		..	*Set of* 2	50·00		

61   62
King George VI and Queen Elizabeth

(Des and photo Waterlow (T **61**). Design recess, name typo B.W. (T **62**))

1948 (1 Dec). *Royal Silver Wedding. Wmk Mult Script CA.*

143	**61**	1½d. red-brown (*p* 14×15)	..	..	30	10
144	**62**	£1 scarlet (*p* 11½×11)	..	..	24·00	45·00

63 Hermes, Globe and Forms of Transport

64 Hemispheres, Vickers Viking Airplane and Steamer

65 Hermes and Globe   66 U.P.U. Monument

(Recess Waterlow (T **63**, **66**). Design recess, name typo B.W. (T **64/5**))

1949 (10 Oct). *75th Anniv of Universal Postal Union. Wmk Mult Script CA.*

145	**63**	1½d. red-brown (*p* 13½–14)	..	30	15
146	**64**	2d. deep blue-green (*p* 11×11½)	..	70	1·75
147	**65**	3d. deep blue (*p* 11×11½)	..	55	1·25
148	**66**	6d. purple (*p* 13½–14)	..	65	2·50
145/8		..	..	*Set of* 4	2·00	5·00

67 Arms of University

68 Princess Alice

(Recess Waterlow)

1951 (16 Feb). *Inauguration of B.W.I. University College. Wmk Mult Script CA. P* 14×14½.

149	**67**	2d. black and red-brown	..	..	30	30
150	**68**	6d. grey-black and purple	..	..	35	30

69 Scout Badge and Map of Caribbean

70 Scout Badge and Map of Jamaica

(Litho B.W.)

1952 (5 Mar). *First Caribbean Scout Jamboree. Wmk Mult Script CA. P 13¹/₂×13 (2d.) or 13×13¹/₂ (6d.).*
151 **69** 2d. blue, apple-green and black	15	10
152 **70** 6d. yellow-green, carmine-red and black	15	30

STAMP BOOKLETS

1938. *Booklet containing twelve ¹/₂d. and eighteen 1d. (Nos. 121/2), each in blocks of 6. Stapled.*
SB9	2s. booklet (black on green cover)	£300
SB10	2s. booklet (black on blue cover)	£190
SB11	2s. booklet (black on yellow cover)	£120

1946. *New Constitution. Black on blue cover. Stapled.*
SB12	2s. booklet containing sixteen 1¹/₂d. (No. 134a) in blocks of 4	£190

1951. *Black on yellow cover. Stapled.*
SB13	2s. booklet containing twelve ¹/₂d and eighteen 1d. (Nos. 121b, 122a), each in blocks of 6	42·00

FREE COLOUR BROCHURE

32 pages of Albums, Catalogues, Handbooks and Accessories.

Available Post Free from:

Stanley Gibbons Publications
5 Parkside, Christchurch Road,
Ringwood, Hants BH24 3SH
Tel; 01425 472363

Kenya, Uganda and Tanganyika

100 cents = 1 East Africa shilling

COMBINED POSTAL ADMINISTRATION

1937 (12 May). *Coronation. As Nos.* 118/20 *of Jamaica.*

128	5 c. green	25	10
129	20 c. orange	55	30
130	30 c. bright blue	85	95
128/30	*Set of* 3	1·50	1·25
128/30 Perf "Specimen"	*Set of* 3	65·00	

15 Dhow on Lake Victoria

Damaged left-hand value tablet (Frame Pl 2–2, with Centre Pl 4B only, R. 9/6)

Retouched value tablet (Frame Pl 2–2, with Centre Pls 4B, 5, 6 or 7, R. 9/6)

Break in bird's breast (Frame Pl 2–2, with Centre Pls 4A or 4B, R. 2/5)

Retouch on 10 c. and 1 s. (Pl 7B, R. 5/10 and 6/7. Ptgs from June 1949 onwards)

With dot

Dot removed

In the 50 c. printing of 14 June 1950, using Frame-plate 3, the dot was removed by retouching on all but five stamps (R. 5/2, 6/1, 7/2, 7/4, and 9/1). In addition, other stamps show traces of the dot where the retouching was not completely effective.

PERFORATIONS. In this issue, to aid identification, the perforations are indicated to the nearest quarter.

(T **10** typo, others recess D.L.R.)

1938 (11 Apr)–**54.** *As T* **8** *to* **14** *(but with portrait of King George VI in place of King George V, as in T* **15**). *Wmk Mult Script CA. Chalk-surfaced paper* (£1).

131	**8**	1 c. black & red-brown (*p* 13¼) (2.5.38)	1·25	65
		a. Perf 13¼×13¾. *Black & choc-brown* (1942)	30	40
		ab. Damaged value tablet	70·00	
		ac. Retouched value tablet	45·00	55·00
		ad. Break in bird's breast	65·00	
		ae. Black & dp chocolate-brn (10.6.46)	1·75	1·50
		af. Ditto. Retouched tablet	50·00	65·00
		ag. Black and red-brown (26.9.51)	1·25	1·25
132	**15**	5 c. black and green (II) (*p* 13×11¾)	1·40	30
133		5 c. reddish brn & orange (*p* 13×11¾) (1.6.49)	40	2·25
		a. Perf 13×12½ (14.6.50)	1·25	3·00
134	**14**	10 c. red-brn & orge (*p* 13×11¾) (2.5.38)	1·00	10
		a. Perf 14 (22.4.41)	95·00	6·50
135		10 c. black and green (*p* 13×11¾) (1.6.49)	30	60
		a. Mountain retouch	65·00	32·00
		b. Perf 13×12½ (14.6.50)	1·00	10
136		10 c. brown and grey (*p* 13×12½) (1.4.52)	75	40
137	**11**	15 c. black and rose-red (*p* 13¼) (2.5.38)	7·50	40
		a. Perf 13¾×13¼ (2.43)	2·50	2·75
138		15 c. black & green (*p* 13¾×13¼) (1.4.52)	1·25	2·50
139	**8**	20 c. black and orange (*p* 13¼) (2.5.38)	35·00	20
		a. Perf 14 (19.5.41)	55·00	1·75
		b. Perf 13¼×13¾ (25.2.42)	5·00	10
		ba. Deep black and deep orange (8.51)	9·00	95
		bw. Wmk inverted	†	—
140	**15**	25 c. blk & carm-red (*p* 13×12½) (1.4.52)	1·25	1·50
141	**12**	30 c. black and dull vio-bl (*p* 13¼) (2.5.38)	50·00	40
		a. Perf 14 (3.7.41)	£140	11·00
		b. Perf 13¼×13¾ (10.5.42)	2·25	10
142		30 c. dull purple and brown (*p* 13¼×13¾) (1.4.52)	80	20
143	**8**	40 c. black & blue (*p* 13¼×13¾) (1.4.52)	1·75	2·50
144	**15**	50 c. purple & blk (II) (*p* 13×11¾) (2.5.38)	10·00	80
		a. Rope not joined to sail (I) (R. 2/5)	£225	£200
		b. Dull claret and black (29.7.47)	21·00	3·50
		c. Brown-purple and black (4.48)	21·00	3·50
		d. Reddish purple and black (28.4.49)	17·00	1·75
		e. Ditto. Perf 13×12½ (10.49)	7·00	45
		ea. Dot removed (14.6.50)	9·00	40
		eb. Ditto. In pair with normal	£200	90·00
145	**14**	1 s. black & yellowish brn (*p* 13×11¾) (2.5.38)	7·50	20
		a. Black and brown (9.42)	6·50	30
		ab. Mountain retouch (7.49)	£350	90·00
		aw. Wmk inverted	†	£1500
		b. Perf 13×12½ (10.49)	7·00	60
		ba. Deep black and brown (clearer impression) (14.6.50)	6·50	85
146	**11**	2 s. lake-brn & brn-pur (*p* 13¼) (2.5.38)	£110	1·50
		a. Perf 14 (1941)	65·00	10·00
		b. Perf 13¾×13¼ (24.2.44)	11·00	30
147	**14**	3 s. dull ultramarine & blk (*p* 13×11¾) (2.5.38)	35·00	3·00
		a. Deep violet-blue and black (29.7.47)	45·00	6·00
		b. Ditto. Perf 13×12½ (14.6.50)	18·00	1·50
148	**12**	5 s. black and carmine (*p* 13¼) (2.5.38)	£130	11·00
		a. Perf 14 (1941)	25·00	1·50
		b. Perf 13¼×13¾ (24.2.44)	18·00	75
149	**8**	10 s. purple and blue (*p* 13¼) (2.5.38)	£120	17·00
		a. Perf 14. *Reddish purple & bl* (1941)	30·00	17·00
		b. Perf 13¼×13¾ (24.2.44)	26·00	2·75
150	**10**	£1 black and red (*p* 11¾×13) (12.10.38)	£300	£110
		a. Perf 14 (1941)	16·00	14·00
		ab. Ordinary paper (24.2.44)	14·00	14·00
		b. Perf 12½ (21.1.54)	10·00	25·00
131/50ab (*cheapest*)		*Set of* 20	£100	27·00
131/50 Perf "Specimen"		*Set of* 13	£400	

Designs: *Vert*—1 c., 20 c., 40 c., 10 s. South African Crowned Cranes; 30 c., 5 s. Jinja Railway Bridge by Ripon Falls; £1 Lion. *Horiz*—10 c., 1 s., 3 s. Lake Naivasha; 15 c., 2 s. Kilimanjaro.

The first printing of the 50 c. utilised the King George V centre plate on which each impression had been individually corrected to show the rope joined to sail. R.2/5 was missed, however, and this continued to show Type I until replaced by a further printing from a new plate in September 1938.

Stamps perf 14, together with Nos. 131a, 137a, 139b, 141b, 146b, 148b and 149b, are known as "Blitz perfs", the differences in perforation being the result of air raid damage to the De La Rue works in which the perforators normally used were destroyed. Where dates of issue are quoted for these stamps they represent earliest known postmark dates.

17 Lake Naivasha

(Recess D.L.R.)

1952 (1 Feb). *Visit of Princess Elizabeth and Duke of Edinburgh. Wmk Mult Script CA. P 13 × 12½.*

163	**17**	10 c. black and green	..	..	10	75
164		1 s. black and brown	..	..	20	1·75

10¢

KENYA
TANGANYIKA
UGANDA

(16)   A screw head in the surcharging forme appears as a crescent moon (R. 20/4)

1941 (1 July)–**42.** *Pictorial Stamps of South Africa variously surch as T* **16** *by Government Printer, Pretoria. Inscr alternately in English and Afrikaans.*

			Un.	Used	Used
			pair	pair	single
151	5 c. on 1d. grey & carmine (No. 56)		60	1·75	15
152	10 c. on 3d. ultramarine (No. 59)	..	1·00	4·25	30
153	20 c. on 6d. green & verm (No. 61a)		60	2·25	20
154	70 c. on 1s. brown and chalky blue				
	(No. 62) (20.4.42)	..	8·00	4·50	40
	a. Crescent moon flaw	..			
151/4	.. .. ..	*Set of* 4	9·25	11·50	95
151/4 Handstamped "Specimen"		*Set of* 4	£180		

1946 (11 Nov). *Victory. As Nos. 141/2 of Jamaica.*

					Unused	Used
155	20 c. red-orange	..	..	..	10	10
156	30 c. blue	..	..	..	10	30
155/6 Perf "Specimen"			*Set of* 2	50·00		

Examples of Nos. 155/6 were prereleased at Lindi on 15 October 1946.

1948 (1 Dec). *Royal Silver Wedding. As Nos. 143/4 of Jamaica.*

157	20 c. orange	..	..	..	..	15	10
158	£1 scarlet	..	..	..	..	35·00	45·00

1949 (10 Oct). *75th Anniv of Universal Postal Union. As Nos. 145/8 of Jamaica.*

159	20 c. red-orange	..	..	..	..	20	10
160	30 c. deep blue	..	..	..	..	75	55
161	50 c. grey	..	..	..	..	50	10
162	1 s. red-brown	..	..	..	..	75	40
159/62	..	..	..	..	*Set of* 4	2·00	1·00

STAMP BOOKLETS

1938. *Black on pink cover. Stapled.*
SB3 3 s. 40, booklet containing twelve 15 c. and eight 20 c. (Nos. 137, 139), each in blocks of 4   .. £180

1949. *Black on yellow cover. Stapled.*
SB4 1 s. booklet containing four 5 c. and eight 10 c. (Nos. 133, 135), each in blocks of 4 .. .. 90·00

1952–53? *Black on yellow cover. Stapled.*
SB5 1 s. booklet containing five 5 c. and eight 10 c. (Nos. 133a, 135b), each in blocks of 4 ..
   a. Stitched .. .. 35·00
   ab. Contents as No. SB5, but 10 c. changed to No. 136 (1953?) .. .. 35·00

POSTAGE DUE STAMPS

D 2

(Typo D.L.R.)

1935 (1 May)–**60.** *Wmk Mult Script CA. P 14.*

D 7	**D 2**	5 c. violet	..	..	..	2·25	1·00
D 8		10 c. scarlet	..	..	..	30	30
D 9		20 c. green	..	..	..	40	30
D10		30 c. brown	..	..	..	60	50
		a. Bistre-brown (19.7.60)		..	..	2·75	5·50
D11		40 c. ultramarine	..	..	..	1·50	30
D12		1 s. grey	..	..	..	15·00	19·00
D7/12	..	..	..	..	*Set of* 6	18·00	22·00
D7/12 Perf "Specimen"		..	..	*Set of* 6	95·00	

Kuwait

16 annas = 1 rupee

INDIAN POSTAL ADMINISTRATION

1939. *Nos. 248, 250/1, 253, 255/63 of India (King George VI) optd with T* **3** *or* **4** *(rupee values).*

36	¹/₂ a. red-brown	..	..	9·00	1·75
38	1 a. carmine	..	..	9·00	1·50
39	2 a. vermilion	..	..	9·00	2·50
41	3 a. yellow-green	..	..	9·00	2·00
43	4 a. brown ..	..	..	35·00	12·00
44	6 a. turquoise-green	..	..	28·00	7·50
45	8 a. slate-violet	..	..	32·00	32·00
46	12 a. lake	..	..	23·00	40·00
47	1 r. grey and red-brown	..	..	5·00	2·50
	a. Extended "T" ..	..		£250	
	b. Opt triple, one inverted	..			
48	2 r. purple and brown	..	..	3·75	11·00
	a. Extended "T" ..	..		£225	
49	5 r. green and blue	..	..	12·00	17·00
	a. Extended "T" ..	..		£375	
50	10 r. purple and claret	..	..	60·00	65·00
	a. Opt double	..		£300	
	b. Extended "T" ..	..		£500	
51	15 r. brown and green	..	..	£120	£180
	a. Extended "T" ..	..		£750	
	w. Wmk inverted	..	..	85·00	£150
36/51	..	..	*Set of* 13	£275	£300

On later printings the extended "T" variety was corrected in two stages.

Examples of most values are known showing a forged Kuwait postmark dated "17 NOV 39".

Following the rebellion in Iraq control of the Kuwait postal service was assumed by the Indian authorities on 2 June 1941.
Unoverprinted stamps of INDIA were used in Kuwait between 1941 and 1945.

1945. *Nos. 265/8 and 269a of India (King George VI, on white background) optd with T* **3**.

52	3 p. slate	..	..	1·00	2·00
53	¹/₂ a. purple	..	..	1·00	2·00
54	9 p. green	..	..	2·00	6·50
55	1 a. carmine	..	..	1·50	1·50
56	1¹/₂ a. dull violet	..	..	2·75	6·00
57	2 a. vermilion	..	..	3·00	2·25
58	3 a. bright violet	..	..	3·00	3·00
59	3¹/₂ a. bright blue	..	..	4·00	6·00
60	4 a. brown	..	..	3·00	2·00
60a	6 a. turquoise-green	..	..	14·00	8·50
61	8 a. slate-violet	..	..	7·00	2·50
62	12 a. lake ..	..	..	7·00	2·75
63	14 a. purple	..	..	12·00	14·00
52/63	..	..	*Set of* 13	55·00	50·00

Following a short period of Pakistani control, from August 1947 the Kuwait postal service passed to British administration on 1 April 1948.

BRITISH POSTAL ADMINISTRATION

(5)

(6)

NOTE. From 1948 onwards, for stamps with similar surcharges, but without name of country, see British Postal Agencies in Eastern Arabia.

1948 (1 Apr)–49. *Nos. 470, 475, 476a/7, 478a and 485/90 of Great Britain (King George VI), surch as T* **5** *or* **6** *(rupee values).*

64	¹/₂ a. on ¹/₂d. pale green	..	..	80	90
65	1 a. on 1d. pale scarlet	..	..	80	90
66	1¹/₂ a. on 1¹/₂d. pale red-brown	..	..	1·00	75
67	2 a. on 2d. pale orange	..	..	80	90
68	2¹/₂ a. on 2¹/₂d. light ultramarine	..	..	1·00	1·00
69	3 a. on 3d. pale violet	..	..	80	30
	a. Pair, one surch albino	..			
70	6 a. on 6d. purple ..	..	..	80	50
71	1 r. on 1s. bistre-brown	..	..	1·50	85
72	2 r. on 2s. 6d. yellow-green	..	..	2·50	3·75
73	5 r. on 5s. red	..	..	3·50	4·50
73a	10 r. on 10s. ultramarine (4.7.49)	..	..	38·00	6·00
64/73a	..	..	*Set of* 11	45·00	18·00

(7)

(8)

1948 (1 May). *Royal Silver Wedding. Nos. 493/4 of Great Britain surch with T* **7** *or* **8**.

74	2¹/₂ a. on 2¹/₂d. ultramarine	..	..	75	50
75	15 r. on £1 blue	..	..	30·00	30·00
	a. Short bars (R. 3/4)	..	..	£130	

No. 75a has the bars cancelling the original face value 3 mm long instead of the 3¹/₂ mm of the normal surcharge.

1948 (29 July). *Olympic Games. Nos. 495/8 of Great Britain surch as T* **7**, *but in one line (6 a.) or two lines (others).*

76	2¹/₂ a. on 2¹/₂d. ultramarine ..	..	..	1·00	1·50
77	3 a. on 3d. violet ..	..	..	1·00	1·50
78	6 a. on 6d. bright purple ..	..	..	1·25	1·50
79	1 r. on 1s. brown ..	..	..	1·25	1·50
76/9	..	..	*Set of* 4	4·00	5·50

1949 (10 Oct). *75th Anniv of U.P.U. Nos. 499/502 of Great Britain surch* "KUWAIT" *and new values.*

80	2¹/₂ a. on 2¹/₂d. ultramarine ..	..	..	90	1·50
81	3 a. on 3d. violet ..	..	..	1·25	2·00
82	6 a. on 6d. bright purple ..	..	..	1·40	2·00
83	1 r. on 1s. brown ..	..	..	1·60	1·25
80/3	..	..	*Set of* 4	4·75	6·00

(8a)

KUWAIT

Type I

10 RUPEES ☰

KUWAIT

Type II

10 RUPEES ☰

(8b)

2 r. Type I Type-set surcharge. "2" level with "RUPEES". Surcharge sharp.
Type II. Plate-printed surcharge. "2" raised. Surcharge worn.
10 r. Type I. Type-set surcharge. "1" and "O" spaced. Surcharge sharp and clean.
Type II. Plate-printed surcharge. "1" and "O" closer together. Surcharge appears heavy and worn, see especially "A", "R" and "P".

☰ **KUWAIT**   ☰ **KUWAIT**
Extra bar in centre   Extra bar at top
(R. 7/2)   (R. 2/2)

1950 (2 Oct)–54. *Nos. 503/11 of Great Britain (King George VI) surch as T 5 or 8a/b (rupee values).*

84	½ a. on ½d. pale orange (3.5.51)	..	1·25	1·50
85	1 a. on 1d. light ultramarine (3.5.51)	..	1·25	85
86	1½ a. on 1½d. pale green (3.5.51)	..	1·25	2·25
87	2 a. on 2d. pale red-brown (3.5.51)	..	1·25	85
88	2½ a. on 2½d. pale scarlet (3.5.51)	..	1·25	2·25
89	4 a. on 4d. light ultramarine	..	1·25	80
90	2 r. on 2s. 6d. yellow-green (I) (3.5.51)	..	15·00	4·50
	a. Extra bar in centre	..	£350	£275
	b. Type II surch (1954)	..	£180	45·00
91	5 r. on 5s. red (3.5.51)	..	21·00	5·00
	a. Extra bar at top	..	£250	£180
92	10 r. on 10s. ultramarine (I) (3.5.51)	..	29·00	6·50
	a. Type II surch (1952)	..	£225	50·00
84/92		*Set of* 9	65·00	22·00

No. 92a is known with surch spaced 10 mm apart instead of 9 mm.

Leeward Islands

1937. 12 pence (d) = 1 shilling; 20 shillings = 1 pound
1951. 100 cents = 1 West Indian dollar

FEDERAL COLONY

1937 (12 May). *Coronation. As Nos. 118/20 of Jamaica.*
92	1d. scarlet	..	..	..	30	15
93	1½d. buff	..	..	..	40	35
94	2½d. bright blue	..	..	..	40	45
92/4	..	..	*Set of* 3	1·00	85
92/4 Perf "Specimen"	..	..	*Set of* 3	60·00	

14

15

Gash in chin
(R. 2/5. 1942 ptgs
only)

(Die A)

(Die B)

In Die B the figure "1" has a broader top and more projecting serif.

"ISLANDS" flaw (R. 1/2
of right pane)

Broken second "E" in
"LEEWARD" (R. 4/1 of
right pane) (Pl. 3 ptgs
from December 1943 until
corrected in June 1949)

Broken lower right
scroll (R. 5/12. 1942
ptgs only)

Missing pearl
(R. 5/1. 1944 ptgs
only)

1938 (25 Nov)–**51**. *T* **14** (*and similar type, but shaded value tablet,* ½d., 1d., 2½d., 6d.) *and* **15** (10s., £1). *Chalk-surfaced paper* (3d. *to* £1). *P* 14.

(a) Wmk Mult Script CA

95	¼d. brown	..	..	30	75
	a. Chalk-surfaced paper. *Dp brn* (13.6.49)			10	60
96	½d. emerald	..	..	50	60
	a. "ISLANDS" flaw	..	.. 35·00	
97	½d. slate-grey (*chalk-surfaced paper*) (1.7.49)		..	30	80
98	1d. scarlet (Die A)	..	..	9·00	1·75
99	1d. scarlet (*shades*) (Die B) (1940)	..	1·25	1·50
	a. "D I" flaw (9.47)	..	..	£110	
	b. *Carmine* (9.42)	..	..	75	3·50
	c. *Red* (13.9.48) ..	..	..	4·50	2·75
	ca. "D I" flaw	..	..	£120	
100	1d. blue-green (*chalk-surfaced paper*) (1.7.49)		..	55	15
	a. "D I" flaw	..	..	£110	
101	1½d. chestnut	..	..	80	50
102	1½d. yellow-orange and black (*chalk-surfaced paper*) (1.7.49)		..	50	30
103	2d. olive-grey	..	..	1·40	1·00
	a. *Slate-grey* (11.42)	..	..	5·50	2·75
104	2d. scarlet (*chalk-surfaced paper*) (1.7.49)		1·40	80
	a. *Vermilion* (24.10.51) ..	..	.. 15·00	9·00
105	2½d. bright blue	..	..	7·50	2·25
	a. *Light bright blue* (11.42)	..	60	1·25
106	2½d. black and purple (*chalk-surfaced paper*) (1.7.49)		..	55	15
107	3d. orange	..	.. 35·00	2·75
	a. Ordinary paper. *Pale orange* (11.42)		40	85
108	3d. bright blue (1.7.49)	..	..	65	15
109	6d. deep dull purple and bright purple		18·00	4·75
	a. Ordinary paper (8.42)	..	4·50	2·25
	ab. Broken "E"	..	..	£150	
	b. *Purple and deep magenta* (9.47)		4·00	2·75
	ba. Broken "E"	..	..	£140	
110	1s. black/*emerald*	..	.. 12·00	1·75
	a. "D I" flaw	..	..	£225	
	b. Ordinary paper (3.42)	..	4·00	90
	ba. *Grey and black/emerald* (8.42)	.. 23·00	4·00
	bb. *Black and grey/emerald* (11.42)	.. £130 11·00
111	2s. reddish purple and blue/*blue*	.. 20·00	1·75
	a. Ordinary paper (3.42)	.. 10·00	1·25
	ab. *Deep purple and blue/blue* (29.9.47)	10·00	1·75
112	5s. green and red/*yellow* ..	.. 45·00 15·00
	a. Ordinary paper (12.43)	.. 32·00 14·00
	ab. Broken "E"	..	..	£375	
	b. *Bright green and red/yellow* (24.10.51)	50·00 30·00

113	10s. bluish green and deep red/*green*	£190 £120
	a. Ordinary paper. *Pale green and dull*	
	red/green (26.6.44*)	£375 £250
	ae. Broken lower right scroll	£2250
	af. Gash in chin	£2000
	b. Ordinary paper. *Green and red/green*	
	(22.2.45*)	£150 60·00
	c. Ordinary paper. *Deep green and deep*	
	vermilion/green (17.7.48*)	£120 65·00
	ca. Missing pearl	£950
	(*b*) *Wmk Mult Crown CA*	
114	£1 brown-purple and black/*red*	£300 £190
	a. Purple and black/carmine (21.9.42*)	80·00 40·00
	ae. Broken lower right scroll	£900 £475
	af. Gash in chin	£900 £475
	b. Brown-purple & black/salmon (5.2.45*)	35·00 24·00
	ba. Missing pearl	£800 £550
	c. Perf 13. *Violet & black/scarlet* (4.1.52*)	32·00 35·00
	ca. Wmk sideways	£3000
	cw. Wmk inverted	£2250
95/114*b*	*Set of* 19	£190 £100
95/114 Perf "Specimen"	*Set of* 13	£500

*Dates quoted for Nos. 113a/14c are earliest known postmark dates. Nos. 113a and 114a were despatched to the Leeward Islands in March 1942, Nos. 113b and 114*b* in December 1943, No. 113c in June 1944 and No. 114c on 13 December 1951.

For illustration of Nos. 99a, 99ca, 100a and 110a see above No. 58.

Nos. 96, 98/9 and 99b exist in coils constructed from normal sheets.

1946 (1 Nov).   *Victory. As Nos. 141/2 of Jamaica.*

115	1½d. brown	15 10
116	3d. red-orange	15 20
115/16 Perf "Specimen"	*Set of* 2	55·00

1949 (2 Jan).   *Royal Silver Wedding. As Nos. 143/4 of Jamaica.*

117	2½d. ultramarine	10 10
118	5s. green	3·75 2·75

1949 (10 Oct).   *75th Anniv of Universal Postal Union. As Nos. 145/8 of Jamaica.*

119	2½d. blue-black	15 30
120	3d. deep blue	75 70
121	6d. magenta	40 70
122	1s. blue-green	45 70
119/22	*Set of* 4	1·60 2·25

(**New Currency. 100 cents = 1 B.W.I. dollar**)

1951 (16 Feb).   *Inauguration of B.W.I. University College. As Nos. 149/50 of Jamaica.*

123	3 c. orange and black	30 40
124	12 c. rose-carmine and reddish violet	60 40

Malaya

100 cents = 1 Malayan dollar

STRAITS SETTLEMENTS

CROWN COLONY

1937 (12 May). *Coronation. As Nos. 118/20 of Jamaica.*

275	4 c. orange		30	10
276	8 c. grey-black		70	10
277	12 c. bright blue		1·25	60
275/7		*Set of 3*	2·00	65
275/7 Perf "Specimen"		*Set of 3*	60·00	

58

1937–41. *Chalk-surfaced paper. Wmk Mult Script CA. P 14 or 15×14 (15 c.).* (a) *Die I (printed at two operations).*

278	58	1 c. black (1.1.38)	4·00	10
279		2 c. green (6.12.37)	18·00	10
280		4 c. orange (1.1.38)	13·00	20
281		5 c. brown (19.11.37)	23·00	30
282		6 c. scarlet (10.1.38)	10·00	40
283		8 c. grey (26.1.38)	42·00	10
284		10 c. dull purple (8.11.37)	7·50	10
285		12 c. ultramarine (10.1.38)	8·00	30
286		25 c. dull purple and scarlet (11.12.37)	42·00	95
287		30 c. dull purple and orange (1.12.37)	42·00	1·50
288		40 c. scarlet and dull purple (20.12.37)	10·00	2·00
289		50 c. black/*emerald* (26.1.38)	9·00	10
290		$1 black and red/*blue* (26.1.38)	10·00	20
291		$2 green and scarlet (26.1.38)	22·00	3·75
292		$5 green and red/*emerald* (26.1.38)	25·00	3·00

(b) *Die II (printed at one operation)*

293	58	2 c. green (28.12.38)	45·00	30
294		2 c. orange (6.10.41)	1·75	8·00
295		3 c. green (*ordinary paper*) (5.9.41)	3·25	3·50
296		4 c. orange (29.10.38)	70·00	10
297		5 c. brown (18.2.39)	28·00	10
298		15 c. ultram (*ordinary paper*) (6.10.41)	4·25	9·00
278/98		*Set of 18*	£275	30·00
278/92, 294/5, 298 Perf "Specimen"		*Set of 18*	£325	

Die I. Lines of background outside central oval touch the oval and the foliage of the palm tree is usually joined to the oval frame. The downward-pointing palm frond, opposite the King's eye, has two points.

Die II. Lines of background are separated from the oval by a white line and the foliage of the palm trees does not touch the outer frame. The palm frond has only one point.

The 6 c. grey, 8 c. scarlet and $5 purple and orange were issued only with the BMA overprint, but the 8 c. without overprint is known although in this state it was never issued (*Price* £13).

STAMP BOOKLETS

1938. *Black on buff (No. SB11) or black on green (No. SB12) covers. Stapled.*

SB11	$1 booklet containing twenty 5 c. (No. 281) in blocks of 10	£1000
SB12	$1.30, booklet containing 5 c. and 8 c. (Nos. 281, 283) in blocks of 10 and pane of airmail labels	£1300

MALAYAN POSTAL UNION

The Malayan Postal Union was organised in 1934 and, initially, covered the Straits Settlements and the Federated Malay States. Stamps of the Straits Settlements together with issues for the individual States continued to be used, but Malayan Postal Union postage due stamps were introduced in 1936.

Following the end of the Second World War the use of these postage dues spread throughout Malaya and to Singapore.

POSTAGE DUE STAMPS

10 cents

D 1   (D 2)

(Typo Waterlow until 1961, then D.L.R.)

1936 (June)–**38.** *Wmk Mult Script CA. P 15×14.*

D1	D 1	1 c. slate-purple (4.38)		3·50	70
D2		4 c. green (9.36)		9·00	1·00
D3		8 c. scarlet		4·00	3·50
D4		10 c. yellow-orange		4·00	30
D5		12 c. pale ultramarine (9.36)		7·50	9·50
D6		50 c. black (1.38)		28·00	5·50
D1/6			*Set of 6*	50·00	18·00
D1/6 Perf "Specimen"			*Set of 6*	£130	

For use in Negri Sembilan, Pahang, Perak, Selangor and Straits Settlements including Singapore.

1945–49. *New values and colours. Wmk Mult Script CA. P 15×14.*

D 7	D 1	1 c. purple		2·75	1·75
D 8		3 c. green		7·00	11·00
D 9		5 c. scarlet		8·00	7·50
D10		8 c. yell-orange (1949) (Perf S. £75)		16·00	16·00
D11		9 c. yellow-orange		50·00	48·00
D12		15 c. pale ultramarine		£120	35·00
D13		20 c. blue (1948) (Perf S. £75)		10·00	6·00
D7/13			*Set of 7*	£190	£110

1951 (8 Aug)–**63.** *Wmk Mult Script CA. P 14.*

D14	D 1	1 c. purple (21.8.52)		30	80
D15		2 c. deep slate-blue (16.11.53)		50	1·25
		a. Perf 12½ (15.11.60)		40	8·50
		ab. Chalk-surfaced paper (10.7.62)		35	6·00
		ac. Ditto. Imperf between (vert pair)			
D16		3 c. deep green (21.8.52)		16·00	12·00
D17		4 c. sepia (16.11.53)		45	3·75
		a. Perf 12½ (15.11.60)		60	13·00
		ab. Chalk-surfaced paper. *Bistre-brown* (10.7.62)		70	11·00
D18		5 c. vermilion		38·00	12·00
D19		8 c. yellow-orange		1·75	3·75
D20		12 c. bright purple (1.2.54)		1·00	5·00
		a. Perf 12½. Chalk-surfaced paper (10.7.62)		1·50	19·00
D21		20 c. blue		4·00	6·00
		a. Perf 12½. *Deep blue* (10.12.57)		5·50	25·00
		ab. Chalk-surfaced paper (15.10.63)		3·00	29·00
D14/21			*Set of 8*	55·00	40·00

Nos. D7 to D21b were for use in the Federation and Singapore, and from 1963 throughout Malaysia.

MALAYA (BRITISH MILITARY ADMINISTRATION)

For use throughout all Malay States and in Singapore. From 1948 this general issue was gradually replaced by individual issues for each state. The last usage was in Kelantan where B M A overprints were not withdrawn until 10 July 1951.

B M A
MALAYA
(1)

1945 (19 Oct)–48. *T 58 of Straits Settlements from Die I (double-plate printing) or Die II (single-plate printing) optd with* **T 1.** *Wmk Mult Script CA. Chalk-surfaced paper. P 14 or 15×14 (No. 11).*

1	1 c. black (I) (R.)	..	..	1·50	40
	a. Ordinary paper	..	..	10	20
2	2 c. black (II) (8.7.47)	..	..	3·25	55
	a. Ordinary paper (19.10.45)	..	20	10
	w. Wmk inverted			† £1200
3	2 c. orange (I) (*ordinary paper*) (9.46)	..	10·00	3·25
4	3 c. yellow-green (II) (*ordinary paper*)	30	40
	a. *Blue-green* (27.1.47)	..	..	3·00	2·50
	b. Chalk-surfaced paper. *Blue-grn* (8.7.47)	6·00	50
5	5 c. brown (II) (11.45)	..	70	50
6	6 c. grey (II) (22.3.48)	..	7·00	1·75
	a. Ordinary paper (19.10.45)	..	30	20
7	8 c. scarlet (II) (*ordinary paper*)	..	30	10
8	10 c. purple (I) (12.45)	..	..	2·75	50
	a. Ordinary paper (19.10.45)	..	40	10
	b. *Slate-purple* (12.45)	..	..	2·25	30
	c. *Magenta* (22.3.48)	..	..	3·75	55
9	10 c. purple (II) (28.7.48)	..	15·00	2·00
10	12 c. bright ultramarine (II) (11.45)	..	1·75	3·75
11	15 c. brt ultram (II) (*ordinary paper*) (11.45)	2·25	5·50
12	15 c. bright ultramarine (II) (R.) (22.3.48)	16·00	90
	a. Ordinary paper (12.45)	..	75	20
	b. *Blue* (27.11.47)	..	..	35·00	85
	ba. Ordinary paper (8.7.47)	..	75·00	12·00
13	25 c. dull purple and scarlet (I) (22.3.48)	5·50	80
	a. Ordinary paper (12.45)	..	1·40	20
	ab. Opt double	..	..	£3750
14	50 c. black/*emerald* (I) (R.) (12.45)	..	8·50	1·25
	a. Ordinary paper	..	..	60	10
15	$1 black and red (I) (*ordinary paper*) (12.45)	2·00	10
16	$2 green & scar (I) (*ordinary paper*) (12.45)	2·75	75
17	$5 green and red/*emerald* (I) (11.45)	..	70·00	65·00
18	$5 pur & orge (I) (*ordinary paper*) (12.45)	3·75	2·75
1/18			*Set of 15*	75·00	65·00
1/11, 13/16, 18 Perf "Specimen"			*Set of 14*	£400

The 8 c. grey with "B.M.A." opt was prepared but not officially issued (*Price £200 unused*).

Nos. 3 and 9 do not exist without the overprint

Nos. 1, 2, 6, 7, 8 and 13 also exist on thin, rough ordinary paper.

No. 8 with reddish purple medallion and dull purple frame is from a 1947 printing with the head in fugitive ink which discolours with moisture.

Postal forgeries of the 50 c. value exist made by dyeing examples of the 1 c. and then altering the face value to 50 c.

In 1946 8 c. and 15 c. stamps in the Crown Colony Victory design were prepared for the Malayan Union, but not issued. Examples of the 8 c. carmine from this issue exist from unofficial leakages (*Price £250 unused*).

MALAYAN STATES

JOHORE

38   Sultan Sir Ibrahim   **39**

(Recess D.L.R.)

1940 (Feb). *Wmk Mult Script CA. P 13½.*

130	**38**	8 c. black and pale blue	..	..	14·00	30
130	Perf "Specimen"	..	..	..	38·00

1948 (1 Dec). *Royal Silver Wedding. As Nos. 143/4 of Jamaica.*

131	10 c. violet	..	..	20	30
132	$5 green	..	..	24·00	32·00

1949 (2 May)–**55.** *Wmk Mult Script CA. Chalk-surfaced paper. P 17½ × 18.*

133	**39**	1 c. black	..	..	10	10
134		2 c. orange	..	..	10	10
		a. *Orange-yellow* (22.1.52)	..	10	40
135		3 c. green	..	..	35	40
		a. *Yellow-green* (22.1.52)	..	5·00	1·60
136		4 c. brown	..	..	10	10
136a		5 c. bright purple (1.9.52)	..	30	30
137		6 c. grey	..	..	20	10
		a. *Pale grey* (22.1.52)	..	30	20
		ac. Error. St. Edward's Crown W 9*b*	..	£850
138		8 c. scarlet	..	..	1·50	90
138a		8 c. green (1.9.52)	..	..	2·25	1·25
139		10 c. magenta	..	..	80	10
		aa. Imperf (pair)	..	..	£1200
139a		12 c. scarlet (1.9.52)	..	2·25	2·50
140		15 c. ultramarine	..	..	1·50	10
141		20 c. black and green	..	..	45	1·00
141a		20 c. bright blue (1.9.52)	..	80	10
142		25 c. purple and orange	..	50	10
142a		30 c. scarlet and purple (5.9.55)	1·75	2·25
142b		35 c. scarlet and purple (1.9.52)	2·75	1·00
143		40 c. red and purple	..	2·50	6·50
144		50 c. black and blue	..	70	10
145		$1 blue and purple	..	3·50	1·25
146		$2 green and scarlet	..	14·00	3·50
147		$5 green and brown	..	40·00	9·00
133/47		..	..	..	*Set of 21*	70·00	26·00

1949 (10 Oct). *75th Anniv of U.P.U. As Nos. 145/8 of Jamaica.*

148	10 c. purple	..	..	30	15
149	15 c. deep blue	..	..	1·00	1·00
150	25 c. orange	..	..	65	1·75
151	50 c. blue-black	..	..	1·25	2·00
148/51	..	..	*Set of 4*	2·75	4·50

POSTAGE DUE STAMPS

D 1

(Typo Waterlow)

1938 (1 Jan). *Wmk Mult Script CA. P 12½.*

D1	**D 1**	1 c. carmine	..	..	11·00	29·00
D2		4 c. green	..	..	38·00	38·00
D3		8 c. orange	..	..	45·00	£130
D4		10 c. brown	..	..	45·00	45·00
D5		12 c. purple	..	..	55·00	£110
D1/5	..	..	..	*Set of 5*	£170	£325
D1/5 Perf "Specimen"	..	..	*Set of 5*	£120

PRICES OF SETS

Set prices are given for many issues, generally those containing three stamps or more. Definitive sets include one of each value or major colour change, but do not cover different perforations die types or minor shades. Where a choice i possible the set prices are based on the cheapes versions of the stamps included in the listings.

KEDAH

1 Sheaf of Rice

    I   II   I   II

1938 (May)–**40.** *As Nos. 52 and 27, but face values redrawn as Types* II.

68a	**1**	1 c. black	..	..	..	..	70·00	4·00
69		2 c. bright green (1940)	..	..	..	£140	8·00

1 c. Type II. Figures "1" have square-cut corners instead of rounded, and larger top serif. Larger "C". Line perf. Produced from a new electrotyped Plate 2 with different engraved face values. Printings exist from either the "wet" or "dry" methods.

2 c. Type II. Figures "2" have circular instead of oval drops and the letters "c" are thin and tall instead of thick and rounded. Produced from a new plate, made from a transfer die, and printed by the "dry" method.

1948 (1 Dec). *Royal Silver Wedding. As Nos. 143/4 of Jamaica.*

70		10 c. violet	..	..	..	..	20	20
71		$5 carmine	..	..	..	..	25·00	32·00

1949 (10 Oct). *75th Anniv of U.P.U. As Nos. 145/8 of Jamaica.*

72		10 c. purple	..	..	..	..	25	20
73		15 c. deep blue	..	..	..	1·00	1·25
74		25 c. orange	..	..	..	65	1·25
75		50 c. blue-black	..	..	..	1·25	2·25
72/5	..	..	..	..	*Set of* 4	2·75	4·50

7 Sheaf of Rice   8 Sultan Badlishah

1950 (1 June)–**55.** *Wmk Mult Script CA. Chalk-surfaced paper.* P 17½ × 18.

76	**7**	1 c. black	..	..	..		10	30
77		2 c. orange	..	..	..		10	15
78		3 c. green	..	..	..		55	1·00
79		4 c. brown	..	..	..		40	10
79a		5 c. bright purple (1.9.52)	..		35	80
		ab. *Bright mauve* (24.9.53)	..		35	30
80		6 c. grey	..	..	..		40	15
81		8 c. scarlet	..	..	..		65	1·75
81a		8 c. green (1.9.52)	..	..		75	1·75
		ab. *Deep green* (24.9.53)	..		6·00	6·50
82		10 c. magenta	..	..	..		30	10
82a		12 c. scarlet (1.9.52)	..	..		85	2·50
83		15 c. ultramarine	..	..		55	35
84		20 c. black and green	..	..		50	2·50
84a		20 c. bright blue (1.9.52)	..		85	10
85	**8**	25 c. purple and orange	..		55	30
85a		30 c. scarlet and purple (5.9.55)		1·25	1·25
85b		35 c. scarlet and purple (1.9.52)		85	1·50
86		40 c. red and purple	..	..		1·25	6·00
87		50 c. black and blue	..	..		1·00	20
88		$1 blue and purple	..	..		2·75	2·00
89		$2 green and scarlet	..	..		20·00	22·00
90		$5 green and brown	..	..		42·00	32·00
76/90	..	..	..	..	*Set of* 21	65·00	65·00

KELANTAN

4 Sultan Ismail

(Recess B.W.)

1937 (July)–**40.** *Wmk Mult Script CA.* P 12.

40	**4**	1 c. grey-olive and yellow	..	..		30	45
41		2 c. green	..	..	..		2·50	10
42		4 c. scarlet	..	..	..		4·75	55
43		5 c. red-brown	..	..	..		4·75	10
44		6 c. lake (10.37)	..	..	..	11·00	3·75
45		8 c. grey-olive	..	..	..		4·75	10
46		10 c. purple (10.37)	..	..		22·00	2·75
47		12 c. blue	..	..	..		3·25	4·00
48		25 c. vermilion and violet	..	..		4·75	3·50
49		30 c. violet and scarlet (10.37)	..	40·00	16·00
50		40 c. orange and blue-green	..		8·00	22·00
51		50 c. grey-olive and orange (10.37)	..	55·00	4·75
52		$1 violet and blue-green (10.37)	..	48·00	12·00
53		$2 red-brown and scarlet (3.40)	..	£160	£180
54		$5 vermilion and lake (3.40)	..	£300	£450
40/54	..	..	..		*Set of* 15	£600	£650
40/54 Perf "Specimen"			*Set of* 15	£400

For above issue surcharged see issues under "Japanese Occupation".

1948 (1 Dec). *Royal Silver Wedding. As Nos. 143/4 of Jamaica.*

55		10 c. violet	..	..	..	..	60	1·25
56		$5 carmine	..	..	..		23·00	48·00

1949 (10 Oct). *75th Anniv of U.P.U. As Nos. 145/8 of Jamaica.*

57		10 c. purple	..	..	..		25	30
58		15 c. deep blue	..	..	..	1·00	90
59		25 c. orange	..	..	..		60	2·25
60		50 c. blue-black	..	..	..	1·25	2·25
57/60	..	..	..	..	*Set of* 4	2·75	5·00

5 Sultan Ibrahim   6 Sultan Yahya Petra and Crest of Kelantan

Normal   No. 62a
Tiny stop (R. 1/2)

1951 (11 July)–**55.** *Chalk-surfaced paper. Wmk Mult Script CA.* P 17½ × 18.

61	**5**	1 c. black	..	..	..		10	30
62		2 c. orange	..	..	..		30	55
		a. Tiny stop	..	..	..	18·00	
		b. *Orange-yellow* (11.5.55)	..	1·00	30
63		3 c. green	..	..	..		3·00	1·25
64		4 c. brown	..	..	..		15	15
65		5 c. bright purple (1.9.52)	..		45	50
		a. *Bright mauve* (9.12.53)	..	1·00	50
66		6 c. grey	..	..	..		20	20
67		8 c. scarlet	..	..	..		85	3·25

68	**5**	8 c. green (1.9.52)	..	..	..	75	1·75
69		10 c. magenta	..	..	..	20	10
70		12 c. scarlet (1.9.52)	..	..	..	75	2·25
71		15 c. ultramarine	..	..	..	2·75	60
72		20 c. black and green	..	..	..	45	5·00
73		20 c. bright blue (1.9.52)	..	..	..	80	25
74		25 c. purple and orange	..	..	..	55	55
75		30 c. scarlet and purple (5.9.55)	..	..	1·25	1·75
76		35 c. scarlet and purple (1.9.52)	..	..	90	1·50
77		40 c. red and purple	..	..	..	4·25	10·00
78		50 c. black and blue	..	..	..	1·00	40
79		$1 blue and purple	..	..	..	6·00	4·00
80		$2 green and scarlet	..	..	..	22·00	20·00
81		$5 green and brown	..	..	..	48·00	40·00
		a. Green and sepia (8.12.53)	..	75·00	80·00
61/81		..	..	..	..	*Set of* 21	85·00	80·00

MALACCA

1948 (1 Dec). *Royal Silver Wedding. As Nos. 143/4 of Jamaica.*

1	10 c. violet	..	..	..	..	30	60
2	$5 brown	..	..	..	..	26·00	45·00

1949 (1 Mar)—**52**. *As T* **58** *of Straits Settlements, but inscr* "MALACCA" *at foot. Wmk Mult Script CA. Chalk-surfaced paper. P* 17½ × 18.

3	1 c. black	..	..	..	..	10	70
4	2 c. orange	..	..	..	..	50	45
5	3 c. green	..	..	..	..	30	1·50
6	4 c. brown	..	..	..	..	15	10
6a	5 c. bright purple (1.9.52)	..	..	45	1·50
7	6 c. grey	..	..	..	..	40	75
8	8 c. scarlet	..	..	..	..	30	4·50
8a	8 c. green (1.9.52)	..	..	..	85	4·50
9	10 c. purple	..	..	..	..	15	10
9a	12 c. scarlet (1.9.52)	..	..	..	95	3·50
10	15 c. ultramarine	..	..	..	30	60
11	20 c. black and green	..	..	..	30	5·00
11a	20 c. bright blue (1.9.52)	..	..	1·25	2·50
12	25 c. purple and orange	..	..	30	70
12a	35 c. scarlet and purple (1.9.52)	..	1·00	3·00
13	40 c. red and purple	..	..	1·25	11·00
14	50 c. black and blue	..	..	..	50	10
15	$1 blue and purple	..	..	..	5·00	14·00
16	$2 green and scarlet..	..	..	18·00	17·00
17	$5 green and brown..	..	..	40·00	35·00
3/17	..	..	..	..	*Set of* 20	65·00	95·00

1949 (10 Oct). *75th Anniv of U.P.U. As Nos. 145/8 of Jamaica.*

18	10 c. purple	..	..	..	..	20	45
19	15 c. deep blue..	..	..	..	75	1·75
20	25 c. orange	..	..	..	..	45	3·50
21	50 c. blue-black	..	..	..	1·00	3·75
18/21	..	..	..	..	*Set of* 4	2·25	8·50

NEGRI SEMBILAN

6   Arms of Negri Sembilan   **7**

1935 (2 Dec)—**41**. *Wmk Mult Script CA. Ordinary paper (6 c. grey, 15 c.) or chalk-surfaced paper (others). P* 14.

21	**6**	1 c. black (1.1.36)	..	..	..	75	10
22		2 c. green (1.1.36)	..	..	..	80	20
23		2 c. orange (11.12.41)	..	..	2·50	45·00
24		3 c. green (21.8.41)	..	..	4·50	7·00
		a. Ordinary paper	..	..	12·00	7·00
25		4 c. orange	..	..	..	50	10
26		5 c. brown (5.12.35)	..	..	30	10
27		6 c. scarlet (1.1.37)	..	..	8·00	2·25
		a. Stop omitted at right (R. 10/4)	..	£200	80·00
28		6 c. grey (18.12.41)	..	..	3·50	70·06
		a. Stop omitted at right (R. 10/4)	..	95·00	£350
29		8 c. grey	..	..	..	..	2·00	10
30		10 c. dull purple (1.1.36)	..	..	70	10

31	**6**	12 c. bright ultramarine (1.1.36)	..	..	1·40	40
32		15 c. ultramarine (1.10.41)	..	..	6·50	45·00
33		25 c. dull purple and scarlet (1.4.36)	..	90	70
34		30 c. dull purple and orange (1.1.36)	..	4·50	2·00
35		40 c. scarlet and dull purple	..	..	85	2·00
36		50 c. black/*emerald* (1.2.36)	..	..	3·75	1·50
37		$1 black and red/*blue* (1.4.36)	..	..	2·25	2·75
38		$2 green and scarlet (16.5.36)	..	..	23·00	16·00
39		$5 green and red/*emerald* (16.5.36)	..	14·00	45·00
21/39		..	..	..	*Set of* 19	70·00	£225
21/39 Perf "Specimen"		..	..	*Set of* 19	£200

An 8 c. scarlet was issued but only with opt during Japanese Occupation of Malaya. Unoverprinted specimens result from leakages.

During shortages in 1941 stamps of STRAITS SETTLE-MENTS (2 c.), SELANGOR (2 c., 8 c.), PERAK (2 c., 25 c., 50 c.) and PAHANG (8 c.) were issued in Negri Sembilan.

1948 (1 Dec). *Royal Silver Wedding. As Nos. 143/4 of Jamaica.*

40	10 c. violet	..	..	..	..	15	50
41	$5 green	..	..	..	..	18·00	28·00

1949 (1 Apr)—**55**. *Chalk-surfaced paper. Wmk Mult Script CA. P* 17½ × 18.

42	**7**	1 c. black..	..	..	..	10	10
43		2 c. orange	..	..	..	10	10
44		3 c. green	..	..	..	10	30
45		4 c. brown	..	..	..	10	10
46		5 c. bright purple (1.9.52)	..	..	30	50
		a. Bright mauve (25.8.53)	..	..	30	45
47		6 c. grey	..	..	..	30	10
		a. Pale grey (25.8.53)	..	..	2·25	10
48		8 c. scarlet	..	..	..	20	75
49		8 c. green (1.9.52)	..	..	1·50	1·60
50		10 c. purple	..	..	..	15	10
51		12 c. scarlet (1.9.52)	..	..	1·50	2·00
52		15 c. ultramarine	..	..	1·75	10
53		20 c. black and green	..	..	25	75
54		20 c. bright blue (1.9.52)	..	..	80	10
55		25 c. purple and orange	..	..	25	10
56		30 c. scarlet and purple (5.9.55)	..	1·25	2·50
57		35 c. scarlet and purple (1.9.52)	..	70	1·00
58		40 c. red and purple	..	..	80	3·75
59		50 c. black and blue	..	..	70	20
60		$1 blue and purple	..	..	3·00	1·75
61		$2 green and scarlet	..	..	12·00	12·00
62		$5 green and brown	..	..	50·00	35·00
42/62		..	..	..	*Set of* 21	65·00	55·00

1949 (10 Oct). *75th Anniv of U.P.U. As Nos. 145/8 of Jamaica.*

63	10 c. purple	..	..	..	..	20	10
64	15 c. deep blue..	..	..	..	75	1·50
65	25 c. orange	..	..	..	..	40	10
66	50 c. blue-black	..	..	..	1·00	2·50
63/6	..	..	..	..	*Set of* 4	2·25	5·50

STAMP BOOKLETS

1935. *Stapled.*

SB1 $1 booklet containing twenty 5 c. (No. 26) in blocks of 10 .. ..

SB2 $1.30, booklet containing 5 c. and 8 c. (Nos. 26, 29), each in block of 10 .. .. ..

PAHANG

15 Sultan Sir Abu Bakar   **16** Sultan Sir Abu Bakar

1935 (2 Dec)–**41.** *Chalk-surfaced paper. Wmk Mult Script CA.*
P 14.

29	**15**	1 c. black (1.1.36)	.. .. ..	15	40
30		2 c. green (1.1.36)	.. .. ..	60	50
31		3 c. green (21.8.41)	.. ..	8·00	11·00
		a. Ordinary paper	.. ..	15·00	4·25
32		4 c. orange	.. .. ..	30	40
33		5 c. brown (5.12.35)	.. ..	60	10
34		6 c. scarlet (1.1.37)	.. ..	8·50	2·25
35		8 c. grey	.. .. ..	60	10
36		8 c. scarlet (11.12.41)	.. ..	1·00	40·00
37		10 c. dull purple (1.1.36) ..	..	30	10
38		12 c. bright ultramarine (1.1.36)	..	1·50	1·75
39		15 c. ultram (*ordinary paper*) (1.10.41)	..	6·00	48·00
40		25 c. dull purple and scarlet (1.4.36)	..	80	1·40
41		30 c. dull purple and orange (1.1.36)	..	80	1·10
42		40 c. scarlet and dull purple	..	75	2·00
43		50 c. black/*emerald* (1.2.36)	..	3·25	1·75
44		$1 black and red/*blue* (1.4.36) ..	..	2·25	7·00
45		$2 green and scarlet (16.5.36) ..	..	18·00	26·00
46		$5 green and red/*emerald* (16.5.36)	..	8·00	50·00
29/46		.. ..	*Set of* 18	55·00	£170
29/46 Perf "Specimen"			*Set of* 18	£190	

A 2 c. orange and a 6 c. grey were prepared but not officially issued. (*Price mint* £4 *each*).

During shortages in 1941 stamps of STRAITS SETTLE-MENTS (2 c.), SELANGOR (2 c., 8 c.) and PERAK (2 c.) were issued in Pahang.

1948 (1 Dec). *Royal Silver Wedding. As Nos.* 143/4 *of Jamaica.*

47		10 c. violet	.. ..	15	60
48		$5 green	.. ..	22·00	40·00

1949 (10 Oct). *75th Anniv of U.P.U. As Nos.* 145/8 *of Jamaica.*

49		10 c. purple	.. .. ..	30	20
50		15 c. deep blue ..	.. ..	65	70
51		25 c. orange	.. .. ..	35	1·10
52		50 c. blue-black	.. ..	70	2·00
49/52 ..		.. .. ..	*Set of* 4	1·75	3·50

1950 (1 June)–**56.** *Wmk Mult Script CA. Chalk-surfaced paper.* P 17½×18.

53	**16**	1 c. black	.. .. ..	10	10
54		2 c. orange	.. .. ..	10	10
55		3 c. green	.. .. ..	20	25
56		4 c. brown	.. .. ..	15	10
		a. Chocolate (24.3.54) ..	..	3·50	1·50
57		5 c. bright purple (1.9.52)	..	25	50
		a. Bright mauve (10.9.53)	..	25	15
58		6 c. grey	.. .. ..	15	10
59		8 c. scarlet	.. .. ..	20	1·00
60		8 c. green (1.9.52)	.. ..	85	75
61		10 c. magenta	.. .. ..	15	10
62		12 c. scarlet (1.9.52)	.. ..	85	1·25
63		15 c. ultramarine	.. ..	30	10
64		20 c. black and green	.. ..	25	2·25
65		20 c. bright blue (1.9.52)	..	75	10
		a. Ultramarine (8.3.56)	..	3·75	2·25
66		25 c. purple and orange	.. ..	30	10
67		30 c. scarlet and brown-purple (5.9.55)	..	1·25	35
		a. Scarlet and purple (8.3.56) ..	..	8·00	3·00
68		35 c. scarlet and purple (1.9.52)	..	60	25
69		40 c. red and purple	.. ..	90	7·00
70		50 c. black and blue	.. ..	75	10
71		$1 blue and purple	.. ..	2·50	2·00
72		$2 green and scarlet	.. ..	13·00	18·00
73		$5 green and brown	.. ..	55·00	38·00
		a. Green and sepia (24.3.54)	..	70·00	70·00
53/73		.. .. ..	*Set of* 21	70·00	60·00

STAMP BOOKLETS

1935. *Stapled.*

SB1		$1 booklet containing twenty 5 c. (No. 33) in blocks of 10	
SB2		$1.30, booklet containing 5 c. and 8 c. (Nos. 33, 35) each in block of 10	

PENANG

1948 (1 Dec). *Royal Silver Wedding. As Nos.* 143/4 *of Jamaica.*

1		10 c. violet	.. .. ..	30	20
2		$5 brown	.. ..	30·00	26·00

1949 (21 Feb)–**52.** *As T* 58 *of Straits Settlements, but inscr* "PENANG" *at foot. Wmk Mult Script CA. Chalk-surfaced paper.* P 17½ × 18.

3		1 c. black	.. .. ..	10	10
4		2 c. orange	.. .. ..	10	10
5		3 c. green	.. .. ..	10	30
6		4 c. brown	.. .. ..	10	10
7		5 c. bright purple (1.9.52)	.. ..	40	1·00
8		6 c. grey	.. .. ..	15	10
9		8 c. scarlet	.. .. ..	30	2·75
10		8 c. green (1.9.52)	.. ..	80	1·00
11		10 c. purple	.. .. ..	15	10
12		12 c. scarlet (1.9.52)	.. ..	80	2·25
13		15 c. ultramarine	.. ..	20	30
14		20 c. black and green	.. ..	20	1·00
15		20 c. bright blue (1.9.52)	..	55	30
16		25 c. purple and orange	..	75	10
17		35 c. scarlet and purple (1.9.52)	..	60	80
18		40 c. red and purple	.. ..	75	7·00
19		50 c. black and blue	.. ..	1·00	15
20		$1 blue and purple ..	..	11·00	1·50
21		$2 green and scarlet..	..	12·00	1·75
22		$5 green and brown ..	..	48·00	1·75
3/22		.. ..	*Set of* 20	70·00	20·00

1949 (10 Oct). *75th Anniv of U.P.U. As Nos.* 145/8 *of Jamaica.*

23		10 c. purple	.. .. ..	20	10
24		15 c. deep blue ..	.. ..	90	75
25		25 c. orange	.. .. ..	45	1·25
26		50 c. blue-black	.. ..	1·50	2·00
23/6		.. .. ..	*Set of* 4	2·75	3·50

PERAK

50   Sultan Iskandar   51

1935 (2 Dec)–**37.** *Chalk-surfaced paper. Wmk Mult Script CA.* P 14.

88	**50**	1 c. black (1.1.36)..	.. .. ..	30	10
89		2 c. green (1.1.36)..	.. ..	30	10
90		4 c. orange	.. .. ..	30	10
91		5 c. brown (5.12.35)	.. ..	30	10
92		6 c. scarlet (1.1.37)	.. ..	7·50	2·75
93		8 c. grey	.. .. ..	50	10
94		10 c. dull purple (1.1.36) ..	..	30	15
95		12 c. bright ultramarine (1.1.36) ..	..	70	90
96		25 c. dull purple and scarlet (1.4.36)	..	85	85
97		30 c. dull purple and orange (1.1.36)	..	90	1·50
98		40 c. scarlet and dull purple	..	2·50	4·25
99		50 c. black/*emerald* (1.2.36)	..	3·50	90
100		$1 black and red/*blue* (1.4.36) ..	..	2·00	90
101		$2 green and scarlet (16.5.36) ..	..	15·00	8·50
102		$5 green and red/*emerald* (16.5.36)	..	50·00	45·00
88/102		.. ..	*Set of* 15	75·00	45·00
88/102 Perf "Specimen"			*Set of* 15	£160	

No. 91 exists in coils constructed from normal sheets in 1936.

1938 (2 May)–**41.** *Wmk Mult Script CA. Chalk-surfaced paper.* P 14.

103	**51**	1 c. black (4.39)	.. .. ..	4·25	10
104		2 c. green (13.1.39)	.. ..	2·75	10
105		2 c. orange (30.10.41)	.. ..	1·50	6·00
		a. Ordinary paper	.. ..	2·00	14·00
106		3 c. green (21.8.41)	.. ..	1·75	3·25

107	**51**	4 c. orange (5.39)	.. .. ..	30·00	10
108		5 c. brown (1.2.39)	.. .. ..	3·50	10
109		6 c. scarlet (12.39)	.. .. ..	25·00	10
110		8 c. grey (1.12.38)	.. .. ..	22·00	10
111		8 c. scarlet (18.12.41)	.. ..	1·00	55·00
112		10 c. dull purple (17.10.38)	..	22·00	10
113		12 c. bright ultramarine (17.10.38)	..	20·00	2·00
114		15 c. brt ultram (*ordinary paper*) (8.41)	1·75	13·00
115		25 c. dull purple and scarlet (12.39)	..	80·00	4·25
116		30 c. dull purple and orange (17.10.38)	9·50	3·00
117		40 c. scarlet and dull purple	.. ..	50·00	2·00
118		50 c. black/*emerald* (17.10.38)	..	26·00	75
119		$1 black and *blue* (7.40)	.. ..	£130	14·00
120		$2 green and scarlet (9.40)	.. ..	£130	55·00
121		$5 green and red/*emerald* (1.41)	..	£180	£225
103/21			*Set of* 19	£650	£350
103/21 Perf "Specimen"	..	..	*Set of* 19	£300	

No. 108 exists in coils constructed from normal sheets.

During shortages in 1941 stamps of STRAITS SETTLE-MENTS (2 c.), SELANGOR (2 c., 3 c.) and PAHANG (8 c.) were issued in Perak.

1948 (1 Dec). *Royal Silver Wedding. As Nos. 143/4 of Jamaica.*

122	10 c. violet	.. ..	15	10
123	$5 green	.. .. ..	20·00	24·00

1949 (10 Oct). *75th Anniv of U.P.U. As Nos. 145/8 of Jamaica.*

124	10 c. purple	.. ..	15	10
125	15 c. deep blue..	.. .. ..	70	60
126	25 c. orange	.. .. ..	45	45
127	50 c. blue-black	.. .. ..	1·75	2·25
124/7	.. ..	..	*Set of* 4	2·75	3·00

52 Sultan Yussuf 'Izzuddin Shah   **53** Sultan Idris Shah

1950 (17 Aug)–**56**. *Chalk-surfaced paper. Wmk Mult Script CA. P* 17½×18.

128	**52**	1 c. black	.. ..	10	10
129		2 c. orange	.. .. ..	10	10
130		3 c. green	.. .. ..	1·50	10
		a. Yellowish green (15.11.51)	..	3·50	3·50
131		4 c. brown	.. .. ..	10	10
		a. Yellow-brown (20.6.56)	..	2·00	10
132		5 c. bright purple (1.9.52)	..	50	80
		a. Bright mauve (10.11.54)	..	1·25	80
133		6 c. grey	.. .. ..	10	10
134		8 c. scarlet	.. .. ..	30	75
135		8 c. green (1.9.52)	.. ..	1·00	60
136		10 c. purple	.. .. ..	10	10
		a. Brown-purple (20.6.56)	..	2·50	30
137		12 c. scarlet (1.9.52)	.. ..	1·00	2·00
138		15 c. ultramarine	.. ..	30	10
139		20 c. black and green	.. ..	30	30
140		20 c. bright blue (1.9.52)	..	75	10
141		25 c. purple and orange	..	30	10
142		30 c. scarlet and purple (5.9.55)	..	1·25	20
143		35 c. scarlet and purple (1.9.52)	..	70	25
144		40 c. red and purple	.. ..	1·50	3·50
145		50 c. black and blue	.. ..	55	10
146		$1 blue and purple	.. ..	7·00	30
147		$2 green and scarlet	.. ..	13·00	4·00
148		$5 green and brown	.. ..	38·00	11·00
128/48	.. ..	*Set of* 21	60·00	21·00

STAMP BOOKLETS

1935.
SB1 $1 booklet containing twenty 5 c. (No. 91) in
     blocks of 10 .. ..
SB2 $1.30, booklet containing 5 c. and 8 c. (Nos. 91,
     93), each in block of 10 .. .. ..

1938.
SB3 $1 booklet containing twenty 5 c. (No. 108) in
     blocks of 10 .. ..
SB4 $1.30, booklet containing 5 c. and 8 c. (Nos. 108,
     110), each in block of 10 .. .. ..

PERLIS

1948 (1 Dec). *Royal Silver Wedding. As Nos. 143/4 of Jamaica.*

1	10 c. violet	.. ..	30	1·75
2	$5 brown	.. ..	28·00	42·00

1949 (10 Oct). *75th Anniv of U.P.U. As Nos. 145/8 of Jamaica.*

3	10 c. purple	.. ..	30	60
4	15 c. deep blue..	.. .. ..	1·00	3·00
5	25 c. orange	.. ..	45	2·00
6	50 c. blue-black	.. .. ..	1·40	3·75
3/6	.. ..	*Set of* 4	3·00	8·50

1 Raja Syed Putra   **2** *Vanda hookeriana*

1951 (26 Mar)–**55**. *Chalk-surfaced paper. Wmk Mult Script CA. P* 17½ × 18.

7	**1**	1 c. black	.. ..	10	80
8		2 c. orange	.. .. ..	15	40
9		3 c. green	.. .. ..	50	2·50
10		4 c. brown..	.. .. ..	60	30
11		5 c. bright purple (1.9.52)	..	30	1·50
12		6 c. grey	.. .. ..	60	1·00
13		8 c. scarlet	.. .. ..	1·00	3·75
14		8 c. green (1.9.52)..	.. ..	75	2·00
15		10 c. purple	.. .. ..	30	20
16		12 c. scarlet (1.9.52)	.. ..	75	2·50
17		15 c. ultramarine	.. ..	1·50	2·50
18		20 c. black and green	.. ..	80	4·50
19		20 c. bright blue (1.9.52)	..	85	65
20		25 c. purple and orange	..	1·00	1·25
21		30 c. scarlet and purple (5.9.55)	..	1·75	8·00
22		35 c. scarlet and purple (1.9.52)	..	75	3·00
23		40 c. red and purple	.. ..	1·50	13·00
24		50 c. black and blue	.. ..	2·25	3·25
25		$1 blue and purple	.. ..	4·50	11·00
26		$2 green and scarlet	.. ..	12·00	18·00
27		$5 green and brown	.. ..	50·00	55·00
7/27	.. ..	*Set of* 21	75·00	£120

SELANGOR

46 Mosque at Palace,   **47** Sultan Suleiman
     Klang

(Des E. J. McNaughton)

1935 (2 Dec)–**41**. *Wmk Mult Script CA* (*sideways on T* **46**). *Chalk-surfaced paper. P* 14 *or* 14×14½ (*No.* 70).

68	**46**	1 c. black (1.1.36)	.. ..	30	1C
69		2 c. green (1.1.36)	.. ..	60	1C
70		2 c. orange (*ordinary paper*) (*p* 14×14½)		
		(21.8.41)	.. .. ..	2·25	1·1
		a. Perf 14. Ordinary paper (9.41)	..	20·00	6·5
		ab. Chalk-surfaced paper	..	24·00	6·5
71		3 c. green (21.8.41)	.. ..	11·00	2·7
		a. Ordinary paper	.. ..	75	7·0

72	**46**	4 c. orange	30	10
73		5 c. brown (5.12.35)	60	10
74		6 c. scarlet (1.1.37)	4·50	10
75		8 c. grey	50	10
76		10 c. dull purple (1.1.36)	50	10
77		12 c. bright ultramarine (1.1.36) ..	1·50	10
78		15 c. brt ultram (*ordinary paper*) (1.10.41)	7·50	32·00
79		25 c. dull purple and scarlet (1.4.36) ..	1·50	60
80		30 c. dull purple and orange (1.1.36) ..	1·25	85
81		40 c. scarlet and dull purple	1·75	1·25
82		50 c. black/*emerald* (1.2.36)	1·50	15
83	**47**	$1 black and rose/*blue* (1.4.36) ..	4·75	50
84		$2 green and scarlet (16.5.36) ..	18·00	7·50
85		$5 green and red/*emerald* (16.5.36)	48·00	23·00
68/85		.. .. .. *Set of* 18	85·00	60·00
68/85 Perf "Specimen" .. .. *Set of* 18			£250	

Supplies of an unissued 8 c. scarlet were diverted to Australia in 1941. Examples circulating result from leakages of this supply (*Price* £350).

48   Sultan Hisamud-din Alam Shah   49

1941. *Wmk Mult Script CA. Chalk-surfaced paper. P* 14.

86	**48**	$1 black and red/*blue* (15.4.41) ..	9·50	5·50
87		$2 green and scarlet (7.7.41) (Perf S. £70)	48·00	27·00

A $5 green and red on emerald, T **48**, was issued overprinted during the Japanese occupation of Malaya. Unoverprinted examples are known, but were not issued (*Price* £95).

During shortages in 1941 stamps of STRAITS SETTLE-MENTS (2 c.) and PERAK (25 c.) were issued in Selangor.

1948 (1 Dec). *Royal Silver Wedding. As Nos.* 143/4 *of Jamaica.*

88		10 c. violet	20	10
89		$5 green	23·00	14·00

1949 (12 Sept)–**55.** *Wmk Mult Script CA. Chalk-surfaced paper. P* 17½×18.

90	**49**	1 c. black	10	10
91		2 c. orange	10	10
92		3 c. green	30	1·25
93		4 c. brown	10	10
94		5 c. bright purple (1.9.52)	30	80
		a. Bright mauve (17.9.53)	30	10
95		6 c. grey	10	10
96		8 c. scarlet	25	65
97		8 c. green (1.9.52)	65	80
98		10 c. purple	10	10
99		12 c. scarlet (1.9.52)	80	2·25
		w. Wmk inverted	£150	
100		15 c. ultramarine	1·00	10
101		20 c. black and green	30	10
102		20 c. bright blue (1.9.52)	80	10
103		25 c. purple and orange	75	10
104		30 c. scarlet and purple (5.9.55) ..	1·25	80
105		35 c. scarlet and purple (1.9.52) ..	70	90
106		40 c. scarlet and purple	2·50	2·75
107		50 c. black and blue	70	10
108		$1 blue and purple	2·75	20
109		$2 green and scarlet	8·50	30
110		$5 green and brown	45·00	1·50
90/110		.. .. .. *Set of* 21	60·00	10·50

1949 (10 Oct). *75th Anniv of U.P.U. As Nos.* 145/8 *of Jamaica.*

111		10 c. purple	30	10
112		15 c. deep blue	75	65
113		25 c. orange	50	2·00
114		50 c. blue-black	1·90	1·50
111/14		.. .. .. *Set of* 4	3·00	3·75

STAMP BOOKLETS

1935. *Stapled.*

SB1	$1 booklet containing twenty 5 c. (No. 73) in blocks of 10	
SB2	$1.30, booklet containing 5 c. and 8 c. (Nos. 73, 75), each in block of 10	

TRENGGANU

4   Sultan Suleiman   5

2 CENTS

(6)

1924–38. *New values, etc. Wmk Mult Script CA. Chalk-surfaced paper. P* 14.

48	**4**	1 c. black (1926)	1·25	70
49		3 c. green (1926)	1·50	75
50		3 c. reddish brown (1938) ..	17·00	8·50
		a. Chestnut	—	8·50
51		5 c. purple/*yellow* (1926) ..	1·75	60
52		6 c. orange	2·50	30
53		8 c. grey (1938)	17·00	3·25
54		12 c. bright ultramarine (1926) ..	4·25	3·25
55		35 c. carmine/*yellow* (1926) ..	4·50	8·00
56		$1 purple and blue/*blue* (1929) ..	9·00	3·50
57		$3 green and lake/*green* (1926) ..	50·00	90·00
		a. Green and brown-red/green ..		
58	**5**	$5 green and red/*yellow* (1938) ..	£250	£1200
48/58		.. .. .. *Set of* 11	£325	£1200
48/58 Optd/Perf "Specimen" .. *Set of* 11			£300	

The 2 c. yellow, 6 c. grey, 8 c. red and 15 c. blue were prepared, but not officially issued (*Price* £110 *each, unused*).

The used price for No. 58 is for an example with an identifiable cancellation from the 1938–41 period.

1941 (1 May). *Nos.* 51 *and* 29 *surch as T* **6.**

59	**4**	2 c. on 5 c. purple/*yellow* ..	6·00	3·50
60		8 c. on 10 c. bright blue	7·00	3·50

1948 (2 Dec). *Royal Silver Wedding. As Nos.* 143/4 *of Jamaica.*

61		10 c. violet	15	60
62		$5 carmine	20·00	32·00

1949 (10 Oct). *75th Anniv of U.P.U. As Nos.* 145/8 *of Jamaica.*

63		10 c. purple	30	35
64		15 c. deep blue	75	1·60
65		25 c. orange	55	2·25
66		50 c. blue-black	1·40	2·50
63/6		.. .. .. *Set of* 4	2·75	6·00

7 Sultan Ismail   8 *Vanda hookeriana*

1949 (27 Dec)–**55.** *Wmk Mult Script CA. Chalk-surfaced paper. P* 17½×18.

67	**7**	1 c. black	10	20
68		2 c. orange	10	20
69		3 c. green	30	2·00
70		4 c. brown	10	20
71		5 c. bright purple (1.9.52) ..	30	70
72		6 c. grey	15	30
73		8 c. scarlet	20	1·50
74		8 c. green (1.9.52)	65	1·00
		a. Deep green (11.8.53) ..	2·75	4·00

75	7	10 c. purple				15	10
76		12 c. scarlet (1.9.52)				65	1·75
77		15 c. ultramarine				30	30
78		20 c. black and green				30	2·00
79		20 c. bright blue (1.9.52)				80	30
80		25 c. purple and orange				40	75
81		30 c. scarlet and purple (5.9.55)				1·25	1·25
82		35 c. scarlet and purple (1.9.52)				70	1·40
83		40 c. red and purple				2·25	11·00
84		50 c. black and blue				50	1·10
85		$1 blue and purple				3·00	4·25
86		$2 green and scarlet				16·00	13·00
87		$5 green and brown				50·00	42·00
67/87					Set of 21	70·00	75·00

POSTAGE DUE STAMPS

D 1

1937 (10 Aug). *Wmk Mult Script CA. P* 14.

D1	D 1	1 c. scarlet					7·50	50·00
D2		4 c. green					8·00	55·00
D3		8 c. yellow					50·00	£250
D4		10 c. brown					£100	90·00
D1/4					Set of 4		£150	£400
D1/4 Perf "Specimen"				Set of 4		£130	

POSTAGE DUE STAMPS

(1) (Upright)   (2)   Second character sideways (R.6/3)

1942 (Apr). *Nos.* D1/5 *of Johore optd as T* 1. A. *In brown.* B. *In black.*

					A	B
JD1	D 1	1 c. carmine			80·00	— 35·00 80·00
JD2		4 c. green			80·00	— 60·00 80·00
JD3		8 c. orange			£110	— 75·00 90·00
JD4		10 c. brown			38·00	— 15·00 50·00
JD5		12 c. purple			48·00	— 25·00 50·00

1943. *Nos.* D1/5 *of Johore optd with T* 2.

JD 6	D 1	1 c. carmine			2·75	16·00
		a. Second character sideways			£110	£225
JD 7		4 c. green			3·75	16·00
		a. Second character sideways			£130	£225
JD 8		8 c. orange			4·00	18·00
		a. Second character sideways			£160	£275
JD 9		10 c. brown			3·50	22·00
		a. Second character sideways			£160	£300
JD10		12 c. purple			4·50	30·00
		a. Second character sideways			£170	£350

JAPANESE OCCUPATION OF MALAYA

Japanese forces invaded Malaya on 8 December 1941 with the initial landings taking place at Kota Bharu on the east coast. Penang fell, to a force which crossed the border from Thailand, on 19 December, Kuala Lumpur on 11 January 1942 and the conquest of the Malay penisula was completed by the capture of Singapore on 15 February.

During the Japanese Occupation various small Dutch East Indies islands near Singapore were administered as part of Malaya. Stamps of the Japanese Occupation of Malaya were issued to the post offices of Dabo Singkep, Puloe Samboe, Tanjong Balei, Tanjong Batu, Tanjong Pinang and Terempa between 1942 and 1945. The overprinted issues were also used by a number of districts in Northern Sumatra whose postal services were administered from Singapore until the end of March 1943.

Malayan post offices were also opened in October 1943 to serve camps of civilians working on railway construction and maintenance in Thailand. Overprinted stamps of the Japanese Occupation of Malaya were used at these offices between October 1943 and the end of the year after which mail from the camps was carried free. Their postmarks were inscribed in Japanese Katakana characters, and, uniquely, showed the Japanese postal symbol.

JOHORE

The postal service in Johore was reconstituted in mid-April 1942 using Nos. J146/60 and subsequently other general issues. Stamps of Johore overprinted "DAI NIPPON 2602" were, however, only used for fiscal purposes. Overprinted Johore postage due stamps were not issued for use elsewhere in Malaya.

KEDAH

Postal services resumed on 10 February 1942 using unoverprinted Kedah values from 1 c. to 8 c.

During the Japanese occupation Perlis was administered as part of Kedah.

DAI NIPPON   DAI NIPPON

2602   2602

(3)   (4)

1942 (13 May)–43. *Stamps of Kedah (Script wmk) optd with T* 3 (1 *c. to* 8 *c.*) *or* 4 (10 *c. to* $5), *both in red.*

J 1	1	1 c. black				3·00	4·25
J 2		2 c. bright green				24·00	30·00
J 3		4 c. violet				3·50	4·00
J 4		5 c. yellow				2·25	3·25
		a. Black opt (1943)				£200	£225
J 5		6 c. carmine-red (Blk.)				1·90	6·00
J 6		8 c. grey-black				2·75	1·75
J 7	6	10 c. ultramarine and sepia				7·00	7·00
J 8		12 c. black and violet				17·00	22·00
J 9		25 c. ultramarine and purple				5·50	9·00
		a. Black opt (1943)				£250	£250
J10		30 c. green and scarlet				65·00	75·00
J11		40 c. black and purple				22·00	32·00
J12		50 c. brown and blue				24·00	35·00
J13		$1 black and green				£130	£150
		a. Opt inverted				£500	£550
J14		$2 green and brown				£150	£160
J15		$5 black and scarlet				60·00	70·00
		a. Black opt (1943)				£700	£750

Nos. J1/15 were gradually replaced by issues intended for use throughout Malaya. Kedah and Perlis were ceded to Thailand by the Japanese on 19 October 1943.

KELANTAN

Postal services resumed on 1 June 1942. Stamps used in Kelantan were overprinted with the personal seals of Sunagawa, the Japanese Governor, and of Handa, the Assistant Governor.

(5) Sunagawa Seal   (6) Handa Seal

40 CENTS   **$1.00**

(7)   (8)

1 Cents

(9)

1942 (June). *Stamps of Kelantan surch*

  (a) *As T **7** or **8** (dollar values). Optd with T **5** in red*

				Un.	Used
J16	4	1 c. on 50 c. grey-olive and orange	..	£200	£180
J17		2 c. on 40 c. orange and blue-green	..	£325	£250
J18		4 c. on 30 c. violet and scarlet	..	£1100	£1100
J19		5 c. on 12 c. blue (R.)	..	£190	£180
J20		6 c. on 25 c. vermilion and violet	..	£200	£190
J21		8 c. on 5 c. red-brown (R.)	..	£250	£140
J22		10 c. on 6 c. lake	..	75·00	£120
J23		12 c. on 8 c. grey-olive (R.)	..	48·00	£110
J24		25 c. on 10 c. purple (R.)	..	£1000	£1100
J25		30 c. on 4 c. scarlet	..	£1600	£1700
J26		40 c. on 2 c. green (R.)	..	50·00	85·00
J27		50 c. on 1 c. grey-olive and yellow	..	£1200	£1100
J28	1	$1 on 4 c. black & red (R., bars Blk.)		50·00	75·00
J29		$2 on 5 c. green and red/*yellow*		50·00	75·00
J30		$5 on 6 c. scarlet	..	50·00	75·00

  (b) *As T **7**. Optd with T **6** in red.*

J31	4	12 c. on 8 c. grey-olive (R.)	..	£120	£180

  (c) *As T **9**. Optd with T **5** in red.*

J32	4	1 c. on 50 c. grey-olive and orange	..	£110	85·00
		a. "Cente" for "Cents" (R. 5/1)	..	£850	£700
J33		2 c. on 40 c. orange and blue-green	..	£110	90·00
		a. "Cente" for "Cents" (R. 5/1)	..	£850	
J34		5 c. on 12 c. blue (R.)	..	95·00	£100
		a. "Cente" for "Cents" (R. 5/1)	..	£750	
J35		8 c. on 5 c. red-brown (R.)	..	95·00	70·00
		a. "Cente" for "Cents" (R. 5/1)	..	£750	£600
J36		10 c. on 6 c. lake ..	..	£150	£160
		a. "Cente" for "Cents" (R. 5/1)	..	£1200	
J37		12 c. on 8 c. grey-olive (R.)	..	£275	£300
		a. "Cente" for "Cents" (R. 5/1)	..	£1500	
J38		30 c. on 4 c. scarlet	..	£1400	£1500
		a. "Cente" for "Cents" (R. 5/1)	..		
J39		40 c. on 2 c. green (R.)	..	£300	£325
		a. "Cente" for "Cents" (R. 5/1)	..	£1600	
J40		50 c. on 1 c. grey-olive and yellow	..	£800	£850
		a. "Cente" for "Cents" (R. 5/1)	..		

  (d) *As T **9**. Optd with T **6** in red.*

J41	4	1 c. on 50 c. grey-olive and orange	..	85·00	£120
		a. "Cente" for "Cents" (R. 5/1)	..	£700	
J42		2 c. on 40 c. orange and blue-green	..	85·00	£130
		a. "Cente" for "Cents" (R. 5/1)	..	£700	
J43		8 c. on 5 c. red-brown (R.)	..	60·00	£110
		a. "Cente" for "Cents" (R. 5/1)	..	£600	
J44		10 c. on 6 c. lake	..	80·00	£130
		a. "Cente" for "Cents" (R. 5/1)	..	£700	

As stamps of the above series became exhausted the equivalent values from the series intended for use throughout Malaya were introduced. Stamps as Nos. J28/30, J32/3 and J35/40, but without Type **5** or **6**, are from remainders sent to Singapore or Kuala Lumpur after the state had been ceded to Thailand (*Price from £15 each unused*).

Kelantan was ceded to Thailand by the Japanese on 19 October 1943.

MALACCA

Postal services from Malacca resumed on 21 April 1942, but there were no stamps available for two days.

PRICES. Those quoted are for single stamps. Blocks of four showing the complete handstamp are worth from six times the price of a single stamp.

(10) Seal of the Government Office of the Malacca Military Dept

1942 (23 Apr). *Stamps of Straits Settlemexmts handstamped as T **10**, in red, each impression covering four stamps.*

							Single
						Un.	*Used*
J45	58	1 c. black	..	..	..	75·00	65·00
J46		2 c. orange	..	..	..	55·00	65·00
J47		3 c. green	..	..	..	55·00	65·00
J48		5 c. brown	..	..	..	£100	£110
J49		8 c. grey..	..	..	..	£160	£100
J50		10 c. dull purple ..	..	..	65·00	70·00
J51		12 c. ultramarine	..	..	90·00	95·00
J52		15 c. ultramarine	..	..	60·00	70·00
J53		40 c. scarlet and dull purple	..	£550	£600
J54		50 c. black/*emerald*	..	..	£800	£800
J55		$1 black and red/*blue* ..	..	£900	£850

The 30c., $2 and $5 also exist with this overprint, but these values were not available to the public.

POSTAGE DUE STAMPS

1942 (23 Apr). *Postage Due stamps of Malayan Postal Union handstamped as T **10**, in red, each impression covering four stamps.*

JD11	D 1	1 c. slate-purple	..	..	..	£150	£150
JD12		4 c. green	..	..	..	£225	£225
JD13		8 c. scarlet	..	..	..	£1500	£1300
JD14		10 c. yellow-orange	..	..	£275	£275
JD15		12 c. ultramarine	..	..	£450	£450
JD16		15 c. black	..	..	..	£1400	£1200

Nos. J45/55 and JD11/16 were replaced during May 1942 by the overprinted issues intended for use throughout Malaya.

PENANG

Postal services on Penang Island resumed on 30 March 1942 using Straits Settlements stamps overprinted by Japanese seals.

DAI NIPPON

2602

PENANG

(11) Okugawa Seal   (12) Ochiburi Seal   (13)

1942 (30 Mar). *Straits Settlements stamps optd.*

(a) *As T* **11** (*three forms of the seal*)

J56	**58**	1 c. black	..	..	..	9·50 11·00
J57		2 c. orange		..	..	24·00 22·00
J58		3 c. green		..	..	20·00 22·00
J59		5 c. brown	..	..	..	24·00 24·00
J60		8 c. grey	..	..	..	26·00 26·00
J61		10 c. dull purple	..		..	45·00 45·00
J62		12 c. ultramarine		..		26·00 30·00
J63		15 c. ultramarine		..		28·00 38·00
J64		40 c. scarlet and dull purple		..		90·00 95·00
J65		50 c. black/*emerald*	..			£160 £170
J66		$1 black and red/*blue*	..			£180 £190
J67		$2 green and scarlet		..		£425 £450
J68		$5 green and red/*emerald*		..		£1200 £1300

(b) *With T* **12**

J69	**58**	1 c. black		..	..	85·00 85·00
J70		2 c. orange		..	..	85·00 85·00
J71		3 c. green		..	..	80·00 85·00
J72		5 c. brown		..		£850 £850
J73		8 c. grey		..	..	50·00 65·00
J74		10 c. dull purple	..		..	75·00 85·00
J75		12 c. ultramarine		..		70·00 80·00
J76		15 c. ultramarine		..		70·00 80·00

Straits Settlements stamps overprinted with a similar seal impression, but circular and containing four characters, are believed to be fiscal issues.

1942 (15 Apr). *Straits Settlements stamps optd with T* **13**.

J77	**58**	1 c. black (R.)	..	..		1·50 1·50
		a. Opt inverted		..		£250 £250
		b. Opt double		..		£250 £250
J78		2 c. orange	..		..	3·75 2·75
		a. "PE" for "PENANG"		..		80·00 75·00
		b. Opt inverted		..		£150
		c. Opt double		..		£275
J79		3 c. green (R.)	..		..	2·50 1·75
		a. Opt double, one inverted	..		£250
J80		5 c. brown (R.) ..		..		1·50 3·00
		a. "N PPON"		..		£140
		b. Opt double		..		£250
J81		8 c. grey (R.)	..		..	2·25 1·40
		a. "N PPON"	..		..	48·00 55·00
		b. Opt double, one inverted			£250
J82		10 c. dull purple (R.)		..		1·50 2·00
		a. Opt double		..		£275 £275
		b. Opt double, one inverted			£400 £400
J83		12 c. ultramarine (R.)		..		2·25 8·00
		a. "N PPON"		..		£325
		b. Opt double		..		£325
		c. Opt double, one inverted		£400 £425
J84		15 c. ultramarine (R.)		..		1·75 2·00
		a. "N PPON"		..		£100 £110
		b. Opt inverted		..		£400 £400
		c. Opt double	..			£400
J85		40 c. scarlet and dull purple			3·00 8·00
J86		50 c. black/*emerald* (R.) ..		..	3·75 15·00
J87		$1 black and red/*blue* ..		..	6·00 22·00
J88		$2 green and scarlet	..		..	35·00 70·00
J89		$5 green and red/*emerald*		..	£400 £500

Nos. J77/89 were replaced by the overprinted issues intended for use throughout Malaya.

SELANGOR

Postal services resumed in the Kuala Lumpur area on 3 April 1942 and gradually extended to the remainder of the state. Stamps of the general overprinted issue were used, but the following commemorative set was only available in Selangor.

**SELANGOR
EXHIBITION
DAI NIPPON
2602
MALAYA**

(14)

1942 (3 Nov). *Agri-horticultural Exhibition. Nos.* 294 *and* 283 *of Straits Settlements optd with T* **14**.

J90	**58**	2 c. orange		..		12·00 23·00
		a. "C" for "G" in "SELANGOR" (R. 1/9)	£225 £275
		b. Opt inverted		..		£300 £400
J91		8 c. grey		..		13·00 23·00
		a. "C" for "G" in "SELANGOR" (R. 1/9)	£225 £275
		b. Opt inverted		..		£300 £400

SINGAPORE

The first post offices re-opened in Singapore on 16 March 1942.

(15) Seal of
Post Office of
Malayan
Military Dept

(Handstamped at Singapore)

1942 (16 Mar). *Stamps of Straits Settlements optd with T* **15** *in red.*

J92	**58**	1 c. black		..	..	10·00 15·00
J93		2 c. orange		..	..	10·00 13·00
		a. Pair, one without handstamp		£900
J94		3 c. green		..	..	48·00 70·00
J95		8 c. grey		..	..	22·00 18·00
J96		15 c. ultramarine		..	..	15·00 15·00

The overprint Type **15** has a double-lined frame, although the two lines are not always apparent, as in the illustration. Three chops were used, differing slightly in the shape of the characters, but forgeries also exist. It is distinguishable from Type **1**, used for the general issues, by its extra width, measuring approximately 14 mm against 12½ mm.

The 6, 10, 30, 40, 50 c., $2 and $5 also exist with this overprint, but were not sold to the public.

Nos. J92/6 were replaced on the 3 May 1942 by the stamps overprinted with Type **1** which were intended for use throughout Malaya.

TRENGGANU

Postal services resumed in Trengganu during March 1942 using unoverprinted stamps up to the 35 c. value.

1942 (Sept). *Stamps of Trengganu (Script wmk) optd as T* **1** *at Kuala Lumpur.*

J 97	**4**	1 c. black		..	..	95·00 85·00
		a. Red opt		..		£160 £180
		b. Brown opt		..		£375 £250
J 98		2 c. green		..		£140 £140
		a. Red opt		..		£180 £200
		b. Brown opt		..		£400 £300
J 99		2 c. on 5 c. purple/*yellow* (No. 59)	60·00 75·00
		a. Red opt		..		45·00 70·00
J100		3 c. chestnut		..		80·00 80·00
		a. Brown opt		..		£425 £325
J101		4 c. scarlet-vermilion		..		£140 £140
J102		5 c. purple/*yellow*		..		10·00 17·00
		a. Red opt		..		19·00
J103		6 c. orange		..		8·50 22·00
		a. Red opt		..		50·00
		b. Brown opt	..			£350 £350
J104		8 c. grey ..		..		9·00 13·00
		a. Brown to red opt		..		50·00 65·00

J105   4   8 c. on 10 c. bright blue (No. 60)   .. 13·00   30·00
     a. Red opt   ..   ..   ..   21·00
J106   10 c. bright blue ..   ..   .. 13·00   23·00
     a. Red opt   ..   ..   ..   55·00
     b. Brown opt £350   £350
J107   12 c. bright ultramarine..   ..   8·00   24·00
     a. Red opt   ..   ..   ..   27·00
J108   20 c. dull purple and orange   ..   8·50   22·00
     a. Red opt   ..   ..   20·00
J109   25 c. green and deep purple   ..   7·50   26·00
     a. Red opt   ..   ..   22·00
     b. Brown opt £350   £350
J110   30 c. dull purple and black   ..   8·00   22·00
     a. Red opt   ..   ..   22·00
J111   35 c. carmine/*yellow*   ..   .. 17·00   28·00
     a. Red opt   ..   ..   20·00
J112   50 c. green and bright carmine ..   60·00   70·00
J113 $1 purple and blue £1800 £1800
J114 $3 green and brown-red/*green*   48·00   80·00
     a. Red opt   ..   ..   ..   60·00
J115   5 $5 green and red/*yellow*   ..   £130   £180
J116 $25 purple and blue £850
     a. Red opt £2250
J117 $50 green and yellow   ..   £6000
J118 $100 green and scarlet   ..   £900

DAI NIPPON

2602

MALAYA

(16)

1942 (Sept). *Stamps of Trengganu (Script wmk) optd with*
T **16.**
J119   4   1 c. black   ..   ..   ..   11·00   10·00
J120   2 c. green £160   £180
J121   2 c. on 5 c. purple/*yellow* (No. 59)   ..   6·00   8·00
J122   3 c. chestnut   ..   ..   ..   9·00   14·00
J123   4 c. scarlet-vermilion   ..   ..   8·50   11·00
J124   5 c. purple/*yellow*   ..   ..   5·50   10·00
J125   6 c. orange   ..   ..   5·00   11·00
J126   8 c. grey   ..   ..   ..   70·00   22·00
J127   8 c. on 10 c. bright blue (No. 60)   ..   5·50   10·00
J128   12 c. bright ultramarine   ..   5·00   15·00
J129   20 c. dull purple and orange   ..   8·00   13·00
J130   25 c. green and deep purple   ..   7·00   23·00
J131   30 c. dull purple and black   ..   7·50   20·00
J132 $3 green and brown-red/*green*   ..   60·00   £110

1943. *Stamps of Trengganu (Script wmk) optd with T* **2.**
J133   4   1 c. black   ..   ..   ..   8·00   16·00
J134   2 c. green   ..   ..   ..   7·00   21·00
J135   2 c. on 5 c. purple/*yellow* (No. 59)   ..   6·00   18·00
J136   5 c. purple/*yellow*   ..   ..   6·50   21·00
J137   6 c. orange   ..   ..   ..   8·00   24·00
J138   8 c. grey..   ..   ..   ..   55·00   70·00
J139   8 c. on 10 c. bright blue (No. 60)   ..   17·00   35·00
J140   10 c. bright blue ..   ..   75·00   £160
J141   12 c. bright ultramarine..   ..   11·00   30·00
J142   20 c. dull purple and orange   ..   11·00   30·00
J143   25 c. green and deep purple   ..   10·00   32·00
J144   30 c. dull purple and black   ..   13·00   35·00
J145   35 c. carmine/*yellow*   ..   ..   13·00   38·00

POSTAGE DUE STAMPS

1942 (Sept). *Nos. D1/4 of Trengganu optd with T* **1** *sideways.*
JD17   D **1**   1 c. scarlet   ..   ..   ..   50·00   80·00
JD18   4 c. green   ..   ..   ..   70·00   90·00
     a. Brown opt   ..   ..   ..   50·00   85·00
JD19   8 c. yellow   ..   ..   ..   14·00   50·00
JD20   10 c. brown   ..   ..   ..   14·00   50·00
The Trengganu 8 c. postage due also exists overprinted with
Type **16,** but this was not issued (*Price* £350 *unused*).

Trengganu was ceded to Thailand by the Japanese on 19
October 1943.

GENERAL ISSUES

The following stamps were produced for use throughout
Malaya, except for Trengganu.

1942 (3 Apr). *Stamps optd as T* **1.** (*a*) *On Straits Settlements.*
J146   58   1 c. black (R.) ..   ..   3·25   3·25
     a. Black opt £250   £275
     b. Violet opt £400   £400
J147   2 c. green (V.) £1400 £1400
J148   2 c. orange (R.)   ..   ..   3·00   2·25
     a. Black opt ..   ..   90·00   £100
     b. Violet opt £150   £150
     c. Brown opt £400   £400
J149   3 c. green (R.)..   ..   2·75   2·25
     a. Black opt £200   £225
     b. Violet opt £400   £400
J150   5 c. brown (R.)   ..   ..   22·00   28·00
     a. Black opt £400   £400
J151   8 c. grey (R.) ..   ..   3·50   2·25
     a. Black opt £200   £225
J152   10 c. dull purple (R.) ..   38·00   40·00
     a. Brown opt £500   £500
J153   12 c. ultramarine (R.) ..   75·00   95·00
J154   15 c. ultramarine (R.) ..   3·50   3·00
     a. Violet opt £450   £400
J155   30 c. dull purple and orange (R.) ..£1200 £1300
J156   40 c. scarlet and dull purple (R.)   75·00   90·00
     a. Brown opt £375   £300
J157   50 c. black/*emerald* (R.) ..   45·00   48·00
J158 $1 black and red/*blue* (R.) ..   75·00   75·00
J159 $2 green and scarlet (R.)   ...   £120   £130
J160 $5 green and red/*emerald* (R.) ..   £170   £180

(b) On Negri Sembilan

J161   6   1 c. black (R.)   ..   ..   19·00   13·00
     a. Violet opt   ..   ..   22·00   20·00
     b. Brown opt   ..   ..   15·00   14·00
     c. Black opt ..   ..   42·00   38·00
J162   2 c. orange (R.)   ..   ..   17·00   14·00
     a. Violet opt   ..   ..   38·00   27·00
     b. Black opt ..   ..   32·00   28·00
     c. Brown opt   ..   ..   45·00   42·00
J163   3 c. green (R.)   ..   ..   22·00   20·00
     a. Violet opt   ..   ..   23·00   29·00
     b. Violet opt (sideways)   ..   £200   £250
     c. Brown opt   ..   ..   65·00   48·00
     d. Black opt ..   ..   42·00   40·00
J164   5 c. brown   ..   ..   ..   25·00   20·00
     a. Brown opt   ..   ..   17·00   15·00
     b. Red opt   ..   ..   14·00   11·00
     c. Violet opt   ..   ..   42·00   38·00
J165   6 c. grey £130   £120
J166   8 c. scarlet £325   £325
J167   10 c. dull purple   ..   ..   60·00   55·00
J167   10 c. dull purple   ..   £110   £110
     a. Red opt £140   £140
     b. Brown opt £250   £250
J168   12 c. bright ultramarine (Br.) ..   £950   £950
J169   15 c. ultramarine (R.) ..   17·00   8·00
     a. Violet opt   ..   ..   42·00   28·00
     b. Brown opt   ..   ..   25·00   12·00
J170   25 c. dull purple and scarlet   ..   28·00   38·00
     a. Red opt   ..   ..   60·00   75·00
     b. Brown opt £225   £225
J171   30 c. dull purple and orange   ..   £150   £150
     a. Brown opt £650   £650
J172   40 c. scarlet and dull purple   ..   £700   £700
     a. Brown opt £750   £750
J173   50 c. black/*emerald* £350   £350
J174 $1 black and red/*blue*   ..   £130   £140
     a. Red opt £130   £140
     b. Brown opt £450   £450
J175 $5 green and red/*emerald*   ..   £400   £425
     a. Red opt £550   £600

(c) On Pahang

J176   15   1 c. black   ..   ..   35·00   32·00
     a. Red opt   ..   ..   35·00   32·00
     b. Violet opt £225   £225
     c. Brown opt £160   £160
J177   3 c. green £150   £160
     a. Red opt £225   £275
     b. Violet opt £500   £475
J178   5 c. brown   ..   ..   12·00   8·00
     a. Red opt £120   £100
     b. Brown opt £150   £100
     c. Violet opt £350   £250

J179	**15**	8 c. grey ..		£250	£250
J180		8 c. scarlet		22·00	10·00
		a. Red opt		85·00	60·00
		b. Violet opt		90·00	65·00
		c. Brown opt		95·00	85·00
J181		10 c. dull purple ..		90·00	80·00
		a. Red opt		£140	£150
		b. Brown opt		£250	£225
J182		12 c. bright ultramarine ..		£1300	£1300
		a. Red opt		£1200	£1200
J183		15 c. ultramarine		85·00	85·00
		a. Red opt		£160	£160
		b. Violet opt		£550	£475
		c. Brown opt		£350	£300
J184		25 c. dull purple and scarlet		18·00	29·00
J185		30 c. dull purple and orange		12·00	27·00
		a. Red opt		£140	£170
J186		40 c. scarlet and dull purple		16·00	30·00
		a. Brown opt		£200	£200
		b. Red opt		55·00	60·00
J187		50 c. black/*emerald*		£375	£400
		a. Red opt		£425	£450
J188		$1 black and red/*blue* (R.)		95·00	£110
		a. Black opt		£250	£250
		b. Brown opt		£475	£475
J189		$5 green and red/*emerald*		£600	£700
		a. Red opt		£850	£950

(d) On Perak

J190	**51**	1 c. black		42·00	32·00
		a. Violet opt		£120	£100
		b. Brown opt		80·00	80·00
J191		2 c. orange		23·00	19·00
		a. Violet opt		70·00	70·00
		b. Red opt		45·00	35·00
		c. Brown opt		55·00	55·00
J192		3 c. green		23·00	26·00
		a. Violet opt		£275	£275
		b. Brown opt		£160	£150
		c. Red opt		£250	£225
J193		5 c. brown		7·00	6·00
		a. Brown opt		23·00	23·00
		b. Violet opt		£140	£140
		c. Red opt		£140	£140
J194		8 c. grey ..		45·00	35·00
		a. Red opt		£325	£225
		b. Brown opt		£275	£225
J195		8 c. scarlet		22·00	35·00
		a. Violet opt		£325	£250
J196		10 c. dull purple ..		20·00	24·00
		a. Red opt		£180	£160
J197		12 c. bright ultramarine ..		£180	£180
J198		15 c. ultramarine		20·00	27·00
		a. Brown opt		£130	£130
		b. Violet opt		£225	£190
		c. Red opt		£225	£190
J199		25 c. dull purple and scarlet		14·00	23·00
J200		30 c. dull purple and orange		17·00	32·00
		a. Brown opt		£250	£250
		b. Red opt		32·00	50·00
J201		40 c. scarlet and dull purple		£200	£225
		a. Brown opt		£375	£375
J202		50 c. black/*emerald*		38·00	48·00
		a. Red opt		48·00	60·00
		b. Brown opt		£225	£225
J203		$1 black and red/*blue* ..		£350	£350
		a. Brown opt		£700	£550
J204		$2 green and scarlet		£1700	£1700
J205		$5 green and red/*emerald*		£475	
		a. Brown opt		£1200	

(e) On Selangor

J206	**46**	1 c. black, S		12·00	20·00
		a. Red opt, SU		21·00	26·00
		b. Violet opt, SU		30·00	32·00
J207		2 c. green, SU		£650	£650
		a. Violet opt, U		£800	£800
J208		2 c. orange (*p* 14×14½), S		42·00	45·00
		a. Red opt, U		£130	£140
		b. Violet opt, U		£200	£150
		c. Brown opt, S		60·00	65·00
J209		2 c. orange (*p* 14), S		70·00	65·00
		a. Red opt, U		£130	£140
		b. Violet opt, U		£200	£150
J210		3 c. green, SU		20·00	16·00
		a. Red opt, SU		18·00	16·00
		b. Violet opt, SU		35·00	50·00
		c. Brown opt, SU		18·00	16·00

J211	**46**	5 c. brown, SU ..		5·50	5·50
		a. Red opt, SU..		11·00	14·00
		b. Violet opt, SU		21·00	25·00
		c. Brown opt, SU		60·00	60·00
J212		6 c. scarlet, S		£225	£225
		a. Red opt, S		£200	£200
		b. Brown opt, S		£425	
J213		8 c. grey, S		17·00	17·00
		a. Red opt, SU..		38·00	30·00
		b. Violet opt, U		35·00	32·00
		c. Brown opt, S		80·00	48·00
J214		10 c. dull purple, S		13·00	21·00
		a. Red opt, S		45·00	45·00
		b. Brown opt, S		90·00	55·00
J215		12 c. bright ultramarine, S		45·00	45·00
		a. Red opt, S		£110	£110
		b. Brown opt, S		£110	£110
J216		15 c. ultramarine, S		16·00	20·00
		a. Red opt, SU..		40·00	40·00
		b. Violet opt, U		£120	90·00
		c. Brown opt, S		60·00	50·00
J217		25 c. dull purple and scarlet, S ..		70·00	80·00
		a. Red opt, S		55·00	75·00
J218		30 c. dull purple and orange, S ..		11·00	23·00
		a. Brown opt, S		£225	£180
J219		40 c. scarlet and dull purple, S ..		£100	£100
		a. Brown opt, S		£225	£170
J220		50 c. black/*emerald*, S		70·00	70·00
		a. Red opt, S		70·00	75·00
		b. Brown opt, S		£200	£200
J221	**48**	$1 black and red/*blue* ..		30·00	42·00
		a. Red opt		£100	£120
J222		$2 green and scarlet		35·00	60·00
		a. Red opt		£325	£325
J223		$5 green and red/*emerald*		60·00	80·00

On T **46** the overprint is normally sideways (with "top" to either right or left), but on T **47** it is always upright.

S=Sideways
U=Upright
SU=Sideways or upright (our prices being for the cheaper).
Specialists recognise nine slightly different chops as Type **1**. Initial supplies with the overprint in red were produced at Singapore. Later overprintings took place at Kuala Lumpur in violet, red or brown and, finally, black. No. J155 was from the Kuala Lumpur printing only. Except where noted these overprints were used widely in Malaya and, in some instances, Sumatra.

The following stamps also exist with this overprint, but were not available to the public:
Straits Settlements (in red) 6, 25 c.
Kelantan (in black) 10 c.
Negri Sembilan 2 c. green (Blk. or Brn.), 4 c. (Blk.), 6 c. scarlet (Blk.), 8 c. grey (Blk.), 12 c. (Blk.), $2 (Blk. or Brn.)
Pahang (in black, 2 c. also in brown) 2, 4, 6 c., $2
Perak 2 c. green (R.), 6 c. (Blk.)
Selangor 4 c. (Blk.)

1942 (May). *Optd with T* **16**. (*a*) *On Straits Settlements.*

J224	**58**	2 c. orange		60	50
		a. Opt inverted		8·00	15·00
		b. Opt double, one inverted		45·00	60·00
J225		3 c. green		48·00	60·00
J226		8 c. grey ..		2·75	1·75
		a. Opt inverted		13·00	26·00
J227		15 c. blue ..		7·50	5·50

(b) On Negri Sembilan

J228	**6**	1 c. black		1·25	60
		a. Opt inverted		9·00	24·00
		b. Opt double, one inverted		35·00	48·00
J229		2 c. orange		3·00	50
J230		3 c. green		2·00	45
J231		5 c. brown		50	55
J232		6 c. grey ..		1·75	1·00
		a. Opt inverted		—	£900
		b. Stop omitted at right (R. 10/4)		60·00	65·00
J233		8 c. scarlet		2·25	1·25
J234		10 c. dull purple		3·00	2·50
J235		15 c. ultramarine		7·50	2·50
J236		25 c. dull purple and scarlet		2·25	7·00
J237		30 c. dull purple and orange		4·25	3·00
J238		$1 black and red/*blue* ..		£100	£110

(c) On Pahang

J239	**15**	1 c. black		1·25	1·10
J240		5 c. brown		1·00	70
J241		8 c. scarlet		25·00	2·50
J242		10 c. dull purple ..		8·50	6·00

J243	15	12 c. bright ultramarine ..	..	1·00	6·00
J244		25 c. dull purple and scarlet	..	3·75	11·00
J245		30 c. dull purple and orange	..	1·25	5·00

(d) On Perak

J246	51	2 c. orange	..	1·25	70
		a. Opt inverted	..	20·00	24·00
J247		3 c. green	..	60	60
		a. Opt inverted	..	10·00	22·00
		b. Opt omitted (in pair with normal) £500			
J248		8 c. scarlet	..	60	40
		a. Opt inverted	..	4·50	7·00
		b. Opt double, one inverted ..	£200	£225
		c. Opt omitted (in horiz pair with normal)	..	£400	
J249		10 c. dull purple	..	6·50	5·00
J250		15 c. ultramarine	..	3·50	2·00
J251		50 c. black/*emerald*	..	1·75	2·75
J252		$1 black and red/*blue* ..	..	£300	£350
J253		$5 green and red/*emerald* ..	..	30·00	60·00
		a. Opt inverted	..	£275	£325

(e) On Selangor

J254	46	3 c. green	..	40	1·00
J255		12 c. bright ultramarine ..	..	1·10	7·00
J256		15 c. ultramarine	..	2·75	1·50
J257		40 c. scarlet and dull purple	..	2·00	2·50
J258	48	$2 green and scarlet ..	..	10·00	25·00

On T **46** the overprint is sideways, with "top" to left or right. The following stamps also exist with this overprint, but were not available to the public.

Perak 1, 5, 30 c. (*Price for set of 3 £300 unused*).
Selangor 1, 5, 10, 30 c., $1, $5 (*Price for set of 6 £550 unused*).

DAI NIPPON
2602
MALAYA

2 Cents

(17)

DAI NIPPON

YUBIN

2 Cents

(18)
"Japanese
Postal Service"

1942 (Nov). *No. 108 of Perak surch with T* **17**.
J259	51	2 c. on 5 c. brown ..	..	1·25	1·00

1942 (Nov). *Perak stamps surch or opt only, as in T* **18**.
J260	51	1 c. black	..	2·00	5·00
		a. Opt inverted	..	19·00	38·00
J261		2 c. on 5 c. brown ..	..	2·00	6·50
		a. "DAI NIPPON YUBIN" inverted	17·00	35·00
		b. Ditto and "2 Cents" omitted ..	42·00	65·00
J262		8 c. scarlet	..	2·75	1·50
		a. Opt inverted	..	11·00	22·00

A similar overprint exists on the Selangor 3 c. but this was not available to the public (*Price £325 unused*).

On 8 December 1942 contemporary Japanese 3, 5, 8 and 25 s. stamps were issued without overprint in Malaya and the 1, 2, 4, 6, 7, 10, 30 and 50 s. and 1 y. values followed on 15 February 1943.

大日本郵便
(19)

6 cts.
(20)

6 cts.
(21)

2 Cents
(22)

6 cts.
(23)

$1·00
(24)

1942 (4 Dec)–44. *Stamps of various Malayan territories optd "Japanese Postal Service" in Kanji characters as T* **2** *or* **19**, *some additionally surch as T* **20** *to* **24**.

(a) Stamps of Straits Settlements optd with T **2**

J263	58	8 c. grey (Blk.) (1943) ..	..	1·40	50
		a. Opt inverted	32·00	42·00
		b. Red opt	1·25	1·25
J264		12 c. ultramarine (1943) ..	55	5·00
J265		40 c. scarlet and dull purple (1943) ..	65	2·00

(b) Stamps of Negri Sembilan optd with T **2** *or surch also*

J266	6	1 c. black		30	40
		a. Opt inverted	8·00	20·00
		b. Sideways second character	24·00	25·00
		ba. Opt inverted with sideways second character	£475	
J267		2 c. on 5 c. brown (surch as T **20**)	40	45
J268		6 c. on 5 c. brown (surch T **21**) (1943)	40	85
		a. Opt Type **2** and surch as Type **21** both inverted ..	£225	£225
J269		25 c. dull purple and scarlet (1943)	1·10	8·00

(c) Stamp of Pahang optd with T **2** *and surch also*

J270	15	6 c. on 5 c. brown (surch T **20**) (1943)	50	75
J271		6 c. on 5 c. brown (surch T **21**) (1943)	1·00	1·50

(d) Stamps of Perak optd with T **2** *or surch also*

J272	51	1 c. black		80	60
		a. Sideways second character	£150	£160
J273		2 c. on 5 c. brown (surch as T **20**)	50	50
		a. Opt Type **2** and surch Type **20** both inverted	18·00	32·00
		b. Opt Type **2** inverted ..	18·00	32·00
		c. Sideways second character	50·00	50·00
J274		2 c. on 5 c. brown (surch T **22**)	45	45
		a. Opt Type **2** and surch Type **22** both inverted	18·00	32·00
		b. Surch Type **22** inverted	18·00	32·00
		c. Sideways second character	25·00	28·00
		ca. Opt Type **2** with sideways second character and surch T **22** both inverted ..	£800	
		cb. Surch Type **22** inverted ..	£800	
		d. Inverted "s" in Type **22** (R. 3/5) ..	50·00	
J275		5 c. brown		45	40
		a. Opt inverted ..	27·00	35·00
		b. Sideways second character	£300	£325
J276		8 c. scarlet		55	50
		a. Opt inverted ..	15·00	26·00
		b. Sideways second character	50·00	60·00
		ba. Opt inverted with sideways second character ..	£600	
J277		10 c. dull purple (1943) ..	60	50
J278		30 c. dull purple and orange (1943)	1·25	2·50
J279		50 c. black/*emerald* (1943) ..	3·00	10·00
J280		$5 green and red/*emerald* (1943) ..	48·00	75·00

(e) Stamps of Selangor optd with T **2** *(sideways on T* **46***)*

J281	46	1 c. black (1943)	90	90
J282		3 c. green	40	45
		a. Sideways second character	17·00	25·00
J283		12 c. bright ultramarine ..	45	1·60
		a. Sideways second character	26·00	40·00
J284		15 c. ultramarine	2·75	3·00
		a. Sideways second character	42·00	48·00
J285	48	$1 black and red/*blue* ..	3·00	13·00
		a. Opt inverted ..	£225	£225
		b. Sideways second character	£225	£250
J286		$2 green and scarlet (1943) ..	10·00	32·00
J287		$5 green and red/*emerald* (1943)	22·00	70·00
		a. Opt inverted ..	£225	£225

(f) Stamps of Selangor optd with T **19** *or surch also*

J288	46	1 c. black (1943)	35	50
J289		2 c. on 5 c. brown (surch as T **21**) (R.) (1943) ..	30	50
J290		3 c. on 5 c. brown (surch T **21**) (1943)	30	2·25
		a. "s" in "cts." inverted (R. 4/3) ..	27·00	50·00
		b. Comma after "cts" (R. 9/3) ..	27·00	50·00
J291		5 c. brown (R.) (1944) ..	30	2·00
J292		6 c. on 5 c. brown (surch T **21**) (1944)	30	80
J293		6 c. on 5 c. brown (surch T **23**) (1944)	20	70
		a. "6" inverted (R. 7/8) ..	£500	
		b. Surch and opt double	£275	
J294		15 c. ultramarine	4·00	4·00
J295		$1 on 10 c. dull purple (surch T **24**) (18.12.1944) ..	30	1·00
J296		$1.50 on 30 c. dull purple and orange (surch T **24**) (18.12.1944) ..	30	1·00

The error showing the second character in Type **2** sideways occurred on R. 6/3 in the first of four settings only.

The 2 c. orange, 3 c. and 8 c. grey of Perak also exist overprinted with Type **2**, but these stamps were not available to the public (*Price for set of 3 £100 unused*).

Examples of No. J275 are known postally used from the Shan States (part of pre-war Burma).

25 Tapping Rubber

26 Fruit

27 Japanese Shrine, Singapore

(Litho Kolff & Co, Batavia)

1943 (29 Apr–1 Oct). *T* **25/7** *and similar designs. P* 12½.

J297	**25**	1 c. grey-green (1 Oct)			15	55
J298	**26**	2 c. pale emerald (1 June)			15	15
J299	**25**	3 c. drab (1 Oct)			15	15
J300	–	4 c. carmine-rose			15	15
J301	–	8 c. dull blue			15	15
J302	–	10 c. brown-purple (1 Oct)			15	15
J303	**27**	15 c. violet (1 Oct)			35	1·75
J304	–	30 c. olive-green (1 Oct)			35	35
J305	–	50 c. blue (1 Oct)			1·00	1·60
J306	–	70 c. blue (1 Oct)			16·00	10·00
J297/306	..			*Set of 10*	17·00	13·50

Designs: *Vert*—4 c. Tin dredger; 8 c. War Memorial, Bukit Timah, Singapore; 10 c. Fishing village; 30 c. Sago palms; 50 c. Straits of Johore. *Horiz*—70 c. Malay Mosque, Kuala Lumpur.

28 Ploughman

29 Rice-planting

1943 (1 Sept). *Savings Campaign. Litho. P* 12½.

J307	**28**	8 c. violet	..	..	7·50	2·75
J308		15 c. scarlet	..	..	6·00	2·75

(Des Hon Chin. Litho)

1944 (15 Feb). *"Re-birth" of Malaya. P* 12½.

J309	**29**	8 c. rose-red	..	..	9·00	2·75
J310		15 c. magenta	..	..	4·00	3·00

大日本

マライ郵便

50 セント

(30)

大日本

マライ郵便

1 ドル

(31)

大日本

マライ郵便

1½ ドル

(32)

1944 (16 Dec). *Stamps intended for use on Red Cross letters. Surch with T* **30/2** *in red.* (a) *On Straits Settlements.*

J311	**58**	50 c. on 50 c. black/*emerald*	..	10·00	23·00
J312		$1 on $1 black and red/*blue*	..	17·00	35·00
J313		$1.50 on $2 green and scarlet	..	28·00	70·00

(b) *On Johore*

J314	**29**	50 c. on 50 c. dull purple and red	..	8·00	18·00
J315		$1.50 on $2 green and carmine	..	5·50	12·00

(c) *On Selangor*

J316	**48**	$1 on $1 black and red/*blue*	..	4·00	12·00
J317		$1.50 on $2 green and scarlet	..	6·50	18·00

Nos. J311/17 were issued in Singapore but were withdrawn after one day, probably because supplies of Nos. J295/6 were received and issued on the 18 December.

POSTAGE DUE STAMPS

Postage Due stamps of the Malayan Postal Union overprinted.

1942 (3 Apr). *Handstamped as T* **1** *in black.*

JD21	D **1**	1 c. slate-purple			12·00	18·00
		a. Red opt ..			60·00	60·00
		b. Brown opt			80·00	85·00
JD22		3 c. green			38·00	40·00
		a. Red opt ..			85·00	90·00
JD23		4 c. green			22·00	22·00
		a. Red opt ..			38·00	38·00
		b. Brown opt			85·00	95·00
JD24		8 c. scarlet ..			42·00	45·00
		a. Red opt ..			75·00	75·00
		b. Brown opt			£100	£100
JD25		10 c. yellow-orange			20·00	24·00
		a. Red opt ..			60·00	60·00
		b. Brown opt			45·00	48·00
JD26		12 c. ultramarine			20·00	30·00
		a. Red opt ..			95·00	95·00
JD27		50 c. black			50·00	60·00
		a. Red opt ..			£200	£225

1942. *Optd with T* **16**.

JD28	D **1**	1 c. slate-purple			1·25	6·00
JD29		3 c. green			8·50	12·00
JD30		4 c. green			6·50	9·50
JD31		8 c. scarlet			9·00	12·00
JD32		10 c. yellow-orange			1·60	8·00
JD33		12 c. ultramarine			1·60	19·00

The 9 c. and 15 c. also exist with this overprint, but these were not issued (*Price £350 each unused*).

1943–45. *Optd with T* **2**.

JD34	D **1**	1 c. slate-purple			40	2·25
JD35		3 c. green ..			40	2·25
		a. Opt omitted (in pair with normal)			£650	
JD36		4 c. green			32·00	35·00
JD37		5 c. scarlet ..			50	2·75
JD38		9 c. yellow-orange ..			60	4·00
		a. Opt inverted			24·00	32·00
JD39		10 c. yellow-orange			60	4·00
		a. Opt inverted			48·00	50·00
JD40		12 c. ultramarine			60	7·00
JD41		15 c. ultramarine			60	4·50

THAI OCCUPATION OF MALAYA

Stamps issued for use in the Malay States of Kedah (renamed Syburi), Kelantan, Perlis and Trengganu, ceded by Japan to Thailand on 19 October 1943. British rule was restored on 9 (Kelantan), 18 (Perlis), 22 (Kedah) and 24 September 1945 (Trengganu). Nos. TM1/6 continued to be used for postage until replaced by the overprinted B.M.A. Malaya issues on 10 October 1945.

KELANTAN

TK 1

(Typo Kelantan Ptg Dept, Khota Baru)

1943 (15 Nov). *Handstamped with State arms in violet. No gum. P* 11.

TK1	TK 1	1 c. black	..	..	£180	£250
TK2		2 c. black	..	..	£200	£200
		a. Handstamp omitted	..		£650	
TK3		4 c. black	..	..	£200	£250
		a. Handstamp omitted	..		£750	
TK4		8 c. black	..	..	£200	£200
		a. Handstamp omitted	..		£500	
TK5		10 c. black	..	..	£250	£350

Nos. TK1/5 were printed in sheets of 84 (12×7) and have sheet watermarks in the form of "STANDARD" in block capitals with curved "CROWN" above and "AGENTS" below in double-lined capitals. This watermark occurs four times in the sheet. Sheets were imperforate at top and left so that stamps exist imperforate at top, left or at top and left.
Similar stamps, but with red handstamps, were for fiscal use.

GENERAL ISSUE

TM 1 War Memorial

(Litho Defence Ministry, Bangkok)

1944 (15 Jan–4 Mar). *Thick opaque, or thin semi-transparent paper. Gummed or ungummed. P* 12½.

TM1	TM 1	1 c. yellow (4 Mar) ..	..	..	30·00	32·00
TM2		2 c. red-brown	..	..	12·00	20·00
		a. Imperf (pair)	..	..	£850	
		b. Perf 12½×11 ..	..	..	20·00	20·00
TM3		3 c. green (4 Mar) ..	..	..	20·00	38·00
		a. Perf 12½×11 ..	..	..	30·00	42·00
TM4		4 c. purple (4 Mar)	..	..	14·00	28·00
		a. Perf 12½×11 ..	..	..	20·00	35·00
TM5		8 c. carmine (4 Mar)	..	..	14·00	20·00
		a. Perf 12½×11 ..	..	..	20·00	20·00
TM6		15 c. blue (4 Mar) ..	..	..	38·00	60·00
		a. Perf 12½×11 ..	..	..	42·00	60·00

5 c. and 10 c. stamps in this design were prepared, but never issued.

TRENGGANU

TRENGGANU

(TT 1)

(Overprinted at Trengganu Survey Office)

1944 (1 Dec). *Various stamps optd with Type* **TT 1**.

(a) On Trengganu without Japanese opt

TT 1	4	1 c. black (48)	..	..	..
TT 2		30 c. dull purple and black (32)		..	

(b) On Trengganu stamp optd as T **1** *of Japanese Occupation*

TT 3	**4**	8 c. grey (J104)	..	..	£350	£250

(c) On stamps optd with T **16** *of Japanese Occupation.*
(i) Pahang

TT 4	**15**	12 c. bright ultramarine (J243)	..	£250	£120

(ii) Trengganu

TT 5	**4**	2 c. on 5 c. purple/*yellow* (J121)*	..	£350	£350
TT 6		8 c. on 10 c. brt blue (J127) (inverted)		£275	£275
TT 7		12 c. brt ultramarine (J128) (inverted)		£275	£275

"This is spelt "TRENGANU" with one "G".

(d) On stamps optd with T **2** *of Japanese Occupation.*
(i) Straits Settlements

TT 8	**58**	12 c. ultramarine (J264)	..	£325	£325
TT 9		40 c. scarlet and dull purple (J265)	..	£325	£325

(ii) Pahang

TT10	**15**	6 c. on 5 c. brown (J271)	..		

(iii) Perak

TT11	**51**	1 c. black (J272)	..		
TT12		10 c. dull purple (J277)	..		
TT13		30 c. dull purple and orange (J278)	..	£550	£325

(iv) Selangor

TT14	**46**	3 c. green (J282)	..	£225	£225
TT15		12 c. brt ultramarine (J283) (L. to R.)		£140	£110
TT16		12 c. brt ultramarine (J283) (R. to L.)		£140	£110
		a. Sideways second character	..	£1600	£1600

(e) On Selangor stamps optd with T **19** *of Japanese Occupation*

TT17	**46**	2 c. on 5 c. brown (J289)	..	£325	£325
TT18		3 c. on 5 c. brown (J290)	..	£325	£325

(f) On pictorials of 1943 *(Nos. J297/306)*

TT19	**25**	1 c. grey-green	..	£250	£250
TT20	**26**	2 c. pale emerald	..	£250	£150
TT21	**25**	3 c. drab	..	£180	£120
TT22	–	4 c. carmine-rose	..	£225	£150
TT23	–	8 c. dull blue	..	£375	£375
TT24	–	10 c. brown-purple	..	£750	£600
TT25	**27**	15 c. violet	..	£250	£150
TT26	–	30 c. olive-green	..	£275	£130
TT27	–	50 c. blue	..	£350	£250
TT28	–	70 c. blue	..	£750	£600

(g) On Savings Campaign stamps (Nos. J307/8)

TT29	**28**	8 c. violet	..	£375	£375
TT30		15 c. scarlet	..	£275	£160

(h) On stamps of Japan

TT31	–	3 s. green (No. 319)	..		
TT32	–	5 s. claret (No. 396) ..	..	£300	£300
TT33	–	25 c. brown and chocolate (No. 329)		£160	£110
TT34	–	30 c. blue-green (No. 330)	..	£300	£160

(i) On Trengganu Postage Due stamp optd with T **1** *of Japanese Occupation*

TT35	D **1**	1 c. scarlet (JD17)	..	..	£1100 £1100

Maldive Islands

100 larees = 1 rupee

PROTECTORATE

5 Palm Tree and Dhow

(Recess B.W.)

7 Fish

8 Native Products

(Recess B.W.)

1950 (24 Dec). *P* 13.

21	5	2 l. olive-green	..	..	..	..	1·00	40
22		3 l. blue	..	..	..	..	5·50	40
23		5 l. emerald-green	..	..	..	5·50	50
24		6 l. red-brown	..	..	..	..	60	30
25		10 l. scarlet	..	..	..	..	70	30
26		15 l. orange	..	..	..	..	70	30
27		25 l. purple	..	..	..	..	60	30
28		50 l. violet	..	..	..	..	70	30
29		1 r. chocolate	..	..	..	8·00	25·00
21/9	..	..	..	..	*Set of* 9	21·00	25·00

1952. *P* 13.

30	7	3 l. blue	..	..	..	..	60	30
31	8	5 l. emerald	..	..	..	..	50	80

Malta

12 pence (d) = 1 shilling; 20 shillings = 1 pound

CROWN COLONY

1937 (12 May). *Coronation. As Nos. 118/20 of Jamaica.*

214	½d. green	..	.. ..	10	10
215	1½d. scarlet	..	.. .. ..	50	15
	a. Brown-lake	..	.. .. ..	£550	£550
216	2½d. bright blue	..	.. ..	50	35
214/16		.. ..	*Set of* 3	1·00	50
214/16 Perf "Specimen"		.. ..	*Set of* 3	60·00	

37 Grand Harbour, Valletta

38 H.M.S. *St. Angelo*

39 Verdala Palace

40 Hypogeum, Hal Saflieni

Broken cross
(Right pane R. 5/7)

Damaged value
tablet (R. 4/9)

Semaphore flaw
(R. 2/7)

(Recess Waterlow)

1938 (17 Feb*)–**43.** *T* 37/40 *and similar designs. Wmk Mult Script CA* (*sideways on No.* 217). *P* 12½.

217	37	¼d. brown	..	.. ..	10	10
218	38	½d. green	..	.. ..	1·50	10
218a		½d. red-brown (8.3.43)		..	55	30
219	39	1d. red-brown	..	..	4·25	30
219a		1d. green (8.3.43)	..	..	60	10
220	40	1½d. scarlet	..	..	1·00	15
		a. Broken cross	..	..	45·00	
220b		1½d. slate-black (8.3.43)		..	30	15
		ba. Broken cross	..	..	40·00	
221	–	2d. slate-black	..	..	30	1·00
221a	–	2d. scarlet (8.3.43)	..	..	40	10
222	–	2½d. greyish blue	..	..	65	30
222a	–	2½d. dull violet (8.3.43)		..	60	10
223	–	3d. dull violet	..	..	30	70
223a	–	3d. blue (8.3.43)	..	..	30	10
224	–	4½d. olive-green and yellow-brown	..	50	10
225	–	6d. olive-green and scarlet	..	75	15
226	–	1s. black	..	..	75	30
227	–	1s. 6d. black and olive-green	..	7·00	3·50
228	–	2s. green and deep blue	..	3·25	3·00
229	–	2s. 6d. black and scarlet	..	7·00	4·50
		a. Damaged value tablet	..	£120	
230	–	5s. black and green	..	..	7·00	5·50
		a. Semaphore flaw	..	..	65·00	
231	–	10s. black and carmine	..	14·00	14·00
217/31		.. .. ..	*Set of* 21	45·00	30·00
217/31 Perf "Specimen"		..	*Set of* 21	£350	

Designs: *Horiz* (as *T* 39)—2d. Victoria and citadel, Gozo; 2½d. De l'Isle Adam entering Mdina; 4½d. Ruins at Mnajdra; 1s. 6d. St. Publius; 2s. Mdina Cathedral; 2s. 6d. Statue of Neptune, *Vert* (as *T* 40)—3d. St. John's Co-Cathedral; 6d. Statue of Manoel de Vilhena; 1s. Maltese girl wearing faldetta; 5s. Palace Square, Valletta; 10s. St. Paul.

*This is the local date of issue but the stamps were released in London on 15 February.

1946 (3 Dec). *Victory. As Nos. 141/2 of Jamaica, but inscr* "MALTA" *between Maltese Cross and George Cross.*

232	1d. green	..	.. ..	10	10
233	3d. blue	..	.. .. ..	10	15
232/3 Perf "Specimen"		..	*Set of* 2	50·00	

SELF-GOVERNMENT

(52)

"NT" joined
(R. 4/10)

NEW INFORMATION

The editor is always interested to correspond with people who have new information that will improve or correct the Catalogue.

Halation flaw (Pl 2 R. 2/5)   Cracked plate (Pl 2
(ptg of 8 Jan 1953)   R. 5/1) (ptg of 8 Jan 1953)

(Optd by Waterlow)

1948 (25 Nov)–53. *New Constitution. As Nos.* 217/31 *but optd as T* **52**; *reading up on* ½d. *and* 5s., *down on other values, and smaller on* ¼d. *value.*

234	**37**	¼d. brown	..	20	20
235	**38**	½d. red-brown	..	20	10
		a. "NT" joined	.. ..	14·00	
236	**39**	1d. green	..	20	10
236a		1d. grey (R.) (8.1.53) ..	..	20	10
237	**40**	1½d. blue-black (R.)	..	75	10
		a. Broken cross	..	38·00	
237b		1½d. green (8.1.53)	..	30	10
		ba. Albino opt	..	†£10000	
238	–	2d. scarlet	..	75	10
238a	–	2d. yellow-ochre (8.1.53)	..	30	10
		ab. Halation flaw	..	85·00	
		ac. Cracked plate	..	85·00	
239	–	2½d. dull violet (R.)	..	80	10
239a	–	2½d. scarlet-vermilion (8.1.53)	..	30	85
240	–	3d. blue (R.) ..	..	30	15
240a	–	3d. dull violet (R.) (8.1.53) ..	..	35	15
241	–	4½d. olive-green and yellow-brown	..	2·00	1·50
241a	–	4½d. olive-green & dp ultram (R.) (8.1.53)	..	50	90
242	–	6d. olive-green and scarlet ..	..	1·25	15
243	–	1s. black	..	2·25	40
244	–	1s. 6d. black and olive-green	..	2·50	45
245	–	2s. green and deep blue (R.)	..	5·00	1·50
246	–	2s. 6d. black and scarlet	..	14·00	2·50
		a. Damaged value tablet	..	£170	
247	–	5s. black and green (R.)	..	£140	5·50
		a. "NT" joined	..	£140	
		b. Semaphore flaw ..	..	£800	
248	–	10s. black and carmine	..	19·00	19·00
234/48		.. .. ..	Set of 21	60·00	30·00

1949 (4 Jan). *Royal Silver Wedding. As Nos.* 143/4 *of Jamaica, but inscr* "MALTA" *between Maltese Cross and George Cross and with* £1 *ptd in recess.*

249	1d. green	..	..	50	10
250	£1 indigo	..	..	38·00	35·00

1949 (10 Oct). *75th Anniv of U.P.U. As Nos.* 145/8 *of Jamaica, but inscr* "MALTA" *in recess.*

251	2½d. violet	..	..	30	10
252	3d. deep blue	..	..	2·25	50
253	6d. carmine-red	..	..	1·50	50
254	1s. blue-black	..	..	1·50	1·75
251/4	.. ..	..	Set of 4	5·00	2·50

53 Queen Elizabeth II   54 "Our Lady of
when Princess   Mount Carmel"
                (attrib Palladino)

(T **53**/4. Recess B.W.)

1950 (1 Dec). *Visit of Princess Elizabeth to Malta. Wmk Mult Script CA. P* 12 × 11½.

255	**53**	1d. green	..	10	10
256		3d. blue ..	..	20	10
257		1s. black	.. ..	55	45
255/7	..	.. ..	Set of 3	70	55

1951 (12 July). *Seventh Centenary of the Scapular. Wmk Mult Script CA. P* 12 × 11½.

258	**54**	1d. green	..	10	10
259		3d. violet	..	15	10
260		1s. black	..	55	40
258/60		.. ..	Set of 3	70	50

Mauritius

100 cents = 1 rupee

CROWN COLONY

51

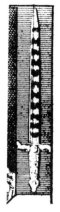

Line through sword
(R. 2/2)

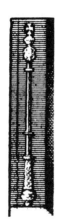

Line by sceptre (R. 5/3)

1937 (12 May). *Coronation. As Nos. 118/20 of Jamaica.*
249	5 c. violet..	.. .. ..	55	10
250	12 c. scarlet	.. .. ..	55	1·25
251	20 c. bright blue ..	.. .. ..	55	10
	a. Line through sword ..	.. ..	45·00	
	b. Line by sceptre	.. ..	45·00	
249/51	.. .. ..	Set of 3	1·50	1·25
249/51 Perf "Specimen" ..	..	Set of 3	48·00	

Sliced "S" at right
(R. 2/2, 3/2, right
pane)

Sliced "S" at top (R. 4/1,
left pane and R. 8/4,
right pane, Duty Plate 1)

Broken frame under "A"
of "MAURITIUS" (R. 9/3
of left pane)

"IJ" flaw (R. 3/6 of right
pane)

Battered "A" (R. 6/1 of
right pane)

(Typo D.L.R.)

1938–49. *T* 51 *and similar types. Wmk Mult Script CA. Chalk-surfaced paper (25 c. to 10 r.). P* 14.
252	2 c. olive-grey (9.3.38)	..	..	30	10
	a. Perf 15×14 (1942)	..	..	1·00	10
253	3 c. reddish purple and scarlet (27.10.38)		2·00	1·00
	a. Sliced "S" at right	..	..	60·00	
	b. Reddish lilac and red (4.43) ..		2·00	2·00
	ba. Sliced "S" at right	..	..	60·00	
254	4 c. dull green (26.2.38)	..	..	2·25	1·00
	a. Deep dull green (4.43)		..	1·00	1·00
255	5 c. slate-lilac (23.2.38)	..	..	5·50	50
	a. Pale lilac (shades) (4.43)	..	..	2·00	20
	b. Perf 15×14 (1942)	..	..	32·00	10
256	10 c. rose-red (9.3.38)	..	..	2·25	20
	a. Sliced "S" at top	..	..	75·00	
	b. Deep reddish rose (shades) (4.43)	..	2·25	10
	ba. Sliced "S" at top	..	..	75·00	
	c. Perf 15×14. Pale reddish rose (1942)	26·00	85
	ca. Sliced "S" at top	..	..	£200	
257	12 c. salmon (shades) (26.2.38)	..	..	1·00	20
	a. Perf 15×14 (1942)	..	..	50·00	75
258	20 c. blue (26.2.38)..	..	..	1·00	10
	a. Broken frame	..	..	70·00	
259	25 c. brown-purple (2.3.38)	..	..	5·50	20
	a. "IJ" flaw	..	..	£140	
	b. Ordinary paper (8.4.43)	..	..	3·25	10
	ba. "IJ" flaw	..	..	90·00	
260	1 r. grey-brown (2.3.38)	..	..	17·00	1·50
	a. Battered "A" ..	..	..	£200	
	b. Ordinary paper (8.4.43)	..	..	12·00	70
	ba. Battered "A" ..	..	..	£160	
	c. Drab (4.49)	..	..	17·00	3·50
	ca. Battered "A" ..	..	..	£200	
261	2 r. 50, pale violet (2.3.38)	..	..	38·00	10·00
	a. Ordinary paper (8.4.43)	..	..	23·00	8·00
	b. Slate-violet (4.48)	..	..	35·00	17·00
262	5 r. olive-green (2.3.38)	..	..	48·00	22·00
	a. Ordinary paper. Sage-green (8.4.43)	27·00	22·00
263	10 r. reddish purple (shades) (2.3.38)	..	42·00	25·00
	a. Ordinary paper (8.4.43)	..	..	9·50	18·00
252/63a	.. ..	..	Set of 12	75·00	45·00
252/63 Perf "Specimen" ..	..	Set of 12	£150	

The stamps perf 15 × 14 were printed by Bradbury, Wilkinson
from De La Rue plates and issued only in the colony in 1942. De La
Rue printings of the 2 c. to 20 c. in 1943–45 were on thin, whiter
paper. 1943–45 printings of the 25 c. to 10 r. were on unsurfaced
paper.

1946 (20 Nov). *Victory. As Nos. 141/2 of Jamaica.*
264	5 c. lilac	.. .. ..	10	10
265	20 c. blue	.. .. ..	10	10
264/5 Perf "Specimen"	..	Set of 2	48·00	

52 1d. "Post Office" Mauritius and King George VI

(Recess B.W.)

1948 (22 Mar). *Centenary of First British Colonial Postage Stamp. Wmk Mult Script CA. P* 11½×11.

266	**52**	5 c. orange and magenta		10	30
267		12 c. orange and green		10	10
268	–	20 c. blue and light blue		10	10
269	–	1 r. blue and red-brown		15	30
266/9			*Set of* 4	40	60
266/9 Perf "Specimen"			*Set of* 4	90·00	

Design:–20 c., 1 r. As T **52** but showing 2d. "Post Office" Mauritius.

1948 (25 Oct). *Royal Silver Wedding. As Nos.* 143/4 *of Jamaica.*

270	5 c. violet		10	10
271	10 r. magenta		9·00	18·00

1949 (10 Oct). *75th Anniv of U.P.U. As Nos.* 145/8 *of Jamaica.*

272	12 c. carmine		60	65
273	20 c. deep blue		1·00	1·00
274	35 c. purple		60	60
275	1 r. sepia		60	20
272/5		*Set of* 4	2·50	2·25

53 Labourdonnais Sugar Factory

55 Aloe Plant

(Photo Harrison)

1950 (1 July). *T* **53, 55** *and similar designs. Wmk Mult Script CA. Chalk surfaced paper. P* 13½ × 14½ (horiz), 14½ × 13½ (vert).

276	1 c. bright purple		10	50
277	2 c. rose-carmine		15	10
278	3 c. yellow-green		60	2·00
279	4 c. green		20	85
280	5 c. blue		15	10
281	10 c. scarlet		30	75
282	12 c. olive-green		1·25	1·25
283	20 c. ultramarine		60	15
284	25 c. brown-purple		1·25	40
285	35 c. violet		30	10
286	50 c. emerald-green		2·00	50
287	1 r. sepia		4·25	10
288	2 r. 50, orange		12·00	5·50
289	5 r. red-brown		13·00	13·00
290	10 r. dull blue		14·00	15·00
276/290		*Set of* 15	45·00	35·00

Designs: *Horiz*—2 c. Grand Port; 5 c. Rempart Mountain; 10 c. Transporting cane; 12 c. Mauritius Dodo and map; 35 c. Government House, Reduit; 1 r. Timor Deer; 2 r. 50, Port Louis; 5 r. Beach scene; 10 r. Arms of Mauritius. *Vert*—4 c. Tamarind Falls; 20 c. Legend of Paul and Virginie (inscr "VIRGINIA"); 25 c. Labourdonnais statue; 50 c. Pieter Both Mountain.

The latitude is incorrectly shown on No. 282. This was corrected before the same design was used for No. 302a.

STAMP BOOKLETS

1953 (10 Oct). *Black on white cover. Stapled.*

SB1   5 r. booklet containing four 5 c., eight 10 c. and 50 c. (Nos. 280, 286, 291) in blocks of 4 and one pane of 4 air mail labels £180

Montserrat

1937. 12 pence (d) = 1 shilling; 20 shillings = 1 pound
1951. 100 cents = 1 West Indian dollar

PRESIDENCY

1937 (12 May). *Coronation. As Nos. 118/20 of Jamaica.*

98	1d. scarlet			30	40
99	1½d. yellow-brown			40	25
100	2½d. bright blue			40	60
98/100			Set of 3	1·00	1·10
98/100 Perf "Specimen"			Set of 3	50·00	

11 Carr's Bay   12 Sea Island Cotton

13 Botanic Station

(Recess D.L.R.)

1938 (2 Aug)–48. *Wmk Mult Script CA. P 12* (10s., £1) *or* 13 (*others*).

101	11	½d. blue-green			1·50	1·10
		a. Perf 14 (1942)			15	20
102	12	1d. carmine			1·50	40
		a. Perf 14 (1943)			30	30
103		1½d. purple			9·50	50
		a. Perf 14 (1942)			30	50
		ab. "A" of "CA" missing from wmk				
104	13	2d. orange			7·00	60
		a. Perf 14 (1942)			85	70
105	12	2½d. ultramarine			65	60
		a. Perf 14 (1943)			40	30
106	11	3d. brown			1·00	40
		a. Perf 14, *Red-brown* (1942)			1·25	40
		ab. *Deep brown* (1943)			6·00	4·75
107	13	6d. violet			5·50	70
		a. Perf 14 (1943)			2·00	60
108	11	1s. lake			7·00	70
		a. Perf 14 (1942)			2·00	30
109	13	2s. 6d. slate-blue			16·00	80
		a. Perf 14 (1943)			16·00	2·50
110	11	5s. rose-carmine			22·00	8·00
		a. Perf 14 (1942)			21·00	3·00
111	13	10s. pale blue (1948)			13·00	17·00
112	11	£1 black (1948)			13·00	26·00
101a/12				Set of 12	65·00	45·00
101/12 Perf "Specimen"			Set of 12	£250	

1946 (1 Nov). *Victory. As Nos. 141/2 of Jamaica.*

113	1½d. purple			10	10
114	3d. chocolate			10	10
113/14 Perf "Specimen"		Set of 2	55·00	

1949 (3 Jan). *Royal Silver Wedding. As Nos. 143/4 of Jamaica.*

115	2½d. ultramarine			10	10
116	5s. carmine				4·50	4·50

1949 (10 Oct). *75th Anniv of U.P.U. As Nos. 145/8 of Jamaica.*

117	2½d. ultramarine			20	30
118	3d. brown			1·00	30
119	6d. purple			40	30
120	1s. purple			40	30
117/20			Set of 4	1·75	1·10

(New Currency. 100 cents = 1 West Indies, later Eastern Caribbean dollar)

1951 (16 Feb). *Inauguration of B.W.I. University College. As Nos. 149/50 of Jamaica.*

121	3 c. black and purple			20	40
122	12 c. black and violet			20	40

14 Government House   18 Badge of Presidency

(Recess B.W.)

1951 (17 Sept). *T* **14**, **18** *and similar horiz designs. Wmk Mult Script CA. P* 11½ × 11.

123	14	1 c. black			10	1·25
124	–	2 c. green			15	70
125	–	3 c. orange-brown			30	70
126	–	4 c. carmine			30	30
127	–	5 c. reddish violet			30	70
128	18	6 c. olive-brown			30	30
129	–	8 c. deep blue			35	20
130	–	12 c. blue and chocolate			35	30
131	–	24 c. carmine and yellow-green			85	30
132	–	60 c. black and carmine			4·50	2·50
133	–	$1.20, yellow-green and blue			5·50	3·75
134	–	$2.40, black and green			4·50	12·00
135	18	$4.80, black and purple			16·00	16·00
123/135				Set of 13	29·00	32·00

Designs:—2 c., $1.20, Sea Island cotton: cultivation; 3 c. Map of colony; 4, 24 c. Picking tomatoes; 5, 12 c. St. Anthony's Church; 8, 60 c. Sea Island cotton: ginning; $2.40, Government House.

Morocco Agencies

BRITISH CURRENCY

From 3 June 1937 unoverprinted stamps of Great Britain were supplied to the post offices at Tangier and Tetuan (Spanish Zone) as local stocks of issues overprinted "MOROCCO AGENCIES" were exhausted.

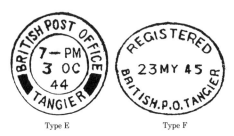

Type E	Type F

Stamps of GREAT BRITAIN *cancelled as Types* E *or* F *at Tangier.*

1937–39. *King George VI (Nos. 462/75).*
Z178	½d. green					
Z179	1d. scarlet					
Z180	1½d. red-brown					
Z181	2d. orange					
Z182	2½d. ultramarine					
Z183	3d. violet					8·00
Z184	4d. grey-green					
Z185	5d. brown					
Z186	6d. purple					5·00
Z187	7d. emerald-green					
Z188	8d. bright carmine					
Z189	9d. deep olive-green					10·00
Z190	10d. turquoise-blue					
Z191	1s. bistre-brown					5·00

1939–42. *King George VI (Nos. 476/8a).*
Z192	2s. 6d. brown				30·00
Z193	2s. 6d. yellow-green				10·00
Z194	5s. red				15·00
Z195	10s. dark blue				60·00
Z196	10s. ultramarine				25·00

1941–42. *King George VI pale colours (Nos. 485/90).*
Z197	½d. pale green				
Z198	1d. pale scarlet				
Z199	1½d. pale red-brown				
Z200	2d. pale orange				
Z201	2½d. light ultramarine				
Z202	3d. pale violet				5·00

1946. *Victory (Nos. 491/2).*
Z203	2½d. ultramarine				7·00
Z204	3d. violet				7·00

NEW INFORMATION

The editor is always interested to correspond with people who have new information that will improve or correct the Catalogue.

Type G

Stamps of GREAT BRITAIN *cancelled as Type* G *at Tetuan.*

1937–39. *King George VI (Nos. 465/75)*
Z211	2d. orange					
Z212	2½d. ultramarine					
Z213	3d. violet					
Z214	4d. grey-green					
Z215	6d. purple					10·00
Z216	9d. deep olive-green					
Z217	1s. bistre-brown					10·00

1939–42. *King George VI (Nos. 476/7).*
Z218	2s. 6d. brown					
Z219	2s. 6d. yellow-green					30·00
Z220	5s. red					40·00

1941. *King George VI pale colours (Nos. 485/90).*
Z221	½d. pale green					
Z222	2d. pale orange					
Z223	2½d. light ultramarine					
Z224	3d. pale violet					10·00

Other unoverprinted stamps of Great Britain are known with Morocco Agencies postmarks during this period, but it is believed that only Nos. Z170/224 were sold by the local post offices.

The use of unoverprinted stamps in Tangier ceased with the issue of Nos. 261/75 on 1 January 1949. Stamps overprinted "MOROCCO AGENCIES" replaced the unoverprinted values at Tetuan on 16 August 1949.

MOROCCO AGENCIES	MOROCCO AGENCIES
(9)	(10)

1949 (16 Aug). *King George VI, optd with T* **9** *or* **10** *(2s. 6d., 5s.).*
77	½d. pale green					1·75	4·0C
78	1d. pale scarlet					2·75	6·50
79	1½d. pale red-brown					2·75	5·50
80	2d. pale orange					3·00	6·50
81	2½d. light ultramarine					3·25	7·0C
82	3d. pale violet					1·50	9£
83	4d. grey-green					45	
84	5d. brown					3·00	12·0C
85	6d. purple					1·50	1·0C
86	7d. emerald-green					40	13·0C
87	8d. bright carmine					3·00	5·0C
88	9d. deep olive-green					40	9·5c
89	10d. turquoise-blue					40	4·5c
90	11d. plum					70	4·5c
91	1s. bistre-brown					2·75	4·5c
92	2s. 6d. yellow-green					10·00	24·0c
93	5s. red					28·00	45·0c
77/93					*Set of 17*	60·00	£14

1951 (3 May). *King George VI (Nos. 503/7, 509/10), optd with T 9 or 10 (2s. 6d., 5s.).*
94	¹/₂d. pale orange	..	..	..	1·75	40
95	1d. light ultramarine	..	..	..	1·75	40
96	1¹/₂d. pale green	..	..	..	1·75	90
97	2d. pale red-brown	..	..	..	1·75	2·50
98	2¹/₂d. pale scarlet	..	..	..	1·75	2·00
99	2s. 6d. yellow-green (H.M.S. *Victory*)	..	10·00	15·00
100	5s. red (Dover)	..	..	..	11·00	17·00
94/100	..	..	..	*Set of 7*	27·00	35·00

SPANISH CURRENCY

(19)

1937 (13 May). *Coronation (No. 461), surch as T 19.*
164	15 c. on 1¹/₂d. maroon (B.) ..	..	..	50	30

MOROCCO
AGENCIES   MOROCCO AGENCIES

**10
CENTIMOS**
(20)

**10
CENTIMOS**
(21)

1937 (June)–52. *King George VI (Nos. 462/4, 466, 468, 471 and 474), surch as T 20.*
165	5 c. on ¹/₂d. green (B.)	..	..	55	15
166	10 c. on 1d. scarlet	..	..	50	10
167	15 c. on 1¹/₂d. red-brown (B.) (4.8.37)	..	55	25
168	25 c. on 2¹/₂d. ultramarine	..	..	60	50
169	40 c. on 4d. grey-green (9.40)	..	20·00	9·00
170	70 c. on 7d. emerald-green (9.40)	..	50	8·00
171	1 p. on 10d. turquoise-blue (16.6.52)	..	50	3·50
165/71	..	..	*Set of 7*	21·00	19·00

1940 (6 May). *Centenary of First Adhesive Postage Stamps (Nos. 479/81 and 483), surch as T 21.*
172	5 c. on ¹/₂d. green (B.)	..	..	30	1·25
173	10 c. on 1d. scarlet	..	..	2·10	1·75
174	15 c. on 1d. red-brown (B.)	..	..	30	1·50
175	25 c. on 2¹/₂d. ultramarine	..	..	30	50
172/5	..	..	*Set of 4*	2·75	4·50

**25
CENTIMOS**

**45 PESETAS
MOROCCO AGENCIES**

MOROCCO AGENCIES
(22)

(23)

1948 (26 Apr). *Silver Wedding (Nos. 493/4), surch with T 22 or 23.*
176	25 c. on 2¹/₂d. ultramarine	..	..	40	15
177	45 p. on £1 blue	..	..	16·00	22·00

1948 (29 July). *Olympic Games (Nos. 495/8), variously surch as T 22.*
178	25 c. on 2¹/₂d. ultramarine	..	..	40	50
179	30 c. on 3d. violet ..	..	..	40	50
180	60 c. on 6d. bright purple ..	..	40	50
181	1 p. 20 c. on 1s. brown	..	..	55	50
	a. Surch double ..	..	..	£550	
178/81	..	..	..	*Set of 4*	1·60	1·75

1951 (3 May)–52. *King George VI (Nos. 503/5 and 507/8), surch as T 20.*
182	5 c. on ¹/₂d. pale orange	..	..	2·00	1·50
183	10 c. on 1d. light ultramarine	..	3·25	2·75
184	15 c. on 1¹/₂d. pale green	..	..	1·75	10·00
185	25 c. on 2¹/₂d. pale scarlet ..	..	1·75	2·75
186	40 c. on 4d. light ultramarine (26.5.52)	..	60	9·00
182/6	..	..	..	*Set of 5*	8·50	23·00

FRENCH CURRENCY

1937 (13 May). *Coronation (No. 461), surch as T 19, but in French currency.*
229	15 c. on 1¹/₂d. maroon (B.) ..	..	..	30	20

1937 (June). *King George VI, surch as T 20, but in French currency.*
230	5 c. on ¹/₂d. green (B.)	..	..	60	1·25

Stamps surcharged in French currency were withdrawn from sale on 8 January 1938.

TANGIER INTERNATIONAL ZONE

(28)

TANGIER
(29)

1937 (13 May). *Coronation (No. 461), optd with T 28.*
244	1¹/₂d. maroon (B.) ..	..	..	..	40	15

1937. *King George VI (Nos. 462/4), optd with T 29.*
245	¹/₂d. green (B.) (June)	..	..	60	30
246	1d. scarlet (June)	..	..	2·50	30
247	1¹/₂d. red-brown (B.) (4 Aug)	..	60	10
245/7	..	..	..	*Set of 3*	3·25	60

TANGIER
(30)

TANGIER
(31)

1940 (6 May). *Centenary of First Adhesive Postage Stamps (Nos. 479/81), optd with T 30.*
248	¹/₂d. green (B.)	..	..	..	30	2·75
249	1d. scarlet	..	..	..	45	40
250	1¹/₂d. red-brown (B.)	..	..	2·00	1·75
248/50	..	..	*Set of 3*	2·50	4·50

1944. *King George VI pale colours (Nos. 485/6), optd with T 29.*
251	¹/₂d. pale green (B.)	..	..	5·00	2·00
252	1d. pale scarlet ..	..	..	5·00	1·75

1946 (11 June). *Victory (Nos. 491/2), optd as T 31.*
253	2¹/₂d. ultramarine ..	..	..	30	20
254	3d. violet	..	..	..	30	30

The opt on No. 254 is smaller (23×2¹/₂ mm).

1948 (26 Apr). *Royal Silver Wedding (Nos. 493/4), optd with T 30.*
255	2¹/₂d. ultramarine ..	..	..	..	30	15
	a. Opt omitted (in vert pair with stamp					
	optd at top) ..	..	..	.. £2500		
256	£1 blue ..	..	..	..	24·00	25·00

No. 255a comes from a sheet on which the overprint is misplaced downwards resulting in the complete absence of the opt from the six stamps of the top row. On the rest of the sheet the opt falls at the top of each stamp instead of at the foot (*Price £250, unused*).

1948 (29 July). *Olympic Games (Nos. 495/8), optd with T 30.*
257	2¹/₂d. ultramarine ..	..	..	..	65	90
258	3d. violet	..	..	..	65	75
259	6d. bright purple	..	..	..	65	90
260	1s. brown	..	..	..	65	40
257/60	..	..	..	Set of 4	2·40	2·75

1949 (1 Jan). *King George VI, optd with T 29.*
261	2d. pale orange ..	..	..	..	3·25	2·25
262	2¹/₂d. light ultramarine	..	..	..	35	2·25
263	3d. pale violet	..	..	..	35	30
264	4d. grey-green	..	..	..	4·00	7·50
265	5d. brown	..	..	..	2·00	7·50
266	6d. purple	..	..	..	35	30
267	7d. emerald-green	..	..	..	80	7·50
268	8d. bright carmine	..	..	..	1·50	6·00
269	9d. deep olive-green	..	..	..	50	10·00

270	10d. turquoise-blue	..	..	..	50	9·50
271	11d. plum ..	..	..	..	50	6·50
272	1s. bistre-brown ..	..	..	..	60	1·00
273	2s. 6d. yellow-green	..	..	..	4·00	7·50
274	5s. red ..	..	..	..	9·00	29·00
275	10s. ultramarine ..	..	..	..	35·00	80·00
261/75	..	..	..	Set of 15	55·00	£150

1949 (10 Oct). *75th Anniv of U.P.U. (Nos. 499/502), optd with T 30.*
276	2¹/₂d. ultramarine ..	..	..	..	50	90
277	3d. violet	..	..	..	50	75
278	6d. bright purple	..	..	..	50	75
279	1s. brown	..	..	..	50	1·40
276/9	..	..	..	Set of 4	1·75	3·50

1950 (2 Oct)–**51.** *King George VI, optd with T 29 or 30 (shilling values).*
280	¹/₂d. pale orange (3.5.51) ..	..	..	45	60
281	1d. light ultramarine (3.5.51)	..	..	70	1·75
282	1¹/₂d. pale green (3.5.51) ..	..	..	70	10·00
283	2d. pale red-brown (3.5.51)	..	..	70	1·10
284	2¹/₂d. pale scarlet (3.5.51) ..	..	..	70	2·00
285	4d. light ultramarine	..	..	..	80	2·25
286	2s. 6d. yell-grn (H.M.S. *Victory*) (3.5.51)		6·50	3·75
287	5s. red (Dover) (3.5.51) ..	..	..	11·00	13·00
288	10s. ultramarine (St. George) (3.5.51)	..	15·00	13·00
280/8	..	..	..	Set of 9	32·00	42·00

Muscat

12 pies = 1 anna; 16 annas = 1 rupee

INDIAN POSTAL ADMINISTRATION

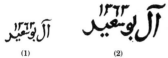

(1)   (2)

1944 (20 Nov). *Bicentenary of Al-Busaid Dynasty. Nos.* 259/60, 265/8 *and* 269a/77 *(King George VI) of India optd* ("AL BUSAID 1363" *in Arabic script) as* T **1** *or* **2** *(rupee values).*

1	3 p. slate ..	..	..	..	30	4·00
2	½ a. purple	..	..	..	30	4·00
3	9 p. green ..	..	..	..	30	4·00
4	1 a. carmine	..	..	..	30	4·00
5	1½ a. dull violet	..	..	..	30	4·00
6	2 a. vermilion	..	..	..	30	4·00
7	3 a. bright violet ..	..	..	50	4·00
8	3½ a. bright blue	..	..	..	50	4·00
9	4 a. brown	..	..	..	50	4·00
10	6 a. turquoise-green	..	..	65	4·00
11	8 a. slate-violet	..	..	..	65	4·25
12	12 a. lake ..	..	..	..	80	5·00
13	14 a. purple	..	..	..	1·00	7·00
14	1 r. grey and red-brown ..	..	..	50	9·00
15	2 r. purple and brown	..	..	70	14·00
1/15	..	..	..	*Set of* 15	7·00	70·00

OFFICIAL STAMPS

1944 (20 Nov). *Bicentenary of Al-Busaid Dynasty. Nos.* O138, O143, O144a/6 *and* 146b/50 *of India optd as* T **1** *or* **2** (1 r.).

O 1	3 p. slate	..	..	..	50	8·50
O 2	½ a. purple	..	..	..	50	8·50
O 3	9 p. green	..	..	..	50	8·50
O 4	1 a. carmine	..	..	..	50	8·50
O 5	1½ a. dull violet ..	..	..	50	8·50
O 6	2 a. vermilion ..	..	..	50	8·50
O 7	2½ a. bright violet	..	..	1·00	8·50
O 8	4 a. brown	..	..	..	1·00	8·50
O 9	8 a. slate-violet ..	..	..	1·00	9·00
O10	1 r. grey and red-brown	..	..	2·25	18·00
O1/10	..	..	..	*Set of* 10	7·50	85·00

From December 1947 there was a Pakistani postal administration and stamps of Pakistan were used until 31 March 1948. The subsequent British administration operated from 1 April 1948 to 29 April 1966 when the stamps of the BRITISH POSTAL AGENCIES IN EASTERN ARABIA were used.

Newfoundland

100 cents = 1 dollar

GOVERNMENT BY COMMISSION

107 Codfish

111 Reindeer

Die I

Die II

No. 258. In Die II the shading of the King's face is heavier and dots have been added down the ridge of the nose. The top frame line is thicker and more uniform.

113 Salmon

114 Newfoundland Dog

115 Harp Seal

116 Cape Race

117 Sealing Fleet

118 Fishing Fleet

Fish-hook flaw (R. 1/7 or 3/3 from different plates)

Re-entry to right of design (inscr oval, tree and value) (R.4/8)

(Recess P.B.)

121 Paper Mills

122 Bell Island

1937 (12 May). *Coronation Issue. As Nos. 95/7 of Antigua, but name and value uncoloured on coloured background. P* 11×11½.

254	2 c. green	..	..	..	1·00	2·00
255	4 c. carmine	..	..	..	1·60	2·25
256	5 c. purple	..	..	..	3·00	2·50
254/6	..	..	..	*Set of* 3	5·00	6·00
254/6 Perf "Specimen"	..	..	*Set of* 3	70·00

144 Codfish

1937 (12 May). *Additional Coronation Issue. T* **144** *and similar horiz designs. W* **106**. *A. P* 14–13½ *(line). B. P* 13 *(comb)*.*

				A		B	
257	1 c. grey	..	..	..	1·50	20	22·00	38·00
	a. Pair, with and without wmk	..	..	19·00	—	—	—
	b. Fish-hook flaw	..	..	16·00	—	£170	—
258	3 c. orange-brown (I)	..	3·50	2·00	2·50	1·75
	a. Pair, with and without wmk	..	..	50·00	—	†
	b. Die I. Imperf between (horiz or vert pair)	..	£350	—	†
	c. Die II	..	..	2·50	2·50	4·00	1·75
	d. Die II. Imperf between (horiz or vert pair)	..	£450	—	†
	e. Die II. Pair, with and without wmk	..	—	—	85·00	—
259	7 c. bright ultramarine	..	2·00	75	£250	£325
	a. Pair, with and without wmk	..	..	—	—	†
	b. Re-entry at right	..	40·00	—	—	—
260	8 c. scarlet	..	..	1·75	2·00	5·50	6·00
	a. Pair, with and without wmk	..	..	50·00	—	†
	b. Imperf between (horiz or vert pair)	..	£500	—	†
	c. Imperf (pair)	..	..	£250	—	†

261 10 c. blackish brown .. .. 3·25 5·00 3·25 8·00
  a. Pair, with and without
    wmk .. .. .. 55·00 — †
  w. Wmk inverted .. .. † 75·00 —
262 14 c. black .. .. .. 1·40 2·00 £4000 £2000
  a. Pair, with and without
    wmk .. .. .. 42·00 — †
263 15 c. claret .. .. .. 8·50 4·00 16·00 17·00
  a. Pair, with and without
    wmk .. .. .. 55·00 — 85·00 —
  b. Imperf between (vert
    pair) .. .. .. £350 — †
  w. Wmk inverted .. .. 75·00 — †
264 20 c. green .. .. .. 2·25 4·50 2·50 7·00
  a. Pair, with and without
    wmk .. .. .. 95·00 — †
  b. Imperf between (vert
    pair) .. .. .. £600 — †
265 24 c. light blue .. .. 2·25 2·50 18·00 18·00
  a. Pair, with and without
    wmk .. .. .. 95·00 — †
  b. Imperf between (vert
    pair) .. .. .. £600 — †
266 25 c. slate .. .. .. 2·75 1·75 18·00 30·00
  a. Pair, with and without
    wmk .. .. .. 95·00 — †
267 48 c. slate-purple .. .. 8·50 4·50 28·00 45·00
  a. Pair, with and without
    wmk .. .. .. £130 — †
  b. Imperf between (vert
    pair) .. .. .. £600 — †
257/67 .. .. Set of 11 32·00 26·00
Designs:—3 c. Map of Newfoundland; 7 c. Reindeer; 8 c. Corner Brook paper mills; 10 c. Salmon; 14 c. Newfoundland dog; 15 c. Harp Seal; 20 c. Cape Race; 24 c. Bell Island; 25 c. Sealing fleet; 48 c. The Banks fishing fleet.
*The line perforation A was produced by two machines measuring respectively 13.7 and 14.1. The comb perforation B measures 13.3×13.2.
Four used examples of No. 259B have now been identified on separate covers.
The paper used had the watermarks spaced for smaller format stamps. In consequence the individual watermarks are out of alignment so that stamps from the second vertical row were without watermark.

155 King George VI   **156** Queen Mother

(Recess P.B.)

1938 (12 May). T 155/6 and similar vert designs. W 106 (sideways). P 13½ (comb).
268 2 c. green .. .. .. 1·50 50
  a. Pair, with and without wmk £130
  b. Imperf (pair) .. .. .. 75·00
269 3 c. carmine .. .. .. 1·00 50
  a. Perf 14 (line) £325 £180
  b. Pair, with and without wmk £180
  c. Imperf (pair) .. .. .. 70·00
270 4 c. light blue.. .. .. 1·75 20
  a. Pair, with and without wmk .. .. 80·00
  b. Pair, with and without wmk .. .. 70·00
271 7 c. deep ultramarine .. .. 75 3·25
  a. Imperf (pair) .. .. .. 90·00
268/71 .. .. .. Set of 4 4·50 4·00
Designs:— 4 c. Queen Elizabeth II as princess; 7 c. Queen Mary. For similar designs, perf 12½, see Nos. 277/281.

NEW INFORMATION

The editor is always interested to correspond with people who have new information that will improve or correct the Catalogue.

159 King George VI and Queen Elizabeth

(Recess B.W.)

1939 (17 June). Royal Visit. No wmk. P 13½.
272 **159** 5 c. deep ultramarine .. .. .. 1·00 30

2

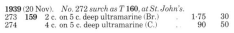

▲   **CENTS**   ▲
(160)

1939 (20 Nov). No. 272 surch as T 160, at St. John's.
273 **159** 2 c. on 5 c. deep ultramarine (Br.) . 1·75 30
274   4 c. on 5 c. deep ultramarine (C.) .. 90 50

161 Grenfell on the Strathcona **162** Memorial University
(after painting by Gribble)   College

(Recess C.B.N.)

1941 (1 Dec). Sir Wilfred Grenfell's Labrador Mission. P 12.
275 **161** 5 c. blue 30 45

(Recess Waterlow)

1941–44. W 106 (sideways* on vert designs). P 12½ (line).
276 **107** 1 c. grey 20 30
277 **155** 2 c. green 30 20
  w. Wmk top of shield to right .. 35·00
278 **156** 3 c. carmine 30 10
  a. Pair, with and without wmk .. 70·00
  w. Wmk top of shield to right .. 35·00
279 **–** 4 c. blue (As No. 270) .. .. 2·25 20
  a. Pair, with and without wmk .. £130
  w. Wmk top of shield to right .. 35·00
280 **111** 5 c. violet (Die I) (p 13½ comb) .. 85·00
  a. Perf 12½ (line) (6.42) .. .. 2·75 30
  ab. Pair, with and without wmk .. £110
  ac. Printed double £275
  ad. Imperf vert (horiz pair) £325
  b. Imperf (pair) £120
281 **–** 7 c. deep ultramarine (As No. 271) . 6·00 8·00
  a. Pair, with and without wmk .. £130
282 **121** 8 c. rose-red .. .. .. 1·00 1·75
  a. Pair, with and without wmk .. £130
283 **113** 10 c. black-brown .. .. .. 1·75 75
284 **114** 14 c. black .. .. 2·00 4·00
285 **115** 15 c. claret .. .. 5·50 7·00
286 **116** 20 c. green .. .. 5·50 5·50
287 **122** 24 c. blue .. .. 3·25 9·00
288 **117** 25 c. slate .. .. 6·50 7·50
289 **118** 48 c. red-brown (1944) .. .. 3·00 5·50
276/89 .. .. Set of 14 35·00 45·00
*The normal sideways watermark shows the top of the shield to left, as seen from the back of the stamp.
Nos. 276/89 are redrawn versions of previous designs with slightly larger dimensions; the 5 c. for example, measures 21 mm in width as opposed to the 20.4 mm of the Perkins Bacon printings.
No. 280. For Die I see note relating to No. 225.

(Recess C.B.N.)

1943 (2 Jan). *P* 12.

290 **162** 30 c. carmine .. .. 1·00 1·10

163 St. John's

TWO

CENTS

(164)

(Recess C.B.N.)

1943 (1 June). *Air. P* 12.

291 **163** 7 c. ultramarine 40 55

1946 (21 Mar). *No.* 290 *surch locally with T* **164**.

292 **162** 2 c. on 30 c. carmine 30 45

165 Queen Elizabeth II
when Princess

166 Cabot off Cape Bonavista

(Recess Waterlow)

1947 (21 Apr). *Princess Elizabeth's 21st Birthday. W* **106** (*sideways*). *P* 12½.

293 **165** 4 c. light blue 30 45

   a. Imperf vert (horiz pair) £225

(Recess Waterlow)

1947 (23 June). *450th Anniv of Cabot's Discovery of Newfoundland. W* **106** (*sideways*). *P* 12½.

294 **166** 5 c. mauve 20 60

   a. Imperf between (horiz pair) . £1100

POSTAGE DUE STAMPS

D 1

D 6ac

(Litho John Dickinson & Co, Ltd)

1939 (1 May)–**49**. *P* 10.

D1	D 1	1 c. green	..	..	2·00	7·50
		a. Perf 11 (1949)	..	..	3·00	8·50
D2		2 c. vermilion	..	..	8·00	6·50
		a. Perf 11 × 9 (1946) ..	..	..	8·50	17·00
D3		3 c. ultramarine	..	..	4·50	18·00
		a. Perf 11 × 9 (1949) ..	..	..	10·00	24·00
		b. Perf 9	..	..	£425	
D4		4 c. orange	..	..	7·50	15·00
		a. Perf 11 × 9 (May 1948)	..	..	11·00	45·00
D5		5 c. brown	..	..	5·50	22·00
D6		10 c. violet	..	..	6·00	15·00
		a. Perf 11 (W **106**) (1949)	..	..	22·00	70·00
		ab. Ditto. Imperf between (vert pair)	..	£650	
		ac. "POSTAGE LUE" (R 3/3 or 3/8)	..	90·00	£225
D1/6 ..		..	..	..	*Set of* 6	30·00	75·00

Newfoundland joined the Dominion of Canada on 31 March 1949.

New Hebrides

100 gold centimes = 1 gold franc

ANGLO-FRENCH CONDOMINIUM

STAMPS INSCRIBED IN ENGLISH

6 Lopevi Is and Outrigger Canoe

(Des J. Kerhor. Eng J. G. Hall. Recess B.W.)

1938 (1 June). *Gold Currency. Wmk Mult Script CA. P 12.*

52	**6**	5 c. blue-green			2·50	2·75
53		10 c. orange			1·25	60
54		15 c. bright violet			3·00	2·75
55		20 c. scarlet			1·60	1·40
56		25 c. reddish brown			1·60	1·40
57		30 c. blue			1·90	1·25
58		40 c. grey-olive			4·50	3·00
59		50 c. purple			1·60	60
60		1 f. red/*green*			4·00	7·50
61		2 f. blue/*green*			30·00	16·00
62		5 f. red/*yellow*			70·00	48·00
63		10 f. violet/*blue*			£200	75·00
52/63				*Set of* 12	£300	£140
52/63 Perf "Specimen"				*Set of* 12	£225	

(Recess Waterlow)

1949 (10 Oct). *75th Anniv of U.P.U. As Nos. 145/8 of Jamaica. Wmk Mult Script CA. P 13¹/₂×14.*

64		10 c. red-orange			30	15
65		15 c. violet			30	15
66		30 c. ultramarine			30	15
67		50 c. purple			40	20
64/7				*Set of* 4	1·10	60

POSTAGE DUE STAMPS

POSTAGE DUE

(D 2)

1938 (1 June). *Optd with Type* D 2, *by B.W.*

D 6	**6**	5 c. blue-green			19·00	27·00
D 7		10 c. orange			19·00	27·00
D 8		20 c. scarlet			25·00	38·00
D 9		40 c. grey-olive			35·00	48·00
D10		1 f. red/*green*			45·00	60·00
D6/10				*Set of* 5	£130	£180
D6/10 Perf "Specimen"				*Set of* 5	£120	

STAMPS INSCRIBED IN FRENCH

1938 (1 June). *Gold Currency. Wmk "R F" in sheet or without wmk. P* 12.

F53	**6**	5 c. blue-green			1·60	2·00
F54		10 c. orange			1·60	1·40
F55		15 c. bright violet			1·25	2·00
F56		20 c. scarlet			1·60	1·75
F57		25 c. reddish brown			4·00	2·25
F58		30 c. blue			4·00	1·75
F59		40 c. grey-olive			1·25	4·00
F60		50 c. purple			1·25	1·40

F61	**6**	1 f. lake/*pale green* (*shades*)			1·60	3·00
F62		2 f. blue/*pale green* (*shades*)			24·00	25·00
F63		5 f. red/*yellow*			45·00	38·00
F64		10 f. violet/*blue*			£110	80·00
F53/64				*Set of* 12	£170	£140
F53/64 Perf "Specimen"				*Set of* 12	£300	

France Libre

(F 6)

1941 (15 Apr). *Adherence to General de Gaulle. Optd with Type* F 6, *at Nouméa, New Caledonia.*

F65	**6**	5 c. blue-green			2·50	17·00
F66		10 c. orange			4·00	16·00
F67		15 c. bright violet			5·50	22·00
F68		20 c. scarlet			14·00	21·00
F69		25 c. reddish brown			14·00	24·00
F70		30 c. blue			14·00	22·00
F71		40 c. grey-olive			14·00	24·00
F72		50 c. purple			14·00	21·00
F73		1 f. lake/*pale green*			14·00	21·00
F74		2 f. blue/*pale green*			14·00	24·00
F75		5 f. red/*yellow*			14·00	24·00
F76		10 f. violet/*blue*			14·00	24·00
F65/76				*Set of* 12	£120	£225

1949 (10 Oct). *75th Anniv of U.P.U. As Nos. 64/7. Wmk "R F" in sheet or without wmk. P* 13¹/₂.

F77		10 c. red-orange			2·25	3·50
F78		15 c. violet			4·50	5·50
F79		30 c. ultramarine			5·75	8·50
F80		50 c. purple			6·75	9·00
F77/80				*Set of* 4	17·00	24·00

POSTAGE DUE STAMPS

CHIFFRE TAXE

(FD 2)

1938 (1 June). *Optd with Type* FD 2, *by Bradbury, Wilkinson.*

FD65	**6**	5 c. blue-green			13·00	30·00
FD66		10 c. orange			16·00	30·00
FD67		20 c. scarlet			22·00	40·00
FD68		40 c. grey-olive			42·00	75·00
FD69		1 f. lake/*pale green*			45·00	80·00
FD65/9				*Set of* 5	£120	£225
FD65/9 Optd "Specimen"				*Set of* 5	£200	

1941 (15 Apr). *Nos. FD65/9 optd with Type* F 6 *at Nouméa, New Caledonia.*

FD77	**6**	5 c. blue-green			8·75	29·00
FD78		10 c. orange			8·75	29·00
FD79		20 c. scarlet			8·75	29·00
FD80		40 c. grey-olive			8·75	29·00
FD81		1 f. lake/*pale green*			15·00	29·00
FD77/81				*Set of* 5	45·00	£130

MINIMUM PRICE

The minimum price quote is 10p which represents a handling charge rather than a basis for valuing common stamps. For further notes about prices see introductory pages.

New Zealand

12 pence (d) = 1 shilling; 20 shillings = 1 pound

DOMINION

43 "Single" Wmk

98 "Multiple Wmk"

Broken ribbon flaw (R. 6/6 of Pl 8)

(Des W. J. Cooch. Recess B.W.)

1938–44. W 98. P 14×13½.

603	108	½d. green (1.3.38) ..	..	.. 6·50	10
		w. Wmk inverted ..	..	.. 9·50	2·00
604		½d. orange-brown (10.7.41)	..	20	10
		w. Wmk inverted ..	..		
605		1d. scarlet (1.7.38)	..	.. 5·00	10
		a. Broken ribbon ..	..	.. 40·00	
		w. Wmk inverted ..	..	.. 9·50	2·00
606		1d. green (21.7.41)	..	20	10
		w. Wmk inverted ..	..	.. 25·00	15·00
607	108a	1½d. purple-brown (26.7.38)	..	.. 26·00	1·60
		w. Wmk inverted ..	..	.. 38·00	3·50
608		1½d. scarlet (1.2.44)	..	20	30
		w. Wmk inverted ..	..	—	55·00
609		3d. blue (26.9.41) ..	..	20	10
		w. Wmk inverted ..	..	—	40·00
603/9		.. ..	Set of 7	35·00	1·90

For other values see Nos. 680/9.

106 King George VI and
Queen Elizabeth

(Recess B.W.)

1937 (13 May). *Coronation.* W 98. P 14 × 13½.

599	106	1d. carmine ..	.. ..	30	10
600		2½d. Prussian blue	.. ..	1·25	1·75
601		6d. red-orange ..	.. ..	1·75	1·40
599/601		.. .. ..	Set of 3	3·00	2·75

109 Children playing

110 Beach Ball

(Des J. Berry. Recess B.W.)

1938 (1 Oct). *Health Stamp.* W 98. P 14 × 13½.

610	109	1d. + 1d. scarlet	.. ..	.. 3·50	1·60

(Des S. Hall. Recess Note Printing Branch, Commonwealth Bank
of Australia, Melbourne)

1939 (16 Oct). *Health Stamps. Surcharged with new value.* W 43.
P 11.

611	110	1d. on ½d. + ½d. green	..	.. 2·50	3·25
612		2d. on 1d. + 1d. scarlet..	..	.. 3·50	3·25

107 Rock climbing

108　　King George VI

108a

(Des G. Bull and J. Berry. Recess John Ash, Melbourne)

1937 (1 Oct). *Health Stamp.* W 43. P 11.

602	107	1d. + 1d. scarlet	.. ..	.. 1·75	2·50

111 Arrival of the Maoris, 1350

115 Signing Treaty of
Waitangi, 1840

(Des L. C. Mitchell (½d., 3d., 4d.); J. Berry (others). Recess B.W.)

1940 (2 Jan–8 Mar).   *Centenary of Proclamation of British Sovereignty. T* 111, 115 *and similar designs. W* 98. *P* 14 × 13½ (2½d.), 13½ × 14 (5d.) *or* 13½ (*others*).

613	½d. blue-green	..	30	10
614	1d. chocolate and scarlet	..	2·75	10
615	1½d. light blue and mauve	..	30	20
616	2d. blue-green and chocolate	..	1·50	10
617	2½d. blue-green and blue	..	1·75	55
618	3d. purple and carmine	..	3·00	45
619	4d. chocolate and lake	..	15·00	90
620	5d. pale blue and brown	..	6·00	2·75
621	6d. emerald-green and violet	..	13·00	70
622	7d. black and red	..	1·50	3·75
623	8d. black and red (8.3)	..	13·00	2·00
624	9d. olive-green and orange ..	..	7·50	1·50
625	1s. sage-green and deep green	..	17·00	3·00
613/25	..	*Set of* 13	75·00	14·00

Designs: *Horiz* (*as T* 111)—1d. H.M.S. *Endeavour*, chart of N.Z., and Capt. Cook; 1½d. British Monarchs; 2d. Tasman with *Heemskerk* and chart; 3d. Landing of immigrants, 1840; 4d. Road, Rail, Sea and Air transport; 6d. *Dunedin* and "Frozen Mutton Route" to London; 7d., 8d. Maori council; 9d. Gold mining in 1861 and 1940. (*As T* 115)—5d. H.M.S. *Britomart* at Akaroa, 1840. *Vert* (*as T* 111)—1s. Giant Kauri tree.

1940 (1 Oct).   *Health Stamps. As T* 110, *but without extra surcharge. W* 43. *P* 11.

626	110	1d. + ½d. blue-green	..	11·00	11·00
627		2d. + 1d. brown-orange	..	11·00	11·00

1^D   1^D

(123)   Inserted "2"   (124)

2,D 1941

1941.   *Surch as T* 123.

628	108	1d. on ½d. green (1.5.41)	..	..	70	10
629	108a	2d. on 1½d. purple-brown (4.41)	..	70	10
		a. Inserted "2"	..	..	£500	£300

The surcharge on No. 629 has only one figure, at top left, and there is only one square to obliterate the original value at bottom right.

The variety "Inserted 2" occurs on the 10th stamp, 10th row. It is identified by the presence of remnants of the damaged "2", and by the spacing of "2" and "D" which is variable and different from the normal.

(Typo Govt Printing Office, Wellington)

1941.   *As T* 91 (*Maori panel*) *but smaller* (17½×20½ *mm*). *Chalk-surfaced paper. P* 14×15. (*a*) *W* 43.

630	91	9d. scarlet and black (5.41)	..	80·00	22·00
		w. Wmk inverted	..	..	

(*b*) *W* 98

631	91	9d. scarlet and black (29.9.41)	..	3·00	2·00
		w. Wmk inverted	..	90·00	65·00

1941 (4 Oct).   *Health Stamps. Nos.* 626/7 *optd with T* 124.

632	110	1d. + ½d. blue-green	..	25	1·50
633		2d. + 1d. brown-orange	..	25	1·50

125 Boy and Girl on Swing

126 Princess Margaret

(Des S. Hall. Recess Note Printing Branch, Commonwealth Bank of Australia, Melbourne)

1942 (1 Oct).   *Health Stamps. W* 43. *P* 11.

634	125	1d. + ½d. blue-green	..	..	15	55
635		2d. + 1d. orange-red	..	..	15	50

(Des J. Berry. Recess B.W.)

1943 (1 Oct).   *Health Stamps. T* 126 *and similar triangular design. W* 98. *P* 12.

636		1d. + ½d. green	..	..	10	60
		a. Imperf between (vert pair)	..	£4500	
637		2d. + 1d. red-brown..	..	..	10	10
		a. Imperf between (vert pair)	..	£4500	£4500

Design:—2d. Queen Elizabeth II as Princess.

✦ TENPENCE ✦

(128)

1944 (1 May).   *No.* 615 *surch with T* 128.

662		10d. on 1½d. light blue and mauve	..	..	10	10

129 Queen Elizabeth II as Princess and Princess Margaret

130 Statue of Peter Pan, Kensington Gardens

(Recess B.W.)

1944 (9 Oct).   *Health Stamps. W* 98. *P* 13½.

663	129	1d. + ½d. green	..	..	15	15
664		2d. + 1d. blue	..	..	15	15

(Des J. Berry. Recess B.W.)

1945 (1 Oct).   *Health Stamps. W* 98. *P* 13½.

665	130	1d. + ½d. green and buff	..	..	10	15
		w. Wmk inverted	..	..	40·00	30·00
666		2d. + 1d. carmine and buff	..	10	15
		w. Wmk inverted	..	..	50·00	40·00

131 Lake Matheson

132 King George VI and Parliament House, Wellington

133 St. Paul's Cathedral

139 "St. George" (Wellington College War Memorial Window)

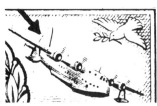

Printer's guide mark (R. 12/3)
Completed rudder (R. 2/4 of Pl 42883 and R. 3/2 of Pl 42796)

(Des J. Berry. Photo Harrison (1½d. and 1s.). Recess B.W. (1d. and 2d.) and Waterlow (others))

1946 (1 Apr). *Peace issue.* T **131/3, 139** *and similar designs.* W **98** (*sideways on* 1½*d.*). P 13 (1*d.,* 2*d.*), 14×14½ (1½*d.,* 1*s.*), 13½ (*others*).

667	½d. green and brown	..	.. 15	20
	a. Printer's guide mark	..	.. 5·50	
	w. Wmk inverted	..	.. 45·00	35·00
668	1d. green ..	..	.. 10	10
	w. Wmk inverted	..	. 32·00	22·00
669	1½d. scarlet	..	.. 10	10
	w. Wmk sideways inverted	..	.. 10	10
670	2d. purple	..	.. 15	10
671	3d. ultramarine and grey	..	.. 20	15
	a. Completed rudder	..	.. 5·00	
672	4d. bronze-green and orange	..	.. 20	20
	w. Wmk inverted	..	.. 80·00	35·00
673	5d. green and ultramarine	..	.. 20	30
674	6d. chocolate and vermilion	..	.. 15	10
675	8d. black and carmine	..	.. 15	10
676	9d. blue and black	..	.. 15	10
677	1s. grey-black	..	.. 15	15
667/77	.. .. ..	..	*Set of* 11 1·50	1·40

Designs: *Horiz* (*as* T **132**)—2d. The Royal Family. (*As* T **131**)—3d. R.N.Z.A.F. badge and airplanes; 4d. Army badge, tank and plough; 5d. Navy badge, H.M.N.Z.S. *Achilles* (cruiser) and *Dominion Monarch* (liner); 6d. N.Z. coat of arms, foundry and farm; 9d. Southern Alps and Franz Josef Glacier. *Vert* (*as* T **139**)—1s. National Memorial Campanile.

142 Soldier helping Child over Stile

(Des J. Berry. Recess Waterlow)

1946 (24 Oct). *Health Stamps.* W **98**. P 13½.

678	**142**	1d. + ½d. green and orange-brown	.. 10	10
		a. Yellow-green and orange-brown	.. 4·50	4·50
		w. Wmk inverted	.. 11·00	11·00
679		2d. + 1d. chocolate and orange-brown	10	10

144 King George VI   **145** Statue of Eros

Plate 1   Plate 2

(Des W. J. Cooch. Recess T **108***a*, B.W.; T **144**, D.L.R.)

1947–52. W **98** (*sideways on "shilling" values*). (*a*) P 14×13½.

680	108*a*	2d. orange	..	.. ..	15	10
		w. Wmk inverted	..	.. ..	70·00	
681		4d. bright purple	..	..	60	30
682		5d. slate	..	.. ..	50	50
683		6d. carmine ..	..	.. ..	40	10
		w. Wmk inverted	..	..	60·00	12·00
684		8d. violet	..	.. ..	65	30
685		9d. purple-brown	..	..	1·50	30
		w. Wmk inverted	..	..	30·00	7·50

(*b*) P 14

686	144	1s. red-brown and carmine (Plate 1)		1·40	60
		aw. Wmk sideways inverted		.. 9·00	6·00
		b. Wmk upright (Plate 1) ..		50	50
		c. Wmk upright (Plate 2) ..		2·25	60
		cw. Wmk inverted	..	.. 42·00	14·00
687		1s. 3d. red-brown and blue (Plate 2)		1·00	60
		aw. Wmk sideways inverted		.. 7·00	4·50
		b. Wmk upright (14.1.52) ..		2·25	3·25
		bw. Wmk inverted	..	..		
688		2s. brown-orange and green (Plate 1)		2·50	1·25
		aw. Wmk sideways inverted		.. 14·00	8·00
		b. Wmk upright (Plate 1) ..		2·50	4·25
689		3s. red-brown and grey (Plate 2)		2·50	2·75
		w. Wmk sideways inverted		.. 28·00	12·00
680/9		.. .. ..		*Set of* 9 9·25	6·00

In head-plate 2 the diagonal lines of the background have been strengthened and result in the upper corners and sides appearing more deeply shaded.

(Des J. Berry. Recess Waterlow)

1947 (1 Oct). *Health Stamps.* W **98** (*sideways*). P 13½.

690	145	1d. + ½d. green	..	.. 10	10
		w. Wmk sideways inverted	..	.. 20·00	20·00
691		2d. + 1d. carmine	..	.. 10	10
		w. Wmk sideways inverted	..	.. 32·00	32·00

146 Port Chalmers, 1848   **148** First Church, Dunedin

(Des J. Berry. Recess B.W.)

1948 (23 Feb). *Centennial of Otago.* T **146, 148** *and similar designs.* W **98** (*sideways on* 3*d.*). P 13½.

692		1d. blue and green	..	.. 10	2
		w. Wmk inverted ..	..	.. 22·00	20·0
693		2d. green and brown	..	.. 10	2
694		3d. purple ..	..	.. 10	2
695		6d. black and rose ..	..	.. 10	2
		w. Wmk inverted ..	..	.. —	£15
692/5		.. .. ..	..	*Set of* 4 30	7

Designs: *Horiz*—2d. Cromwell, Otago; 6d. University Otago.

150 Boy Sunbathing and Children   **151** Nurse and Child
Playing

(Des E. Linzell. Recess B.W.)

1948 (1 Oct).   *Health Stamps. W* **98**. *P* 13¹/₂.
696 **150** 1d. + ¹/₂d. blue and green 10   10
          w. Wmk inverted   ..   .. 18·00 17·00
697   2d. + 1d. purple and scarlet 10   10

1949 ROYAL VISIT ISSUE. Four stamps were prepared to
commemorate this event: 2d. Treaty House, Waitangi; 3d. H.M.S.
Vanguard; 5d. Royal portraits; 6d. Crown and sceptre. The visit did
not take place and the stamps were destroyed, although a few
examples of the 3d. later appeared on the market. A similar set was
prepared in 1952, but was, likewise, not issued.

(Des J. Berry. Photo Harrison)

1949 (3 Oct).   *Health Stamps. W* **98**. *P* 14 × 14¹/₂.
698 **151** 1d. + ¹/₂d. green 15   15
699   2d. + 1d. ultramarine 15   15
          a. No stop below "D" of "1D." (R.1/2) 6·50 15·00

1½d.

POSTAGE

(152)   **153** Queen Elizabeth II
and Prince Charles

1950 (28 July).   *As Type F* **6**, *but without value, surch with*
T 152. *W* **98** (*inverted*). *Chalk-surfaced paper. P* 14.
700 **F 6** 1¹/₂d. carmine 10   10
          w. Wmk upright ..   .. 1·50 1·50

(Des J. Berry and R. S. Phillips. Photo Harrison)

1950 (2 Oct).   *Health Stamps. W* **98**. *P* 14×14¹/₂.
701 **153** 1d. +¹/₂d. green 15   10
          w. Wmk inverted ..   .. 4·25 4·25
702   2d. +1d. plum 15   10
          w. Wmk inverted ..   .. 14·00 14·00

154 Christchurch   **155** Cairn on Lyttleton Hills
Cathedral

(Des L. C. Mitchell (2d.), J. A. Johnstone (3d.) and J. Berry (others).
Recess B.W.)

1950 (20 Nov).   *Centennial of Canterbury, N.Z. T* **154/5** *and*
similar designs. W **98** (*sideways on* 1d. *and* 3d.). *P* 13¹/₂.
703 1d. green and blue 15   25
704 2d. carmine and orange 15   25
705 3d. dark blue and blue 20   30
706 6d. brown and blue 20   40
707 1s. reddish purple and blue 20   50
703/7 ..   ..   ..   *Set of* 5 80 1·50
    Designs: *Vert* (*as T* **154**)—3d. John Robert Godley. *Horiz* (*as*
T **155**)—6d. Canterbury University College; 1s. Aerial view of
Timaru.

159 "Takapuna" class Yachts

(Des J. Berry and R. S. Phillips. Recess B.W.)

1951 (1 Nov).   *Health Stamps. W* **98**. *P* 13¹/₂.
708 **159** 1¹/₂d. + ¹/₂d. scarlet and yellow .. 15   50
709   2d. + 1d. deep green and yellow .. 15   10
          w. Wmk inverted ..   .. 40·00 40·00

STAMP BOOKLETS

B 1

1938 (Nov).   *Cream* (*No.* SB18) *or blue* (*No.* SB19) *covers as*
Type B **1**.
SB18 2s. booklet containing twelve ¹/₂d. and eighteen
          1d. (Nos. 603, 605) in blocks of 6 ..   .. £250
SB19 2s. 3d. booklet containing eighteen 1¹/₂d. (No.
          607) in blocks of 6 ..   ..   .. £225

POSTAGE DUE STAMPS

D 2   D 3

1937–38.   *"Wiggins Teape" thin, hard chalky paper. W* **43**.
P 14 × 15.
D37 **D 2** ¹/₂d. carmine and yellow-green (2.38) .. 18·00 32·00
D38   1d. carmine and yellow-green (1.37) .. 11·00 3·75
D39   2d. carmine and yellow-green (6.37) .. 27·00 13·00
D40   3d. carmine and yellow-green (11.37) 85·00 55·00
D37/40 ..   ..   ..   *Set of* 4 £120 95·00

(Des J. Berry. Typo Govt Printing Office, Wellington)

1939–49.   *P* 15×14. (*a*) *W* **43** (*sideways inverted*) (16.8.39).
D41 **D 3** ¹/₂d. turquoise-green ..   .. 5·00 5·00
D42   1d. carmine ..   ..   .. 2·50   30
          w. Wmk sideways ..   ..   — 1·50
D43   2d. bright blue ..   ..   .. 6·00 2·75
D44   3d. orange-brown ..   .. 19·00 24·00
          w. Wmk sideways
D41/4 ..   ..   ..   *Set of* 4 29·00 29·00

(b) W 98 (sideways (1d.) or sideways inverted (2d.))

D45	D 3	1d. carmine (4.49)	..	..	15·00 5·50*
D46		2d. bright blue (12.46)	..	..	7·00 1·00
		w. Wmk sideways (4.49)	..	..	2·50 8·00
D47		3d. orange-brown (1943)	..	..	40·00 32·00
		a. Wmk sideways inverted (6.45)			12·00 5·00
		aw. Wmk sideways (28.11.49)		..	8·00 8·00
D45/7	..	..	..	Set of 3	23·00 10·00*

*The use of Postage Due stamps ceased in 1951, our used price for No. D45 being for stamps postmarked after this date (price for examples clearly cancelled 1949–51, £27).

OFFICIAL STAMPS

Official   Official
(O 4)   (O 5)

1938–51. Nos. 603 etc., optd with Type O 4.

O134	108	½d. green (1.3.38)	..	..	13·00 1·75
O135		½d. brown-orange (1946)	..	1·60 2·50
O136		1d. scarlet (1.7.38)	..	..	14·00 15
O137		1d. green (10.7.41)	..	..	2·25 10
O138	108a	1½d. purple-brown (26.7.38)	..	..	75·00 18·00
O139		1½d. scarlet (2.4.51)	..	..	9·00 5·00
O140		3d. blue (16.10.41)	..	..	2·25 10
O134/40	..	..	..	Set of 7	£100 24·00

1940 (2 Jan–8 Mar). Centennial. Nos. 613, etc., optd with Type O 5.

O141		½d. blue-green (R.)	..	..	1·50 35
		a. "ff" joined, as Type O 4	..	50·00 60·00
O142		1d. chocolate and scarlet	..	..	4·00 10
		a. "ff" joined, as Type O 4	..	60·00 60·00
O143		1½d. light blue and mauve	..	..	2·25 2·00
O144		2d. blue-green and chocolate	..	..	4·00 10
		a. "ff" joined, as Type O 4	..	60·00 60·00
O145		2½d. blue-green and ultramarine	..	3·75 2·75
		a. "ff" joined, as Type O 4	..	60·00 65·00
O146		3d. purple and carmine (R.)	..	..	8·00 90
		a. "ff" joined, as Type O 4	..	42·00 60·00
O147		4d. chocolate and lake	..	..	48·00 2·00
		a. "ff" joined, as Type O 4	..	£140 80·00
O148		6d. emerald-green and violet	..	25·00 2·00
		a. "ff" joined, as Type O 4	..	70·00 70·00
O149		8d. black and red (8.3)	..	..	30·0Ω 17·00
		a. "ff" joined, as Type O 4	..	75·00 £100
O150		9d. olive-green and vermilion	..	10·00 7·00
O151		1s. sage-green and deep green	..	48·00 4·00
O141/51	..	..	..	Set of 11	£160 35·00

For this issue the Type O 4 overprint occurs on R.4/3 of the 2½d. and on R.1/10 of the other values.

1947–49. Nos. 680, etc., optd with Type O 4.

O152	108a	2d. orange	..	..	1·50 10
O153		4d. bright purple	..	..	4·00 1·00
O154		6d. carmine	..	..	10·00 40
O155		8d. violet	..	..	8·00 6·50
O156		9d. purple-brown	..	..	9·00 6·50
O157	144	1s. red-brown and carmine (wmk upright) (Plate 1)	..	16·00 95
		a. Wmk sideways (Plate 1) (1949)	8·00 8·00
		aw. Wmk sideways inverted	..	30·00
		b. Wmk upright (Plate 2)	..	20·00 7·00
		bw. Wmk inverted	..	..	50·00 26·00
O158		2s. brown-orange and green (wmk sideways) (Plate 1)	..	22·00 16·00
		a. Wmk upright (Plate 1)	..	32·00 35·00
O152/8	..	..	..	Set of 7	55·00 28·00

LIFE INSURANCE DEPARTMENT

L 2 Lighthouse

1944–47. W 98. P 14 × 15.

L37	L 2	½d. yellow-green (7.47)	..	..	4·00 6·50
L38		1d. scarlet (6.44)	..	..	2·00 1·75
L39		2d. yellow (1946)	..	..	9·00 12·00
L40		3d. brown-lake (10.46)	..	14·00 24·00
L41		6d. pink (7.47)	..	..	10·00 27·00
L37/41	..	..	..	Set of 5	35·00 65·00

L 3 Castlepoint Lighthouse   L 6 Cape Campbell Lighthouse

(Des J. Berry. Recess B.W.).

1947 (1 Aug)–65. Type L 3, L 6 and similar designs. W 98 (sideways on 1d., 2d., 2½d.). P 13½.

L42		½d. grey-green and orange-red	..	1·00 60
L43		1d. olive-green and pale blue	..	1·00 50
L44		2d. deep blue and grey-black	..	70 30
L45		2½d. black and bright blue (white opaque paper) (4.11.63)	..	9·50 13·00
L46		3d. mauve and pale blue	..	..	2·50 35
L47		4d. brown and yellow-orange	..	2·50 85
		a. Wmk sideways (white opaque paper) (13.10.65)	5·00 13·00
L48		6d. chocolate and blue	..	..	3·00 1·25
L49		1s. red-brown and blue	..	..	3·25 2·00
L42/49	..	..	..	Set of 8	21·00 17·00

Designs: Horiz (as Type L 3)–1d Taiaroa lighthouse; 2d. Cape Palliser lighthouse; 6d. The Brothers lighthouse. Vert (as Type L 6)–3d. Eddystone lighthouse; 4d. Stephens Island lighthouse; 1s. Cape Brett lighthouse.

POSTAL FISCAL STAMPS

35/-

F 6   (F 7)

(Des H. L. Richardson. Typo Govt Ptg Office)

1931–40. As Type F 6 (various frames). W 43. P 14.

(i) Thick, opaque, chalk-surfaced "Cowan" paper, with horizontal mesh (1931–35)

F145	1s. 3d. lemon (4.31)	..	..	..	10·00 35·0C
F146	1s. 3d. orange-yellow	..	..	4·25 4·25
F147	2s. 6d. deep brown	..	..	13·00 3·75
F148	4s. red	..	..	..	14·00 4·5C
F149	5s. green	..	..	..	15·00 6·5C
F150	6s. carmine-rose	..	..	32·00 12·0C
F151	7s. blue	..	..	..	27·00 16·0C
F152	7s. 6d. olive-grey	..	..	55·00 80·0C
F153	8s. slate-violet	..	..	28·00 25·0€
F154	9s. brown-orange	..	..	30·00 25·0€
F155	10s. carmine-lake	..	..	24·00 8·0€
F156	12s. 6d. deep plum (9.35)	..	..	£140 £14:
F157	15s. sage-green	..	..	60·00 28·0€
F158	£1 pink	..	..	..	60·00 17·0€
F159	25s. greenish blue	..	..	£250 £37!
F160	30s. brown (1935)	..	..	£250 £14!
F161	35s. orange-yellow	..	..	£2250 £275€
F162	£2 bright purple	..	..	£300 60·0€
F163	£2 10s. red	..	..	£225 £30€

F164	£3 green	.. .. ..	£300	£170
F165	£3 10s. rose (1935)	.. ..	£1200	£1000
F166	£4 light blue (1935)	.. ..	£325	£130
F167	£4 10s. deep olive-grey (1935)	..	£1100	£1100
F168	£5 indigo-blue	.. .. ..	£325	90·00

(ii) *Thin, hard "Wiggins Teape" paper with vertical mesh* (1936–40)

(a) Chalk-surfaced (1936–39)

F169	1s. 3d. pale orange-yellow	..	9·00	2·50
F170	2s. 6d. dull brown	.. ..	35·00	2·75
F171	4s. pale red-brown	.. ..	48·00	4·75
F172	5s. green	.. ..	55·00	6·00
	w. Wmk inverted	.. ..		
F173	6s. carmine-rose	.. ..	55·00	21·00
F174	7s. pale blue	.. .. ..	60·00	25·00
F175	8s. slate-violet ..	.. ..	85·00	40·00
F176	9s. brown-orange	.. ..	90·00	55·00
F177	10s. pale carmine-lake ..	..	90·00	6·50
F178	15s. sage-green ..	.. ..	£140	45·00
F179	£1 pink	.. .. ..	£100	23·00
F180	30s. brown (1.39)	.. ..	£350	£130
F181	35s. orange-yellow	.. ..	£3000	£3000
F182	£2 bright purple (1937)	..	£400	75·00
	w. Wmk inverted	.. ..		
F183	£3 green (1937)	.. ..	£425	£180
F184	£5 indigo-blue (1937) ..	..	£600	£150

(b) Unsurfaced (1940)

F185	7s. 6d. olive-grey ..	.. ..	£140	90·00

Not all values listed above were stocked at ordinary post offices as some of them were primarily required for fiscal purposes but all were valid for postage.

1939. *No.* F161 *surch with Type* F *7.*

F186	35/- on 35s. orange-yellow ..	..	£400	£225

Because the 35s. orange-yellow could so easily be confused with the 1s. 3d. in the same colour it was surcharged.

1940 (June). *New values surch as Type* F *7.* W *43. "Wiggins Teape" chalk-surfaced paper.* P *14.*

F187	3/6 on 3s. 6d. grey-green ..	..	45·00	14·00
F188	5/6 on 5s. 6d. lilac ..	..	75·00	42·00
F189	11/- on 11s. yellow ..	..	£130	95·00
F190	22/- on 22s. scarlet ..	..	£325	£225
F187/90	.. .. ..	*Set of* 4	£500	£325

These values were primarily needed for fiscal use.

1940–58. *As Type* F *6* (*various frames*). W *98.*

(i) P *14. "Wiggins Teape" chalk-surfaced paper with vertical mesh* (1940–56)

F191	1s. 3d. orange-yellow ..	..	6·00	1·25
	w. Wmk inverted	..		
F192	1s. 3d. yellow and black (*wmk inverted*) (14.6.55) ..	..	1·00	60
	aw. Wmk upright (9.9.55)	..	25·00	25·00
	b. Error. Yellow and blue (*wmk inverted*) (7.56) ..	..	3·00	5·50
F193	2s. 6d. deep brown	..	6·50	30
	w. Wmk inverted (3.49)		6·50	30
F194	4s. red-brown ..	..	11·00	70
	w. Wmk inverted (3.49)		13·00	70
F195	5s. green	..	17·00	80
	w. Wmk inverted (1.5.50)		19·00	80
F196	6s. carmine-rose	..	30·00	3·25
	w. Wmk inverted (1948)		30·00	2·50
F197	7s. pale blue ..	..	30·00	4·25
F198	7s. 6d. ol-grey (*wmk inverted*) (21.12.50)	60·00	50·00
F199	8s. slate-violet ..	..	48·00	17·00
	w. Wmk inverted (6.12.50)		42·00	17·00
F200	9s. brown-orange (1.46)	..	21·00	32·00
	w. Wmk inverted (9.1.51)		38·00	32·00
F201	10s. carmine-lake	..	27·00	2·25
	w. Wmk inverted (4.50)		27·00	2·50
F202	15s. sage-green ..	..	42·00	17·00
	w. Wmk inverted (8.12.50)		50·00	25·00
F203	£1 pink ..	..	26·00	3·50
	w. Wmk inverted (1.2.50)		38·00	4·00
F204	25s. greenish blue (1946)	..	£325	£350
	w. Wmk inverted (7.53)		£350	£375
F205	30s. brown (1946)	..	£225	£100
	w. Wmk inverted (9.49)		£200	£100
F206	£2 bright purple (1946)	..	80·00	18·00
	w. Wmk inverted (17.6.52)		80·00	18·00

F207	£2 10s. red (*wmk inverted*) (9.8.51)	..	£225	£225
F208	£3 green (1946)	.. ..	£110	48·00
	w. Wmk inverted (17.6.52)	..	£100	45·00
F209	£3 10s. rose (11.48)	..	£1400	£1000
	w. Wmk inverted (5.52)	..	£1400	£1000
F210	£4 light blue (*wmk inverted*) (12.2.52)	£120	80·00
	w. Wmk upright	.. ..	†	—
F211	£5 indigo-blue ..	.. ..	£200	48·00
	w. Wmk inverted (11.9.50)	..	£160	45·00
F191/211	.. .. ..	*Set of* 21	£2500	£1700

 I.

 II.

3s. 6d.

Type I. Broad serifed capitals

Type II. Taller capitals, without serifs

Surcharged as Type F *7*

F212	3/6 on 3s. 6d. grey-green (I) (1942)	..	20·00	6·00
	w. Wmk inverted (12.10.50)	..	24·00	6·50
F213	3/6 on 3s. 6d. grey-green (II) (6.53)	..	12·00	35·00
	w. Wmk inverted (6.53)	..	28·00	35·00
F214	5/6 on 5s. 6d. lilac (1944)	..	35·00	15·00
	w. Wmk inverted (13.9.50)	..	35·00	15·00
F215	11/- on 11s. yellow (1942)	..	70·00	45·00
F216	22/- on 22s. scarlet (1945)	..	£225	£130
	w. Wmk inverted (1.3.50)	..	£225	£130
F212/16	.. .. ..	*Set of* 5	£325	£200

(ii) P *14×13½. "Wiggins Teape" unsurfaced paper with horizontal mesh* (1956–58)

F217	1s. 3d. yellow and black (11.56)	..	1·50	1·50
	w. Wmk inverted	..	16·00	16·00
F218	£1 pink (20.10.58)	.. ..	32·00	12·00

No. F192b had the inscription printed in blue in error but as many as 378,000 were printed.

From 1949–53 inferior paper had to be used and for technical reasons it was necessary to feed the paper into the machine in a certain way which resulted in whole printings with the watermark inverted for most values.

COOK ISLANDS

20 Capt. Cook landing

21 Capt. Cook

22 Double Maori Canoe

23 Natives working Cargo

24 Port of Avarua

25 R.M.S. *Monowai*

1936 (15 July)–**44**.   *Stamps of New Zealand optd with T* **19**. W **43**. *P* 14.

(*a*) *T* **72** (*King George V*). *Cowan thick, opaque chalk-surfaced paper*

| 116 | 2s. light blue (No. 469) .. | .. | .. | 12·00 | 42·00 |
| 117 | 3s. pale mauve (No. 470) | .. | .. | 13·00 | 60·00 |

(*b*) *Type* F **6**. *Cowan thick, opaque chalk-surfaced paper*

118	2s. 6d. deep brown (No. F147)	..	..	17·00	55·00
119	5s. green (No. F149) (R.)	..	..	20·00	75·00
120	10s. carmine-lake (No. F155)	..	..	38·00	£120
121	£1 pink (No. F158)	..	..	55·00	£150
118/21	..	..	*Set of* 4	£110	£350

(*c*) *Type* F **6**. *Thin, hard, chalk-surfaced Wiggins, Teape paper*

122	2s. 6d. dull brown (No. F170) (12.40)	..	80·00	80·00
123	5s. green (No. F172) (R.) (10.40)		£275	£275
123*a*	10s. pale carmine-lake (No. F177) (11.44)		£120	£150
123*b*	£3 green (No. F183) (R.) (date?)	..	£325	£500
122/3*b*	..	..	..	*Set of* 4	£700	£900

COOK
IS'DS.

(28)

IS'DS.

Small second "S"
(R. 1/2)

1937 (1 June). *Coronation. Nos.* 599/601 *of New Zealand* (*inscr* "12th MAY 1937") *optd with T* **28**.

124	1d. carmine	..	..	..	40	10
	a. Small second "S"	..	..	9·00	
125	2½d. Prussian blue..	..	..	80	20
	a. Small second "S"	..	..	17·00	
126	6d. red-orange	..	..	..	80	20
	a. Small second "S"	..	..	17·00	
124/6	..	..	..	*Set of* 3	1·75	45

29 King George VI

30 Native Village

31 Native Canoe   32 Tropical Landscape

(Des J. Berry (2s., 3s., and frame of 1s.). Eng B.W. Recess Govt Ptg. Office, Wellington)

1938 (2 May). W **43** *of New Zealand. P* 14.

127	29	1s. black and violet	..	..	5·00	6·50
128	30	2s. black and red-brown	..	16·00	8·50
129	31	3s. light blue and emerald-green	..	35·00	27·00
127/9	..	..	..	*Set of* 3	50·00	38·00

(Recess B.W.)

1940 (2 Sept). *Surch as in T* **32**. W **98** *of New Zealand. P* 13½ × 14.

| 130 | **32** | 3d. on 1½d. black and purple .. | .. | 20 | 30 |

Type **32** was not issued without surcharge.

1943–54. *Postal Fiscal stamps as Type* F **6** *of New Zealand optd with T* **19**. W **98**. *Wiggins, Teape chalk-surfaced paper. P* 14.

131	2s. 6d. dull brown (No. F170) (3.46)	..	23·00	32·00
	w. Wmk inverted (2.4.51)	..	10·00	14·00
132	5s. green (No. F172) (R.) (11.43)	..	6·00	17·00
	w. Wmk inverted (5.54)	..	13·00	18·00
133	10s. pale carmine-lake (No. F177) (10.48)	40·00	60·00
	w. Wmk inverted (10.51)	..	32·00	55·00
134	£1 pink (No. F179) (11.47)	..	38·00	60·00
	w. Wmk inverted (19.5.54)	..	38·00	60·00

135	£3 green (No. F183) (R.) (1946?)	..	£350	£500
	w. Wmk inverted (28.5.53)	..	55·00	£160
136	£5 indigo-blue (No. F184) (R.) (25.10.50)	£225	£350
	w. Wmk inverted (19.5.54)	..	£225	£350
131/6	..	..	..	*Set of* 6	£325	£600

The £3 and £5 were mainly used for fiscal purposes.

(Recess Govt Ptg Office, Wellington)

1944–46. W **98** *of New Zealand* (*sideways on* ½d. 1d., 1s., *and* 2s.). *P* 14.

137	20	½d. black and deep green (11.44)	..	1·00	3·50
		w. Wmk sideways inverted ..		7·00	
138	21	1d. black and scarlet (5.44) ..	..	2·00	35
		w. Wmk sideways inverted ..		10·00	
139	22	2d. black and brown (2.46) ..	..	1·25	4·00
140	23	2½d. black and deep blue (5.45)	..	1·25	75
141	24	4d. black and blue (4.44)	..	3·50	6·50
142	25	6d. black and orange (6.44) ..	..	1·25	1·25
143	29	1s. black and violet (9.44)	..	1·25	2·00
144	30	2s. black and red-brown (8.45)	..	18·00	16·00
145	31	3s. light blue and emerald-green (6.45)	25·00	16·00
137/45	..	..	..	*Set of* 9	48·00	45·00

COOK
ISLANDS

(33)

1946 (4 June). *Peace. Nos.* 668, 670, 674/5 *of New Zealand optd with T* **33** (*reading up and down at sides on* 2d.).

146	1d. green (Parliament House)	..	..	15	10
147	2d. purple (Royal family) (B.)	..	..	15	30
148	6d. chocolate and vermilion (Coat of arms, foundry and farm)	..	..	20	30
149	8d. black and carmine ("St. George") (B.)	..	20	30
146/9	..	..	..	*Set of* 4	60	80

34 Ngatangiia Channel,   41 Map and Statue
Rarotonga   of Capt. Cook

(Des J. Berry. Recess Waterlow)

1949 (1 Aug)–**61**. *T* **34**, **41** *and similar designs. W* **98** *of New Zealand* (*sideways on shilling values*). *P* 13½ × 13 (*horiz*) *or* 13 × 13½ (*vert*).

150	½d. violet and brown	..	..	10	1·00
151	1d. chestnut and green	..	..	2·50	2·00
152	2d. reddish brown and scarlet	..	60	2·00
153	3d. green and ultramarine	..	..	80	2·00
	aw. Wmk inverted	..	..	£100	
	b. Wmk sideways (white opaque paper) (22.5.61)	..	..	3·50	2·50
154	5d. emerald-green and violet	..	2·50	1·50
155	6d. black and carmine	..	..	3·25	2·75
156	8d. olive-green and orange	..	..	40	3·75
	w. Wmk inverted	..	..	85·00	50·00
157	1s. light blue and chocolate	..	..	4·25	3·75
158	2s. yellow-brown and carmine	..	3·00	8·50
	w. Wmk sideways inverted	..		
159	3s. light blue and bluish green	..	6·00	12·00
150/9	..	..	..	*Set of* 10	21·00	35·00

Designs: *Horiz*—1d. Capt. Cook and map of Hervey Islands; 2d. Rarotonga and Revd. John Williams; 3d. Aitutaki and palm trees; 5d. Rarotonga Airfield; 6d. Penrhyn village; 8d. Native hut. *Vert*—2s. Native hut and palms; 3s. *Matua* (inter-island freighter).

See note on white opaque paper below No. 736 of New Zealand.

NIUE

NIUE

(13)   14 King George VI   15 Tropical
                                                    Landscape

1937 (13 May). *Coronation Issue. Nos.* 599/601 *of New Zealand*
  optd with T 13.
72   1d. carmine   30   10
73   2½d. Prussian blue   40   30
74   6d. red-orange   40   20
72/4 ..   ..   *Set of* 3   1·00   50

1938 (2 May). *T* 14 *and similar designs inscr* "NIUE COOK
  ISLANDS". *W* 43 *of New Zealand. P* 14.
75   1s. black and violet ..   ..   ..   4·25   4·50
76   2s. black and red-brown   ..   ..   12·00 14·00
77   3s. light blue and emerald-green ..   30·00 16·00
75/7 ..   ..   *Set of* 3 42·00 30·00
Designs: *Vert*—2s. Island village. *Horiz*—3s. Cook Islands
canoe.

1940 (2 Sept). *Surch as in T* 15. *W* 98 *of New Zealand.*
  P 13½×14.
78   3d. on 1½d. black and purple   15   10

NIUE.

(16)

1941–67. *Postal Fiscal stamps as Type F* 6 *of New Zealand*
  with thin opt, T 16. *P* 14.
(i) *Thin, hard, chalk-surfaced "Wiggins Teape" paper with vertical*
  mesh (1941–43). (a) W 43 *of New Zealand*
79   2s. 6d. deep brown (B.) (4.41)   ..   50·00 55·00
80   5s. green (R.) (4.41) £200 £170
81   10s. pale carmine-lake (B.) (6.42) ..   £100 £160
82   £1 pink (B.) (2.43?) £170 £250
79/82 ..   ..   *Set of* 4 £475 £550
            (b) W 98 *of New Zealand* (1944–54)
83   2s. 6d. deep brown (B.) (3.45)   ..   3·50   7·00
           w. Wmk inverted (11.51)   ..   ..   5·00   8·50
84   5s. green (R.) (11.44)   ..   ..   7·50   9·50
           w. Wmk inverted (19.5.54)   ..   7·50   9·50
85   10s. carmine-lake (B.) (11.45)   .. 55·00 90·00
           w. Wmk inverted   ..   ..   55·00 90·00
86   £1 pink (B.) (6.42)   ..   ..   42·00 50·00
83/6 ..   ..   *Set of* 4 95·00 £140

(ii) *Unsurfaced "Wiggins Teape" paper with horizontal mesh. W* 98
  of New Zealand (1957–67)
87   2s. 6d. deep brown (*p* 14 × 13½) (1.11.57) ..   5·00   8·00
88   5s. pale yellowish green (*wmk sideways*)
           (6.67)   ..   ..   42·00 75·00
No. 88 came from a late printing made to fill demands from
Wellington, but no supplies were sent to Niue. It exists in both
line and comb perf.

1944–46. *As Nos.* 62/7 *and* 75/7, *but W* 98 *of New Zealand*
  (*sideways on* ½d., 1d., 1s. *and* 2s.).
89 12   ½d. black and emerald   50   1·75
90   –   1d. black and deep lake   50   70
91   –   2d. black and red-brown   ..   4·75   5·50
92   –   2½d. black and slate-blue (1946)   ..   60   95
93   –   4d. black and greenish blue ..   2·50   90
           w. Wmk inverted and reversed   ..   16·00
94   –   6d. black and red-orange   ..   70   1·40
95 14   1s. black and violet   ..   1·25   85
96   –   2s. black and red-brown (1945)   ..   8·50   2·75
97   –   3s. light blue and emerald-green (1945) 13·00   7·00
89/97 ..   ..   *Set of* 9 29·00 20·00
Designs: *Vert*—½d. Landing of Captain Cook; 1d. Captain
Cook. *Horiz*—2d. Double Maori canoe; 2½d. Islanders working
cargo; 4d. Port of Avarua; 6d. R.M.S. *Monowai.*

1946 (4 June). *Peace. Nos.* 668, 670, 674/5 *of New Zealand optd*
  as T 16 *without stop* (*twice, reading up and down on* 2d.).
98   1d. green (Blk.)   10   10
99   2d. purple (B.)   10   10
100   6d. chocolate and vermilion (Blk.)   ..   10   10
           a. Opt double, one albino £200
101   8d. black and carmine (B.)   10   10
98/101 ..   ..   *Set of* 4   35   30
Nos. 102/112 are no longer used.

17 Map of Niue   18 H.M.S. *Resolution*

23 Bananas   24 Matapa Chasm

(Des J. Berry. Recess B.W.)

1950 (3 July). *T* 17/18, 23/24 *and similar designs. W* 98 *of New*
  Zealand (*sideways inverted on* 1d., 2d., 3d., 4d., 6d. *and* 1s.).
  P 13½×14 (*horiz*) *or* 14×13½ (*vert*).
113   ½d. orange and blue   10   20
114   1d. brown and blue-green   ..   ..   2·25   1·25
115   2d. black and carmine   20   20
116   3d. blue and violet-blue   10   15
117   4d. olive-green and purple-brown ..   10   15
118   6d. green and brown-orange..   ..   60   30
119   9d. orange and brown   10   30
120   1s. purple and black   10   15
121   2s. brown-orange and dull green ..   1·00   3·50
122   3s. blue and black   ..   ..   ..   4·50   4·00
113/22 ..   ..   *Set of* 10   8·00   9·00
Designs: *Horiz* (as *T* 18)—2d. Alofi landing; 3d. Native hut;
4d. Arch at Hikutavake; 6d. Alofi bay; 1s. Cave, Makefu. *Vert*
(as *T* 17)—9d. Spearing fish.

TOKELAU ISLANDS

1 Atafu Village and Map

(Des J. Berry from photographs by T. T. C. Humphrey. Recess B.W.)

1948 (22 June). *T* 1 *and similar horiz designs. Wmk T* 98 *of New*
  Zealand (*Mult N Z and Star*). *P* 13½.
1   ½d. red-brown and purple   15   30
2   1d. chestnut and green   15   30
           w. Wmk inverted £275
3   2d. green and ultramarine   15   30
1/3 ..   ..   *Set of* 3   40   80
Designs:—1d. Nukunono hut and map; 2d. Fakaofo village
and map.
Covers are known postmarked 16 June 1948, but this was in
error for 16 July.

WESTERN SAMOA

NEW ZEALAND MANDATE

WESTERN
SAMOA.

(27)

1935–42. *Postal Fiscal stamps as Type F 6 of New Zealand optd with T 27. W 43 of New Zealand. P 14.*

(a) *Thick, opaque chalk-surfaced "Cowan" paper* (7.8.35)
189	2s. 6d. deep brown (B.)	..	..	..	4·75 14·00
190	5s. green (B.)	..	..	..	10·00 18·00
191	10s. carmine-lake (B.)	..	..	..	45·00 60·00
192	£1 pink (B.)	..	..	..	60·00 95·00
193	£2 bright purple (R.)	..	..	..	£140 £300
194	£5 indigo-blue (R.)..	..	..	..	£250 £550

(b) *Thin, hard chalk-surfaced "Wiggins, Teape" paper* (1941–42)
194a	5s. green (B.) (6.42)	..	..	..	75·00 85·00
194b	10s. pale carmine-lake (B.) (6.41)	.:	..	£120 £130
194c	£2 bright purple (R.) (2.42)	..	..	£475 £650
194d	£5 indigo-blue (R.) (2.42)	..	..	£800 £950

The £2 and £5 values were primarily for fiscal use.
See also Nos. 207/14.

28 Coastal Scene

31 Robert Louis
Stevenson

(Des J. Berry (1d. and 1½d.). L. C. Mitchell (2½d. and 7d.). Recess B.W.)

1939 (29 Aug). *25th Anniv of New Zealand Control. T 28, 31 and similar horiz designs. W 98 of New Zealand. P 13½ × 14 or 14 × 13½ (7d.).*
195	1d. olive-green and scarlet ..	..	..	30	10
196	1½d. light blue and red-brown	..	..	45	30
197	2½d. red-brown and blue	..	..	90	65
198	7d. violet and slate-green ..	..	..	6·50	2·25
195/8 ..	..	..	..	..	*Set of 4*	7·50 3·00

Designs:—1½d. Western Samoa; 2½d. Samoan dancing party.

32 Samoan Chief

33 Apia Post Office

(Recess B.W.)
1940 (2 Sept). *W 98 of New Zealand (Mult "N Z" and Star). P 14 × 13½.*
199	32	3d. on 1½d. brown	..	..	..	10 10

T 32 was not issued without surcharge.

(T 33. Des L. C. Mitchell. Recess B.W.)
1944–49. *As Nos. 180, 182/3 and T 33. W 98 of New Zealand (Mult "N Z" and Star) (sideways on 2½d.). P 14 or 13½ × 14 (5d.).*
200	½d. green	..	..	..	..	30 11·00
202	2d. black and orange	..	..	..	2·50 5·50
203	2½d. black and blue (1948)	..	..	4·25 20·00
205	5d. sepia and blue (8.6.49) ..	..	..	75 50
200/5 ..	..	..	..	..	*Set of 4*	7·00 32·00

Designs: *Vert*—½d. Samoan girl; 2½d. Chief and wife. *Horiz*—2d. River scene.

1945–53. *Postal Fiscal stamps as Type F 6 of New Zealand optd with T 27. W 98 of New Zealand. Thin hard, chalk-surfaced "Wiggins Teape" paper. P 14.*
207	2s. 6d. deep brown (B.) (6.45)	..	..	3·50 10·00
	w. Wmk inverted	..	..	..	3·50 8·00
208	5s. green (B.) (5.45)	..	..	..	7·50 8·50
	w. Wmk inverted	..	..	..	8·50 9·50
209	10s. carmine-lake (B.) (4.46)	..	..	17·00 17·00
	w. Wmk inverted	..	..	..	21·00 22·00
210	£1 pink (B.) (6.48)	..	..	..	90·00 £150
	w. Wmk inverted	..	..	..	..
211	30s. brown (8.48)	..	..	..	£150 £300
	w. Wmk inverted	..	..	..	£200 £325
212	£2 bright purple (R.) (11.47)	..	..	£150 £275
	w. Wmk inverted	..	..	..	£170 £275
213	£3 green (8.48) ..	..	..	..	£180 £375
	w. Wmk inverted	..	..	..	£225 £400
214	£5 indigo-blue (R.) (1946)	..	..	£275 £425
	w. Wmk inverted (5.53) ..	..	..	£325 £450
207/10 ..	..	..	..	..	*Set of 4*	£100 £160

The £2 to £5 values were mainly used for fiscal purposes.
See also Nos. 232/5.

WESTERN
SAMOA

(34)

1946 (4 June). *Peace Issue. Nos. 668, 670 and 674/5 of New Zealand optd with T 34 (reading up and down at sides on 2d.).*
215	1d. green	..	..	..	..	10 10
	w. Wmk inverted ..	..	..	..	£130
216	2d. purple (B.)	..	..	..	10 10
217	6d. chocolate and vermilion	..	..	10 10
218	8d. black and carmine (B.)	..	..	10 10
215/18	..	..	..	..	*Set of 4*	35 30

Nigeria

12 pence (d) = 1 shilling; 20 shillings = 1 pound

CROWN COLONY

1937 (12 May). *Coronation. As Nos. 118/20 of Jamaica, but ptd by B.W. & Co. P* 11×11½.

46	1d. carmine	..	.. .. ..	30	1·50
47	1½d. brown	..	.. .. ..	1·25	2·00
48	3d. blue	..	.. .. ..	1·40	2·00
46/8	..	..	*Set of* 3	2·75	5·00
46/8 Perf "Specimen"		.. ..	*Set of* 3	55·00	

15 King George VI   16 Victoria-Buẹa Road

(Recess B.W. (T **15**), D.L.R. (others)

1938 (1 May)–**51**. *Designs as* T **15/16**. *Wmk Mult Script CA. P* 12 (T **15**) *or* 13×11½ (*others*).

49	**15**	½d. green	..	..	10	10
		a. Perf 11½ (15.2.50)	..	..	30	10
50		1d. carmine	..	..	19·00	2·50
		a. Rose-red (*shades*)	..		75	20
50*b*		1d. bright purple (1.12.44)	..	..	10	20
		ba. Perf 11½ (15.2.50)		..	20	50
51		1½d. brown	..	..	20	10
		a. Perf 11½ (15.11.50)	..	..	10	10
52		2d. black	..	..	10	80
52*aa*		2d. rose-red (1.12.44)	..	..	10	80
		ab. Perf 11½ (15.2.50)	..	..	10	40
52*a*		2½d. orange (4.41)	..	..	10	70
53		3d. blue	..	..	10	10
		a. Wmk sideways	..	..	† £2250	
53*b*		3d. black (1.12.44)	..	..	10	30

54	**15**	4d. orange	..	.. ..	48·00	2·50
54*a*		4d. blue (1.12.44)		.. ..	15	1·75
55		6d. blackish purple	..	..	40	10
		a. Perf 11½ (17.4.51)	..	..	40	60
56		1s. sage-green	..	..	60	10
		a. Perf 11½ (15.2.50)	..	..	15	10
57		1s. 3d. light blue (1940)	..	..	60	20
		a. Perf 11½ (14.6.50)	..	..	50	70
		b. Wmk sideways (Perf 11½)	..	..	— £2000	
58	**16**	2s. 6d. black and blue	..	..	60·00	11·00
		a. Perf 13½ (6.42)	..	..	3·50	4·00
		ab. Perf 13½. *Black and deep blue* (1946)			48·00	40·00
		b. Perf 14 (1942)	..	..	2·00	2·75
		c. Perf 12 (15.8.51)	..	..	1·75	2·75
59	–	5s. black and orange	..	..	£110	11·00
		a. Perf 13½ (8.42)	..	..	5·50	4·50
		b. Perf 14 (1948)	..	..	6·00	3·00
		c. Perf 12 (19.5.49)	..	..	5·50	4·00
49/59*c*		..	..	*Set of* 16	50·00	11·50
49/52*aa*, 53/9 Perf "Specimen"		..	*Set of* 15	£200		

Design: *Horiz as* T **16**—5s. R. Niger at Jebba.

1946 (21 Oct). *Victory. As Nos.* 141/2 *of Jamaica.*

60	1½d. chocolate	..	..	..	20	10
61	4d. blue	..	..	..	20	90
60/1 Perf "Specimen"		..	..	*Set of* 2	55·00	

1948 (20 Dec). *Royal Silver Wedding. As Nos.* 143/4 *of Jamaica.*

62	1d. bright purple	..	..	35	30
63	5s. brown-orange	..	..	5·00	8·00

1949 (10 Oct). *75th Anniv of U.P.U. As Nos.* 145/8 *of Jamaica.*

64	1d. bright reddish purple	..	..	..	20	10
65	3d. deep blue	..	..	..	75	1·50
66	6d. purple	..	..	..	70	1·75
67	1s. olive	..	..	..	80	1·75
64/7	..	..	..	*Set of* 4	2·25	4·50

North Borneo

100 cents = 1 Malayan dollar

BRITISH NORTH BORNEO COMPANY ADMINISTRATION

81 Buffalo Transport   82 Palm Cockatoo

(Eng J. A. C. Harrison. Recess Waterlow)

1939 (1 Jan). *T* **81/2** *and similar designs.* P 12½.

303	1 c. green and red-brown	..	65	75
304	2 c. purple and greenish blue	..	4·00	75
305	3 c. slate-blue and green	..	1·50	2·00
306	4 c. bronze-green and violet ..	..	2·25	50
307	6 c. deep blue and claret	..	1·50	3·00
308	8 c. scarlet ..	..	6·00	1·50
309	10 c. violet and bronze-green ..	..	38·00	6·00
310	12 c. green and royal blue	..	13·00	4·00
	a. *Green and blue* ..	..	22·00	6·00
311	15 c. blue-green and brown	..	15·00	5·50
312	20 c. violet and slate-blue	..	8·50	3·25
313	25 c. green and chocolate	..	11·00	6·00
314	50 c. chocolate and violet	..	13·00	5·50
315	$1 brown and carmine	..	65·00	18·00
316	$2 violet and olive-green ..	..	90·00	75·00
317	$5 indigo and pale blue	..	£300	£190
303/17		*Set of* 15	£500	£275
303/17 Perf "Specimen"		*Set of* 15	£275	

Designs: *Vert*—3 c. Native; 4 c. Proboscis Monkey; 6 c. Mounted Bajaus; 10 c. Orang-Utan; 15 c. Dyak; $1, $2 Badge of the Company. *Horiz*—8 c. Eastern Archipelago; 12 c. Murut with blow-pipe; 20 c. River scene; 25 c. Native boat; 50 c. Mt Kinabalu; $5 Arms of the Company.

WAR TAX
(96)

WAR TAX
(97)

1941 (24 Feb). *Nos.* 303/4 *optd with T* **96/7.**

318	1 c. green and red-brown	..	50	1·50
	a. Optd front and back ..	..	£250	
319	2 c. purple and greenish blue	..	3·50	3·00

BRITISH MILITARY ADMINISTRATION

North Borneo, including Labuan, was occupied by the Japanese in January 1942. Australian forces landed on Labuan on 10 June 1945 and by the end of the war against Japan on 14 August had liberated much of western North Borneo. The territory was placed under British Military Administration on 5 January 1946.

BMA
(98)

(99)

1945 (17 Dec). *Nos.* 303/17 *optd with T* **98.**

320	1 c. green and red-brown	..	4·25	90
321	2 c. purple and greenish blue	..	10·00	1·00
	a. Opt double	..	£4500	
322	3 c. slate-blue and green	..	1·25	1·25
323	4 c. bronze-green and violet ..	..	16·00	13·00
324	6 c. deep blue and claret	..	1·25	30

325	8 c. scarlet ..	..	3·00	55
326	10 c. violet and bronze-green ..	..	3·00	30
327	12 c. green and blue ..	..	4·75	1·00
	a. *Green and royal blue* ..	..		
328	15 c. blue-green and brown	..	1·50	1·00
329	20 c. violet and slate-blue	..	2·50	1·25
330	25 c. green and chocolate	..	3·75	1·25
331	50 c. chocolate and violet	..	3·00	1·00
332	$1 brown and carmine	..	35·00	24·00
333	$2 violet and olive-green	..	35·00	19·00
	a. Opt double	..	£2250	
334	$5 indigo and pale blue	..	12·00	8·50
320/34	..	*Set of* 15	£120	65·00

These stamps and the similarly overprinted stamps of Sarawak were obtainable at all post offices throughout British Borneo (Brunei, Labuan, North Borneo and Sarawak), for use on local and overseas mail.

CROWN COLONY

North Borneo became a Crown Colony on 15 July 1946.

Lower bar broken at right (R. 8/3)   Lower bar broken at left (R. 8/4)

1947 (1 Sept–22 Dec). *Nos.* 303 *to* 317 *optd with T* **99** *and bars obliterating words* "THE STATE OF" *and* "BRITISH PROTECTORATE".

335	1 c. green and red-brown (15.12) ..	..	15	1·00
	b. Lower bar broken at right ..	..	12·00	
	c. Lower bar broken at left	..	12·00	
336	2 c. purple and greenish blue (22.12)	..	70	90
337	3 c. slate-blue and green (R.) (22.12)	..	15	70
338	4 c. bronze-green and violet	..	30	30
339	6 c. deep blue and claret (R.) (22.12)	..	15	20
340	8 c. scarlet	..	20	20
	b. Lower bar broken at right ..	..	13·00	
341	10 c. violet and bronze-green (15.12)	..	40	40
342	12 c. green and royal blue (22.12) ..	..	1·50	1·75
	a. *Green and blue*	..		
343	15 c. blue-green and brown (22.12)	..	2·00	30
344	20 c. violet and slate-blue (22.12)	..	60	60
	b. Lower bar broken at right ..	..	24·00	
345	25 c. green and chocolate (22.12)	..	1·25	45
	b. Lower bar broken at right	..	32·00	
346	50 c. chocolate and violet (22.12)	..	90	85
	b. Lower bar broken at right	..	32·00	
	c. Lower bar broken at left	..	32·00	
347	$1 brown and carmine (22.12) ..	..	90	1·10
348	$2 violet and olive-green (22.12)	..	3·50	7·50
349	$5 indigo and pale blue (R.) (22.12)	..	12·00	9·50
	b. Lower bar broken at right	..	80·00	
335/49	..	*Set of* 15	22·00	23·00
335/49 Perf "Specimen" ..	..	*Set of* 15	£250	

1948 (1 Nov). *Royal Silver Wedding. As Nos.* 143/4 *of Jamaica.*

350	8 c. scarlet ..	..	30	80
351	$10 mauve ..	..	20·00	35·00

1949 (10 Oct). *75th Anniv of U.P.U. As Nos.* 145/8 *of Jamaica.*

352	8 c. carmine ..	..	40	30
353	10 c. brown ..	..	1·75	1·00
354	30 c. orange-brown ..	..	90	1·75
355	55 c. blue ..	..	90	2·25
352/5 ..	..	*Set of* 4	3·50	4·75

100 Mount Kinabalu   102 Coconut Grove

(1)   2 Mt Kinabalu   3 Borneo Scene

(Photo Harrison)

1950 (1 July)–52. *T* 100, 102 *and similar designs. Wmk Mult Script CA. Chalk-surfaced paper. P* 13½ × 14½ *(horiz), 14½ × 13½ (vert).*

356	1 c. red-brown	..	..	..	15	60
357	2 c. blue	..	..	..	15	50
358	3 c. green	..	..	..	15	15
359	4 c. bright purple	..	..	..	15	10
360	5 c. violet	..	..	..	15	10
361	8 c. scarlet	..	..	..	75	85
362	10 c. maroon	..	..	..	60	15
363	15 c. ultramarine	..	..	..	1·00	65
364	20 c. brown	..	..	..	80	10
365	30 c. olive-brown	..	..	1·50	20
366	50 c. rose-carmine ("JESSLETON")	..		85	2·75
366a	50 c. rose-carmine ("JESSELTON") (1.5.52)	..	5·50	1·75
367	$1 red-orange	..	..	..	1·50	1·00
368	$2 grey-green	..	..	..	2·00	7·00
369	$5 emerald-green	..	..	..	10·00	14·00
370	$10 dull blue	..	..	..	30·00	40·00
356/70			*Set of* 16	48·00	65·00

Designs: *Horiz*—2 c. Native musical instrument; 8 c. Map; 10 c. Log pond; 15 c. Malay prau, Sandakan; 20 c. Bajau Chief; $2 Murut with blowpipe; $5 Net-fishing; $10 Arms of North Borneo. *Vert*—4 c. Hemp drying; 5 c. Cattle at Kota Belud; 30 c. Suluk river canoe, Lahad Datu; 50 c. Clock tower, Jesselton; $1 Bajau horsemen.

POSTAGE DUE STAMPS

D 2 Crest of the Company

(Recess Waterlow)

1939 (1 Jan). *P* 12½.

D66	D 2	2 c. brown	..	..	..	6·00	65·00
D67		4 c. scarlet	..	..	..	6·00	85·00
D68		6 c. violet	..	..	..	17·00	£110
D69		8 c. green	..	..	..	17·00	£170
D70		10 c. blue	..	..	..	35·00	£275
D66/70			..	*Set of* 5	70·00	£650
D66/70 Perf "Specimen"				*Set of* 5	£140	

JAPANESE OCCUPATION OF NORTH BORNEO

Japanese forces landed in Northern Borneo on 15 December 1941 and the whole of North Borneo had been occupied by 19 January 1942.

Brunei, North Borneo, Sarawak and, after a short period, Labuan, were administered as a single territory by the Japanese. Until September–October 1942, previous stamp issues, without overprint, continued to be used in conjunction with existing postmarks. From October 1942 onwards unoverprinted stamps of Japan were made available and examples can be found used from the area for much of the remainder of the War. Japanese Occupation issues for Brunei, North Borneo and Sarawak were equally valid throughout the combined territory but not, in practice, equally available.

1942 (30 Sept). *Stamps of North Borneo handstamped with T* 1.

(*a*) *In violet on Nos.* 303/17

J 1	1 c. green and red-brown	..	..	£110	£160
	a. Black opt	..	..	£160	£160
J 2	2 c. purple and greenish blue	..	£110	£160
	a. Black opt	..	..	£160	£160
J 3	3 c. slate-blue and green	..	..	95·00	£160
	a. Black opt	..	..	£160	£160
J 4	4 c. bronze-green and violet	..	90·00	£160
	a. Black opt	..	..	45·00	90·00
J 5	6 c. deep blue and claret	..	..	£100	£160
	a. Black opt	..	..	£150	£160
J 6	8 c. scarlet	..	..	95·00	£140
	a. Pair, one without opt	..	£1000	
	b. Black opt	..	..	£150	£140
J 7	10 c. violet and bronze-green	..	£110	£160
	a. Black opt	..	..	£160	£160
J 8	12 c. green and bright blue	..	£120	£250
	a. Black opt	..	..	£250	£250
J 9	15 c. blue-green and brown	..	£120	£250
	a. Black opt	..	..	£250	£250
J10	20 c. violet and slate-blue	..	£160	£300
	a. Black opt	..	..	£300	£300
J11	25 c. green and chocolate	..	£160	£300
	a. Black opt	..	..	£300	£300
J12	50 c. chocolate and violet	..	£200	£350
	a. Black opt	..	..	£350	£350
J13	$1 brown and carmine	..	£200	£425
	a. Black opt	..	..	£425	£425
J14	$2 violet and olive-green	..	£325	£550
	a. Pair, one without opt	..	£1800	
	b. Black opt	..	..	£550	£550
J15	$5 indigo and pale blue	..	£375	£650
	a. Black opt	..	..	£650	£650

(*b*) *In black on Nos.* 318/19 ("WAR TAX")

J16	1 c. green and red-brown	..	£350	£200
J17	2 c. purple and greenish blue	..	£950	£300

(Litho Kolff & Co., Batavia)

1943 (29 Apr). *P* 12½.

J18	2	4 c. red	..	..	..	14·00	28·00
J19	3	8 c. blue	..	..	..	14·00	28·00

(4)   (5)

("Imperial Japanese Postal Service North Borneo")

1944 (30 Sept). *Nos.* 303/15 *of North Borneo optd as T* 4.

J20	1 c. green and red-brown	..	..	3·75	8·50
J21	2 c. purple and greenish blue	..	..	7·50	8·50
	a. Optd on No. J2	..	..	£350	
J22	3 c. slate-blue and green	..	..	2·75	6·00
	a. Optd on No. J3	..	..	£350	
J23	4 c. bronze-green and violet	..	..	3·75	8·00
J24	6 c. deep blue and claret	..	..	3·50	6·00
J25	8 c. scarlet	..	..	..	5·50	16·00
	a. Optd on No. J6	..	..	£350	

J26	10 c. violet and bronze-green	..	..	6·50	13·00
	a. Optd on No. J7	..	..	£350	
	b. Optd on No. J7a	..	..	£180	£350
J27	12 c. green and bright blue		..	5·00	13·00
	a. Optd on No. J8	..	..	£350	
J28	15 c. blue-green and brown	..	..	4·00	14·00
	a. Optd on No. J9	..	..	£350	
J29	20 c. violet and slate-blue ..	..	..	14·00	32·00
J30	25 c. green and chocolate ..	..	..	14·00	32·00
J31	50 c. chocolate and violet ..	..	..	50·00	90·00
J32	$1 brown and carmine	..	..	80·00	£140
J20/32	..	..	..	*Set of* 13	£180 £350

The spacing between the second and third lines of the overprint
is 12 mm on the horizontal stamps, and 15 mm on the upright.

1944 (11 May). *No.* J1 *surch with T* **5.**

J33	**81**	$2 on 1 c. green and red-brown	..	£4500 £3750

(6)　　　**7** Girl War-worker　　　(8) ("North Borneo")

1944 (11 May). *North Borneo No.* 315 *surch with T* **6.**

J34	$5 on $1 brown and carmine	..	..	£3750 £2750

1944 (2 Oct)–**45.** *Contemporary stamps of Japan as T* **7** (*various subjects*) *optd with T* **8** *at Chinese Press, Kuching.*

J35	1 s. red-brown (No. 391) (1945)	..	..	4·50	11·00
J36	2 s. scarlet (No. 318) (1945)		..	4·50	11·00
J37	3 s. emerald-green (No. 319) (12.44)		..	3·50	11·00
J38	4 s. yellow-green (No. 395) (1945)		..	4·50	10·00
J39	5 s. claret (No. 396) (1945)		..	5·50	12·00
J40	6 s. orange (No. 322) (1945)	..	..	6·00	12·00
	a. Opt double, one inverted	..	..		
J41	8 s. violet (No. 324) (1945)		..	3·50	13·00
J42	10 s. carmine and pink (No. 399) (1945)	..	4·00	13·00
J43	15 s. blue (No. 401) (11.44)		..	5·50	13·00
J44	20 s. blue-slate (No. 328) (11.44)	..	..	80·00	80·00
J45	25 s. brown and chocolate (No. 329) (1945)		50·00	65·00
J46	30 s. turquoise-blue (No. 330)	..	..	£160	95·00
J47	50 s. olive and bistre (No. 331) (1945)	..	55·00	60·00
J48	1 y. red-brown & chocolate (No. 332) (1945)	55·00	75·00
J35/48	..	..	..	*Set of* 14	£400 £425

Designs:—2 s. General Nogi; 3 s. Hydro-electric Works; 4 s. Hyuga Monument and Mt Fuji; 5 s. Admiral Togo; 6 s. Garambi Lighthouse, Formosa; 8 s. Meiji Shrine; 10 s. Palms and map of S.E. Asia; 15 s. Airman; 20 s. Mt Fuji and cherry blossoms; 25 s. Horyu Temple; 30 s. Torii, Itsukushima Shrine at Miyajima; 50 s. Kinkaku Temple; 1 y. Great Buddha, Kamakura.

Examples of some values have been found with hand-painted forged overprints.

Northern Rhodesia

12 pence (d) = 1 shilling; 20 shillings = 1 pound

CROWN COLONY

THERN_RHODE

Hyphen between
"NORTHERN" AND "RHODESIA"
(R. 9/6)

1937 (12 May). *Coronation. As Nos. 118/20 of Jamaica, but ptd by B.W. P* 11×11½.

22	1½d. carmine ..	..	..	..	..	40	35
23	2d. buff	..	..	..	..	70	35
24	3d. blue	..	..	..	..	1·25	1·75
	a. Hyphen flaw	..	..	..	£120		
22/4 ..		..	..	*Set of 3*	2·10	2·25
22/4 Perf "Specimen"		..	..	*Set of 3*	60·00	

3   4

"Tick bird" flaw
(R. 7/1)

(Recess Waterlow)

1938 (1 Mar)–**52**. *Wmk Mult Script CA. P* 12½.

25	3	½d. green	..	..	..	..	10	10
		a. "C" of "CA" missing from wmk	..			
26		½d. chocolate (15.11.51)	..		10	70
		a. Perf 12½×14 (22.10.52)	..	..	1·40	4·25
27		1d. brown	..	..	..	10	10
		a. Chocolate (1948)	..	..	1·60	60
28		1d. green (15.11.51)	..	..	60	80
29		1½d. carmine-red	..	..	45·00	30
		a. Imperf between (horiz pair)	..	£11000	
		b. "Tick bird" flaw	..	..	£1600	£140
30		1½d. yellow-brown (10.1.41)	..	30	10
		b. "Tick bird" flaw	..	..	48·00	22·00
31		2d. yellow-brown	..	..	60·00	85
32		2d. carmine-red (10.1.41)	..	..	30	20
33		2d. purple (1.12.51)	..	..	45	65
34		3d. ultramarine	..	..	..	30	10
35		3d. scarlet (1.12.51)	..	..	50	1·50

36	3	4d. dull violet ..	..	..	..	30	40
37		4½d. blue (5.5.52)	..	..	..	40	3·75
38		6d. grey	..	..	..	..	30	10
39		9d. violet (5.5.52)	..	..	..	40	2·00
40	4	1s. yellow-brown and black	..	..	1·75	40
41		2s. 6d. black and green	..	..	7·00	1·50
42		3s. violet and blue	..	..	..	13·00	4·00
43		5s. grey and dull violet	..	..	8·00	4·50
44		10s. green and black	..	..	11·00	12·00
45		20s. carmine-red and rose-purple	..	35·00	45·00
25/45 ..		..	..	..	..	*Set of 21*	£160	70·00
25/45 Perf "Specimen"		..	..	*Set of 15*	£275	

Nos. 26a and 28 exist in coils, constructed from normal sheets.

1946 (26 Nov). *Victory. As Nos. 141/2 of Jamaica. P* 13½×14.

46	1½d. red-orange	..	..	..	..	10	10
	a. Perf 14 × 13½	..	..	..	9·50	10·00
47	2d. carmine ..	..	..	..	10	30
46/7 Perf "Specimen"		..	..	*Set of 2*	50·00	

1948 (1 Dec). *Royal Silver Wedding. As Nos. 143/4 of Jamaica, but* 20s. *ptd in recess.*

48	1½d. orange ..	..	..	..	..	30	10
49	20s. brown-lake	..	..	..	40·00	45·00

1949 (10 Oct). *75th Anniv of U.P.U. As Nos. 145/8 of Jamaica.*

50	2d. carmine ..	..	..	..	..	30	30
51	3d. deep blue ..	..	..	..	1·50	1·25
52	6d. grey	..	..	..	..	1·00	1·25
53	1s. red-orange	..	..	..	1·00	1·00
50/3 ..		..	..	..	*Set of 4*	3·50	3·50

POSTAGE DUE STAMPS

D 1

(Typo D.L.R.)

1929–52. *Wmk Mult Script CA. Ordinary paper. P* 14.

D1	D 1	1d. grey-black ..	..	..	..	2·50	2·50
		a. Chalk-surfaced paper. *Blk* (22.1.52)	20·00	75·00
		ab. Error. St. Edward's Crown, *W9b*	..	£1100
D2		2d. grey-black ..	..	..	..	3·00	3·00
D3		3d. grey-black ..	..	..	..	3·00	21·00
		a. Chalk-surfaced paper. *Blk* (22.1.52)	7·00	60·00
		ab. Error. Crown missing, *W9a*	..	£190
		ac. Error. St. Edward's Crown, *W9b*	..	£140
D4		4d. grey-black ..	..	..	..	9·00	27·00
D1/4			..	..	..	*Set of 4*	16·00	48·00
D1/4 Perf "Specimen"		..	..	*Set of 4*	80·00	

The 2d. is known bisected and used as a 1d. at Luanshya or Nkana on various dates between 1937 and 1951 and on understamped letters from South Africa at Chingola in May 1950 (*Price on cover from* £325).

Nyasaland

12 pence (d) = 1 shilling; 20 shillings = 1 pound

PROTECTORATE

1937 (12 May). *Coronation. As Nos.* 118/20 *of Jamaica, but ptd by B.W. P* 11×11½.

127	½d. green		..	..	30	50
128	1d. brown	..	..	..	70	40
129	2d. grey-black	..	..	..	70	90
127/9	..	..	..	*Set of* 3	1·50	1·60
127/9 Perf "Specimen"		..	..	*Set of* 3	55·00	

18 Symbol of the Protectorate   **19**

(T **18** recess Waterlow; T **19** typo D.L.R.)

1938 (1 Jan)–**44**. *Chalk-surfaced paper* (2s. *to* £1). *P* 12½. (T **18**) *or* 14 (T **19**). (*a*) *Wmk Mult Script CA*

130	**18**	½d. green	..	..	30	75
130*a*		½d. brown (12.12.42) ..		..	10	90
131		1d. brown	..	..	40	15
131*a*		1d. green (12.12.42) ..		..	30	40
132		1½d. carmine ..	..	..	1·25	3·50
132*a*		1½d. grey (12.12.42)	..		30	2·75
133		2d. grey	..	..	2·50	85
133*a*		2d. carmine (12.12.42)		..	30	60
134		3d. blue	..	..	60	20
135		4d. bright magenta ..		..	1·50	60
136		6d. violet	..	..	1·60	60
137		9d. olive-bistre	..	..	2·50	2·25
138		1s. black and orange	..		2·50	90
139	**19**	2s. purple and blue/*blue*	..		10·00	7·00
140		2s. 6d. black and red/*blue*	..		12·00	7·00
141		5s. pale green and red/*yellow*	40·00	17·00
		a. Ordinary paper. *Green and red/ pale yellow* (3.44)	..	95·00	65·00
142		10s. emerald and deep red/*pale green*	60·00	23·00
		a. Ordinary paper. *Bluish green and brown-red/pale green* (1.38)	..	£300	£160

(*b*) *Wmk Mult Crown CA*

143	**19**	£1 purple and black/*red*	..	30·00	23·00
130/43		..	..	*Set of* 18	£150	80·00
130/43 Perf "Specimen"		..	*Set of* 18	£600	

No. 141a has a yellow surfacing often applied in horizontal lines giving the appearance of laid paper.

The printer's archives record the despatch of No. 142a to Nyasaland in January 1938, but no used examples have been reported before 1945.

20 Lake Nyasa   **21** King's African Rifles

(Recess B.W.)

1945 (1 Sept). *T* **20/1** *and similar designs. Wmk Mult Script CA* (*sideways on horiz designs*). *P* 12.

144	½d. black and chocolate	..	..	10	10
145	1d. black and emerald	..	..	30	70
146	1½d. black and grey-green	..	..	20	50
147	2d. black and scarlet	..	..	30	30
148	3d. black and light blue	..	..	20	30
149	4d. black and claret..	..	..	75	45
150	6d. black and violet..	..	..	1·00	40
151	9d. black and olive ..	..	..	1·00	2·50
152	1s. indigo and deep green	..	..	1·00	20
153	2s. emerald and maroon	..	..	3·50	4·00
154	2s. 6d. emerald and blue	..	..	7·00	3·75
155	5s. purple and blue ..	..	..	4·50	5·50
156	10s. claret and emerald	..	..	11·00	9·00
157	20s. scarlet and black	..	..	17·00	19·00
144/57	..	..	..	*Set of* 14	42·00	42·00
144/57 Perf "Specimen"	..		*Set of* 14	£250	

Designs: *Horiz*—1½d., 6d. Tea estate; 2d., 1s., 10s. Map of Nyasaland; 4d., 2s. 6d. Tobacco; 9d. Type **20** ; 5s., 20s. Badge of Nyasaland. *Vert*—3d., 2s. Fishing Village.

1946 (16 Dec). *Victory. As Nos.* 141/2 *of Jamaica.*

158	1d. green	..	..	..	10	10
159	2d. red-orange	..	..	..	20	10
158/9 Perf "Specimen"	..	..	*Set of* 2	50·00	

26 Symbol of the   **27** Arms in 1891 and 1951
Protectorate

(Recess B.W.)

1947 (20 Oct). *Wmk Mult Script CA. P* 12.

160	**26**	1d. red-brown and yellow-green ..	..	30	10
160 Perf "Specimen"	..	..		45·00	

1948 (15 Dec). *Royal Silver Wedding. As Nos.* 143/4 *of Jamaica.*

161	1d. green	..	..	..	15	10
162	10s. mauve	..	..	..	15·00	22·00

1949 (21 Nov). *75th Anniv of U.P.U. As Nos.* 145/8 *of Jamaica.*

163	1d. blue-green	..	..	..	50	20
164	3d. greenish blue	..	..	..	1·50	1·50
165	6d. purple	..	..	..	1·00	50
166	1s. ultramarine	..	..	..	1·00	50
163/6 ..	..	..	..	*Set of* 4	3·50	2·40

(Des C. Twynam. Recess B.W.)

1951 (15 May). *Diamond Jubilee of Protectorate. Wmk Mult Script CA. P* 11 × 12.

167	**27**	2d. black and scarlet	..	..	90	75
168		3d. black and turquoise-blue	..	..	90	75
169		6d. black and violet	..	..	90	1·25
170		5s. black and indigo	..	..	1·50	6·00
167/70	..	..	..	*Set of* 4	3·75	8·00

POSTAGE DUE STAMPS

D 1

(Typo D.L.R.)

1950 (1 July). *Wmk Mult Script CA. P* 14.

D1	D 1	1d. scarlet			3·00	12·00
D2		2d. ultramarine			7·00	20·00
D3		3d. green			7·50	5·50
D4		4d. purple			14·00	35·00
D5		6d. yellow-orange			22·00	80·00
D1/5				*Set of* 5	48·00	£140

Pakistan

12 pies = 1 anna; 16 annas = 1 rupee

DOMINION

1947 (1 Oct). *Nos. 259/68 and 269a/77 (King George VI) of India optd by litho at Nasik, as T* **1** *(3 p. to 12 a.) or* **2** *(14 a. and rupee values).*

1	3 p. slate ..		..	..	..	10	10
2	½ a. purple		..	..	..	10	10
3	9 p. green ..		..	..	..	10	10
4	1 a. carmine		..	..	..	10	10
5	1½ a. dull violet		..	..	..	10	10
6	2 a. vermilion		..	..	..	10	20
7	3 a. bright violet ..		..	..		10	20
8	3½ a. bright blue	..		..	..	65	2·25
9	4 a. brown	..		..	..	20	10
10	6 a. turquoise-green		..	..		1·00	75
11	8 a. slate-violet	..		..	..	30	60
12	12 a. lake ..		..	..	..	1·00	20
13	14 a. purple		..	..	..	2·50	65
14	1 r. grey and red-brown		..	..		1·75	50
15	2 r. purple and brown		..	..		3·25	75
16	5 r. green and blue		..	..		4·00	3·00
17	10 r. purple and claret		..	..		4·00	2·00
18	15 r. brown and green		..		..	48·00	75·00
19	25 r. slate-violet and purple			..		55·00	35·00
1/19					*Set of* 19	£110	£110

Numerous provisional "PAKISTAN" overprints, both hand-stamped and machine-printed, in various sizes and colours, on Postage and Official stamps, also exist.

These were made under authority of Provincial Governments, District Head Postmasters or Local Postmasters and are of considerable philatelic interest.

The 1 a. 3 p. (India No. 269) exists only as a local issue (*Price*, Karachi opt 90p. *unused*; £1.75 *used*).

The 12 a., as No. 12 but overprinted at Karachi, exists with overprint inverted (*Price £60 unused*).

The 1 r. value with local overprint exists with overprint inverted (*Price £150 unused*) or as a pair with one stamp without overprint (*Price £600 unused*).

3 Constituent Assembly
Building, Karachi

6 Crescent and Stars

(Des A. R. Chughtai (1 r.). Recess D.L.R.)

1948 (9 July). *Independence. T* **3, 6** *and similar horiz designs. P* 13½ × 14 *or* 11½ (1 r.).

20	1½ a. ultramarine	..		..	70	50
21	2½ a. green	..		..	70	10
22	3 a. purple-brown	..		..	70	20
23	1 r. scarlet ..		..	..	70	50
	a. Perf 14 × 13½ ..			..	4·25	12·00
20/3	..			*Set of* 4	2·50	1·10

Designs:—2½ a. Karachi Airport entrance; 3 a. Gateway to Lahore Fort.

7 Scales of Justice

8 Star and Crescent

9 Lloyds Barrage

10 Karachi Airport

13 Khyber Pass

(Des M. M. A. Suharwardi (T **8**). Recess Pakistan Security Ptg Corp Ltd, Karachi (P 13 and 13½), D.L.R. (others))

1948 (14 Aug)–**56**?. *T* **7/10. 13** *and similar designs.*

24	7	3 p. red (p 12½)		..	..	10	10
		a. Perf 13½ (1954?)		..	..	20	10
25		6 p. violet (p 12½)		..	..	80	10
		a. Perf 13½ (1954?)		..	..	1·50	60
26		9 p. green (p 12½)		..	..	50	10
		a. Perf 13½ (1954?)		..	..	60	10
27	8	1 a. blue (p 12½)		..	..	10	30
28		1½ a. grey-green (p 12½)		..		10	10
29		2 a. red (p 12½)		..	..	20	30
30	9	2½ a. green (p 14×13½)		..		2·50	5·00
31	10	3 a. green (p 14)		..	..	5·50	40
32	9	3½ a. bright blue (p 14×13½)		..		3·50	3·50
33		4 a. reddish brown (p 12½)		..		50	10
34		6 a. blue (p 14×13½)		..		50	50
35		8 a. black (p 12½)		..	..	50	40
36	10	10 a. scarlet (p 14)		..	..	4·50	6·00
37	–	12 a. scarlet (p 14×13½)		..		6·50	55
38	–	1 r. ultramarine (p 14)		..		5·50	10
		a. Perf 13½ (1954?)		..	..	11·00	1·50
39	–	2 r. chocolate (p 14)		..	..	20·00	30
		a. Perf 13½ (1954?)		..	..	20·00	75
40	–	5 r. carmine (p 14)		..	..	15·00	50
		a. Perf 13½ (7.53)		..	..	9·00	20
41	13	10 r. magenta (p 14)		..	..	9·00	12·00
		a. Perf 12		..	..	60·00	4·25
		b. Perf 13 (1951)		..	..	16·00	30
42		15 r. blue-green (p 12)		..	..	16·00	9·00
		a. Perf 14		..	..	13·00	30·00
		b. Perf 13 (1956?)		..	..	17·00	12·00
43		25 r. violet (p 14)		..	..	55·00	65·00
		a. Perf 12		..	..	25·00	30·00
		b. Perf 13 (1954)		..	..	32·00	18·00
24/43		..			*Set of* 20	95·00	40·00

Designs: *Vert (as T* **7**)—6 a., 8 a., 12 a. Karachi Port Trust. (*As T* **10**)—1 r., 2 r., 5 r. Salimullah Hostel, Dacca.

For 25 r. with W **98**, see No. 210.

14 Star and Crescent

15 Karachi Airport

(Recess Pakistan Security Ptg Corp (P 13½), D.L.R. (others).

1949 (Feb)–**53**? *Redrawn. Crescent moon with points to left as T* **14/15.**

44	14	1 a. blue (p 12½)		..	..	3·75	40
		a. Perf 13½ (1953?)		..	..	3·25	10
45		1½ a. grey-green (p 12½)		..		3·75	40
		a. Perf 13½ (1952?)		..	..	3·00	10
46		2 a. red (p 12½)		..	..	3·75	10
		a. Perf 13½ (1953?)		..	..	3·25	10

47	15	3 a. green (p 14)	.. ..	..	4·50	65
48	–	6 a. blue (as No. 34) (p 14×13½)		..	8·00	20
49	–	8 a. black (as No. 35) (p 12½)	..	..	3·50	75
50	15	10 a. scarlet (p 14)	.. ..	..	10·00	90
51	–	12 a. scarlet (as No. 37) (p 14×13½)		..	17·00	2·00
44/51		.. .. ..	Set of 8		48·00	2·50

16

(Recess D.L.R.)

1949 (11 Sept). *First Death Anniv of Mohammed Ali Jinnah. T 16 and similar design. P 14.*

52	16	1½ a. brown	.. ..	..	1·25	65
53	–	3 a. green	.. ..	..	1·25	65
54	–	10 a. black	.. ..	..	2·75	4·75
52/4		.. ..	Set of 3		4·75	5·50

Design:—10 a. Similar inscription reading "QUAID-I-AZAM/ MOHAMMAD ALI JINNAH" etc.

17 Pottery

18 Aeroplane and Hour-glass

Two Types of 3½ a.:

I

II

19 Saracenic Leaf Pattern

20 Archway and Lamp

(Des A. R. Chughtai. Recess D.L.R., later printings, Pakistan Security Ptg Corp)

1951 (14 Aug)–**56.** *Fourth Anniv of Independence. P 13.*

55	17	2½ a. carmine	.. ..	..	80	35
56	18	3 a. purple	.. ..	..	40	10
57	17	3½ a. blue (I)	.. ..	..	75	2·25
57a		3½ a. blue (II)(12.56)	..	..	3·25	1·25
58	19	4 a. green	.. ..	..	35	10
59	–	6 a. brown-orange	.. ..	..	45	10
60	20	8 a. sepia	.. ..	..	4·00	10
61	–	10 a. violet	.. ..	..	80	60
62	18	12 a. slate	.. ..	..	90	10
55/62		.. ..	Set of 9		10·50	4·00

The above and the stamps issued on the 14 August 1954, 1955 and 1956, are basically definitive issues, although issued on the Anniversary date of Independence.

OFFICIAL STAMPS

PAKISTAN

(O 1)

1947. *Nos. O138/41 and O143/50 (King George VI) of India, optd as Type O 1 (Nos. O1/9) or as T 2 (Nos. O10/13) both in litho by Nasik.*

O 1	3 p. slate	..	..	..	80	10
O 2	½ a. purple	..	..	..	30	10
O 3	9 p. green	..	..	..	3·50	2·50
O 4	1 a. carmine	..	..	..	30	10
O 5	1½ a. dull violet	..	..	..	30	10
O 6	2 a. vermilion	..	..	..	30	10
O 7	2½ a. bright violet	..	..	..	5·00	6·50
O 8	4 a. brown	..	..	..	1·25	30
O 9	8 a. slate-violet	..	..	..	1·50	90
O10	1 r. grey and red-brown	..	..	..	80	85
O11	2 r. purple and brown	..	..	..	3·50	2·50
O12	5 r. green and blue	..	..	..	14·00	23·00
O13	10 r. purple and claret	..	..	..	35·00	75·00
O1/13	.. .. ..	Set of 13			60·00	£100

See note after No. 19. The 1 a. 3 p. (India No. O146a) exists as a local issue (*Price*, Karachi opt, £4.25 mint, £11 used).

SERVICE

(O 2)

SERVICE

(O 3)

NOTE. Apart from a slight difference in size, Types O 2 and O 3 can easily be distinguished by the difference in the shape of the "c".

PRINTERS. Type O 2 was overprinted by De La Rue and Types O 3 and O 4 by the Pakistan Security Ptg Corp.

1948 (14 Aug)–**54?** *Optd with Type O 2.*

O14	7	3 p. red (No. 24) ..		..	10	10
O15		6 p. violet (No. 25) (R.) ..		..	10	10
O16		9 p. green (No. 26) (R.) ..		..	10	10
O17	8	1 a. blue (No. 27) (R.)	..	..	3·75	10
O18		1½ a. grey-green (No. 28) (R.)		..	3·50	10
O19		2 a. red (No. 29)..		..	1·50	10
O20	10	3 a. green (No. 31)	..	..	16·00	4·25
O21	9	4 a. reddish brown (No. 33)		..	80	10
O22	–	8 a. black (No. 35) (R.)	..	..	1·25	4·50
O23	–	1 r. ultramarine (No. 38)	..	..	1·00	10
O24	–	2 r. chocolate (No. 39)	..	..	13·00	5·00
O25	–	5 r. carmine (No. 40)	..	..	18·00	5·00
O26	13	10 r. magenta (No. 41)	..	..	13·00	35·00
		a. Perf 12 (10.10.51)	..	..	15·00	35·00
		b. Perf 13 (1954?)	..	..	13·00	45·00
O14/26		.. .. ..	Set of 13		65·00	48·00

1949. *Optd with Type O 2.*

O27		1 a. blue (No. 44) (R.)	..	..	1·00	10
O28		1½ a. grey-green (No. 45) (R.)		..	30	10
		a. Opt inverted	..	..	£200	38·00
O29		2 a. red (No. 46)	..	..	1·00	10
		a. Opt omitted (in pair with normal)	..	—	£120
O30		3 a. green (No. 47)	..	..	13·00	3·50
O31		8 a. black (No. 49) (R.)	..	..	23·00	11·00
O27/31		.. .. ..	Set of 5		35·00	13·00

1951 (14 Aug). *4th Anniv of Independence. As Nos. 56, 58 and 60, but inscr "SERVICE" instead of "PAKISTAN POSTAGE".*

O32	18	3 a. purple	..	..	4·00	5·00
O33	19	4 a. green	..	..	1·50	10
O34	20	8 a. sepia	..	..	5·50	2·25
O32/4 ..			Set of 3		10·00	6·50

1953. *Optd with Type O 3.*

O35		3 p. red (No. 24a)	..	..	10	10
O36		6 p. violet (No. 25a) (R.)	..	..	10	10
O37		9 p. green (No. 26a) (R.)	..	..	10	10
O38		1 a. blue (No. 44a) (R.)	..	..	10	10
O39		1½ a. grey-green (No. 45a) (R.)	..	10	10
O40		2 a. red (No. 46a) (1953?)	..	..	15	10
O41		1 r. ultramarine (No. 38a)	..	..	6·00	2·00
O42		2 r. chocolate (No. 39a)	..	..	3·00	10
O43		5 r. carmine (No. 40a)	..	..	18·00	8·50
O44		10 r. magenta (No. 41b) (date?)	..	18·00	45·00
O35/44		.. .. ..	Set of 10		40·00	50·00

BAHAWALPUR

Bahawalpur, a former feudatory state situated to the west of the Punjab, was briefly independent following the partition of India on 15 August 1947 before acceding to Pakistan on 3 October of the same year.

East India Company and later Indian Empire post offices operated in Bahawalpur from 1854. By a postal agreement of 1879 internal mail from the state administration was carried unstamped, but this arrangement was superseded by the issue of Official stamps in 1945.

These had been preceded by a series of pictorial stamps prepared in 1933–34 on unwatermarked paper. It was intended that these would be used as state postage stamps, but permission for such use was withheld by the Indian Government so they were used for revenue purposes. The same designs were utilised for the 1945 Official series, Nos. O1/6, on paper watermarked Star and Crescent. Residual stocks of the unwatermarked 1 a., 8 a., 1 r. and 2 r. were used for the provisional Officials, Nos. O7 and O11/13.

A commemorative 1 a. Receipt stamp was produced to mark the centenary of the alliance with Great Britain. This may not have been ready until 1935, but an example of this stamp is known used on cover from Deh Rawal to Sadiq Garh and postmarked 14 August 1933. Both this 1 a. and the same value from the unwatermarked set also exist with Official Arabic overprint in black. These were not issued for postal purposes although one used example of the latter has been recorded.

Stamps of India were overprinted in the interim period between 15 August and 3 October 1947. After the state joined Pakistan postage stamps were issued for internal use until 1953.

Nawab (from 1947 Amir) Sadiq Mohammad Khan Abbasi V, 1907–1966

(1)

1947 (15 Aug). *Nos. 265/8, 269a/77 and 259/62 (King George VI) of India optd locally with* **T 1.**

1	3 p. slate (R.)	..	..	..	11·00
2	½ a. purple ..	..	..	..	11·00
3	9 p. green (R.)	..	..	..	11·00
4	1 a. carmine	..	..	..	11·00
5	1½ a. dull violet (R.)..	..	..	11·00
6	2 a. vermilion	..	..	..	11·00
	a. Opt double	..	..	..	£700
7	3 a. bright violet (R.)	..	..	11·00
8	3½ a. bright blue (R.)	..	..	11·00
9	4 a. brown ..	..	..	..	11·00
10	6 a. turquoise-green (R.)	..	..	11·00
	a. Opt double	..	..	..	£700
11	8 a. slate-violet (R.)	..	..	11·00
12	12 a. lake	..	..	..	11·00
13	14 a. purple ..	..	..	..	45·00
14	1 r. grey and red-brown	..	..	18·00
15	2 r. purple and brown (R.)	..	..	£700
16	5 r. green and blue (R.)	..	..	£700
17	10 r. purple and claret	..	..	£700
1/17	..	..	..	*Set of* 17	£2000

Nos. 1/17 were issued during the interim period, following the implementation of the Indian Independence Act, during which time Bahawalpur was part of neither of the two Dominions created. The Amir acceded to the Dominion of Pakistan on 3 October 1947 and these overprinted stamps of India were then withdrawn.

The stamps of Bahawalpur only had validity for use within the state. For external mail Pakistan stamps were used.

PRINTERS. All the following issues were recess-printed by De La Rue & Co, Ltd, London.

NEW INFORMATION

The editor is always interested to correspond with people who have new information that will improve or correct the Catalogue.

2 Amir Muhammad Bahawal Khan I Abbasi

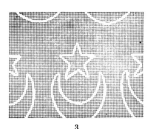

3

1947 (1 Dec). *Bicentenary Commemoration.* W **3** *(sideways).* P 12½ × 11½.

18	2	½ a. black and carmine	..	..	..	1·00	1·25

4 H.H. the Amir of Bahawalpur

5 The Tombs of the Amirs

6 Mosque in Sadiq-Garh

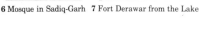

7 Fort Derawar from the Lake

8 Nur-Mahal Palace

9 The Palace, Sadiq-Garh

10 H.H. the Amir of   **11** Three Generations of Rulers; H.H.
Bahawalpur   the Amir in centre

1948 (1 Apr). W **3** (*sideways on vert designs*). P 12½ (*T* **4**),
11½ × 12½ (*T* **5**, **7**, **8** *and* **9**), 12½ × 11½ (*T* **6** *and* **10**) *or*
13½ × 14 (*T* **11**).

19	4	3 p. black and blue	..	..	30 13·00
20		½ a. black and claret		..	30 13·00
21		9 p. black and green		..	30 13·00
22		1 a. black and carmine ..		..	30 13·00
23		1½ a. black and violet		..	30 10·00
24	5	2 a. green and carmine ..		..	50 14·00
25	6	4 a. orange and brown ..		..	60 14·00
26	7	6 a. violet and blue	..	..	70 14·00
27	8	8 a. carmine and violet ..		..	75 14·00
28	9	12 a. green and carmine ..		..	80 19·00
29	10	1 r. violet and brown	..	..	14·00 28·00
30		2 r. green and claret	..	..	24·00 42·00
31		5 r. black and violet	..	..	28·00 55·00
32	11	10 r. scarlet and black	..	..	28·00 70·00
19/32 ..		..	..	..	*Set of* 14 90·00 £300

12 H.H. The Amir of Bahawalpur   **13** Soldiers of 1848
and Mohammed Ali Jinnah   and 1948

1948 (3 Oct). *First Anniv of Union of Bahawalpur with Pakistan.*
W **3**. P 13.
33   **12**   1½ a. carmine and blue-green   60   1·25

1948 (15 Oct). *Multan Campaign Centenary.* W **3**. P 11½.
34   **13**   1½ a. black and lake   70   6·50

1948. *As Nos. 29/32, but colours changed.*
35	10	1 r. deep green and orange	..	60 13·00
36		2 r. black and carmine ..		60 16·00
37		5 r. chocolate and ultramarine ..		60 27·00
38	11	10 r. red-brown and green	..	70 32·00
35/8 ..		.. ..	..	*Set of* 4 2·25 80·00

14 Irrigation   **17** U.P.U. Monument, Berne

1949 (3 Mar). *Silver Jubilee of Accession of H.H. the Amir of
Bahawalpur.* T **14** *and similar horiz designs.* W **3**. P 14.
39		3 p. black and ultramarine	..	..	..	10 8·00
40		½ a. black and brown-orange ..		..	10 8·00
41		9 p. black and green	..		..	10 8·00
42		1 a. black and carmine		..	..	10 8·00
39/42 ..					*Set of* 4	30 29·00

Designs:—½ a. Wheat; 9 p. Cotton; 1 a. Sahiwal bull.
Nos. 39/42 exist imperforate (*Prices, £15 per pair, unused*).

1949 (10 Oct). *75th Anniv of Universal Postal Union.* W **3**. *P* 13.
43	17	9 p. black and green	..	..	20 2·00
		a. Perf 17½ × 17		..	2·50 14·00
44		1 a. black and magenta ..		..	20 2·00
		a. Perf 17½ × 17		..	2·50 14·00
45		1½ a. black and orange		..	20 2·00
		a. Perf 17½ × 17		..	2·50 14·00
46		2½ a. black and blue		..	20 2·00
		a. Perf 17½ × 17		..	2·50 14·00
43/6 ..		.. ..	..	*Set of* 4	70 7·00
43a/6a		.. ..	..	*Set of* 4	9·00 50·00

Nos. 43/6 exist imperforate (*Prices, £10 per pair, unused*).

OFFICIAL STAMPS

O **1** Panjnad Weir   O **2** Dromedary and Calf

O **3** Blackbuck   O **4** Eastern White Pelicans

O **5** Friday Mosque, Fort   O **6** Temple at Pattan
Derawar   Munara

1945 (1 Mar). *Various horizontal pictorial designs, with red
Arabic opt.* W **3**. P 14.
O1	O **1**	½ a. black and green	..	..	2·25 7·50
O2	O **2**	1 a. black and carmine	..	..	3·25 4·75
		a. Opt omitted	..	..	† £600
O3	O **3**	2 a. black and violet	..	..	3·25 7·50
O4	O **4**	4 a. black and olive-green	..	..	7·50 18·00
O5	O **5**	8 a. black and brown ..		..	14·00 9·50
O6	O **6**	1 r. black and orange		..	16·00 9·50
O1/6		.. ..	..	*Set of* 6	42·00 50·00

Permission for the introduction of Nos. O1/6 was granted by
the Imperial Government as from 1 January 1945, but the
stamps were not used until 1 March. First Day covers exist
showing the January date.
Examples of No. O2a come from a sheet used at Rahimya
Khan.

O **7** Baggage Camels   (O **8**)

1945 (10 Mar). *Revenue stamp with red Arabic opt. No wmk.*
P 14.
O7   O **7**   1 a. black and brown   ..   ..   .. 26·00 48·00

1945 (Mar–June). *Surch as Type* O **8** (*at Security Printing Press,*
Nasik) *instead of red Arabic opt. No wmk. P* 14.
O11   O **5**   ½ a. on 8 a. black and purple ..   .. 4·25   3·25
O12   O **6**   1½ a. on 1 r. black and orange ..   .. 24·00 8·00
O13   O **1**   1½ a. on 2 r. black and blue (1 June)   .. 95·00 9·00
O11/13   ..   .. *Set of* 3 £110 18·00
The stamps used as a basis for Nos. O7 and O11/13 were part
of the Revenue series issued in 1933–34.

SERVICE

(O **9**)   O **10** H.H. the Amir of
Bahawalpur

1945. *Optd with Type* O **9** (*by D.L.R.*) *instead of red Arabic opt. No*
wmk. P 14.
O14   O **1**   ½ a. black and carmine..   ..   .. 1·25   8·50
O15   O **2**   1 a. black and carmine..   ..   .. 2·00 11·00
O16   O **3**   2 a. black and orange ..   ..   .. 3·25 30·00
O14/16   ..   .. *Set of* 3 6·00 45·00

1945. *P* 14.
O17   O **10**   3 p. black and blue ..   ..   .. 2·00   5·50
O18   1½ a. black and violet..   ..   .. 11·00 5·50

O **11** Allied Banners

(Des E. Meronti. Recess, background litho)

1946 (1 May). *Victory. P* 14.
O19   O **11**   1½ a. green and grey ..   ..   .. 1·75   2·25

1948.   *Nos. 19, 22, 24/5 and 35/8 optd as Nos.* O1/6.
O20   **4**   3 p. black and blue (R.)   50   8·00
O21   1 a. black and carmine (Blk.) 50   7·00
O22   **5**   2 a. green and carmine (Blk.) 50   8·50
O23   **6**   4 a. orange and brown (Blk.) ..   .. 50 11·00
O24   **10**   1 r. deep green and orange (R.)   .. 50 13·00
O25   2 r. black and carmine (R.)   ..   .. 50 15·00
O26   5 r. chocolate and ultramarine (R.)   .. 50 26·00
O27   **11**   10 r. red-brown and green (R.)   .. 50 29·00
O20/7   ..   .. *Set of* 8 3·50 £110

1949 (10 Oct). *75th Anniv of Universal Postal Union. Nos.* 43/6
optd as Nos. O1/6.
O28   **17**   9 p. black and green   15   4·50
   a. Perf 17½ × 17   ..   ..   .. 2·00 23·00
O29   1 a. black and magenta..   ..   .. 2·00 23·00
   a. Perf 17½ × 17   ..   ..   .. 2·00 23·00
O30   1½ a. black and orange   15   4·50
   a. Perf 17½ × 17   ..   ..   .. 2·00 23·00
O31   2½ a. black and blue   15   4·50
   a. Perf 17½ × 17   ..   ..   .. 2·00 23·00
O28/31   ..   .. *Set of* 4 55 16·00
O28a/31a   ..   .. *Set of* 4 7·50 85·00
Nos. O28/31 exist imperforate (*Prices, £10 per pair, unused*)

From 1947 stamps of Pakistan were used on all external mail.
Bahawalpur issues continued to be used on internal mail until
1953.

Palestine

1000 mils = 1 Palestine pound

BRITISH MANDATE

9 Rachel's Tomb   10 Dome of the Rock

11 Citadel, Jerusalem   12 Sea of Galilee

(Des F. Taylor. Typo Harrison)

1927 (1 June)**-45.** *Wmk Mult Script CA. P* 13½ × 14½ (2 m. to 20 m.) or 14.

90	9	2 m. greenish blue (14.8.27)	..	30	10
91		3 m. yellow-green	.. ..	40	10
92	10	4 m. rose-pink (14.8.27)..	.. ..	3·25	1·25
93	11	5 m. orange (14.8.27)	.. ..	65	10
		a. From coils. Perf 14½×14 (1935)		14·00	18·00
		b. *Yellow* (12.44)	..	65	15
		c. *Yellow.* From coils. Perf 14½ × 14 (1945)		30·00	27·00
94	10	6 m. pale green (14.8.27)	..	3·00	1·75
		a. *Deep green* ..	.. ..	50	20
95	11	7 m. scarlet (14.8.27)	.. ..	4·00	1·25
96	10	8 m. yellow-brown (14.8.27)	..	12·00	5·00
97	9	10 m. slate (14.8.27)	.. ..	40	10
		a. *Grey.* From coils. Perf 14½ × 14 (11.38)		20·00	24·00
		b. *Grey* (1944)..	.. ..	75	10
98	10	13 m. ultramarine	.. ..	3·75	30
99	11	20 m. dull olive-green (14.8.27)	..	1·00	15
		a. *Bright olive-green* (12.44)	..	1·00	15
100	12	50 m. deep dull purple (14.8.27) ..		1·00	30
		a *Bright purple* (12.44)	..	1·25	30
101		90 m. bistre (14.8.27)	.. ..	60·00	60·00
102		100 m. turquoise-blue (14.8.27)	..	2·00	70
103		200 m. deep violet (14.8.27)	..	8·00	5·00
		a. *Bright violet* (1928)	..	27·00	16·00
		b. *Blackish violet* (12.44)	..	6·00	3·50
90/103b			*Set of* 14	85·00	65·00
90/103 H/S "Specimen"			*Set of* 14	£325	

Three sets may be made of the above issue; one on thin paper, one on thicker paper with a ribbed appearance, and another on thick white paper without ribbing.

2 m. stamps in the grey colour of the 10 m., including an example postmarked in 1935, exist as do 50 m. stamps in blue, but it has not been established whether they were issued.

Nos. 90/1 and 93 exist in coils, constructed from normal sheets.

1932 (1 June)**-44.** *New values and colours. Wmk Mult Script CA. P* 13½ × 14½ (4 m. to 15 m.) or 14.

104	10	4 m. purple (1.11.32) ..	.. ..	65	10
105	11	7 m. deep violet	.. ..	45	10

106	10	8 m. scarlet	..	..	60	20
107		13 m. bistre (1.8.32)	..	..	70	10
108		15 m. ultramarine (1.8.32)	..	..	1·25	10
		a. *Grey-blue* (12.44) ..	..	..	1·00	40
		b. *Greenish blue*	..	..	1·10	40
109	12	250 m. brown (15.1.42)	..	..	3·75	1·75
110		500 m. scarlet (15.1.42)	..	..	4·50	3·00
111		£P1 black (15.1.42)	..	..	5·00	3·50
104/11		.. ..	..	*Set of* 8	15·00	8·00
104/11 Perf "Specimen"		..	..	*Set of* 8	£375	

No. 108 exists in coils, constructed from normal sheets.

STAMP BOOKLETS

1929. *Blue cover. Without advertisements on front. Stitched.*
SB1 150 m. booklet containing twelve 2 m., 3 m. and eighteen 5 m. (Nos. 90/1, 93) in blocks of 6 £2000
  a. As No. SB1, but stapled £1600

1937–38. *Red cover. With advertisements on front. Stapled.*
SB2 150 m. booklet containing 2 m., 3 m., 5 m. and 15 m. (Nos. 90/1, 93, 108) in blocks of 6 £1600
  a. Blue cover (1938) £1600

1939. *Pink cover. With advertisements on front. Stapled.*
SB3 120 m. booklet containing six 10 m. and twelve 5 m. (Nos. 93, 97) in blocks of 6 .. .. £1500

POSTAGE DUE STAMPS

D 3 (MIL)

1928 (1 Feb)**-45.** *Wmk Mult Script CA. P* 14.

D12	D 3	1 m. brown	..	..	45	85
		a. Perf 15 × 14 (1944)	..	..	30·00	55·00
D13		2 m. yellow	..	..	55	60
D14		4 m. green	..	..	80	1·60
		a. Perf 15 × 14 (1945)	..	..	50·00	70·00
D15		6 m. orange-brown (10.33)	..	..	11·00	8·50
D16		8 m. carmine ..	..	..	1·75	90
D17		10 m. pale grey	..	..	1·25	60
D18		13 m. ultramarine	..	..	1·50	1·75
D19		20 m. pale olive-green	..	..	1·60	1·25
D20		50 m. violet	..	..	2·50	1·25
D12/20		.. .. ..	..	*Set of* 9	18·00	16·00
D12/20 Perf (D15) or Optd (others) "Specimen"				*Set of* 9	£300	

The British Mandate terminated on 14 May 1948. Later issues of stamps and occupation issues will be found listed under Gaza, Israel and Jordan in Part 19 (*Middle East*) of this catalogue.

Pitcairn Islands

12 pence (d) = 1 shilling; 20 shillings = 1 pound

CROWN COLONY

PRICES. Those quoted for Nos. Z1/47 are for examples showing a virtually complete strike of Type Z 1. Due to the size of the cancellation such examples will usually be on piece.

Z 1

Stamps of New Zealand cancelled with Type Z 1.

1937. *Coronation (Nos. 599/601).*
Z30	1d. carmine	..	..	..	..	26·00
Z31	2½d. Prussian blue	..	..	..	28·00
Z32	6d. red-orange	..	..	..	..	28·00

1937. *Health (No. 602).*
Z33	1d. + 1d. scarlet	..	..	..	50·00

1938. *King George VI (Nos. 603, 605).*
Z34	½d. green	..	..	..	..	50·00
Z35	1d. scarlet	..	..	..	..	50·00

1940. *Centenary of British Sovereignty (Nos. 613/22, 624/5).*
Z36	½d. blue-green	..	..	..	27·00
Z37	1d. chocolate and scarlet	..	..	30·00
Z38	1½d. light blue and mauve	..	..	32·00
Z39	2d. blue-green and chocolate	..	..	32·00
Z40	2½d. blue-green and blue	..	..	35·00
Z41	3d. purple and carmine ..	..	..	35·00
Z42	4d. chocolate and lake ..	..	..	50·00
Z43	5d. pale blue and brown	..	..	55·00
Z44	6d. emerald-green and violet	..	..	55·00
Z45	7d. black and red	..	..	..	75·00
Z46	9d. olive-green and orange	..	..	75·00
Z47	1s. sage-green and deep green	..	..	75·00

1 Cluster of Oranges

2 Christian on *Bounty* and Pitcairn Island

(Recess B.W. (1d., 3d., 4d., 8d. and 2s. 6d.), and Waterlow (others))

1940 (15 Oct)–**51.** *T **1/2** and similar horiz designs. Wmk Mult Script CA. P 11½×11 (1d., 3d., 4d., 8d. and 2s. 6d.) or 12½ (others).*
1	½d. blue-green	..	..	40	60
2	1d. mauve and magenta	..	..	55	70
3	1½d. grey and carmine	..	..	55	50
4	2d. green and brown	..	..	1·75	1·40
5	3d. yellow-green and blue ..	..	1·25	1·40
	aw. Wmk inverted ..	..	..	£1500	
5b	4d. black and emerald-green (1.9.51)	.. 15·00	7·00
6	6d. brown and grey-blue	..	..	5·00	2·25
6a	8d. olive-green and magenta (1.9.51)	.. 15·00	7·00
7	1s. violet and grey	..	..	3·00	2·00
8	2s. 6d. green and brown	..	..	7·50	4·25
1/8	..	..	..	*Set of* 10	45·00	24·00
1/5, 6, 7/8 Perf "Specimen"		*Set of* 8	£750

Designs:—1½d. John Adams and his house; 2d. Lt. Bligh and H.M.S. *Bounty*; 3d. Pitcairn Islands and Pacific Ocean; 4d. *Bounty* Bible; 6d. H.M.S. *Bounty*; 8d. School, 1949; 1s. Fletcher Christian and Pitcairn Island; 2s. 6d. Christian on H.M.S. *Bounty* and Pitcairn Coast.

Flagstaff flaw
(R. 8/2)

1946 (2 Dec). *Victory. As Nos. 141/2 of Jamaica.*
9	2d. brown	..	..	..	40	15
10	3d. blue	..	..	..	40	15
	a. Flagstaff flaw	..	..	23·00	
9/10 Perf "Specimen"	..	..	*Set of* 2	£140

1949 (1 Aug). *Royal Silver Wedding. As Nos. 143/4 of Jamaica.*
11	1½d. scarlet	..	..	..	2·00	1·00
12	10s. mauve	..	..	..	60·00	50·00

1949 (10 Oct). *75th Anniv of U.P.U. As Nos. 145/8 of Jamaica.*
13	2½d. red-brown	..	..	..	2·00	3·00
14	3d. deep blue	..	..	..	11·00	4·00
15	6d. deep blue-green ..	..	..	10·00	5·00
16	1s. purple	..	..	..	10·00	5·00
13/16 ..	..	..	..	*Set of* 4	30·00	15·00

STAMP BOOKLETS

1940 (15 Oct). *Black on deep green cover. Stapled.*
SB1 4s. 8d. booklet containing one each ½d., 1d., 1½d., 2d., 3d., 6d., 1s. and 2s. 6d. (Nos. 1/5, 6, 7/8) £2500

In addition to the stapled booklets, the shipment also contained some empty booklet covers. These were made up on the island, but due to the absence of a stapling machine the booklets were assembled with paper fasteners.

St. Helena

12 pence (d) = 1 shilling; 20 shillings = 1 pound

CROWN COLONY

1937 (19 May). *Coronation. As Nos. 118/20 of Jamaica.*

128	1d. green ..	..	..	..	40	30
129	2d. orange	..	..	..	75	30
130	3d. bright blue	..	..	..	1·25	30
128/30	..	..	..	*Set of* 3	2·25	80
128/30 Perf "Specimen"	..	..	*Set of* 3	55·00		

33 Badge of St. Helena

(Recess Waterlow)

1938 (12 May)–**44.** *Wmk Mult Script CA. P* 12½.

131	**33**	½d. violet	..	..	..	10	40
132		1d. green	..	..	.. 20·00	4·00
132a		1d. yellow-orange (8.7.40)	..	..	20	30
133		1½d. scarlet	..	..	..	20	40
134		2d. red-orange ..	..	..	..	20	15
135		3d. ultramarine	..	..	.. 90·00	25·00
135a		3d. grey (8.7.40)	..	..	30	30
135b		4d. ultramarine (8.7.40)	..	..	2·00	30
136		6d. light blue	..	..	..	2·00	30
136a		8d. sage-green (8.7.40) ..	..	..	3·25	90
		b. Olive-green (24.5.44)	..	..	4·50	4·00

137	**33**	1s. sepia	..	..	..	90	30
138		2s. 6d. maroon ..	..	..	.. 16·00	3·50
139		5s. chocolate	..	..	.. 17·00	7·50
140		10s. purple	..	..	.. 17·00	16·00
131/140		..	..	*Set of* 14	£150	55·00
131/40 Perf "Specimen"		..	..	*Set of* 14	£300	

See also Nos. 149/51.

1946 (21 Oct). *Victory. As Nos. 141/2 of Jamaica.*

141	2d. red-orange	..	..	..	10	10
142	4d. blue	..	..	..	10	10
141/2 Perf "Specimen"	..	..	*Set of* 2	60·00		

1948 (20 Oct). *Royal Silver Wedding. As Nos. 143/4 of Jamaica.*

143	3d. black	..	..	..	30	20
144	10s. violet-blue	..	..	. 22·00	27·00

1949 (10 Oct). *75th Anniv of U.P.U. As Nos. 145/8 of Jamaica.*

145	3d. carmine ..	..	..	..	75	30
146	4d. deep blue ..	..	..	..	2·00	90
147	6d. olive	..	..	..	1·25	90
148	1s. blue-black	..	..	..	1·25	1·10
145/8 ..	..	..	..	*Set of* 4	4·75	3·00

1949 (1 Nov). *Wmk Mult Script CA. P* 12½.

149	**33**	1d. black and green	..	..	..	50	80
150		1½d. black and carmine ..	..	..	50	80
151		2d. black and scarlet ..	..	..	50	80
149/51		..	..	..	*Set of* 3	1·40	2·25

St. Kitts–Nevis

1937. 12 pence (d) = 1 shilling; 20 shillings = 1 pound
1951. 100 cents = 1 West Indian dollar

CROWN COLONY

1937 (12 May). *Coronation. As Nos. 118/20 of Jamaica.*
65	1d. scarlet	.. ..	30	20
66	1½d. buff	.. ..	40	10
67	2½d. bright blue	.. .. ..	60	45
65/7		*Set of* 3	1·10	65
65/7 Perf "Specimen"		*Set of* 3	50·00	

Nos. 61/7 are inscribed "ST. CHRISTOPHER AND NEVIS".

Break in frame above ornament
(R. 2/4) (ptgs between 1941 and 1950)

7 King George VI

8 King George VI and Medicinal Spring

9 King George VI and Christopher Columbus

10 King George VI and Anguilla Island

Break in oval at foot (R. 12/5) (ptgs between 1941 and 1945 only). Sometimes touched-in by hand painting)

Break in oval at left (R. 7/1) (1943 and 1944 ptgs only)

(Typo; centre litho (T 10). D.L.R.)

Break in value tablet (R. 12/5) (1947 ptg only)

Break in oval (R. 12/1) (1938 ptg only)

Break in value tablet frame (R.3/2)

Break in value tablet frame (R.12/3) (ptgs between 1941 and 1945 only)

1938 (15 Aug)–**50.** *Wmk Mult Script CA (sideways on T 8 and 9). Chalk-surfaced paper* (10s., £1). *P* 14 (*T* 7 *and* 10) *or* 13×12 (*T* 8/9).

68	7	½d. green	.. ..	3·00	20
		a. *Blue-green* (5.4.43)	.. ..	10	10
69		1d. scarlet	.. ..	4·00	70
		a. *Carmine* (5.43)	.. ..	50	40
		b. *Carmine-pink* (4.47)	..	60·00	16·00
		c. *Rose-red* (7.47)	.. ..	70	70
70		1½d. orange	.. ..	20	30
71	8	2d. scarlet and grey	.. ..	17·00	2·50
		a. Chalk-surfaced paper. *Carmine and deep grey* (1940)	..	50·00	9·50
		b. Perf 14. *Scarlet and pale grey* (1941)		70	1·25
		ba. *Scarlet and deep grey* (5.43)	..	20·00	5·00
		c. Perf 14. Chalk-surfaced paper. *Scarlet and pale grey* (8.49)	..	1·50	1·50
72	7	2½d. ultramarine	.. ..	3·50	30
		a. *Bright ultramarine* (5.4.43)	..	30	30
73	8	3d. dull reddish purple and scarlet	..	14·00	3·00
		a. Chalk-surfaced paper. *Brown-purple and carmine-red* (1940)		17·00	3·50
		b. Perf 14. Chalk-surfaced paper. *Dull reddish purple & carm-red* (1942)		24·00	3·75
		c. Perf 14. Ordinary paper. *Reddish lilac and scarlet* (5.43)	..	1·75	12·00
		d. Perf 14. Ordinary paper. *Purple and bright scarlet* (1945, 1947)	..	4·25	4·25
		da. Break in value tablet	..	50·00	
		e. Perf 14. Chalk-surfaced paper. *Deep purple and scarlet* (1946)	..	65·00	18·00
		f. Perf 14. Ordinary paper. *Rose-lilac and bright scarlet* (1948)	..	5·00	5·50
		g. Perf 14. Chalk-surfaced paper. *Deep reddish purple & brt scarlet* (1950)		3·00	3·50

74	9	6d. green and bright purple	6·50	1·75
		a. Break in oval	65·00	
		b. Perf 14. Chalk-surfaced paper.		
		Green and deep claret (1942) ..	50·00	11·00
		c. Perf 14. Ordinary paper. Green and		
		purple (5.43)	4·50	1·50
		d. Perf 14. Chalk-surfaced paper.		
		Green and purple (10.48)	3·25	3·00
75	8	1s. black and green	12·00	1·25
		a. Break in value tablet frame ..	90·00	
		b. Perf 14 (1943)	3·75	85
		ba. Break in value tablet frame ..	50·00	
		c. Perf 14. Chalk-surfaced paper		
		(28.7.49)	2·00	2·50
		ca. Break in value tablet frame ..	38·00	
76		2s. 6d. black and scarlet ..	28·00	9·00
		a. Perf 14. Chalk-surfaced paper		
		(1942)	12·00	5·00
		ab. Ordinary paper. (5.43) ..	11·00	3·75
77	9	5s. grey-green and scarlet ..	65·00	16·00
		a. Perf 14. Chalk-surfaced paper		
		(1941)	£130	24·00
		ab. Break in value tablet frame ..	£275	
		ac. Break in frame above ornament ..	£275	
		ad. Break in oval at foot ..	£275	
		ae. Break in oval at left	£275	
		b. Perf 14. Ordinary paper. Bluish		
		green and scarlet (5.43) ..	22·00	9·00
		ba. Break in value tablet frame ..	£120	
		bb. Break in frame above ornament ..	£130	
		bc. Break in oval at foot ..	£110	
		bd. Break in oval at left ..	£120	
		c. Perf 14. Chalk-surfaced paper.		
		Green and scarlet-vermilion (7.6.50)	26·00	18·00
		cb. Break in frame above ornament ..	£130	
77d	10	10s. black and ultramarine (1.9.48) ..	12·00	19·00
77e		£1 black and brown (1.9.48) ..	12·00	23·00
68/77e		.. ..	Set of 12	60·00	55·00
68/77 Perf "Specimen" ..			Set of 10	£180	

1946 (1 Nov). *Victory. As Nos. 141/2 of Jamaica.*

78		1½d. red-orange	10	10
79		3d. carmine	10	10
78/9 Perf "Specimen"		Set of 2	60·00	

1949 (3 Jan). *Royal Silver Wedding. As Nos. 143/4 of Jamaica.*

80		2½d. ultramarine	10	10
81		5s. carmine	4·50	2·50

1949 (10 Oct). *75th Anniv of U.P.U. As Nos. 145/8 of Jamaica.*

82		2½d. ultramarine	35	20
83		3d. carmine-red	60	30
84		6d. magenta	40	30
85		1s. blue-green	40	30
82/5		Set of 4	1·60	1·00

1950 (10 Nov). *Tercentenary of British Settlement in Anguilla. Nos. 69c, 70 and 72a (perf 14) optd as T 11 and new ptgs of T 8/9 on chalk-surfaced paper perf 13×12½ as T 12.*

86	7	1d. rose-red	10	10
87		1½d. orange	10	10
		a. Error. Crown missing, W 9a ..	£1300	
		b. Error. St. Edward's Crown, W 9b ..	£800	
88		2½d. bright ultramarine	10	10
89	8	3d. dull purple and scarlet ..	10	10
90	9	6d. green and bright purple ..	10	10
91	8	1s. black and green (R.)	10	10
		a. Break in value tablet frame ..	8·50	
86/91		.. ..	Set of 6	40	40

Nos. 87a/b occur on a row in the watermark, in which the crowns and letters "CA" alternate.

(New Currency. 100 cents = 1 West Indian, later East Caribbean, dollar)

1951 (16 Feb). *Inauguration of B.W.I. University College. As Nos. 149/50 of Jamaica.*

92		3c. black and yellow-orange..	30	15
93		12c. turquoise-green and magenta	30	50

13 Bath House and   **14** Map of the Islands
Spa, Nevis

(Recess Waterlow)

1952 (14 June). *Vert designs as T 14 (3, 12 c.) or horiz as 13 (others). Wmk Mult Script CA. P 12½.*

94	1 c. deep green and ochre	15	80
95	2 c. green	30	70
96	3 c. carmine-red and violet	30	70
97	4 c. scarlet	20	20
98	5 c. bright blue and grey	20	20
99	6 c. ultramarine	20	15
100	12 c. deep blue and reddish brown	20	10
101	24 c. black and carmine-red	20	10
102	48 c. olive and chocolate	1·50	1·50
103	60 c. ochre and deep green	1·50	1·75
104	$1.20, deep green and ultramarine	5·00	2·25
105	$4.80, green and carmine	12·00	18·00
94/105	.. ..	Set of 12	19·00	23·00

Designs:—2 c. Warner Park; 4 c. Brimstone Hill; 5 c. Nevis from the sea, North; 6 c. Pinney's Beach, Nevis; 12 c. Sir Thomas Warner's Tomb; 24 c. Old Road Bay; 48 c. Sea Island cotton, Nevis; 60 c. The Treasury; $1.20, Salt pond, Anguilla; $4.80, Sugar factory.

St. Lucia

1937. 12 pence (d) = 1 shilling; 20 shillings = 1 pound
1949. 100 cents = 1 West Indian dollar

CROWN COLONY

1937 (12 May). *Coronation. As Nos.* 118/20 *of Jamaica, but ptd by B.W. P* 11×11½.

125	1d. violet	..	30	30
126	1½d. carmine ..	..	55	20
127	2½d. blue	..	55	40
125/7		*Set of* 3	1·25	80
125/7 Perf "Specimen"		*Set of* 3	55·00	

26 King George VI

27 Columbus Square

28 Government House

31 Device of St. Lucia

(Des E. Crafer (T **26**), H. Fleury (5s.). Recess Waterlow (½d. to 3½d., 8d., 3s., 5s., £1), D.L.R. (6d., 1s.) and B.W. (2s., 10s.))

1938 (22 Sept)–48. *T* **26/8, 31** *and similar designs. Wmk Mult Script CA (sideways on* 2s.).

128	**26**	½d. green (*p* 14½ × 14)	..	75	10
		a. Perf 12½ (1943) ..		10	10
129		1d. violet (*p* 14½ × 14)	..	90	75
		a. Perf 12½ (1938) ..		10	15
129b		1d. scarlet (*p* 12½) (1947)	..	10	10
		c. Perf 14½ × 14 (1948)	..	10	10
130		1½d. scarlet (*p* 14½ × 14)	..	1·25	40
		a. Perf 12½ (1943) ..		15	35
131		2d. grey (*p* 14½ × 14)	..	70	80
		a. Perf 12½ (1943) ..		10	10
132		2½d. ultramarine (*p* 14½ × 14)	..	1·25	15
		a. Perf 12½ (1943) ..		10	10
132b		2½d. violet (*p* 12½) (1947)	..	30	10
133		3d. orange (*p* 14½ × 14)	..	15	10
		a. Perf 12½ (1943) ..		10	10
133b		3½d. ultramarine (*p* 12½) (1947)	..	30	15
134	**27**	6d. claret (*p* 13½)	..	2·00	50
		a. *Carmine-lake* (*p* 13½) (1945)	..	1·75	35
		b. Perf 12. *Claret* (1948)	..	1·00	45
134c	**26**	8d. brown (*p* 12½) (1946)	..	2·50	30
135	**28**	1s. brown (*p* 13½)	..	55	30
		a. Perf 12 (1948)	..	40	20
136	–	2s. blue and purple (*p* 12)	..	3·50	1·25
136a	**26**	3s. bright purple (*p* 12½) (1946)	..	8·00	2·75
137	–	5s. black and mauve (*p* 12½)	..	14·00	6·00
138	**31**	10s. black/*yellow* (*p* 12)	..	4·50	9·00
141	**26**	£1 sepia (*p* 12½) (1946)	..	11·00	8·00
128a/141			*Set of* 17	40·00	26·00
128/41 Perf "Specimen"			*Set of* 17	£300	

Designs: *Horiz* (*as T* **28**): 2s. The Pitons; 5s. Loading bananas.

1946 (8 Oct). *Victory. As Nos.* 141/2 *of Jamaica.*

142	1d. lilac	..	..	10	10
143	3½d. blue	..	..	10	10
142/3 Perf "Specimen"		..	*Set of* 2	50·00	

1948 (26 Nov). *Royal Silver Wedding. As Nos.* 143/4 *of Jamaica.*

144	1d. scarlet	..	..	15	10
145	£1 purple-brown	..	..	12·00	35·00

(New Currency. 100 cents = 1 West Indian, later Eastern Caribbean dollar)

32 King George VI

33 Device of St. Lucia

(Recess Waterlow (**32**), B.W. (**33**))

1949 (1 Oct)–50. *Value in cents or dollars. Wmk Mult Script CA. P* 12½ (1 c. *to* 16 c.), 11 × 11½ (*others*).

146	**32**	1 c. green	..	..	10	10
		a. Perf 14 (1949)	..	..	90	40
147		2 c. magenta	..	..	10	10
		a. Perf 14½ × 14 (1949)	..	..	1·50	1·00
148		3 c. scarlet	..	..	10	50
149		4 c. grey	..	..	10	10
		a. Perf 14½ × 14	..	..	† £5000	
150		5 c. violet	..	..	10	10
151		6 c. orange	..	..	15	50
152		7 c. ultramarine	..	..	80	1·00
153		12 c. claret	..	..	2·00	60
		a. Perf 14½ × 14 (1950)	..	£425	£275	
154		16 c. brown	..	..	1·50	20
155	**33**	24 c. light blue ..	..	..	30	10
156		48 c. olive-green..	..	..	1·50	85
157		$1.20, purple ..	..	..	2·25	5·00
158		$2.40, blue-green	..	..	3·00	17·00
159		$4.80, rose-carmine	..	..	7·00	18·00
146/159		..	..	*Set of* 14	17·00	38·00

1949 (10 Oct). *75th Anniv of U.P.U. As Nos.* 145/8 *of Jamaica.*

160	5 c. violet	..	..	20	20
161	6 c. orange	..	..	70	50
162	12 c. magenta ..	..	..	30	20
163	24 c. blue-green	..	..	65	20
160/3		..	*Set of* 4	1·60	1·00

1951 (16 Feb). *Inauguration of B.W.I. University College. As Nos.* 149/50 *of Jamaica.*

164	3 c. black and scarlet..	..	..	45	30
165	12 c. black and deep carmine ..	..	..	45	30

MINIMUM PRICE

The minimum price quote is 10p which represents a handling charge rather than a basis for valuing common stamps. For further notes about prices see introductory pages.

N 1
E 9
W 5
W 1

CONSTITUTION

(35)

34 Phoenix rising from
Burning Buildings

(Flames typo, rest recess B.W.)

1951 (19 June). *Reconstruction of Castries. Wmk Mult Script CA.
P 13½ × 13.*
166 **34** 12 c. red and blue 15 50

1951 (25 Sept). *New Constitution. Nos. 147, 149/50 and 153
optd with T 35 by Waterlow. P 12½.*
167 **32** 2 c. magenta 15 20
168 4 c. grey 15 20
169 5 c. violet 15 15
170 12 c. claret 15 40
167/70 .. .. *Set of* 4 55 85

POSTAGE DUE STAMPS

D 2 D 3

(Typo D.L.R.)
1933–47. *Wmk Mult Script CA. P* 14.
D3 **D 2** 1d. black .. .. .. 4·25 5·00
D4 2d. black .. .. .. 14·00 7·50
D5 4d. black (28.6.47) .. .. 4·25 26·00
D6 8d. black (28.6.47) .. .. 4·25 35·00
D3/6 .. .. *Set of* 4 24·00 65·00
D3/6 Perf "Specimen" .. .. *Set of* 4 £130

1949 (1 Oct)–52. *Value in cents. Wmk Mult Script CA. Typo. P* 14.
D 7 **D 3** 2 c. black .. .. .. 1·75 21·00
  a. Chalk-surfaced paper (27.11.52) 10 6·00
  ab. Error. Crown missing, W **9a** .. 80·00
  ac. Error. St. Edward's Crown, W **9b** 30·00
D 8 4 c. black .. .. .. 3·25 14·00
  a. Chalk-surfaced paper (27.11.52).. 30 7·50
  ab. Error. Crown missing, W **9a** .. £100
  ac. Error. St. Edward's Crown, W **9b** 40·00
D 9 8 c. black .. .. .. 2·75 18·00
  a. Chalk-surfaced paper (27.11.52).. 2·00 24·00
  ac. Error. St. Edward's Crown, W **9b** £180
D10 16 c. black .. .. .. 12·00 50·00
  a. Chalk-surfaced paper (27.11.52).. 3·00 35·00
  ac. Error. St. Edward's Crown, W **9b** £250
D7/10 .. .. *Set of* 4 18·00 95·00
D7a/10a .. .. *Set of* 4 4·75 65·00

St. Vincent

1937. 12 pence (d) = 1 shilling; 20 shillings = 1 pound
1949. 100 cents = 1 West Indian dollar

CROWN COLONY

1937 (12 May). *Coronation. As Nos. 118/20 of Jamaica, but ptd by B.W. P 11×11½.*

146	1d. violet	..	..	35	30
147	1½d. carmine ..	..	..	55	10
148	2½d. blue	..	..	65	1·10
146/8 ..	..	..	*Set of* 3	1·40	1·25
146/8 Perf "Specimen"	..	..	*Set of* 3	50·00	

25

26 Young's Island and Fort Duvernette

27 Kingstown and Fort Charlotte

28 Bathing Beach at Villa

29 Victoria Park, Kingstown

NEW CONSTITUTION 1951

(29*a*)

(Recess B.W.)

1938 (11 Mar)–47. *Wmk Mult Script CA. P 12.*

149	25	½d. blue and green ..	..	..	10	10
150	26	1d. blue and lake-brown	..	..	10	10
151	27	1½d. green and scarlet	..	..	20	10
152	25	2d. green and black	..	..	40	35
153	28	2½d. blue-black and blue-green	..	20	40
153*a*	29	2½d. green and purple-brown (1947)	20	20
154	25	3d. orange and purple	..	..	20	10
154*a*	28	3½d. blue-black and blue-green (1947)	40	95
155	25	6d. black and lake	..	..	1·00	40
156	29	1s. purple and green	..	..	1·00	50
157	25	2s. blue and purple	..	6·00	75
157*a*		2s. 6d. red-brown and blue (1947) ..	1·00	3·50
158		5s. scarlet and deep green .. '	..	10·00	2·50

158*a*	25	10s. violet and brown (1947)		..	3·75	8·00
		aw. Wmk inverted ..		..	..	— £1200
159		£1 purple and black		..	..	16·00	15·00
149/59		..	..	..	..	*Set of* 15	35·00	28·00
149/59 Perf "Specimen"		..	..	*Set of* 15	£250	

1946 (15 Oct). *Victory. As Nos. 141/2 of Jamaica.*

160		1½d. carmine ..	..	..	..	10	10
161		3½d. blue	..	..	..	..	10	10
160/1 Perf "Specimen"		..	..	*Set of* 2	50·00	

1948 (30 Nov). *Royal Silver Wedding. As Nos. 143/4 of Jamaica.*

162		1½d. scarlet ..	..	..	..	10	10
163		£1 bright purple ..	..	..	15·00	16·00

No. 163 was originally printed in black, but the supply of these was stolen in transit. A few archive examples exist, some perforated "Specimen".

(New Currency. 100 cents = 1 West Indian, later East Caribbean dollar)

1949 (26 Mar)–52. *Value in cents and dollars. Wmk Mult Script CA. P 12.*

164	25	1 c. blue and green	..	..	20	65
164*a*		1 c. green and black (10.6.52) ..	..	30	1·25
165	26	2 c. blue and lake-brown	..	..	15	30
166	27	3 c. green and scarlet	..	..	40	40
166*a*	25	3 c. orange and purple (10.6.52)	..	30	1·25
167		4 c. green and black	..	..	35	20
167*a*		4 c. blue and green (10.6.52)	..	30	15
168	29	5 c. green and purple-brown	..	15	10
169	25	6 c. orange and purple ..	..	40	40
169*a*	27	6 c. green and scarlet (10.6.52)..	..	30	1·00
170	28	7 c. blue-black and blue-green ..	..	3·50	40
170*a*		10 c. blue-black and blue-green (10.6.52)	50	20
171	25	12 c. black and lake	..	..	35	15
172	29	24 c. purple and green	..	..	35	45
173	25	48 c. blue and purple	..	..	1·50	1·50
174		60 c. red-brown and blue..	..	1·75	2·00
175		$1.20, scarlet and deep green .. '	..	4·25	4·00
176		$2.40, violet and brown	..	..	6·00	9·00
177		$4.80, purple and black	..	..	11·00	18·00
164/77		..	..	..	..	*Set of* 19	28·00	35·00

1949 (10 Oct). *75th Anniv of U.P.U. As Nos. 145/8 of Jamaica*

178		5 c. blue	..	..	..	..	25	15
179		6 c. purple	..	..	..	..	40	70
180		12 c. magenta ..	..	..	..	30	65
181		24 c. blue-green	..	..	..	50	25
178/81		..	..	..	..	*Set of* 4	1·25	1·60

1951 (16 Feb). *Inauguration of B.W.I. University College. As Nos. 149/50 of Jamaica.*

182		3 c. deep green and scarlet	..	..	30	15
183		12 c. black and purple ..	..	..	30	15

1951 (21 Sept). *New Constitution. Optd with T 29a by B.W.*

184	27	3 c. green and scarlet	..	..	15	30
185	25	4 c. green and black	..	..	15	20
186	29	5 c. green and purple-brown	..	15	20
187	25	12 c. black and lake	..	..	30	20
184/7 ..		..	..	..	..	*Set of* 4	65	80

Sarawak

100 cents = 1 Malayan dollar

BROOKE FAMILY ADMINISTRATION

21 Sir Charles Vyner Brooke

B M A (22)

(Recess B.W.)

1934 (1 May)–**41**. *No wmk. P* 12.

106	**21**	1 c. purple			15	10
107		2 c. green			15	10
107a		2 c. black (1.3.41)			80	1·60
108		3 c. black			15	10
108a		3 c. green (1.3.41)			2·00	3·00
109		4 c. bright purple			20	15
110		5 c. violet			50	10
111		6 c. carmine			60	60
111a		6 c. lake-brown (1.3.41)			3·25	8·00
112		8 c. red-brown			40	10
112a		8 c. carmine (1.3.41)			2·00	10
113		10 c. scarlet			1·25	40
114		12 c. blue			1·25	25
114a		12 c. orange (1.3.41)			1·25	4·75
115		15 c. orange			1·50	4·00
115a		15 c. blue (1.3.41)			3·50	9·00
116		20 c. olive-green and carmine			1·40	70
117		25 c. violet and orange			1·40	1·00
118		30 c. red-brown and violet			1·40	1·60
119		50 c. violet and scarlet			1·40	75
120		$1 scarlet and sepia			60	60
121		$2 bright purple and violet			7·50	7·00
122		$3 carmine and green			20·00	22·00
123		$4 blue and scarlet			20·00	25·00
124		$5 scarlet and red-brown			20·00	26·00
125		$10 black and yellow			18·00	38·00
106/25				*Set of* 26	£100	£140
106/25 Perf "Specimen"				*Set of* 26	£450	

For the 3 c. green, wmkd Mult Script CA, see No. 152a.

BRITISH MILITARY ADMINISTRATION

Following the Japenese surrender elements of the British Military Administration reached Kuching on 11 September 1945. From 5 November 1945 current Australian 1d., 3d., 6d. and 1s. stamps were made available for civilian use until replaced by Nos. 126/45. Other Australian stamps were also accepted as valid for postage during this period.

1945 (17 Dec). *Optd with T* **22**.

126	**21**	1 c. purple			40	50
127		2 c. black (R.)			40	40
		a. Opt double			† £3500	
128		3 c. green			40	30
129		4 c. bright purple			40	30
130		5 c. violet (R.)			40	90
131		6 c. lake-brown			70	75
132		8 c. carmine			11·00	9·00
133		10 c. scarlet			60	70
134		12 c. orange			90	3·75
135		15 c. blue			1·50	40
136		20 c. olive-green and carmine			2·25	1·40
137		25 c. violet and orange (R.)			2·25	2·75
138		30 c. red-brown and violet			3·50	2·75
139		50 c. violet and scarlet			1·25	35
140		$1 scarlet and sepia			2·50	1·25
141		$2 bright purple and violet			9·00	5·50

142	**21**	$3 carmine and green			17·00	32·00
143		$4 blue and scarlet			25·00	29·00
144		$5 scarlet and red-brown			95·00	£110
145		$10 black and yellow (R.)			£100	£130
126/45				*Set of* 20	£250	£300

These stamps, and the similarly overprinted stamps of North Borneo, are obtainable at all post offices throughout British Borneo (Brunei, Labuan, North Borneo and Sarawak), for use on local and overseas mail.

The administration of Sarawak was returned to the Brooke family on 15 April 1946, but the Rajah, after consulting the inhabitants ceded the territory to Great Britain on 1 June 1946.

23 Sir James Brooke, Sir Charles Vyner Brooke and Sir Charles Brooke (24)

(Recess B.W.)

1946 (18 May). *Centenary Issue. P* 12.

146	**23**	8 c. lake			50	30
147		15 c. blue			50	1·60
148		50 c. black and scarlet			80	1·75
149		$1 black and sepia			1·00	10·00
146/9				*Set of* 4	2·50	12·00
146/9 Perf "Specimen"				*Set of* 4	90·00	

CROWN COLONY

1947 (16 Apr). *Optd with T* **24**, *typo by B.W. in blue-black or red. Wmk Mult Script CA. P* 12.

150	**21**	1 c. purple			15	30
151		2 c. black (R.)			15	15
152		3 c. green (R.)			15	15
		a. Albino opt			£3500	
153		4 c. bright purple			15	15
154		6 c. lake-brown			20	90
155		8 c. carmine			40	10
156		10 c. scarlet			20	20
157		12 c. orange			20	90
158		15 c. blue (R.)			20	40
159		20 c. olive-green and carmine (R.)			50	50
160		25 c. violet and orange (R.)			40	30
161		50 c. violet and scarlet (R.)			40	40
162		$1 scarlet and sepia			75	90
163		$2 bright purple and violet			1·40	3·25
164		$5 scarlet and red-brown			3·00	3·25
150/64				*Set of* 15	7·25	10·50
150/64 Perf "Specimen"				*Set of* 15	£250	

No. 152a shows an uninked impression of T **24**.

1948 (25 Oct). *Royal Silver Wedding. As Nos.* 143/4 *of Jamaica.*

165		8 c. scarlet			30	30
166		$5 brown			28·00	28·00

1949 (10 Oct). *75th Anniv of U.P.U. As Nos.* 145/8 *of Jamaica.*

167		8 c. carmine			1·25	1·25
168		15 c. deep blue			2·25	2·25
169		25 c. deep blue-green			2·00	1·50
170		50 c. violet			2·00	4·00
167/70				*Set of* 4	6·75	7·50

Japanese. Until September–October 1942, previous stamp issues, without overprint, continued to be used in conjunction with existing postmarks. From 1 October 1942 onwards unoverprinted stamps of Japan were made available and examples can be found used from the area for much of the remainder of the War. Japanese Occupation issues for Brunei, North Borneo and Sarawak were equally valid throughout the combined territory but not, in practice, equally available.

25 *Trogonoptera brookiana*   **26** Western Tarsier

(Recess; Arms typo B.W.)

1950 (3 Jan). *T* **25/6** *and similar designs. Wmk Mult Script CA.*
P 11½ × 11 (*horiz*) *or* 11 × 11½ (*vert*).

171	1 c. black	..	..	30	30
172	2 c. red-orange	..	..	20	40
173	3 c. green	..	..	10	60
174	4 c. chocolate ..	..	..	10	20
175	6 c. turquoise-blue	..	..	10	15
176	8 c. scarlet	..	..	10	30
177	10 c. orange	..	..	50	3·25
178	12 c. violet	..	..	1·75	1·50
179	15 c. blue	..	..	1·00	15
180	20 c. purple-brown and red-orange	..	..	60	30
181	25 c. green and scarlet..	..	..	90	30
182	50 c. brown and violet..	..	..	1·25	15
183	$1 green and chocolate	..	..	8·50	2·25
184	$2 blue and carmine	..	..	19·00	9·00
185	$5 black, yellow, red and purple	..	19·00	10·00
171/85	..	..	*Set of* 15	48·00	26·00

Designs: *Horiz*—8 c. Dayak dancer; 10 c. Malayan Pangolin; 12 c. Kenyah boys; 15 c. Fire-making; 20 c. Kelemantan rice barn; 25 c. Pepper vines; $1 Kelabit smithy; $2 Map of Sarawak; $5 Arms of Sarawak. *Vert*—3 c. Kayan tomb; 4 c. Kayan girl and boy; 6 c. Bead work; 50 c. Iban woman.

40 Map of Sarawak

(Recess B.W.)

1952 (1 Feb). *Wmk Mult Script CA. P* 11½ × 11.

186	**40**	10 c. orange	..	..	..	75	40

JAPANESE OCCUPATION OF SARAWAK

Japanese forces landed in North Borneo on 16 December 1941 and Sarawak was attacked on 23 December 1941.

Brunei, North Borneo, Sarawak and after a short period Labuan, were administered as a single territory by the

宁及田朱本日大

(1)

("Imperial Japanese Government")

1942 (Oct). *Stamps of Sarawak handstamped with T* **1** *in violet.*

J 1	**21**	1 c. purple	..	..	30·00	48·00
		a. Pair, one without opt	..	..	£850
J 2		2 c. green	..	..	65·00	£110
		a. Black opt ..	..	..	65·00
J 3		2 c. black	..	..	60·00	70·00
		a. Black opt	..	..	75·00
J 4		3 c. black	..	..	£180	£180
J 5		3 c. green	..	..	38·00	55·00
		a. Black opt	..	..	55·00
J 6		4 c. bright purple	..	..	40·00	55·00
		a. Black opt	..	..	55·00
J 7		5 c. violet	..	..	45·00	55·00
		a. Black opt	..	..	55·00
J 8		6 c. carmine	..	..	75·00	80·00
J 9		6 c. lake-brown	..	..	45·00	55·00
		a. Black opt	..	..	55·00
J10		8 c. red-brown ..	..	..	£150	£170
J11		8 c. carmine	..	..	75·00	£110
J12		10 c. scarlet	..	..	40·00	60·00
		a. Black opt	..	..	55·00
J13		12 c. blue	..	..	90·00	£100
		a. Black opt	..	..	£120
J14		12 c. orange	..	..	95·00	£110
J15		15 c. orange	..	..	£180	£180
		a. Black opt	..	..	£200
J16		15 c. blue	..	..	65·00	70·00
J17		20 c. olive-green and carmine	..	38·00	60·00
		a. Black opt	..	..	55·00
J18		25 c. violet and orange	..	..	60·00	60·00
		a. Black opt	..	..	65·00
J19		30 c. red-brown and violet	..	40·00	65·00
		a. Black opt	..	..	55·00
J20		50 c. violet and scarlet	..	..	48·00	65·00
J21		$1 scarlet and sepia	..	..	60·00	80·00
J22		$2 bright purple and violet	..	£130	£160
J23		$3 carmine and green	..	..	£700	£800
J24		$4 blue and scarlet	..	..	£150	£190
J25		$5 scarlet and red-brown	..	£150	£190
J26		$10 black and yellow	..	..	£150	£200

The overprint, being handstamped, exists inverted on all values.

Stamps of T **21** optd with Japanese symbols within an oval frame are revenue stamps, while the same stamps overprinted with three Japanese characters between two vertical double rules, were used as seals.

Nos. J1/26 have been extensively forged. Recent research indicates that complete or part sets on cover cancelled by Japanese circular postmarks in violet dated "17 11 21" (21 Nov 1942) or "18 3 1" (1 Mar 1943) have forged overprints.

Seychelles

100 cents = 1 Mauritius rupee

CROWN COLONY

1937 (12 May). *Coronation. As Nos.* 118/20 *of Jamaica, but ptd by B.W. P* 11×11½.

132	6 c. sage-green	..	..	35	15
133	12 c. orange	..	..	50	30
134	20 c. blue	..	..	70	65
132/4	..	..	*Set of* 3	1·40	1·00
132/4 Perf "Specimen"	..	..	*Set of* 3	55·00	

14 Coco-de-mer Palm

15 Giant Tortoise

16 Fishing Pirogue

(Photo Harrison)

1938 (1 Jan)–**49**. *Wmk Mult Script CA. Chalk-surfaced paper. P* 14½×13½ (*vert*) *or* 13½×14½ (*horiz*).

135	14	2 c. purple-brown (10.2.38)	..	..	85	40
		a. Ordinary paper (18.11.42)	..		20	75
136	15	3 c. green	..	..	6·50	1·25
136a		3 c. orange (8.8.41)	..	..	1·25	50
		ab. Ordinary paper (18.11.42)	..		55	1·25
137	16	6 c. orange	..	..	6·50	2·50
137a		6 c. greyish green (8.8.41)	..		3·00	70
		aw. Wmk inverted	..		£375	
		b. Ordinary paper. *Green* (18.11.42)		55	1·00
		c. *Green* (5.4.49)	..	..	2·00	75
138	14	9 c. blue (10.2.38)	..	..	10·00	2·00
138a		9 c. grey-blue (8.8.41)	..		3·25	40
		ab. Ordinary paper (18.11.42)	..		4·00	90
		ac. Ordinary paper. *Dull bl* (19.11.45)	3·25	1·25
		ad. *Dull blue* (5.4.49)	..		7·50	4·50
		aw. Wmk inverted	..			
139	15	12 c. reddish violet	..	..	38·00	1·25
139a		15 c. brown-carmine (8.8.41)	..		3·75	30
		ab. Ordinary paper. *Brn-red* (18.11.42)	2·50	1·25
139c	14	18 c. carmine-lake (8.8.41)	..		3·50	60
		ca. Ordinary paper (18.11.42)	..		3·00	1·50
		cb. Rose-carmine (5.4.49)	..		7·50	7·00
140	16	20 c. blue	..	..	42·00	5·00
140a		20 c. brown-ochre (8.8.41)	..		3·50	45
		ab. Ordinary paper (18.11.42)	..		2·00	1·25
141	14	25 c. brown-ochre	..	..	60·00	14·00
142	15	30 c. carmine (10.2.38)	..		60·00	9·00
142a		30 c. blue (8.8.41)	..	..	3·50	50
		ab. Ordinary paper (18.11.42)	..		1·40	2·50
143	16	45 c. chocolate (10.2.38)	..		7·50	1·25
		a. Ordinary paper. *Pur-brn* (18.11.42)	1·25	1·75
		b. *Purple-brown* (5.4.49)	..		8·50	8·00
144	14	50 c. deep reddish violet (10.2.38)	..	3·75	60
		a. Ordinary paper (18.11.42)	..		60	2·00
144b		50 c. bright lilac (13.6.49)	..		60	1·50

145	15	75 c. slate-blue (10.2.38)	..		85·00	38·00
145a		75 c. deep slate-lilac (8.8.41)	..		5·00	1·25
		ab. Ordinary paper (18.11.42)	..		1·00	2·00
146	16	1 r. yellow-green (10.2.38)	..		£100	48·00
146a		1 r. grey-black (8.8.41)	..		5·00	85
		ab. Ordinary paper (18.11.42)	..		1·25	2·25
147	14	1 r. 50, ultramarine (10.2.38)	..		9·00	1·50
		a. Ordinary paper (18.11.42)	..		3·75	3·50
148	15	2 r. 25, olive (10.2.38)	..		14·00	4·00
		a. Ordinary paper (18.11.42)	..		9·00	9·00
149	16	5 r. red (10.2.38)	..	..	6·00	3·25
		a. Ordinary paper (18.11.42)	..		11·00	12·00
135/49	..	..	..	*Set of* 25	£400	£120
135/49 (*excl No.* 144b) Perf "Specimen"	*Set of* 24	£350	

Lamp on mast flaw (R. 1/5)

1946 (23 Sept). *Victory. As Nos.* 141/2 *of Jamaica.*

150		9 c. light blue	..	..	10	10
151		30 c. deep blue	..	..	10	10
		a. Lamp on mast flaw	..		10·00	
150/1 Perf "Specimen"	..	..	*Set of* 2	50·00	

Line by crown (R. 1/3)

1948 (5 Nov). *Royal Silver Wedding. As Nos.* 143/4 *of Jamaica.*

152		9 c. ultramarine	..	..	15	25
		a. Line by crown	..		12·00	
153		5 r. carmine	..	..	10·00	18·00

1949 (10 Oct). *75th Anniv of U.P.U. As Nos.* 145/8 *of Jamaica, but inscribed* "SEYCHELLES" *in recess.*

154		18 c. bright reddish purple	..	..	30	15
155		50 c. purple	..	..	75	50
156		1 r. grey	..	..	40	15
157		2 r. 25, olive	..	..	50	60
154/7	..	..	..	*Set of* 4	1·75	1·25

OMNIBUS ISSUES

Details, together with prices for complete sets, of the various Omnibus issues from the 1937 Coronation series to the B.W.I. University College set are included in a special section at the end of the listings.

17 Sail-fish   18 Map of Indian Ocean

(Photo Harrison)

1952 (3 Mar). *Various designs as T* **14/16** *but with new portrait and crown as in T* **17/18.** *Chalk-surfaced paper. Wmk Mult Script CA. P* 14½ × 13½ (*vert*) *or* 13½ × 14½ (*horiz*).

158	17	2 c. lilac ..		50	70
		a. Error. Crown missing, W **9***a*	£325		
		b. Error. St. Edward's Crown, W **9***b*	£110		
159	15	3 c. orange		50	30
		a. Error. Crown missing, W **9***a*	£275		
		b. Error. St. Edward's Crown, W **9***b*	£100		
160	14	9 c. chalky blue ..		50	85
		a. Error. Crown missing, W **9***a*	£450		
		b. Error. St. Edward's Crown, W **9***b*	£170		
161	16	15 c. deep yellow-green		40	75
		a. Error. Crown missing, W **9***a*	£375		
		b. Error. St. Edward's Crown, W **9***b*	£170		
162	18	18 c. carmine-lake		65	20
		a. Error. Crown missing, W **9***a*	£450		
		b. Error. St. Edward's Crown, W **9***b*	£200		
163	16	20 c. orange-yellow		90	60
		a. Error. Crown missing, W **9***a*	£500		
		b. Error. St. Edward's Crown, W **9***b*	£275		
164	15	25 c. vermilion		70	70
		a. Error. Crown missing, W **9***a*	£550		
		b. Error. St. Edward's Crown, W **9***b*	£250		
165	17	40 c. ultramarine..		70	90
		a. Error. Crown missing, W **9***a*	£550		
		b. Error. St. Edward's Crown, W **9***b*	£300		

166	16	45 c. purple-brown		70	30
		a. Error. Crown missing, W **9***a*	£650		
		b. Error. St. Edward's Crown, W **9***b*	£325		
167	14	50 c. reddish violet		1·25	60
		a. Error. Crown missing, W **9***a*	£700		
		b. Error. St. Edward's Crown, W **9***b*	£350		
168	18	1 r. grey-black ..		2·50	1·75
		b. Error. St. Edward's Crown, W **9***b*	£600		
169	14	1 r. 50, blue		5·00	8·00
		b. Error. St. Edward's Crown, W **9***b*	£800		
170	15	2 r. 25, brown-olive		5·50	9·50
		b. Error. St. Edward's Crown, W **9***b*	£650		
171	18	5 r. red ..		5·50	12·00
		b. Error. St. Edward's Crown, W **9***b*	£550		
172	17	10 r. green		12·00	21·00
158/72			*Set of* 15	35·00	50·00

See *Introduction* re the watermark errors.

POSTAGE DUE STAMPS

D 1

(Frame recess, value typo B.W.)

1951 (1 Mar). *Wmk Mult Script CA. P* 11½.

D1	D 1	2 c. scarlet and carmine		80	1·50
D2		3 c. scarlet and green ..		1·25	1·50
D3		6 c. scarlet and bistre ..		1·25	1·25
D4		9 c. scarlet and orange		1·50	1·25
D5		15 c. scarlet and violet ..		1·75	9·00
D6		18 c. scarlet and blue ..		1·75	9·00
D7		20 c. scarlet and brown..		1·75	9·00
D8		30 c. scarlet and claret ..		1·75	7·50
D1/8 ..			*Set of* 8	10·50	35·00

Sierra Leone

12 pence (d) = 1 shilling; 20 shillings = 1 pound

CROWN COLONY

1937 (12 May). *Coronation. As Nos. 118/20 of Jamaica, but ptd by B.W.*

185	1d. orange		70	40
186	2d. purple		90	40
187	3d. blue		2·00	3·00
185/7		*Set of 3*	3·25	3·50
185/7 Perf "Specimen"		*Set of 3*	55·00	

30 Freetown from the Harbour

31 Rice Harvesting

(Recess Waterlow)

1938 (1 May)–44. *Wmk Mult Script CA (sideways). P 12½.*

188	**30**	½d. black and blue-green	15	30
189		1d. black and lake	40	40
		a. Imperf between (vert pair)	†	—

190	**31**	1½d. scarlet	20·00	50
190*a*		1½d. mauve (1.2.41)	20	50
191		2d. mauve	40·00	1·75
191*a*		2d. scarlet (1.2.41)	20	70
192	**30**	3d. black and ultramarine	40	40
193		4d. black and red-brown (20.6.38)	80	1·40
194	**31**	5d. olive-green (20.6.38)	5·00	3·50
195		6d. grey (20.6.38)	75	40
196	**30**	1s. black and olive-green (20.6.38)	1·50	50
196*a*	**31**	1s. 3d. yellow-orange (1.7.44)	40	40
197	**30**	2s. black and sepia (20.6.38)	4·50	1·75
198	**31**	5s. red-brown (20.6.38)	10·00	4·50
199		10s. emerald-green (20.6.38)	16·00	7·00
200	**30**	£1 deep blue (20.6.38)	17·00	16·00
188/200		*Set of 16*	£100	35·00
188/200 Perf "Specimen"		*Set of 16*	£250	

1946 (1 Oct). *Victory. As Nos. 141/2 of Jamaica.*

201	1½d. lilac		15	10
202	3d. ultramarine		15	10
201/2 Perf "Specimen"		*Set of 2*	55·00	

1948 (1 Dec). *Royal Silver Wedding. As Nos. 143/4 of Jamaica.*

203	1½d. bright purple		15	15
204	£1 indigo		16·00	16·00

1949 (10 Oct). *75th Anniv of U.P.U. As Nos. 145/8 of Jamaica.*

205	1½d. purple		20	30
206	3d. deep blue		60	1·60
207	6d. grey		35	2·00
208	1s. olive		35	1·00
205/8		*Set of 4*	1·40	4·50

Singapore

100 cents = 1 Malayan dollar

CROWN COLONY

Stamps in the Crown Colony Victory design with face values of 8 c. and 15 c. were prepared for Singapore in 1946, but were not issued.

(Typo D.L.R.)

1948 (1 Sept)–**52.** *As T 58 of Malaysia (Straits Settlements), but inscribed "SINGAPORE" at foot. Wmk Mult Script CA. Chalk-surfaced paper.* (a) *P* 14.

1	1 c. black	..	..	..	..	15	30
2	2 c. orange	..	..	..	..	15	10
3	3 c. green	..	..	..	..	50	30
4	4 c. brown	..	..	..	..	20	60
5	6 c. grey	..	..	..	..	40	30
6	8 c. scarlet (1.10.48)	..	..	..	30	30
7	10 c. purple	..	..	..	..	20	10
8	15 c. ultramarine (1.10.48)	..	..	7·50	10
9	20 c. black and green (1.10.48)	..	..	3·50	20
10	25 c. purple and orange (1.10.48)	..	3·50	15
11	40 c. red and purple (1.10.48) ..	..	6·50	5·00
12	50 c. black and blue (1.10.48) ..	..	3·25	10
13	$1 blue and purple (1.10.48)	..	..	10·00	1·25
14	$2 green and scarlet (25.10.48)	..	48·00	3·25
15	$5 green and brown (1.10.48)	..	£110	3·50
1/15	..	..	..	..	*Set of* 15	£170	13·50

(b) *P* 17½×18

16	1 c. black (21.5.52)	..	..	..	50	2·50
17	2 c. orange (31.10.49)	..	..	..	70	80
19	4 c. brown (1.7.49)	..	..	..	70	10
19a	5 c. bright purple (1.9.52) ..	..	..	2·50	90
21	6 c. grey (10.12.52)	..	..	..	70	75
21a	8 c. green (1.9.52) ..	..	..	..	4·00	3·00

22	10 c. purple (9.2.50)	..	..	..	50	10
22a	12 c. scarlet (1.9.52)	..	..	..	4·00	6·00
23	15 c. ultramarine (9.2.50) ..	..	10·00	10
24	20 c. black and green (31.10.49)	..	3·00	2·00
24a	20 c. bright blue (1.9.52)	..	..	4·00	10
25	25 c. purple and orange (9.2.50)	..	80	10
25a	35 c. scarlet and purple (1.9.52)	..	4·00	90
26	40 c. red and purple (4.5.51*)	..	22·00	8·50
27	50 c. black and blue (9.2.50)	..	7·50	10
28	$1 blue and purple (31.10.49)	..	12·00	20
	a. Error. St. Edward's Crown, W 9b	£4000	
29	$2 green and scarlet (24.5.51)	..	£110	1·75
	a. Error. St. Edward's Crown. W 9b	£4000	
30	$5 green and brown (19.12.51)	..	£180	1·75
16/30	..	..	..	*Set of* 18	£325	27·00

* Earliest known postmark date.

Nos. 28a and 29a occur on rows in the watermark in which the crowns and letters "CA" alternate.

Postal forgeries of the 50 c., $1 and $2 exist on unwatermarked paper and perforated 14×14½.

1948 (25 Oct). *Royal Silver Wedding. As Nos. 143/4 of Jamaica.*

31	10 c. violet	..	..	..	..	75	30
32	$5 brown	..	..	..	..	£110	29·00

1949 (10 Oct). *75th Anniv of U.P.U. As Nos. 145/8 of Jamaica.*

33	10 c. orange	..	..	..	..	75	30
34	15 c. deep blue ..	..	..	..	6·00	2·25
35	25 c. orange	..	..	..	..	6·00	2·25
36	50 c. blue-black	..	..	..	6·00	3·00
33/6	..	..	..	..	*Set of* 4	17·00	7·00

Somaliland Protectorate

1937. 12 pies = 1 anna; 16 annas = 1 rupee
1951. 100 cents = 1 shilling

PROTECTORATE

1937 (13 May).   *Coronation. As Nos. 118/20 of Jamaica.*
90	1 a. scarlet	..	.. ..	15	10
91	2 a. grey-black	..	.. .. ..	55	85
92	3 a. bright blue	..	.. ..	70	55
90/2	.. ..	..	.. *Set of 3*	1·25	1·40
90/2 Perf "Specimen"		.. ..	*Set of 3*	55·00	

9 Berbera
Blackhead Sheep

5 Cents	1 Shilling
(10)	(11)

6 Berbera Blackhead Sheep   7 Lesser Kudu

8 Somaliland Protectorate

(Des H. W. Claxton. Recess Waterlow)

1938 (10 May).   *Portrait to left. Wmk Mult Script CA. P 12½.*
93	6	½ a. green	..	.. .. ..	15	3·00
94		1 a. scarlet	..	.. .. ..	15	40
95		2 a. maroon	..	.. .. ..	30	50
96		3 a. bright blue	..	.. ..	5·50	7·00
97	7	4 a. sepia	..	.. ..	2·75	3·75
98		6 a. violet	..	.. ..	3·75	8·50
99		8 a. grey	..	.. ..	85	8·50
100		12 a. red-orange	..	.. ..	2·00	9·00
101	8	1 r. green	..	.. ..	8·50	30·00
102		2 r. purple	..	.. ..	9·50	30·00
103		3 r. bright blue	..	.. ..	16·00	20·00
104		5 r. black	..	.. ..	16·00	20·00
		a. Imperf between (horiz pair)			£10000	
93/104		.. ..	..	*Set of 12*	60·00	£130
93/104 Perf "Specimen"		..	*Set of 12*	£140		

Examples of most values are known showing a forged Berbera
postmark dated "15 AU 38".

Following the Italian Occupation during 1940–41 the
stamps of ADEN were used at Berbera from 1 July 1941 until
26 April 1942.

(Recess Waterlow)

1942 (27 Apr).   *As T 6/8 but with full-face portrait of King George
VI, as in T 9. Wmk Mult Script CA. P 12½.*
105	9	½ a. green	..	.. ..	10	10
106		1 a. scarlet	..	.. ..	10	10
107		2 a. maroon	..	.. ..	40	10
108		3 a. bright blue	..	.. ..	80	10
109	7	4 a. sepia	..	.. ..	1·25	10
110		6 a. violet	..	.. ..	2·00	10
111		8 a. grey	..	.. ..	70	10
112		12 a. red-orange	..	.. ..	2·25	10
113	8	1 r. green	..	.. ..	1·00	40
114		2 r. purple	..	.. ..	1·00	3·50
115		3 r. bright blue	..	.. ..	1·25	6·50
116		5 r. black	..	.. ..	4·25	4·00
105/16		.. ..	..	*Set of 12*	13·50	13·50
105/16 Perf "Specimen"		..	*Set of 12*	£140		

1946 (15 Oct).   *Victory. As Nos. 141/2 of Jamaica. P 13½×14.*
117	1 a. carmine	..	.. ..	10	10
	a. Perf 13½	..	.. ..	8·50	40·00
118	3 a. blue	..	.. ..	10	10
117/18 Perf "Specimen"	..	*Set of 2*	45·00		

1949 (28 Jan).   *Royal Silver Wedding. As Nos. 143/4 of
Jamaica.*
119	1 a. scarlet	..	.. ..	10	10
120	5 r. black	..	.. ..	3·50	3·25

1949 (10 Oct).   *75th Anniv of U.P.U. As Nos. 145/8 of Jamaica.
Surch with face values in annas.*
121	1 a. on 10 c. carmine	..	.. ..	30	15
122	3 a. on 30 c. deep blue (R.)	..	.. ..	40	40
123	6 a. on 50 c. purple	..	.. ..	40	40
124	12 a. on 1s. red-orange..		.. ..	55	40
121/4	.. ..		*Set of 4*	1·50	1·25

(New Currency. 100 cents = 1 shilling)

1951 (1 Apr).   *1942 issue surch as T 10/11.*
125	5 c. on ½ a. green	..	.. ..	10	30
126	10 c. on 2 a. maroon	..	.. ..	10	20
127	15 c. on 3 a. bright blue	..	.. ..	30	30
128	20 c. on 4 a. sepia	..	.. ..	50	20
129	30 c. on 6 a. violet	..	.. ..	70	20
130	50 c. on 8 a. grey	..	.. ..	55	20
131	70 c. on 12 a. red-orange	..	.. ..	1·00	2·75
132	1 s. on 1 r. green	..	.. ..	50	20
133	2 s. on 2 r. purple	..	.. ..	2·00	6·00
134	2 s. on 3 r. bright blue	..	.. ..	2·25	2·50
135	5 s. on 5 r. black (R.) ..	..	.. ..	3·00	4·00
125/35	.. .. ..		*Set of 11*	10·00	15·00

South Africa

12 pence = 1 shilling; 20 shillings = 1 pound

DOMINION

PRICES for Nos. 71/135 are for unused horizontal pairs, used horizontal pairs and used singles (either inscription), *unless otherwise indicated*. Vertical pairs are worth 50% of those prices quoted for horizontal pairs.

25

25a

7 *Dromedaris*
(Van Riebeeck's ship)

8 Orange Tree

"Mouse" flaw (R. 4/1)

(Des J. Prentice)

9

1937 (12 May). *Coronation. W* **9** (*sideways**). *P* 14.
71	**25**	½d. grey-black and blue-green ..	25	70	10
		w. Wmk horns to left ..	25	70	10
72		1d. grey-black and carmine	35	50	10
		w. Wmk horns to left ..	35	50	10
73		1½d. orange and greenish blue ..	50	50	10
		a. "Mouse" flaw ..	4·00		
		w. Wmk horns to left ..	50	50	10
74		3d. ultramarine ..	3·00	2·00	10
		w. Wmk horns to left ..	3·00	2·00	10
75		1s. red-brown and turquoise-blue	4·50	4·00	15
		a. Hyphen on Afrikaans stamp omitted (R. 2/13) ..	42·00		
		w. Wmk horns to left ..	4·50	4·00	15
71/5		.. .. *Set of* 5	7·75	7·00	40

*The normal sideways watermark shows the horns of the Springbok pointing to the right, *as seen from the back of the stamp.*

No. 75a shows the hyphen completely omitted and the top of the "K" damaged. A less distinct flaw, on which part of the hyphen is still visible and with no damage to the "K", occurs on R. 4/17.

12a A Native Kraal

13 Black and Blue Wildebeest

1937–40. *W* **9**. *P* 15×14.
75b	**25a**	½d. grey and green ..	7·50	90	10
		ba. Booklet pane of 6 (with blank margins) (1937) ..	42·00		
		bd. Grey and blue-green (1940)	5·50	90	10

The lines of shading in T **25a** are all horizontal and thicker than in T **6**. In Nos. 75b and 75bd the design is composed of solid lines. For stamps with designs composed of dotted lines, see No. 114. Later printings of No. 75bd have a smaller design.

14 Ox-wagon inspanned

15 Ox-wagon outspanned

22a Groot Schuur

26 Voortrekker Ploughing

27 Wagon crossing Drakensberg

28 Signing of Dingaan–Retief Treaty

(Des J. Prentice)

1939 (17 July). *250th Anniv of Huguenot Landing in South Africa and Huguenot Commemoration Fund. W* **9**. *P* 14 (*Nos.* 82/3) *or* 15 × 14 (*No.* 84).

82	32	¹/₂d. + ¹/₂d. brown and green	..	4·75	4·50	30
83	33	1d. + 1d. green and carmine	..	11·00	4·75	30
84	34	1¹/₂d. + 1¹/₂d. blue-green and purple	26·00	11·00	1·00
82/4		.. .. ..	*Set of* 3	38·00	18·00	1·40

29 Voortrekker Monument

(Des W. Coetzer and J. Prentice)

1938 (14 Dec). *Voortrekker Centenary Memorial Fund. W* **9**. *P* 14 (*Nos.* 76/7) *or* 15 × 14 (*others*).

76	26	¹/₂d. + ¹/₂d. blue and green	..	10·00	4·00	30
77	27	1d. + 1d. blue and carmine	..	11·00	5·00	40
78	28	1¹/₂d. + 1¹/₂d. chocolate & blue-grn	15·00	9·50	80
79	29	3d. + 3d. bright blue	..	17·00	11·00	1·00
76/9		.. .. ..	*Set of* 4	48·00	27·00	2·25

30 Wagon Wheel

31 Voortrekker Family

(Des W. Coetzer and J. Prentice)

1938 (14 Dec). *Voortrekker Commemoration. W* **9**. *P* 15 × 14.

80	30	1d. blue and carmine	..	4·00	3·75	30
81	31	1¹/₂d. greenish blue and brown	..	6·00	3·75	30

32 Old Vicarage, Paarl, now a museum

33 Symbol of the Reformation

34 Huguenot Dwelling, Drakenstein Mountain Valley

34a Gold Mine

1941 (Aug)–**48**. *W* **9** (*sideways*). *P* 14 × 15.

87	34a	1¹/₂d. blue-grn and yellow-buff (*shades*)	..	40	30	10
		a. Yellow-buff (centre) omitted	£1500		
		b. Booklet pane of 6 (with postal slogans on margins) (1948)	.. ..	3·50		

35 Infantry

36 Nurse and Ambulance

37 Airman

38 Sailor, Destroyer and Lifebelts

39 Women's Auxiliary Services

40 Artillery

41 Electric Welding

42 Tank Corps

42a Signaller

"Stain" on uniform (R. 14/11)

1941–46. *War Effort.* W **9** (*sideways on 2d., 4d., 6d.*). P 14 (2d., 4d., 6d.) or 15 × 14 (*others*). (*a*) *Inscr alternately.*

88	35	¹/₂d. green (19.11.41)	.. ..	1·25	1·25	10
89	36	1d. carmine (3.10.41) ..		2·00	1·00	10
		a. "Stain" on uniform flaw	..	14·00		
90	37	1¹/₂d. myrtle-green (12.1.42)		1·50	90	10
91	39	3d. blue (1.8.41)	..	20·00	20·00	50
92	40	4d. orange-brown (20.8.41)	..	17·00	11·00	15
		a. Red-brown (6.42) ..		32·00	28·00	1·25
93	41	6d. red-orange (3.9.41) ..		12·00	8·00	15
94	42a	1s. 3d. olive-brown (2.1.43)	..	12·00	6·00	20
		a. Blackish brown (5.46)	..	4·00	6·00	20

(*b*) *Inscr bilingually*

					Un	*Us*
					single	*single*
95	38	2d. violet (15.9.41) ..	.. ..		90	30
96	42	1s. brown (27.10.41)	.. ..		3·25	50
88/96 ..		.. .. Set of 7 pairs and 2 singles		55·00	45·00

43 Infantry   44 Nurse   45 Airman   46 Sailor

47 Women's   48 Electric   49 Heavy Gun in
Auxiliary Services Welding   Concrete Turret

50 Tank Corps

Unit (*pair*)

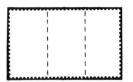

Unit (*triplet*)

1942–44. *War Effort. Reduced sizes. In pairs perf* 14 (P) *or strips of three, perf* 15×14 (T), *subdivided by roulette* 6¹/₂. W **9** (*sideways* * *on* 3d., 4d. *and* 1s.). (*a*) *Inscr alternately.*

				Un	*Us*	*Us*
				unit	*unit*	*single*
97	43	¹/₂d. blue-green (T) (10.42)	..	70	1·00	10
		a. Green (3.43) ..		2·75	1·50	10
		b. Greenish blue (7.44)	..	2·00	1·00	10
		c. Roulette omitted ..		£475		
98	44	1d. carmine-red (T) (5.1.43)	..	1·50	85	10
		a. Bright carmine (3.44)	..	1·00	40	10
		b. Both roulettes omitted	..	£400		
		ba. Left-hand roulette omitted		£500		
99	45	1¹/₂d. red-brown (P) (9.42)	..	65	1·00	10
		a. Roulette 13 (8.42) ..	..	1·50	3·25	15
		b. Roulette omitted ..	..	£225	£250	
100	46	2d. violet (P) (2.43) ..	..	90	1·25	10
		a. Reddish violet (6.43)	..	1·50	50	10
		b. Roulette omitted ..	..	£375		
101	47	3d. blue (T) (10.42) ..	..	7·00	13·00	10
102	48	6d. red-orange (P) (10.42)	..	2·00	1·40	10

(*b*) *Inscr bilingually*

103	49	4d. slate-green (T) (10.42)	..	18·00	4·00	10
104	50	1s. brown (P) (11.42) ..	..	15·00	1·50	10
97/104		.. .. ..	Set of 8	40·00	21·00	65

*The sideways watermark shows springbok heads to left on the 3d. and 1s., and to right on the 4d., all as seen from the back of the stamp.

52   53

1943. *Coil stamps. Redrawn. In single colours with plain background.* W **9.** P 15 × 14.

				Un	*Used*	*Used*
				pair	*pair*	*single*
105	52	¹/₂d. blue-green (18.2.43)	..	75	3·00	20
106	53	1d. carmine (9.43)	.. ..	1·75	2·75	15
		Quoted prices are for *vertical* pairs.				

54 Union Buildings, Pretoria

1945–46. *Redrawn.* W **9.** P 14.

107	54	2d. slate and violet (3.45)	..	9·00	2·50	10
		a. Slate & brt vio (shades) (10.46)	2·50	6·50	15

In Nos. 107 and 107a the Union Buildings are shown at a different angle from Nos. 58 and 58a. Only the centre is screened i.e., composed of very small square dots of colour arranged in straight diagonal lines. For whole design screened and colours changed, see No. 116. No. 107a also shows "2" of "2d." clear of white circle at top.

55 "Victory"   56 "Peace"

"Flying saucer" flaw (Cyl 17 R. 17/2)

I

II

5s.

57 "Hope"

1945 (3 Dec).   *Victory. W 9. P 14.*

108	55	1d. brown and carmine..	20	80	10
109	56	2d. slate-blue and violet	20	85	10
110	57	3d. deep blue and blue ..	20	1·25	10
108/10		.. .. .. Set of 3	55	2·75	25

58 King George VI   59 King George VI and
                                Queen Elizabeth

60 Queen Elizabeth II as Princess,
and Princess Margaret

"Bird" on "2" (Cyl 6912
R. 10/6)

(Des J. Prentice)

1947 (17 Feb).   *Royal Visit. W 9. P 15 × 14.*

111	58	1d. black and carmine	..	..	10	10	10
112	59	2d. violet..	..	..	15	20	10
		a. "Bird" on "2" flaw	..	..	2·50		
113	60	3d. blue ..	..	..	15	20	10
111/13		.. .. .. Set of 3	35	45	20

1947–54.   "SUID-AFRIKA" *hyphenated on Afrikaans stamps.*
Printed from new cylinders with design in screened rotogravure.
W 9. P 15 × 14 (½d., 1d. and 6d.) or 14 (others).

114	25a	½d. grey and green (frame only			
		screened) (1947)	70	1·50	, 10
		a. Booklet pane of 6 (with			
		postal slogans on margins)			
		(1948)	3·00		
		b. Entire design screened			
		(2.49)	70	1·50	10
		ba. Booklet pane of 6 (with			
		margin at right) (1951) ..	3·50		
115	7	1d. grey and carmine (1.9.50)	50	75	10
		a. Booklet pane of 6 (with			
		margin at right) (1951) ..	5·00		
116	54	2d. slate-blue and purple (3.50)	60	4·00	10
117	22a	3d. dull blue (4.49)	2·00	3·75	10
117a		3d. blue (3.51)	2·25	3·00	10
		ab. "Flying saucer" flaw ..	14·00		
		b. *Deep blue* (1954)	60·00	50·00	3·00
118	12a	4d. brown (22.8.52)	1·00	5·50	10
119	8	6d. green & red-orge (III) (1.50)	1·75	40	10
		a. *Grn & brn-orge* (III) (1951)	1·50	40	10
120	13	1s. brown & chalky blue (1.50)	10·00	4·00	10
		a. *Blackish brown & ultram*			
		(4.52)	18·00	7·00	15
121	14	2s. 6d. green and brown (8.49)	10·00	23·00	55
122	15	5s. black and pale blue-grn (I)			
		(9.49)	45·00	35·00	75
122a		5s. black & deep yellow-green			
		(II) (1.54)	70·00	65·00	2·00
114/22		.. .. .. Set of 9	65·00	70·00	1·50

In screened rotogravure the design is composed of very small
squares of colour arranged in straight diagonal lines.
    ½d. Size 17¾ × 21¾ mm. Early printings have only the frame
screened.
    1d. Size 18 × 22 mm. For smaller, redrawn design, see No. 135.
    2d. For earlier issue with centre only screened, and in different
colours, see Nos. 107/a.
    3d. No. 117. Whole stamp screened with irregular grain. Scrolls
above "3d." solid and toneless. Printed from two cylinders.
No. 117a/b. Whole stamp diagonally screened. Printed from one
cylinder. Clouds more pronounced.
    4d. Two groups of white leaves below name tablet and a clear
white line down left and right sides of stamp.

61 Gold Mine   62 King George VI and
                           Queen Elizabeth

1948 (1 Apr).   *W 9 (sideways). In pair, perf 14, sub-divided by*
roulette 6½.

			Un	*Us Used*
			unit of 4	*unit single*
124	61	1½d. blue-green and yellow-buff	1·75	3·00	10

(Des J. Booysen and J. Prentice)

1948 (26 Apr).   *Silver Wedding. W* **9**. *P* 14.

			Un pair	Used pair	Used single
125	62	3d. blue and silver	50	50	10

(Typo Government Printer, Pretoria)

1948 (July).   *W* **9**. *P* 14½ × 14.

126	6	½d. pale grey and blue-green ..	85	8·00	65

This was an economy printing made from the old plates of the 1926 issue for the purpose of using up a stock of cut paper. For the original printing in black and green, see No. 30.

63 *Wanderer* (emigrant ship) entering Durban

Extended rigging on mainmast (R. 14/2)

(Des J. Prentice)

1949 (2 May).   *Centenary of Arrival of British Settlers in Natal. W* **9**. *P* 15 × 14.

127	63	1½d. claret	30	30	10
		a. Extended rigging	5·00		

64 Hermes

65 Wagons approaching Bingham's Berg

"Lake" in East Africa (R. 2/19)

(Des J. Booysen and J. Prentice)

1949 (1 Oct).   *75th Anniv of Universal Postal Union. As T* **64** *inscr* "UNIVERSAL POSTAL UNION" *and* "WERELDPOSUNIE" *alternately. W* **9** *(sideways). P* 14 × 15.

128	64	½d. blue-green	60	85	10
129		1½d. brown-red	60	85	10
130		3d. bright blue	1·00	1·40	10
		a. "Lake" in East Africa ..	16·00		
128/30		.. .. *Set of* 3	2·00	2·75	25

(Des W. Coetzer and J. Prentice)

1949 (1 Dec).   *Inauguration of Voortrekker Monument, Pretoria. T* **65** *and similar horiz designs. W* **9**. *P* 15 × 14.

			Un single	Us single
131		1d. magenta	10	10
132		1½d. blue-green	10	10
133		3d. blue	10	10
131/3		.. .. .. *Set of* 3	20	20

Designs:—1½d. Voortrekker Monument, Pretoria; 3d. Bible, candle and Voortrekkers.

68 Union Buildings, Pretoria

1950 (Apr)–51.   *W* **9** *(sideways). P* 14 × 15.

			Un pair	Used pair	Used single
134	68	2d. blue and violet	30	50	10
		a. Booklet panes of 6 (with margin at right) (1951)	8·00		

1951 (22 Feb).   *As No. 115, but redrawn with the horizon clearly defined. Size reduced to* 17¼ × 21¼ *mm.*

135	7	1d. grey and carmine	75	85	10

STAMP BOOKLETS

1937.   *Black on lemon cover. Advertisement on front cover. Stitched.*

SB10   2s. 6d. booklet containing two panes of six ½d. (No. 75ba) and four panes of six 1d. (No. 56e), all with blank margins £200

1937.   *Machine vended booklets. Red cover. Stitched.*

SB11   6d. booklet containing four ½d. and 1d. (Nos. 75b, 56) in pairs .. .. 7·00

1938.   *Machine vended booklets. Blue cover. Stitched.*

SB12   3d. booklet containing ½d. and 1d. (Nos. 75b, 56), each in pair .. .. 26·00

1938.   *Black on buff cover. Union arms at top left with advertisement at foot. Stitched.*

SB13   2s. 6d. booklet containing twelve ½d. and twenty-four 1d. (Nos. 75b, 56) in blocks of 6 £300

1939.   *Black on buff cover. Union arms centred at top with advertisement at foot. Stitched.*

SB14   2s. 6d. booklet containing twelve ½d. and twenty-four 1d. (Nos. 75b, 56) in blocks of 6 £150

1939–40.   *Green on buff cover. Union arms centred at top with large advertisement at bottom left. Stitched.*

SB15   2s. 6d. booklet containing twelve ½d. and twenty-four 1d. (Nos. 75b, 56) in blocks of 6 £2500
        a. Blue on buff cover .. .. 70·00

1941.   *Blue on buff cover as No. SB15. Stitched.*

SB17   2s. 6d. booklet containing twelve ½d. and 1d. (Nos. 75b, 56) in blocks of 6 and 1½d. (No. 57) in block of 4 .. .. £110

1948.   *Black on buff cover. With advertisement. Stitched.*

SB18   3s. booklet containing two panes of six ½d., 1d. and 1½d. (Nos. 114a, 56h, 87b), all with postal slogans on margins, and pane of air mail labels .. .. 20·00

1951.   *Black on buff cover. Stitched.*

SB19   3s. 6d. booklet containing two panes of six ½d., 1d. and 2d. (Nos. 114ba, 115a, 134a), each with margin at right .. .. .. 15·00

POSTAGE DUE STAMPS

D 2   D 3   D 4

1932–42. *Type* D 2 *redrawn.* W **9.** P 15 × 14.

(a) Frame roto, value typo
D22	¹/₂d. black and blue-green (1934)	..	1·50	1·60
D23	2d. black and deep purple (10.4.33)	..	5·50	1·75

(b) Whole stamp roto
D25	1d. black and carmine (3.34)	..	1·50	10
D26	2d. black and deep purple (1940)	..	16·00	10
	a. Thick (double) "2d." (R. 5/6, R. 18/2)	..	£180	20·00
D27	3d. black and Prussian blue (3.8.32)	..	22·00	14·00
D28	3d. deep blue and blue (1935)	..	5·50	30
	a. Indigo and milky blue (1942)	..	55·00	2·75
D29	6d. green and brown-ochre (7.6.33)	..	23·00	8·00
	a. Green and bright orange (1938)	..	10·00	3·50
D22/9a	.. ..	Set of 7	55·00	18·00

In No. D26 the value, when magnified, has the meshed appearance of a photogravure screen, whereas in No. D23 the black of the value is solid.

1943–44. *Inscr bilingually. Roto.* W **9.** *In units of three, perf* 15 × 14 *subdivided by roulette* 6¹/₂.

				Un unit	Us unit	Us single
D30	D 3	¹/₂d. blue-green (1944)	..	9·50	30·00	30
D31		1d. carmine ..	..	9·00	4·50	10
D32		2d. dull violet ..	..	6·50	10·00	15
		a. Bright violet ..	..	16·00	40·00	65
D33		3d. indigo (1943)	..	45·00	70·00	1·25
D30/3 ..		.. ..	Set of 4	65·00	£100	1·90

Split "D" (R. 7/5 on every fourth sheet)

1948–49. *New figure of value and capital "D". Whole stamp roto.* W **9.** P 15 × 14.
D34	D 4	¹/₂d. black and blue-green	..	6·00	8·50
D35		1d. black and carmine	..	8·00	4·00
D36		2d. black and violet (1949)	..	9·00	4·00
		a. Thick (double) "2D." (R. 15/5–6, R. 16/5–6)	..	50·00	24·00
D37		3d. deep blue and blue	..	15·00	14·00
		a. Split "D"	..	£130	
D38		6d. green and bright orange (1949)		25·00	8·00
D34/8	.. ..	Set of 5	55·00	35·00	

1950–58. *As Type* D **4,** *but* "SUID-AFRIKA" *hyphenated. Whole stamp roto.* W **9.** P 15 × 14.
D39	1d. black and carmine (5.50)	..	70	30
D40	2d. black and violet (4.51)	..	50	20
	a. Thick (double) "2D." (R. 15/5–6, R. 16/5–6)	..	8·00	6·00
	b. Black and reddish violet (12.52)	..	70	20
	ba. Thick (double) "2D." ..	..	8·00	6·00
	bb. Black (value) omitted ..	..	£1600	
D41	3d. deep blue and blue (5.50)	..	4·25	2·00
	a. Split "D"	..	80·00	
D42	4d. deep myrtle-green and emerald (2.58)	11·00	12·00	
D43	6d. green and bright orange (3.50)	..	7·00	8·50
D44	1s. black-brown and purple-brown (2.58)	12·00	12·00	
D39/44	.. ..	Set of 6	32·00	32·00

No. D40bb occurs in horizontal pair with a normal.

OFFICIAL STAMPS

(O 2)

(Approximate measurements of the space between the two lines of overprint are quoted in millimetres, either in the set headings or after individual listings)

1930–47. *Nos.* 42/4 *and* 47/9 ("SUIDAFRIKA" *in one word) optd with Type* O **2.**
O12	6	¹/₂d. black and green (9¹/₂–12¹/₂ mm) (1931) ..	2·25	3·75	40
		a. Stop after "OFFISIEEL" on English inscr stamp ..	35·00	42·00	4·00
		b. Ditto, but on Afrikaans inscr stamp	30·00	38·00	3·50
O13	7	1d. black & carmine (I) (12¹/₂ mm)	4·50	4·50	55
		a. Stop after "OFFISIEEL" on English inscr stamp ..	38·00	45·00	4·00
		b. Ditto, but on Afrikaans inscr stamp	32·00	38·00	3·50
		c. On Type II (No. 43d) (12¹/₂–13¹/₂ mm) (1933) ..	10·00	9·00	90
		ca. Opt double	£275	£300	
O14	11	2d. slate-grey and lilac (20¹/₂–22¹/₂ mm) (1931) ..	6·00	11·00	1·50
O15		2d. blue and violet (20¹/₂–22¹/₂ mm) (1938)	£100	£100	9·00
O16	8	6d. green and orange (12¹/₂–13¹/₂ mm) (1931) ..	7·00	8·50	85
		a. Stop after "OFFISIEEL" on English inscr stamp ..	65·00	70·00	6·50
		b. Ditto, but on Afrikaans inscr stamp	55·00	60·00	5·50
		c. "OFFISIEEL" reading upwards (R. 17/12, 18/12, 19/12, 20/12) (1933)			£350
O17	13	1s. brown & dp bl (19 mm) (1932)	45·00	80·00	8·50
		a. Lines of opt 21 mm apart (1933)	45·00	70·00	7·50
O18	14	2s. 6d. green and brown (17¹/₂–18¹/₂ mm) (1933) ..	75·00	£130	15·00
		a. Lines of opt 21 mm apart (1934)	48·00	75·00	8·50
O19		2s. 6d. blue and brown (19¹/₂–20 mm) (11.47)	27·00	65·00	6·50
		a. Diaeresis over second "E" of "OFFISIEEL" on Afrikaans inscr stamp (R. 6/2) ..		£600	£700
		b. Ditto, but on English inscr stamp (R. 6/3)		£600	£700

The stop varieties for the ¹/₂d., 1d. and 6d. occur on R. 9/10, 9/12, 19/10, 19/12 with English inscriptions and R. 5/3, 5/11, 8/12, 15/3, 15/11, 18/12 with Afrikaans on the 1930 and 1931 overprintings only.

(O 3)   (O 4)

1935–49. *Nos.* 54, 56/8, 61/2 *and* 64a/b ("SUID-AFRIKA" *hyphenated) optd.*
(a) With Type O **2** *(reading downwards with* "OFFICIAL" *at right)*
O20	6	¹/₂d. grey & grn (12¹/₂ mm) (1936)	3·50	18·00	1·75
O21	7	1d. grey & carm (11¹/₂–13 mm) (1937)	1·25	1·75	20
		a. Grey & bright rose-carmine (No. 56i) (1949)	2·25	3·00	30

O22 **22** 1½d. green and bright gold (20
    mm) (1937)   23·00 19·00 1·75
    a. Blue-green and dull gold
    (No. 57b) (1941)   38·00 11·00 1·10
O23 **11** 2d. blue & violet (20 mm) (1939) £100 20·00 2·25
O24 **8** 6d. green and vermilion (I)
    (11½–13 mm) (1937) 80·00 42·00 3·75
    a. "Falling ladder" flaw £225
    b. Die II (No. 61b) (1938) 10·00 10·00 1·25
    c. Die III. Green & red-orange
    (No. 61c) (11.47)   4·00 8·50   85
O25 **13** 1s. brown and chalky blue (20
    mm) (1939)   65·00 26·00 2·25
    a. Diaeresis over second "E" of
    "OFFISIEEL" on both
    English and Afrikaans inscr
    stamps (1941)   £1100 £850
    b. Ditto, but on English inscr
    stamp only (11.47) £1000 £750
O26 **15** 5s. black and blue-green (20
    mm) (6.48)   45·00 £120 13·00
O27 **23** 10s. blue and blackish brown (No.
    64ba) (20 mm) (6.48) 80·00 £180 23·00

(b) With Type O 3 (reading downwards with "OFFICIAL" at
    left and 18–19 mm between lines of opt)
O28 **15** 5s. black and blue-green (1940) 70·00 £100 12·00
O29 **23** 10s. blue and sepia (1940) £325 £325 38·00

(c) With Type O 4 (reading upwards with "OFFICIAL" at right
    and 18½ mm between lines of opt
O30 **11** 2d. grey and dull purple (No.
    58a) (1941)   6·00 21·00 2·25
No. O25a first appeared in the 1941 overprinting where the
variety occurs on stamps 5 and 6 of an unidentified row. The
variety reappears in the November 1947 overprinting where the
stamps involved are R. 6/1 and 2. No. 25b occurs on R. 6/3 of the
same overprinting.
    Horizontal rows of 6 of the 1s. exist with "OFFICIAL" twice on
the first stamp and "OFFISIEEL" twice on the last stamp. Such
rows are believed to come from two half sheets which were
overprinted in 1947, but not placed into normal stock.

OFFICIAL

(O 5)

OFFISIEEL

(O 6)

1937–44. No. 75b (redrawn design) optd. (a) With Type O 2
(reading downwards with "OFFICIAL" at right and 11–12½
mm between lines of opt)
O31 **25a** ½d. grey and green   9·50 11·00 1·25
    a. Grey and blue-green (No.
    75bd) (1944)   1·00 5·50   60

(b) With Type O 5 (reading up and down with "OFFICIAL" at left
and diaeresis over the second "E" of "OFFISIEEL". 10 mm
between lines of opt)
O32 **25a** ½d. grey and blue-green (No.
    75bd) (1944)   14·00 19·00 2·00

1944–50. Nos. 87 and 134 optd. (a) With Type O 2 (reading
downwards with "OFFICIAL" at right)
O33 **34a** 1½d. blue-green and yellow-buff
    (14½ mm)   2·50 8·00   80
    a. With diaeresis over second
    "E" of "OFFISIEEL" £225 £160
    b. Lines of opt 16½ mm apart
    (6.48)   2·25 5·50   50

(b) With Type O 6 (reading upwards with "OFFICIAL" at left
and 16 mm between lines of opt)
O34 **34a** 1½d. bl-green & yell-buff (1949) 28·00 40·00 4·00
O35 **68** 2d. blue and violet (1950) £1400 £1700 £170
    Two different formes were used to overprint Type 34a
between 1944 and 1946. The first, applied to the left halves of
sheets only, had a diaeresis over the second "E" of "OFFISIEEL"
on all positions of the setting, except for R. 1/2, 2/2 and 3/2. The
second form, from which the majority of the stamps came, was
applied twice to overprint complete sheets, had no diaeresis.

1947 (Nov)–49. No. 107 optd with Type O 2 (reading
downwards with "OFFICIAL" at right and 20 mm between
lines of opt).
O36 **54** 2d. slate and violet   2·25 17·00 1·75
    a. With diaeresis over second "E"
    of "OFFISIEEL" (R. 1/5-6,
    11/5-6)   £275 £425
    b. Slate-purple and bright violet
    (No. 107a) (1949)   5·50 14·00 1·60

1949–50. Nos. 114 and 120 optd with Type O 2 (reading
downwards with "OFFICIAL" at right).
O37 **25a** ½d. grey and green (11 mm) 1·25 7·00   70
O38 **13** 1s. brown and chalky blue
    (17½–18½ mm) (1950) 9·00 26·00 2·50

OFFISIEEL   **OFFICIAL**

(O 7)

1950 (June)–54. Optd as Type O 7 using stereo blocks
measuring either 10 (½d., 1d., 6d.), 14½ (1½d., 2d.) or 19 mm
(others) between the lines of opt.
O39 **25a** ½d. grey and blue-green (No.
    75bd) (6.51)   1·00 8·00   75
O40   ½d. grey & grn (No. 114) (2.53)   70 1·50   15
O41 **7** 1d. grey & bright rose-carmine
    (No. 56i)   1·00 5·00   50
O42   1d. grey & car (No. 115) (3.51) 1·00 2·00   20
O43   1d. grey & car (No. 135) (6.52)   90 2·00   20
O44 **34a** 1½d. blue-green and yellow-buff
    (No. 87) (3.51)   1·40 3·00   30
O45 **68** 2d. blue and violet (No. 134) 1·00 2·00   20
    a. Opt inverted   £1200
O46 **8** 6d. green & red-orge (No. 119) 1·00 3·50   35
    a. Green and brown-orange
    (No. 119a) (6.51)   1·50 3·50   35
O47 **13** 1s. brn & chalky bl (No. 120) 5·50 18·00 2·00
    a. Blackish brown and ultram
    (No. 120a) (1.54)   £150 £160 18·00
O48 **14** 2s. 6d. green & brn (No. 121) 8·50 32·00 3·50
O49 **15** 5s. black and blue-green (No.
    64a) (3.51)   £160 90·00 9·00
O50   5s. black and pale blue-green
    (I) (No. 122) (2.53) 45·00 65·00 6·50
    a. Black & deep yellow-green
    (II) (No. 122a) (1.54) 65·00 85·00 9·00
O51 **23** 10s. blue and blackish brown
    (No. 64ba)   65·00 £170 22·00

Southern Rhodesia

12 pence (d) = 1 shilling; 20 shillings = 1 pound

SELF-GOVERNING COLONY

4

1935–41. *Inscr* "POSTAGE AND REVENUE".
35	4	2d. green and chocolate (p 12½)..		..	1·75	7·00
		a. Perf 14 (1941)..	..	..	75	10
35b		3d. deep blue (p 14) (1938)	..	..	2·50	10

10 Cecil John Rhodes (after S. P. Kendrick)

15 Lobengula's Kraal and Govt House, Salisbury

6 Victoria Falls and Railway Bridge

7 King George VI

Recut shirt collar (R. 6/1)

1937 (12 May). *Coronation. P* 12½.
36	6	1d. olive and rose-carmine	..	..	80	50
37		2d. emerald and sepia	..	..	80	1·25
38		3d. violet and blue	..	..	3·75	7·00
39		6d. black and purple	..	..	2·25	3·25
36/9	..	..	..	*Set of* 4	7·00	11·00

1937 (25 Nov). *P* 14.
40	7	½d. green	..	..	50	10
41		1d. scarlet	..	..	30	10
42		1½d. red-brown	..	..	1·00	10
43		4d. red-orange ..	..	..	1·50	10
44		6d. grey-black ..	..	..	1·50	20
45		8d. emerald-green	..	..	2·00	90
46		9d. pale blue	..	..	1·50	20
47		10d. purple	..	..	2·25	1·75
48		1s. black and blue-green	..	..	1·50	10
		a. Double print of frame	..	..	£850	
49		1s. 6d. black and orange-yellow	..	8·00	1·25	
50		2s. black and brown	..	..	11·00	55
51		2s. 6d. ultramarine and purple	..	8·00	4·00	
52		5s. blue and blue-green	..	..	26·00	2·00
40/52	..	..	..	*Set of* 13	60·00	9·50

Nos. 40/1 exist in coils, constructed from normal sheets.

"Cave" flaw (R. 6/6)

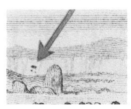

(Des Mrs. L. E. Curtis (½d., 1d., 1½d., 3d.), Mrs I. Mount (others))

1940 (3 June). *British South Africa Company's Golden Jubilee. T* **8/10**, **15** *and similar designs. P* 14.
53		½d. slate-violet and green ..	..	..	10	40
54		1d. violet-blue and scarlet	..	..	10	10
55		1½d. black and red-brown	..	..	15	60
		a. Recut shirt collar	..	..	15·00	
56		2d. green and bright violet	..	..	30	40
57		3d. black and blue	..	..	30	90
		a. Cave flaw	..	..	20·00	
58		4d. green and brown	..	..	1·60	1·75
59		6d. chocolate and green	..	..	30	1·50
60		1s. blue and green	..	..	45	1·75
53/60	..	..	..	*Set of* 8	3·00	6·50

Designs: *Horiz* (*as T* **8**)—2d. Fort Victoria; 3d. Rhodes makes peace. *Vert* (*as T* **10**)—4d. Victoria Falls Bridge; 6d. Statue of Sir Charles Coghlan.

8 British South Africa Co's Arms

9 Fort Salisbury, 1890

NEW INFORMATION

The editor is always interested to correspond with people who have new information that will improve or correct the Catalogue.

16 Mounted Pioneer   Hat brim retouch (P1 1B R. 1/8)

(Roto South African Govt Printer, Pretoria)

1943 (1 Nov). *50th Anniv of Occupation of Matabeleland. W 9 of South Africa (Mult Springbok) sideways. P 14.*
61	16	2d. brown and green	..	..	.. 20	40
		a. Hat brim retouch	..	..	.. 16·00	

17 Queen Elizabeth II when Princess
and Princess Margaret

1947 (1 Apr). *Royal Visit. T 17 and similar horiz design. P 14.*
62		¹⁄₂d. black and green	..	..	.. 15	40
63		1d. black and scarlet..	..	..	.. 15	40

Design:—1d. King George VI and Queen Elizabeth.

19 Queen Elizabeth   20 King George VI   21 Queen Elizabeth II
                                           when Princess

22 Princess Margaret   Damage to
                          right-hand frame
                             (R.1/10)

1947 (8 May). *Victory. P 14.*
64	19	1d. carmine	..	..	 10	10
65	20	2d. slate ..	..	..	.. 10	10
		a. Double print ..	..	..	.. £1000	
		b. Damaged frame	..	..	.. 7·00	
66	21	3d. blue ..	..	..	.. 55	30
67	22	6d. orange	..	..	.. 30	40
64/7		..	..	..	*Set of* 4 90	80

(Recess B.W.)

1949 (10 Oct). *75th Anniv of U.P.U. As Nos. 146/7 of Jamaica.*
68		2d. slate-green	..	..	 80	20
69		3d. blue	..	..	.. .. 1·10	2·75

23 Queen Victoria, Arms and King George VI

1950 (12 Sept). *Diamond Jubilee of Southern Rhodesia. P 14.*
70	23	2d. green and brown	..	..	.. 30	50

POSTAGE DUE STAMPS

SOUTHERN

RHODESIA

(D 1)

1951 (1 Oct). *Postage Due stamps of Great Britain optd with Type D 1.*
D1	D 1	¹⁄₂d. emerald (No. D27)	..	.. 3·25	12·00
D2		1d. violet-blue (No. D36)	..	.. 3·00	2·00
D3		2d. agate (No. D29)	..	.. 4·00	1·75
D4		3d. violet (No. D30)	..	.. 2·75	1·50
D5		4d. blue (No. D38)	..	.. 1·75	3·00
D6		4d. dull grey-green (No. D31)	..	.. £150	£425
D7		1s. deep blue (No. D33)	..	.. 3·00	2·00
D1/5, 7		..	..	*Set of* 6 16·00	20·00

No. D6 is reported to have been issued to Fort Victoria and Gwelo main post offices only.

South West Africa

12 pence (d) = 1 shilling; 20 shillings = 1 pound

SOUTH AFRICAN ADMINISTRATION

PRICES for Nos. 96/140 are for unused horizontal pairs, used horizontal pairs or used singles (either inscr), *unless otherwise stated.*

27 Mail Train    **28**

(Recess B.W.)

1937 (1 Mar). *W 9 of South Africa. P 14 × 13½.*

96	27	1½d. purple-brown	..	13·00	2·75	25

(Recess B.W.)

1937 (12 May). *Coronation. W 9 of South Africa (sideways). P 13½ × 14.*

97	28	½d. black and emerald ..	..	50	15	10
98		1d. black and scarlet	..	50	15	10
99		1½d. black and orange	..	50	15	10
100		2d. black and brown	..	50	15	10
101		3d. black and blue	..	50	15	10
102		4d. black and purple	..	50	20	10
103		6d. black and yellow ..	..	80	2·00	20
104		1s. black and grey-black	..	1·25	2·50	25
97/104		.. ..	*Set of 8*	4·50	5·00	65

1938 (14 Dec). *Voortrekker Centenary Memorial. Nos. 76/9 of South Africa optd as T 11.*

105	½d. + ½d. blue and green..	..	8·00	12·00	1·75
106	1d. + 1d. blue and carmine	..	18·00	6·50	1·00
107	1½d. + 1½d. chocolate & blue-green	22·00	18·00	2·75
108	3d. + 3d. bright blue	..	42·00	45·00	6·50
105/8	.. .. ..	*Set of 4*	80·00	75·00	11·00

1938 (14 Dec). *Voortrekker Commemoration. Nos. 80/1 of South Africa optd as T 11.*

109	1d. blue and carmine	..	10·00	11·00	1·50
110	1½d. greenish blue and brown	..	12·00	13·00	1·75

1939 (17 July). *250th Anniv of Landing of Huguenots in South Africa and Huguenot Commemoration Fund. Nos. 82/4 of South Africa optd as T 11.*

111	½d. + ½d. brown and green	..	8·00	8·00	1·10
112	1d. + 1d. green and carmine	..	13·00	10·00	1·25
113	1½d. + 1½d. blue-green and purple ..	17·00	10·00	1·25
111/13	.. ..	*Set of 3*	35·00	25·00	3·25

SWA   SWA   SWA   S W A

(29)   (30)   (31)   (32)

1941 (1 Oct)–43. *War Effort. Nos. 88/96 of South Africa optd with T 29 or 30 (3d. and 1s.). (a) Inscr alternately.*

114	½d. green (1.12.41)	..	75	2·00	15
	a. Blue-green (1942)	..	65	1·50	15
115	1d. carmine (1.11.41)	..	55	1·75	15
	a. "Stain" on uniform	..	6·00		

116	1½d. myrtle-green (21.1.42)	..	55	1·75	15
117	3d. blue	..	22·00	13·00	1·00
118	4d. orange-brown ..	..	6·50	10·00	1·00
	a. Red-brown ..	..	16·00	22·00	3·00
119	6d. red-orange ..	..	2·50	3·00	50
120	1s. 3d. olive-brown (15.1.43)	..	11·00	12·00	1·25

(b) Inscr bilingually

				Un	*Us*
				single	*single*
121	2d. violet	..	..	50	40
122	1s. brown (17.11.41)	..	..	60	40
114/22		*Set of 7 pairs and 2 singles*	40·00	40·00

1943–44. *War Effort (reduced sizes). Nos. 97/104 of South Africa, optd with T 29 (1½d. and 1s., No. 130), or T 31 (others).*

(a) Inscr alternately

					Un	*Us*	*Us*
					unit	*unit*	*single*
123	½d. blue-green (T) ..	..	..	40	2·25	10
	a. Green ..	..	..	3·00	3·50	15
	b. Greenish blue ..	..	..	3·00	3·50	10
124	1d. carmine-red (T)	..	..	90	2·25	10
	a. Bright carmine..	..	..	2·25	3·25	10
125	1½. red-brown (P) ..	..	..	45	50	10
126	2d. violet (P) ..	..	..	4·00	2·50	10
	a. Reddish violet ..	..	..	5·00	2·75	10
127	3d. blue (T)..	..	..	3·25	8·50	45
128	6d. red-orange (P) ..	..	..	4·00	2·25	30
	a. Opt inverted	..	..	£425		

(b) Inscr bilingually

129	4d. slate-green (T)	..	..	2·00	11·00	45
	a. Opt inverted	..	..	£425	£275	50·00
130	1s. brown (opt T 29) (P)	..	11·00	20·00	2·00
	a. Opt inverted	..	..	£425	£300	
	b. Opt T 31 (1944) ..	..	4·00	3·50	30
	c. Opt T 31 inverted	..	£375	£275	40·00
123/30b		..	*Set of 8*	17·00	29·00	1·75

The "units" referred to above consist of pairs (P) or triplets (T).
No. 128 exists with another type of opt as Type **31**, but with broader "s", narrower "w" and more space between the letters.

1945. *Victory. Nos. 108/10 of South Africa optd with T 30.*

131	1d. brown and carmine	..	..	25	40	10
	a. Opt inverted	..	..	£225	£250	
132	2d. slate-blue and violet	..	..	30	45	10
133	3d. deep blue and blue	..	..	1·00	70	10
131/3	.. .. ..	*Set of 3*	1·40	1·40	20

1947 (17 Feb). *Royal Visit. Nos. 111/13 of South Africa optd as T 31, but 8½ × 2 mm.*

134	1d. black and carmine	..	..	10	10	10
135	2d. violet	..	..	10	20	10
	a. "Bird" on "2" ..	..	..	3·00		
136	3d. blue ..	..	..	15	20	10
134/6	.. ..	*Set of 3*	30	45	15

1948 (26 Apr). *Royal Silver Wedding. No. 125 of South Africa, optd as T 31, but 4 × 2 mm.*

137	3d. blue and silver ..	..	1·50	35	10

1949 (1 Oct). *75th Anniv of U.P.U. Nos. 128/30 of South Africa optd as T 30, but 13 × 4 mm.*

138	1½d. blue-green	..	..	1·25	2·00	25
139	1½d. brown-red	..	..	1·25	1·00	15
140	3d. bright blue	..	..	1·75	1·50	25
	a. "Lake" in East Africa	..	20·00		
138/40	.. .. ..	*Set of 3*	3·75	4·00	60

1949 (1 Dec). *Inauguration of Voortrekker Monument, Pretoria. Nos.* 131/3 *of South Africa optd with T* 32.

							Un single	Us single
141	1d. magenta..	..	..	..	..	..	10	10
142	1½d. blue-green	..	..	..	..	..	10	10
143	3d. blue	..	..	..	..	..	15	25
141/3 ..	..	..	..	..	Set of 3	30	30

1952 (14 Mar). *Tercentenary of Landing of Van Riebeeck. Nos.* 136/40 *of South Africa optd as T* 30, *but* 8 × 3½ mm (1d., 4½d.) *or* 11 × 4 mm (others).

144	½d. brown-purple and olive-grey	..	..	10	40
145	1d. deep blue-green ..	..	..	10	10
146	2d. deep violet	..	..	..	50	10
147	4½d. blue	..	..	..	..	30	2·25
148	1s. brown	..	..	..	..	1·25	20
144/8 ..	..	..	..	Set of 5	2·00	2·75

OFFICIAL STAMPS

OFFICIAL   OFFISIEEL
(O 11)   (O 12)

1938 (1 July). *English stamp optd with Type* O 11 *and Afrikaans with Type* O 12 *in red.*

O17 **27** 1½d. purple-brown   ..   .. 24·00 42·00 6·00

OFFICIAL   OFFISIEEL
(O 13)   (O 14)

1945–50. *English stamp optd with Type* O 13, *and Afrikaans stamp with Type* O 14 *in red.*

O18	**12**	½d. black and emerald ..	..	11·00	26·00	5·00
O19	**13**	1d. indigo and scarlet (1950)	..	3·50	15·00	3·25
		a. Opt double ..	..	£425		
O20	**27**	1½d. purple-brown	..	..	42·00	35·00	6·50
O21	**14**	2d. blue and brown (1947?)	..	£450	£600	£100
O22	**17**	6d. blue and brown	..	..	9·50	38·00	7·00
O18/20, O22		..	..	Set of 4	60·00	£100	20·00

OFFICIAL   OFFISIEEL
(O 15)   (O 16)

1951 (16 Nov)–**52.** *English stamp optd with Type* O 15 *and Afrikaans stamp with Type* O 16, *in red.*

O23	**12**	½d. black and emerald (1952) ..	12·00	20·00	4·50
O24	**13**	1d. indigo and scarlet ..	..	3·50	12·00	1·75
O25	**27**	1½d. purple-brown	..	..	24·00	24·00	5·00
		a. Opts transposed	..	..	70·00	80·00	
O26	**14**	2d. blue and brown	..	..	1·25	15·00	3·50
		a. Opts transposed	..	..	42·00	£100	
O27	**17**	6d. blue and brown	..	..	2·75	35·00	7·50
		a. Opts transposed	..	..	22·00	£110	
O23/7		..	..	..	Set of 5	38·00	95·00	20·00

The above errors refer to stamps with the English overprint on Afrikaans stamp and *vice versa.*

Sudan

10 milliemes = 1 piastre; 100 piastres = 1 Sudanese pound

ANGLO-EGYPTIAN CONDOMINIUM

2 Arab Postman

6   7

10 Statue of Gen. Gordon

1938 (1 July). *Air. Nos. 53c, 55, 57b and 57d surch as T* **16**.
74 10 5 m. on 2½ p. magenta & bl (*p* 11½×12½) 3·50 10
75   3 p. on 3½ p. black and violet (*p* 14) .. 35·00 48·00
    a. Perf 11½×12½ £375 £475
76   3 p. on 7½ p. green and emerald (*p* 14) 7·00 6·50
    a. Perf 11½×12½ £375 £475
77   5 p. on 10 p. brown & greenish blue (*p* 14) 1·75 4·75
    a. Perf 11½×12½ £375 £475
74/7 .. .. *Set of* 4 42·00 55·00
A 5 p. on 2½ p., perf 11½×12½, exists either mint or cancelled from a trial printing (*Price* £350 *unused*).

5 Mills.

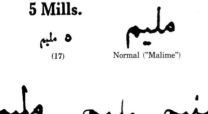

ه ملس

(17)   Normal ("Malime")

"Malmime"   Short "mim"   Broken "lam"
(Left-hand   (Right-hand   (Right-hand
pane R. 5/1)   pane R. 3/1)   pane R. 6/2)

---

5 M

Inserted "5"
(Bottom right-hand
pane R. 4/5)

1940 (25 Feb). *No. 42 surch with T* **17** *by McCorquodale
(Sudan) Ltd, Khartoum.*
78 6 5 m. on 10 m. carmine and black.. .. 50 30
    a. "Malmime" .. .. 42·00 45·00
    b. Two dots omitted (Right-hand pane
       R. 8/6).. .. .. .. 42·00 45·00
    c. Short "mim" .. .. .. 42·00 45·00
    d. Broken "lam".. .. .. .. 42·00 45·00
    e. Inserted "5" £130

4½
Piastres

4½   ٤ ١/٢ قرش
PIASTRES

(18)   (19)

1940–1. *Nos. 41 and 45c surch as T* **18** *or* **19** *at Khartoum.*
79 6 4½ p. on 5 m. olive-brown & blk (9.2.41) .. 48·00 3·00
80 2 4½ p. on 8 p. emerald and black (12.12.40) 32·00 8·00

20 Tuti Island, R. Nile,   21 Tuti Island, R. Nile
near Khartoum   near Khartoum

(Des Miss H. M. Hebbert. Litho Security Printing Press, Nasik,
India)

1941 (25 Mar–10 Aug). *P* 14 × 13½ (*T* **20**) *or P* 13½ × 14 (*T* **21**).
81 20 1 m. slate and orange (10.8) .. .. 60 2·25
82   2 m. orange and chocolate (10.8).. .. 70 2·00
83   3 m. mauve and green (10.8) 70 10
84   4 m. green and chocolate (10.8) 80 20
85   5 m. olive-brown and black (10.8) .. 30 10
86   10 m. carmine and black (10.8) .. .. 7·00 1·75
87   15 m. bright blue and chestnut 70 10
88 21 2 p. purple and orange-yellow (10.8) .. 3·50 60
89   3 p. red-brown and blue 70 10
90   4 p. ultramarine and black 80 10
91   5 p. chestnut and green (10.8) .. .. 4·50 7·50
92   6 p. greenish blue and black (10.8) .. 18·00 40
93   8 p. emerald and black (10.8) .. .. 14·00 45
94   10 p. slate and purple (10.8) .. .. 50·00 75
95   20 p. pale blue and blue (10.8) .. 50·00 26·00
81/95 .. .. *Set of* 15 £140 38·00

119	4 p. brown and light blue	..	..	..	1·00	1·75
120	4½ p. black and ultramarine ..		..	..	2·25	3·50
	a. *Black and steel-blue*		..	..	3·25	4·50
121	6 p. black and carmine	..	..	..	75	1·75
122	20 p. black and purple		..	..	1·75	3·50
115/122	..	..	..	..	*Set of* 8	13·00	13·50

Designs:—2½ p. Kassala Jebel; 3 p. Sagia (water wheel);
3½ p. Port Sudan; 4 p. Gordon Memorial College; 4½ p. *Gordon
Pasha* (Nile mail boat); 6 p. Suakin; 20 p. G.P.O., Khartoum.

22   23

1948 (1 Jan–June). *Arabic inscriptions below camel altered.
Typo.* W 7. *Ordinary paper* (8, 10, 20 *p.*) *or chalk-surfaced
paper* (*others*). *P* 14.

96	**22**	1 m. black and orange ..		..	..	35	2·00
97		2 m. orange and chocolate		..	..	80	2·25
98		3 m. mauve and green ..		..	..	30	2·25
99		4 m. deep green and chocolate		..	..	30	10
100		5 m. olive-brown and black		..	..	3·00	90
101		10 m. rose-red and black		..	..	3·50	10
		a. Centre inverted ..		..	..	†	—
102		15 m. ultramarine and chestnut		..	3·25	10
103	**23**	2 p. purple and orange-yellow		..	5·00	80
104		3 p. red-brown and deep blue ..		..	4·50	20
105		4 p. ultramarine and black		..	3·25	95
106		5 p. brown-orange and deep green		..	3·50	80
107		6 p. greenish blue and black ..		..	4·00	2·75
108		8 p. bluish green and black		..	4·00	2·75
109		10 p. black and mauve ..		..	8·50	2·75
		a. Chalk-surfaced paper (June)		..	16·00	3·50
110		20 p. pale blue and deep blue ..		..	4·50	20
		a. Perf 13. Chalk-surfaced paper (June)		..	48·00	£110
111		50 p. carmine and ultramarine ..		..	6·00	1·50
96/111		..	..	..	*Set of* 16	48·00	18·00

A single used example is known of No. 101a.
For similar stamps, but with different Arabic inscriptions, see
Nos. 37/46b.

24   25

1948 (1 Oct). *Golden Jubilee of "Camel Postman" design. Chalk-
surfaced paper. Typo.* W 7. *P* 13.

112	**24**	2 p. black and light blue	..	..	10	10

1948 (23 Dec). *Opening of Legislative Assembly, Chalk-surfaced paper. Typo.* W 7. *P* 13.

113	**25**	10 m. rose-red and black ..	..	..	15	10
114		5 p. brown-orange and deep green	..	15	40

26 Blue Nile Bridge, Khartoum

(Des Col. W. L. Atkinson (2½ p., 6 p.), G. R. Wilson (3 p.), others
from photographs. Recess)

1950 (1 July). *Air. T* **26** *and similar horiz designs.* W 7. *P* 12.

115	2 p. black and blue-green	..	..	..	4·00	70
116	2½ p. light blue and red-orange	..	..	50	1·00
117	3 p. reddish purple and blue	..	..	3·00	30
118	3½ p. purple-brown and yellow-brown	..	1·00	2·50

34 Ibex   35 Cotton Picking

(Des Col. W. L. Atkinson (1 m., 2 m., 4 m., 5 m., 10 m., 3 p., 3½ p.,
20 p.), Col. E. A. Stanton (50 p.) others from photographs. Typo)

1951 (1 Sept)–**62**? *Designs as T* **34/5**. *Chalk-surfaced paper.*
W 7. *P* 14 (*millieme values*) *or* 13 (*piastre values*).

123	1 m. black and orange	..	..	..	30	90
124	2 m. black and bright blue	..	..	1·25	30
125	3 m. black and green	..	..	..	3·25	1·75
126	4 m. black and yellow-green	..	..	60	1·75
127	5 m. black and purple	..	..	..	85	10
	a. *Black and reddish purple* (1962?)	..	2·50	10
128	10 m. black and pale blue ..	..	..	15	10
129	15 m. black and chestnut ..	..	..	1·75	10
	a. *Black and brown-orange* (1962?)	..	1·75	10
130	2 p. deep blue and pale blue	..	..	15	10
	a. *Deep blue and very pale blue* (1962?)	2·00	10
131	3 p. brown and dull ultramarine	..	3·25	10
	a. *Brown and deep blue* (1962?)	..	5·00	80
132	3½ p. bright green and red-brown	..	60	10
133	4 p. ultramarine and black	..	..	40	10
	a. *Deep blue and black* (1962?)	..	4·00	10
134	5 p. orange-brown and yellow-green	..	30	10
135	6 p. blue and black	..	..	..	5·00	2·25
	a. *Deep blue and black* (1962?)	..	11·00	4·00
136	8 p. blue and brown	..	..	8·00	1·50
	a. *Deep blue and brown* (1962?)	..	9·00	1·00
137	10 p. black and green	..	..	1·00	10
138	20 p. blue-green and black	..	..	4·25	95
139	50 p. carmine and black	..	..	11·00	75
123/139	..	..	..	*Set of* 17	38·00	9·00

Designs: *Vert as T* **34**—2 m. Whale-headed Stork, 3 m. Giraffe;
4 m. Baggara girl; 5 m. Shilluk warrior; 10 m. Hadendowa; 15 m.
Policeman. *Horiz as T* **35**—3 p. Ambatch reed canoe; 3½ p. Nuba
wrestlers; 4 p. Weaving; 5 p. Saluka farming; 6 p. Gum tapping;
8 p. Darfur chief; 10 p. Stack Laboratory; 20 p. Nile Lechwe. *Vert
as T* **35**—50 p. Camel postman.

POSTAGE DUE STAMPS

D 2 Gunboat *Zafir*

1948 (1 Jan). *Arabic inscriptions at foot altered. Chalk-surfaced
paper. Typo.* W 7. *P* 14.

D12	**D 2**	2 m. black and brown-orange ..	..	80	23·00
D13		4 m. brown and green ..	..	2·00	25·00
D14		10 m. green and mauve ..	..	13·00	15·00
D15		20 m. ultramarine and carmine..	..	13·00	15·00
D12/15		..	..	..	*Set of* 4	26·00	80·00

The 10 and 20 m. were reissued in 1980 on Sudan arms
watermarked paper.

OFFICIAL STAMPS

S.G.   S.G.   S.G.

(O 3)   (O 4)   (O 4a)

1948 (1 Jan). *Nos. 96/102 optd with Type O 3, and 103/111 with Type O 4.*

O43	22	1 m. black and orange	..	20	2·50
O44		2 m. orange and chocolate	..	75	10
O45		3 m. mauve and green	..	1·50	4·00
O46		4 m. deep green and chocolate	..	1·50	2·50
O47		5 m. olive-brown and black	..	1·50	10
O48		10 m. rose-red and black	..	1·00	80
O49		15 m. ultramarine and chestnut	..	1·50	10
O50	23	2 p. purple and orange-yellow	..	1·50	10
O51		3 p. red-brown and deep blue	..	1·50	10
O52		4 p. ultramarine and black	..	1·50	10
		a. Perf 13 (optd Type O 4a)	..	13·00	15·00
O53		5 p. brown-orange and deep green	..	1·75	10
O54		6 p. greenish blue and black	..	1·50	10
O55		8 p. bluish green and black	..	1·50	1·75
O56		10 p. black and mauve	..	2·00	20
O57		20 p. pale blue and deep blue	..	3·50	25
O58		50 p. carmine and ultramarine	..	55·00	40·00
O43/58		.. .. ..	*Set of 16*	70·00	48·00

1950 (1 July). *Air. Optd with Type O 4a.*

O59	2 p. black and blue-green (R.)	..		12·00	2·50
O60	2½ p. light blue and red-orange		..	1·50	1·75
O61	3 p. reddish purple and blue	..		80	1·00
O62	3½ p. purple-brown and yellow-brown		..	80	5·50
O63	4 p. brown and light blue	..		80	4·00
O64	4½ p. black and ultramarine (R.)	..		3·25	14·00
	a. Black and steel-blue	..		5·00	14·00

O65	6 p. black and carmine (R.)	..	..	1·00	4·25
O66	20 p. black and purple (R.)	..		5·00	12·00
O59/66	.. .. ..	..	*Set of 8*	22·00	40·00

1951 (1 Sept)–**62**? *Nos. 123/9 optd with Type O 3, and 130/9 with Type O 4a.*

O67	1 m. black and orange (R.)	..	..	30	3·25
O68	2 m. black and bright blue (R.)		..	30	50
O69	3 m. black and green (R.)	..	..	2·50	13·00
O70	4 m. black and yellow-green (R.)		..	10	4·50
O71	5 m. black and purple (R.)	..	..	10	10
O72	10 m. black and pale blue (R.)	..	..	10	10
O73	15 m. black and chestnut (R.)	..	..	10	10
O74	2 p. deep blue and pale blue	..	..	10	10
	a. Opt inverted	..	..	£400	
	b. *Deep blue and very pale blue* (1962)			50	10
O75	3 p. brown and dull ultramarine	..		1·75	10
	a. *Brown and deep blue* (1962?)			3·25	75
O76	3½ p. bright green and red-brown	..		25	10
	a. *Deep blue and black* (1962?)			2·25	75
O77	4 p. ultramarine and black	..		30	10
	a. *Light emerald & red-brown* (1962?)			70	10
O78	5 p. orange-brown and yellow-green	..		25	10
O79	6 p. blue and black	..	..	30	2·75
	a. *Deep blue and black* (1962?)		..	4·00	4·50
O80	8 p. blue and brown	..	..	45	10
	a. *Deep blue and brown* (1962?)		..	2·50	1·25
O81	10 p. black and green (R.)	..	..	50	10
O81a	10 p. black and green (Blk.) (1958)		..	13·00	1·25
O82	20 p. blue-green and black	..		1·25	30
	a. Opt inverted	..	..	—	£550
O83	50 p. carmine and black	..		3·50	1·25
O67/83	.. .. ..	..	*Set of 18*	22·00	24·00

The 5, 10 and 15 m. values were later reissued with a thinner overprint.

Swaziland

12 pence (d) = 1 shilling; 20 shillings = 1 pound

1937 (12 May). *Coronation. As Nos.* 118/20 *of Jamaica, but ptd by B.W. P* 11×11½.

25	1d. carmine	..	..	..	75	1·00
26	2d. yellow-brown		..	..	75	15
27	3d. blue	..	..	..	75	50
25/7	..	..	..	Set of 3	2·00	1·50
25/7 Perf "Specimen"		..	..	Set of 3	60·00	

3 King George VI

(Recess D.L.R.)

1938 (1 Apr)–54. *Wmk Mult Script CA. P* 13½ × 13.

28	3	½d. green	..	..	90	55
		a. Perf 13½ × 14 (1.43)	..	..	20	1·75
		b. Perf 13½ × 14. *Bronze-green* (2.50)		75	3·25
29		1d. rose-red	..	..	1·00	60
		a. Perf 13½ × 14 (1.43)	..	..	80	1·00
30		1½d. light blue	..	..	3·75	65
		a. Perf 14 (1941)	..	..	1·50	95
		b. Perf 13½ × 14 (1.43)	..	..	30	75
31		2d. yellow-brown	..	..	2·50	75
		a. Perf 13½ × 14 (1.43)	..	..	30	50
32		3d. ultramarine	..	..	6·00	1·50
		a. *Deep blue* (10.38]	..	..	8·00	1·50
		b. Perf 13½ × 14. *Ultramarine* (1.43)	1·50	3·25
		c. Perf 13½ × 14. *Light ultram* (10.46)	10·00	7·00
		d. Perf 13½ × 14. *Deep blue* (10.47)	..	6·50	6·50
33		4d. orange	..	..	2·75	95
		a. Perf 13½ × 14 (1.43)	..	..	45	1·40
34		6d. deep magenta	..	..	6·00	1·25
		a. Perf 13½ × 14 (1.43)	..	..	3·50	3·50
		b. Perf 13½ × 14. *Reddish purple* (shades) (7.44)	..	3·50	1·25
		c. Perf 13½ × 14. *Claret* (13.10.54)	..	5·00	3·00
35		1s. brown-olive..	..	..	7·00	1·25
		a. Perf 13½ × 14 (1.43)	..	..	1·25	65
36		2s. 6d. bright violet	..	..	22·00	4·00
		a. Perf 13½ × 14. *Violet* (1.43)	..	6·00	2·50
		b. Perf 13½ × 14. *Reddish violet* (10.47)	..	6·00	5·00
37		5s. grey..	..	..	50·00	8·00
		a. Perf 13½ × 14. *Slate* (1.43)	..	55·00	50·00
		b. Perf 13½ × 14. *Grey* (5.44)..	..	23·00	11·00
38		10s. sepia	..	..	50·00	5·50
		a. Perf 13½ × 14 (1.43)	..	..	6·50	6·00
28/38a		..	..	Set of 11	40·00	20·00
28/38 Perf "Specimen"		..	Set of 11	£200	

The above perforations vary slightly from stamp to stamp, but the average measurements are respectively: 13.3 × 13.2 comb (13½ × 13), 14.2 line (14) and 13.3 × 13.8 comb (13½ × 14).

Swaziland
(4)

1945 (3 Dec). *Victory. Nos.* 108/10 *of South Africa optd with T* 4.

				Un	*Us*	*Us*
					pair	*pair single*
39	1d. brown and carmine	..	..	55	50	10
40	2d. slate-blue and violet	..	..	55	50	10
41	3d. deep blue and blue	..	..	55	1·75	20
39/41	..	..	..	Set of 3	1·50	2·50	30

1947 (17 Feb). *Royal Visit. As Nos.* 32/5 *of Lesotho.*

						Un	*Us*
42	1d. scarlet	..	..	..	..	10	10
43	2d. green	..	..	..	..	10	10
44	3d. ultramarine	..	..	..	10	10
45	1s. mauve	..	..	..	..	10	10
42/5	..	..	..	..	Set of 4	30	30
42/5 Perf "Specimen"	..	..	Set of 4	80·00	

1948 (1 Dec). *Royal Silver Wedding. As Nos.* 143/4 *of Jamaica.*

46	1½d. ultramarine	..	..	..	50	10
47	10s. purple-brown	..	..	..	22·00	22·00

1949 (10 Oct). *75th Anniv of U.P.U. As Nos.* 145/8 *of Jamaica.*

48	1½d. blue	..	..	..	..	20	10
49	3d. deep blue	..	..	..	80	60
50	6d. magenta..	..	..	..	60	60
51	1s. olive	..	..	..	..	60	60
48/51	..	..	..	..	Set of 4	2·00	1·75

POSTAGE DUE STAMPS

D 1

(Typo D.L.R.)

1933 (2 Jan)–57. *Wmk Mult Script CA. P* 14.

D1	D 1	1d. carmine	..	..	..	30	6·00
		a. Chalk-surfaced paper. *Dp carmine* (24.10.51)	..	20	10·00
		ac. Error. St Edward's Crown, W 9b	£120	
D2		2d. pale violet	..	..	1·75	18·00
		a. Chalk-surfaced paper (22.2.57)	..	4·75	26·00
		ab. Large "d" ..	..	..	..	32·00	
D1/2 Perf "Specimen"	..	..	Set of 2	40·00	

For illustration of No. D2ab see above No. D1 of Lesotho.

Tonga

12 pence (d) = 1 shilling; 20 shillings = 1 pound

PROTECTORATE

15 Arms

16 Ovava Tree, Kana-Kubolu

18 Prehistoric Trilith at Haamonga

20 Coral

22 Red Shining Parrot

23 View of Vavau Harbour

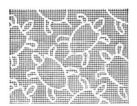

24 Tortoises (*upright*)

26 Queen Salote

29 Queen Salote

(Recess D.L.R.)

1938 (12 Oct). 20th *Anniv of Queen Salote's Accession. Tablet at foot dated* "1918–1938". *W* 24. *P* 14.

71	29	1d. black and scarlet	..	..	55	2·75
72		2d. black and purple	..	..	5·00	2·00
73		2½d. black and ultramarine	..	..	5·00	2·75
71/3	..	..	..	Set of 3	9·50	6·75
71/3 Perf "Specimen"		..	..	Set of 3	65·00	

For Silver Jubilee issue in a similar design, see Nos. 83/87.

Dies of 2d.:

Die II

Die III

Normal

Lopped branch (R. 8/5)
(ptgs from 1934 onwards)

Normal

"2½" recut (note lines on "2" and different "½")
(R. 1/1)

(Recess D.L.R.)

1942–49. *Wmk Mult Script CA* (*sideways on* 5s.). *P* 14.

74	15	½d. yellow-green	..	..	15	1·60
75	16	1d. black and scarlet	..	..	75	1·60
		a. Lopped branch	..	..	15·00	
76	26	2d. black and purple (Die II)	..		2·25	1·50
		a. Die III (4.49)	..	..	3·75	6·00
77		2½d. bright ultramarine	..	..	60	80
		a. Recut "2½"	..	..	6·00	
78	18	3d. black and yellow-green	..	..	30	1·50
79	20	6d. red	..	..	1·50	1·50
80	26	1s. black and red-brown	..	..	1·25	2·25
81	22	2s. 6d. deep purple (1943)	..	..	20·00	20·00

82   **23**   5s. black and brown-red (1943)   . .   16·00 38·00
74/82   . .   . .   *Set of* 9 38·00 60·00
74/82 Perf "Specimen"   . .   . .   *Set of* 9 £170
    In Die III the foot of the "2" is longer than in Die II and
extends towards the right beyond the curve of the loop; the
letters of "PENI-E-UA" are taller and differently shaped.
    Damage to the "2" on R. 4/9 of No. 77 was frequently corrected
by hand-painting.

30

(Recess D.L.R.)

1944 (25 Jan). *Silver Jubilee of Queen Salote's Accession. As T* **29**,
but inscr "1918–1943" *at foot, as T* **30**. *Wmk Mult Script CA. P* 14.
83   1d. black and carmine   15   50
84   2d. black and purple   15   50
85   3d. black and green   15   50
86   6d. black and orange.   30   85
87   1s. black and brown   30   85
83/7   . .   . .   . .   *Set of* 5   95   2·75
83/7 Perf "Specimen"   . .   . .   *Set of* 5 70·00

1949 (10 Oct). *75th Anniv of U.P.U. As Nos.* 145/8 *of Jamaica.*
88   2½d. ultramarine   40   30
89   3d. olive   80   2·00
90   6d. carmine-red   50   30
91   1s. red-brown   50   35
88/91 . .   . .   *Set of* 4   2·00 2·75

31   Queen Salote   **33**

34 Map

32 Queen Salote

(Photo Waterlow)

1950 (1 Nov).   *Queen Salote's Fiftieth Birthday. Wmk Mult Script
CA. P* 12½.
92   **31**   1d. carmine   40   1·00
93   **32**   5d. green   40   1·00
94   **33**   1s. violet   40   1·40
92/4 . .   . .   *Set of* 3   1·10 3·00

35 Palace, Nuku'alofa

(Recess Waterlow)

1951 (2 July). *50th Anniv of Treaty of Friendship between Great
Britain and Tonga. T* **34/5** *and similar designs. Wmk Mult Script
CA. P* 12½ (3*d.*), 13 × 13½ (½*d.*), 13½ × 13 (*others*).
95   ½d. green   20   1·50
96   1d. black and carmine   15   1·00
97   2½d. green and brown   30   1·50
98   3d. yellow and bright blue. .   . .   1·00   1·50
99   5d. carmine and green   65   70
100   1s. yellow-orange and violet   . .   65   70
95/100   . .   . .   *Set of* 6   2·75   6·00
    Designs: *Horiz*—2½d. Beach scene; 5d. Flag; 1s. Arms of Tonga
and G.B. *Vert*—3d. H.M.N.Z.S. *Bellona.*

Transjordan

1000 milliemes = 1 Palestinian pound

BRITISH MANDATE

28   29

(Re-engraved with figures of value at left only. Recess Perkins, Bacon)

1930 (1 June)–**39**. *Wmk Mult Script CA. P* 14.

194b	28	1 m. red-brown (6.2.34)			30	1·00
		c. Perf 13½ × 13 (1939)			2·75	2·75
195		2 m. greenish blue			30	50
		a. Perf 13½ × 13. *Bluish green* (1939)			7·00	2·00
196		3 m. carmine-pink			40	70
196a		3 m. green (6.2.34)			70	85
		b. Perf 13½ × 13 (1939)			13·00	4·00
197		4 m. green			60	1·75
197a		4 m. carmine-pink (6.2.34)			1·50	90
		b. Perf 13½ × 13 (1939)			48·00	14·00
198		5 m. orange			40	40
		a. Coil stamp. P 13½ × 14 (1936)			18·00	12·00
		b. Perf 13½ × 13 (1939)			50·00	3·00
199		10 m. scarlet			70	15
		a. Perf 13½ × 13 (1939)			80·00	4·25
200		15 m. ultramarine			65	20
		a. Coil stamp. P 13½ × 14 (1936)			18·00	12·00
		b. Perf 13½ × 13 (1939)			32·00	3·75
201		20 m. olive-green			1·25	35
		a. Perf 13½ × 13 (1939)			55·00	12·00
202	29	50 m. purple			1·50	1·25
203		90 m. bistre			2·50	4·25
204		100 m. blue			3·75	4·25
205		200 m. violet			8·50	14·00
206		500 m. brown			20·00	35·00
207		£P1 slate-grey			45·00	80·00
194b/207				*Set of* 16	80·00	£130
194b/207	Perf "Specimen"			*Set of* 16	£130	

For stamps perf 12 see Nos. 230/43, and for T **28** lithographed, perf 13½, see Nos. 222/9.

34

(Litho Survey Dept, Cairo)

1942 (18 May). *T* **28**, *but with Arabic characters above portrait and in top left circle modified as in T* **34**. *No wmk. P* 13½.

222	34	1 m. red-brown			80	2·50
223		2 m. green			1·50	1·50
224		3 m. yellow-green			1·75	2·25
225		4 m. carmine-pink			1·75	3·00
226		5 m. yellow-orange			3·00	1·00
227		10 m. scarlet			2·75	2·75
228		15 m. blue			3·50	1·75
229		20 m. olive-green			8·00	9·00
222/9				*Set of* 8	21·00	21·00

(Recess Bradbury, Wilkinson)

1943 (1 Jan)–**44**. *Wmk Mult Script CA. P* 12.

230	28	1 m. red-brown			20	75
231		2 m. bluish green			70	75
232		3 m. green			1·75	1·25
233		4 m. carmine-pink			1·75	1·25
234		5 m. orange			1·25	20
235		10 m. red			3·00	1·25
236		15 m. blue			3·00	30
237		20 m. olive-green (5.44)			2·75	1·00
238	29	50 m. purple (5.44)			3·00	1·00
239		90 m. bistre (5.44)			4·75	4·00
240		100 m. blue (5.44)			5·00	1·75
241		200 m. violet (5.44)			9·00	5·50
242		500 m. brown (5.44)			13·00	12·00
243		£P1 slate-grey (5.44)			24·00	20·00
230/43				*Set of* 14	65·00	45·00

Nos. 237/43 were released in London by the Crown Agents about May 1944 but were not put on sale in Transjordan until 26 August 1946.

Printings of the 3, 4, 10, 12, 15 and 20 m. in changed colours were released on 12 May 1947.

POSTAGE DUE STAMPS

D 26   D 35

(Recess Perkins, Bacon)

1929 (1 Apr)–**39**. *Wmk Mult Script CA. P* 14.

D189	D 26	1 m. red-brown			60	2·50
		a. Perf 13½×13 (1939)			80·00	50·00
D190		2 m. orange-yellow			60	2·75
D191		4 m. green			60	3·25
D192		10 m. scarlet			1·50	3·75
D193		20 m. olive-green			5·50	9·50
D194		50 m. blue			7·00	13·00
D189/94				*Set of* 6	14·00	30·00
D189/94	Perf "Specimen"			*Set of* 6	50·00	

(Litho Survey Dept, Cairo)

1942 (22 Dec). *Redrawn. Top line of Arabic in taller lettering. No wmk. P* 13½.

D230	D 35	1 m. red-brown			80	7·00
D231		2 m. orange-yellow			4·50	7·00
D232		10 m. scarlet			6·00	4·75
D230/2				*Set of* 3	10·00	17·00

(Recess Bradbury, Wilkinson)

1944. *Wmk Mult Script CA. P* 12.

D244	D 26	1 m. red-brown			15	2·00
D245		2 m. orange-yellow			30	2·25
D246		4 m. green			55	3·50
D247		10 m. carmine			85	4·00
D248		20 m. olive-green			16·00	23·00
D244/8				*Set of* 5	16·00	30·00

Trinidad and Tobago

100 cents = 1 West Indian dollar

CROWN COLONY

1937 (12 May). *Coronation. As Nos. 118/20 of Jamaica.*
243	1 c. green	15	10
244	2 c. yellow-brown	35	10
245	8 c. orange	1·25	75
243/5 ..	*Set of 3*	1·60	80
243/5 Perf "Specimen"	*Set of 3*	55·00	

37 First Boca   **47** King George VI
(Recess B.W.)

1938 (2 May)–**44.** *T* **37** *and similar horiz designs, and T* **47.**
Wmk Mult Script CA (sideways on 1 c. *to* 60 c.).

(*a*) *P* 11½×11
246	1 c. blue and green	30	20
247	2 c. blue and yellow-brown	30	20
248	3 c. black and scarlet	11·00	90
248*a*	3 c. green and purple-brown (1941)	30	20
ab.	"A" of "CA" missing from wmk		
249	4 c. chocolate	29·00	1·00
249*a*	4 c. scarlet (1941)	40	60
249*b*	5 c. magenta (1.5.41)	30	15
250	6 c. sepia and blue	90	60
251	8 c. sage-green and vermilion	1·00	60
252	12 c. black and purple	13·00	1·10
a.	*Black and slate-purple* (1944)	2·50	10
253	24 c. black and olive-green	50	10
254	60 c. myrtle-green and carmine	8·50	95

(*b*) *T* **47.** *P* 12
255	$1.20, blue-green (1.40)	10·00	75
256	$4.80, rose-carmine (1.40)	20·00	20·00
246/56	*Set of 14*	75·00	23·00
246/56 *exc* 249*b* Perf "Specimen"	*Set of 13*	£190	

Designs:—2 c. Imperial College of Tropical Agriculture; 3 c. Mt Irvine Bay, Tobago; 4 c. Memorial Park; 5 c. G.P.O. and Treasury; 6 c. Discovery of Lake Asphalt; 8 c. Queen's Park, Savannah; 12 c. Town Hall, San Fernando; 24 c. Government House; 60 c. Blue Basin.

1946 (1 Oct). *Victory. As Nos. 141/2 of Jamaica.*
257	3 c. chocolate ..	10	10
258	6 c. blue	10	80
257/8 Perf "Specimen"	*Set of 2*	45·00	

1948 (22 Nov). *Royal Silver Wedding. As Nos. 143/4 of Jamaica, but $4.80 in recess.*
259	3 c. red-brown	10	10
260	$4.80, carmine	17·00	19·00

1949 (10 Oct). *75th Anniv of U.P.U. As Nos. 145/8 of Jamaica.*
261	5 c. bright reddish purple	40	40
262	6 c. deep blue	75	55

263	12 c. violet ..	40	65
264	24 c. olive ..	40	30
261/4	*Set of 4*	1·75	1·75

1951 (16 Feb). *University College of B.W.I. As Nos. 149/50 of Jamaica.*
265	3 c. green and red-brown	20	30
266	12 c. black and reddish violet ..	20	30

POSTAGE DUE STAMPS

D 1

1923–45. *Wmk Mult Script CA. P* 14.
D18	D 1	1d. black (1923)		60	1·00
D19		2d. black (1923)		60	1·00
D20		3d. black (1925)		60	1·75
D21		4d. black (1929)		1·75	12·00
D22		5d. black (1944)		29·00	65·00
D23		6d. black (1945)		38·00	23·00
D24		8d. black (1945)		38·00	£110
D25		1s. black (1945)		55·00	85·00
D18/25			*Set of 8*	£150	£275
D18/25 Optd/Perf "Specimen"			*Set of 8*	£140	

1947 (1 Sept)–**61.** *Values in cents. Wmk Mult Script CA. Ordinary paper. P* 14.
D26	D 1	2 c. black	95	2·25
		a. Chalk-surfaced paper (20.1.53) ..	20	3·00
		ab. Error. Crown missing. W 9*a*	55·00	
		ac. Error. St. Edward's Crown. W 9*b*	23·00	
D27		4 c. black	85	3·00
		a. Chalk-surfaced paper (10.8.55) ..	1·50	3·75
D28		6 c. black	95	6·00
		a. Chalk-surfaced paper (20.1.53) ..	30	6·00
		ab. Error. Crown missing. W 9*a*	£150	
		ac. Error. St. Edward's Crown. W 9*b*	50·00	
D29		8 c. black	90	16·00
		a. Chalk-surfaced paper (10.9.58) ..	35	13·00
D30		10 c. black	85	2·75
		a. Chalk-surfaced paper (10.8.55) ..	2·50	7·00
D31		12 c. black	90	14·00
		a. Chalk-surfaced paper (20.1.53) ..	40	12·00
		ab. Error. Crown missing. W 9*a*	£180	
		ac. Error. St. Edward's Crown. W 9*b*	£180	
D32		16 c. black	2·00	30·00
		a. Chalk-surfaced paper (22.8.61) ..	6·50	30·00
D33		24 c. black	6·00	7·50
		a. Chalk-surfaced paper (10.8.55) ..	6·00	24·00
D26/33			*Set of 8*	12·00	70·00
D26/33*a* ..			*Set of 8*	13·00	90·00
D26/33 Perf "Specimen"			*Set of 8*	£140	

Tristan da Cunha

12 pence (d) = 1 shilling; 20 shillings = 1 pound

DEPENDENCY OF ST. HELENA

During World War II there was little mail from the island as its function as a meteorological station was cloaked by security. Such covers as are known are generally struck with the "tombstone" naval censor mark and postmarked "maritime mail" or have South African postal markings. A few philatelic items from early in the war bearing cachets exist, but this usage was soon stopped by the military commander and the handstamps were put away until peace returned. Covers from the period would be worth from £75 to, at least, £350.

Cachet VIII

C10 **1946** (8 May). Cachet VIII .. .. .. *from* 85·00

Cachet IX

C11 **1948** (29 Feb). Cachet IX .. .. . *from* 55·00

Cachet X

C12 **1948** (6 Mar). Cachet X .. .. *from* 45·00

TRISTAN DA CUNHA

(1)

1952 (1 Jan). *Nos.* 131, 135a/40 *and* 149/51 *of St. Helena optd with T* 1.

1	½d. violet ..	..	..	..	15	85
2	1d. black and green	..	..	..	40	1·25
3	1½d. black and carmine	..	..	..	40	1·25
4	2d. black and scarlet	..	..	..	40	1·50
5	3d. grey ..	..	..	..	60	1·25
6	4d. ultramarine	..	..	..	2·25	2·00
7	6d. light blue	..	..	..	3·50	2·50
8	8d. sage-green	..	..	..	3·00	3·00
9	1s. sepia ..	..	..	..	3·50	2·00
10	2s. 6d. maroon	..	..	..	19·00	14·00
11	5s. chocolate	..	..	..	23·00	23·00
12	10s. purple	..	..	..	40·00	45·00
1/12	..	..	..	*Set of* 12	85·00	85·00

Turks and Caicos Islands

12 pence (d) = 1 shilling; 20 shillings = 1 pound

DEPENDENCY OF JAMAICA

1937 (12 May). *Coronation. As Nos. 118/20 of Jamaica.*

191	½d. myrtle-green 10	10
	a. *Deep green* .. .. 40·00	
192	2d. grey-black 60	40
193	3d. bright blue 80	40
191/3	.. .. .. *Set of 3* 1·40	75
191/3	Perf "Specimen" .. .. *Set of 3* 55·00	

46 Raking Salt

47 Salt Industry

(Recess Waterlow)

1938 (18 June)–45. *Wmk Mult Script CA. P 12½.*

194	**46**	¼d. black 10	10
195		½d. yellowish green .. .. .. 2·75	15
		a. *Deep green* (6.11.44) 50	70
196		1d. red-brown 40	10
197		1½d. scarlet 40	15
198		2d. grey 40	30
199		2½d. yellow-orange .. .. .. 3·75	80
		a. *Orange* (6.11.44) .. .. .. 1·75	1·40
200		3d. bright blue 30	30
201		6d. mauve .. .. 7·50	1·25
201a		6d. sepia (9.2.45) 15	20
202		1s. yellow-bistre .. .. .. 3·25	7·50
202a		1s. grey-olive (9.2.45) 15	20
203	**47**	2s. deep rose-carmine .. .. 40·00	11·00
		a. *Bright rose-carmine* (6.11.44) .. 17·00	13·00
204		5s. yellowish green .. .. .. 48·00	13·00
		a. *Deep green* (6.11.44) .. .. 35·00	16·00
205		10s. bright violet .. .. .. 11·00	5·50
194/205		.. .. .. *Set of 14* 65·00	35·00
194/205	Perf "Specimen" .. .. *Set of 14* £200	

1946 (4 Nov). *Victory. As Nos. 141/2 of Jamaica.*

206	2d. black 10	10
207	3d. blue 15	10
206/7	Perf "Specimen" .. .. *Set of 2* 55·00	

1948 (13 Sept). *Royal Silver Wedding. As Nos. 143/4 of Jamaica.*

208	1d. red-brown 15	10
209	10s. mauve .. .. 6·00	8·00

50 Badge of the Islands

53 Queen Victoria and King George VI

(Recess Waterlow)

1948 (14 Dec). *Centenary of Separation from Bahamas. T 50, 53 and similar designs. Wmk Mult Script CA. P 12½.*

210	**50**	½d. blue-green 30	15
211		2d. carmine 60	15
212	–	3d. blue 80	15
213	–	6d. violet 50	20
214	**53**	2s. black and bright blue 55	55
215		5s. black and green 90	1·25
216		10s. black and brown 90	3·25
210/16		.. .. *Set of 7* 4·00	5·00

Designs: *Horiz*—3d. Flag of Turks and Caicos Islands; 6d. Map of islands.

1949 (10 Oct). *75th Anniv of U.P.U. As Nos. 145/8 of Jamaica.*

217	2½d. red-orange 40	55
218	3d. deep blue 80	50
219	6d. brown 50	50
220	1s. olive 50	35
217/20	.. .. .. *Set of 4* 2·00	1·75

65 Bulk Salt Loading

66 Dependency's Badge

(Recess Waterlow)

1950 (1 Aug). *T 65 and similar horiz designs, and T 66. Wmk Mult Script CA. P 12½.*

221	½d. green 20	40
222	1d. red-brown 20	75
223	1½d. deep carmine 40	55
224	2d. red-orange 20	40
225	2½d. grey-olive 30	50
226	3d. bright blue 20	40
227	4d. black and rose .. .. .. 2·50	70
228	6d. black and blue .. .. .. 2·00	50
229	1s. black and blue-green 90	50
230	1s. 6d. black and scarlet .. .. 4·00	3·25
231	2s. emerald and ultramarine .. .. 2·00	3·50
232	5s. blue and black .. .. .. 10·00	5·50
233	10s. black and violet .. .. .. 14·00	14·00
221/33	.. .. .. *Set of 13* 32·00	27·00

Designs:—1d. Salt Cay; 1½d. Caicos mail; 2d. Grand Turk; 2½d. Sponge diving; 3d. South Creek; 4d. Map; 6d. Grand Turk Light; 1s. Government House; 1s. 6d. Cockburn Harbour; 2s. Government Offices; 5s. Loading salt.

Virgin Islands

1937. 12 pence (d) = 1 shilling; 20 shillings = 1 pound
1951. 100 cents = 1 West Indian dollar

CROWN COLONY

1937 (12 May). *Coronation. As Nos. 95/7 of Antigua.*
P 11×11½.

107	1d. carmine ..	..	20	70
108	1½d. yellow-brown	..	40	2·25
109	2½d. blue	..	45	80
107/9 ..		Set of 3	95	3·25
107/9 Perf "Specimen"		Set of 3	55·00	

15 King George VI and Badge of Colony   16 Map

(Photo Harrison)

1938 (1 Aug)–47. *Wmk Mult Script CA. Chalk-surfaced paper.*
P 14.

110	**15**	½d. green	..	2·25	1·75
		a. Ordinary paper (10.43)	..	30	90
111		1d. scarlet	..	2·25	1·25
		a. Ordinary paper (10.43)	..	30	60
112		1½d. red-brown ..	..	2·50	2·75
		a. Ordinary paper (10.43)	..	65	95
		w. Wmk inverted	..	†	
113		2d. grey	..	4·00	1·50
		a. Ordinary paper (10.43)	..	40	90
114		2½d. ultramarine	..	3·25	1·25
		a. Ordinary paper (10.43)	..	60	1·50
115		3d. orange	..	4·75	70
		a. Ordinary paper (10.43)	..	40	80
116		6d. mauve	..	3·50	90
		a. Ordinary paper (10.43)	..	1·50	80
117		1s. olive-brown	..	7·00	2·50
		a. Ordinary paper (8.42)	..	1·50	70
118		2s. 6d. sepia ..	..	18·00	4·25
		a. Ordinary paper (8.42)	..	14·00	3·00
119		5s. carmine	..	35·00	5·50
		a. Ordinary paper (8.42)	..	13·00	4·00
120		10s. blue (1.12 47)	..	7·00	8·00
121		£1 black (1.12.47)	..	11·00	20·00
110/21 ..		Set of 12	45·00	38·00
110/21 Perf "Specimen" ..		Set of 12	£225	

The ordinary paper, used as a substitute for the chalk-surfaced for printings between 1942 and 1945, is thick, smooth and opaque.

1946 (1 Nov). *Victory. As Nos.* 110/11 *of Antigua.*

122	1½d. lake-brown	..	10	10
123	3d. orange	..	10	10
122/3 Perf "Specimen"	Set of 2	55·00		

1949 (3 Jan). *Royal Silver Wedding. As Nos.* 112/13 *of Antigua.*

124	2½d. ultramarine	..	10	10
125	£1 black	..	11·00	13·00

1949 (10 Oct). *75th Anniv of U.P.U. As Nos.* 114/17 *of Antigua.*

126	2½d. ultramarine	..	30	45
127	3d. orange	..	50	1·25
128	6d. magenta ..	..	50	40
129	1s. olive	..	50	40
126/9 ..	Set of 4	1·60	2·25	

(New Currency. 100 cents = 1 B.W.I. dollar)

1951. *Inauguration of B.W.I. University College. As Nos.* 118/19 *of Antigua.*

130	3 c. black and brown-red (10.4) ..	..	40	40
131	12 c. black and reddish violet (16.2)	..	40	50

(Recess Waterlow)

1951 (2 Apr). *Restoration of Legislative Council. Wmk Mult Script CA. P* 14½ x 14.

132	**16**	6 c. orange	..	20	50
133		12 c. purple	..	20	50
134		24 c. olive ..	..	20	50
135		$1.20 carmine ..	..	45	75
132/5 ..		Set of 4	95	2·00	

17 Sombrero Lighthouse   18 Map of Jost Van Dyke

(Recess D.L.R.)

1952 (15 Apr). *T* 17/18 *and similar designs. Wmk Mult Script CA. P* 12½ × 13 (*vert*) *or* 13 × 12½ (*horiz*).

136	1 c. black	..	30	90
137	2 c. deep green	..	35	30
138	3 c. black and brown	..	30	80
139	4 c. carmine-red	..	35	90
140	5 c. claret and black	..	90	50
141	8 c. bright blue	..	35	75
142	12 c. dull violet	..	45	75
143	24 c. deep brown	..	35	30
144	60 c. yellow-green and blue ..	..	2·50	11·00
145	$1.20, black and bright blue	..	3·75	12·00
146	$2.40, yellowish green and red-brown	..	10·00	9·00
147	$4.80, bright blue and carmine	..	11·00	14·00
136/47 ..		Set of 12	27·00	45·00

Designs: *Horiz*—3 c. Sheep industry; 4 c. Map of Anegada; 5 c. Cattle industry; 8 c. Map of Virgin Gorda; 12 c. Map of Tortola; 60 c. Dead Man's Chest; $1.20, Sir Francis Drake Channel; $2.40, Road Town; $4.80, Map of Virgin Islands. *Vert*—24 c. Badge of the Presidency.

Zanzibar

100 cents = 1 East Africa shilling

PROTECTORATE

37 *Sham Alam*
(Sultan's dhow)

V
I
C
T
O
R
Y

I
S
S
U
E

8TH JUNE 1946

(38)

1944 (20 Nov). *Bicentenary of Al Busaid Dynasty. Recess. Wmk Mult Script CA. P 14.*

327	**37**	10 c. ultramarine		50	80
328		20 c. red		50	1·50
329		50 c. blue-green		50	30
330		1 s. dull purple		50	45
327/30			*Set of* 4	1·75	2·75
327/30 Perf "Specimen"			*Set of* 4	70·00	

1946 (11 Nov). *Victory. Nos. 311 and 315 optd with T* **38.**

331	**33**	10 c. black (R.)		20	20
332		30 c. ultramarine (R.)		20	40
331/2 Perf "Specimen"		*Set of* 2	45·00		

1949 (10 Jan). *Royal Silver Wedding. As Nos. 143/4 of Jamaica.*

333	20 c. orange		30	90
334	10 s. brown		17·00	26·00

1949 (10 Oct). *75th Anniv of U.P.U. As Nos. 145/8 of Jamaica.*

335	20 c. red-orange		40	1·25
336	30 c. deep blue		1·40	80
337	50 c. magenta		1·50	1·50
338	1 s. blue-green		1·50	2·50
335/8		*Set of* 4	4·25	5·50

POSTAGE DUE STAMPS

D 3

(Typo D.L.R.)

1936 (1 Jan)–**62**. *Wmk Mult Script CA. P* 14.

D25	**D 3**	5 c. violet		1·25	4·50
		a. Chalk-surfaced paper (18.7.56)		30	10·00
D26		10 c. scarlet		90	1·75
		a. Chalk-surfaced paper (6.3.62)		30	4·00
D27		20 c. green		75	3·25
		a. Chalk-surfaced paper (6.3.62)		30	9·50
D28		30 c. brown		4·00	12·00
		a. Chalk-surfaced paper (18.7.56)		30	8·00
D29		40 c. ultramarine		4·00	16·00
		a. Chalk-surfaced paper (18.7.56)		40	16·00
D30		1 s. grey		4·00	22·00
		a. Chalk-surfaced paper (18.7.56)		1·00	14·00
D25/30			*Set of* 6	13·50	55·00
D25a/30a			*Set of* 6	2·40	55·00
D25/30 Perf "Specimen"			*Set of* 6	60·00	

Set Prices for British Commonwealth Omnibus Issues

1937 CORONATION

Country	Cat. Nos.	Stamps
Great Britain	461	1
Aden	13/15	3
Antigua	95/7	3
Ascension	35/7	3
Australia		
Nauru	44/7	4
New Guinea	208/11	4
Papua	154/7	4
Bahamas	146/8	3
Barbados	245/7	3
Basutoland	15/17	3
Bechuanaland	115/17	3
Bermuda	107/9	3
British Guiana	305/7	3
British Honduras	147/9	3
British Solomon Is.	57/9	3
Canada	356	1
Cayman Islands	112/14	3
Ceylon	383/5	3
Cyprus	148/50	3
Dominica	96/8	3
Falkland Islands	143/5	3
Fiji	246/8	3
Gambia	147/9	3
Gibraltar	118/20	3
Gilbert and Ellice Is.	40/2	3
Gold Coast	117/19	3
Grenada	149/51	3
Hong Kong	137/9	3
Jamaica	118/20	3
Kenya, Uganda and Tanganyika	128/30	3
Leeward Islands	92/4	3
Malaya—Straits Settlements	275/7	3
Malta	214/16	3
Mauritius	249/51	3
Montserrat	98/100	3
Morocco Agencies		
Spanish Currency	164	1
French Currency	229	1
Tangier	244	1
Newfoundland	254/6, 257/67	14
New Zealand	599/601	3
Cook Islands	124/6	3
Niue	72/4	3
Nigeria	46/8	3
Northern Rhodesia	22/4	3
Nyasaland	127/9	3
St. Helena	128/30	3
St. Kitts-Nevis	65/7	3
St. Lucia	125/7	3
St. Vincent	146/8	3
Seychelles	132/4	3
Sierra Leone	185/7	3
Somaliland	90/2	3
South Africa	71/5	5 × 2
Southern Rhodesia	36/9	4
South West Africa	97/104	8 × 2
Swaziland	25/7	3
Trinidad and Tobago	243/5	3
Turks & Caicos Is.	191/3	3
Virgin Islands	107/9	3
Total		**202**

Price
Un Used
Complete set of 202 stamps £130 £110

1945–46 VICTORY

Country	Cat. Nos.	Stamps
Great Britain	491/2	2
Aden	28/9	2
Seiyun	12/13	2
Shihr and Mukalla	12/13	2
Antigua	110/11	2
Ascension	48/9	2
Australia	213/15	3
Bahamas	176/7	2
Barbados	262/3	2
Basutoland	29/31	3 × 2
Bechuanaland	129/31	3 × 2
Bermuda	123/4	2
British Guiana	320/1	2
British Honduras	162/3	2
British Solomon Is.	73/4	2
Burma	64/7	4
Cayman Islands	127/8	2
Ceylon	400/1	2
Cyprus	164/5	2
Dominica	110/11	2
Falkland Islands	164/5	2
Falkland Islands Dependencies	G17/18	2
Fiji	268/9	2
Gambia	162/3	2
Gibraltar	132/3	2
Gilbert and Ellice Is.	55/6	2
Gold Coast	133/4	2
Grenada	164/5	2
Hong Kong	169/70	2
India	278/81	4
Hyderabad	53	1
Jamaica	141/2	2
Kenya, Uganda and Tanganyika	155/6	2
Leeward Islands	115/16	2
Malta	232/3	2
Mauritius	264/5	2
Montserrat	113/14	2
Morocco Agencies		
Tangier	253/4	2
New Zealand	667/77	11
Cook Islands	146/9	4
Niue	98/101	4
Western Samoa	215/18	4
Nigeria	60/1	2
Northern Rhodesia	46/7	2
Nyasaland	158/9	2
Pakistan		
Bahawalpur	O19	1
Pitcairn Islands	9/10	2
St. Helena	141/2	2
St. Kitts-Nevis	78/9	2
St. Lucia	142/3	2
St. Vincent	160/1	2
Seychelles	150/1	2
Sierra Leone	201/2	2
Somaliland	117/18	2
South Africa	108/10	3 × 2
Southern Rhodesia	64/7	4
South West Africa	131/3	3 × 2
Swaziland	39/41	3 × 2
Trinidad and Tobago	257/8	2
Turks & Caicos Is.	206/7	2
Virgin Islands	122/3	2
Zanzibar	331/2	2
Total		**164**

Complete set of 164 stamps 28·00 27·00

1948 ROYAL SILVER WEDDING

Country	Cat. Nos.	Stamps
Great Britain	493/4	2
Aden	30/1	2
Seiyun	14/15	2
Shihr and Mukalla	14/15	2
Antigua	112/13	2
Ascension	50/1	2
Bahamas	194/5	2
Bahrain	61/2	2
Barbados	265/6	2
Basutoland	36/7	2
Bechuanaland	136/7	2
Bermuda	125/6	2
British Guiana	322/3	2
British Honduras	164/5	2
British Postal Agencies in Eastern Arabia	25/6	2
British Solomon Is.	75/6	2
Cayman Islands	129/30	2
Cyprus	166/7	2
Dominica	112/13	2
Falkland Islands	166/7	2
Falkland Islands Dependencies	G19/20	2
Fiji	270/1	2
Gambia	164/5	2
Gibraltar	134/5	2
Gilbert and Ellice Is.	57/8	2
Gold Coast	147/8	2
Grenada	166/7	2
Hong Kong	171/2	2
Jamaica	143/4	2
Kenya, Uganda and Tanganyika	157/8	2
Kuwait	74/5	2
Leeward Islands	117/18	2
Malaya		
Johore	131/2	2
Kedah	70/1	2
Kelantan	55/6	2
Malacca	1/2	2
Negri Sembilan	40/1	2
Pahang	47/8	2
Penang	1/2	2
Perak	122/3	2
Perlis	1/2	2
Selangor	88/9	2
Trengganu	61/2	2
Malta	249/50	2
Mauritius	270/1	2
Montserrat	115/16	2
Morocco Agencies		
Spanish Currency	176/7	2
Tangier	255/6	2
Nigeria	62/3	2
North Borneo	350/1	2
Northern Rhodesia	48/9	2
Nyasaland	161/2	2
Pitcairn Islands	11/12	2
St. Helena	143/4	2
St. Kitts-Nevis	80/1	2
St. Lucia	144/5	2
St. Vincent	162/3	2
Sarawak	165/6	2
Seychelles	152/3	2
Sierra Leone	203/4	2
Singapore	31/2	2
Somaliland	119/20	2
South Africa	125	1 × 2
South West Africa	137	1 × 2
Swaziland	46/7	2
Trinidad and Tobago	259/60	2
Turks & Caicos Is.	208/9	2
Virgin Islands	124/5	2

Zanzibar	333/4	2
Total		138

Complete set—138 stamps £1600 £1600

1949 75TH ANNIVERSARY OF U.P.U.

Country	Cat. Nos.	Stamps
Great Britain	499/502	4
Aden	32/5	4
Seiyun	16/19	4
Shihr and Mukalla	16/19	4
Antigua	114/17	4
Ascension	52/5	4
Australia	232	1
Bahamas	196/9	4
Bahrain	67/70	4
Barbados	267/70	4
Basutoland	38/41	4
Bechuanaland	138/41	4
Bermuda	130/3	4
British Guiana	324/7	4
British Honduras	172/5	4
British Postal Agencies in Eastern Arabia	31/4	4
British Solomon Is.	77/80	4
Brunei	96/9	4
Cayman Islands	131/4	4
Ceylon	410/12	3
Cyprus	168/71	4
Dominica	114/17	4
Falkland Islands	168/71	4
Falkland Islands Dependencies	G21/4	4
Fiji	272/5	4
Gambia	166/9	4
Gibraltar	136/9	4
Gilbert and Ellice Is.	59/62	4

Gold Coast	149/52	4
Grenada	168/71	4
Hong Kong	173/6	4
India	325/8	4
Jamaica	145/8	4
Kenya, Uganda and Tanganyika	159/62	4
Kuwait	80/3	4
Leeward Islands	119/22	4
Malaya		
Johore	148/51	4
Kedah	72/5	4
Kelantan	57/60	4
Malacca	18/21	4
Negri Sembilan	63/6	4
Pahang	49/52	4
Penang	23/6	4
Perak	124/7	4
Perlis	3/6	4
Selangor	111/14	4
Trengganu	63/6	4
Malta	251/4	4
Mauritius	272/5	4
Montserrat	117/20	4
Morocco Agencies		
Tangier	276/9	4
New Hebrides	64/7,	
	F77/80	4 + 4
Nigeria	64/7	4
North Borneo	352/5	4
Northern Rhodesia	50/3	4
Nyasaland	163/6	4
Pakistan		
Bahawalpur	43/6,	
	O28/31	4 + 4
Pitcairn Islands	13/16	4
St. Helena	145/8	4
St. Kitts-Nevis	82/5	4
St. Lucia	160/3	4
St. Vincent	178/81	4
Sarawak	167/70	4
Seychelles	154/7	4
Sierra Leone	205/8	4

Singapore	33/6	4
Somaliland	121/4	4
South Africa	128/30	3 × 2
Southern Rhodesia	68/9	2
South West Africa	138/40	3 × 2
Swaziland	48/51	4
Tonga	88/91	4
Trinidad and Tobago	261/4	4
Turks & Caicos Is.	217/20	4
Virgin Islands	126/9	4
Zanzibar	335/8	4
Total		310

Complete set of 310 stamps £325 £300

1951 INAUGURATION OF B.W.I. UNIVERSITY COLLEGE

Country	Cat. Nos.	Stamps
Antigua	118/19	2
Barbados	283/4	2
British Guiana	328/9	2
British Honduras	176/7	2
Dominica	118/19	2
Grenada	185/6	2
Jamaica	149/50	2
Leeward Islands	123/4	2
Montserrat	121/2	2
St. Kitts-Nevis	92/3	2
St. Lucia	164/5	2
St. Vincent	182/3	2
Trinidad and Tobago	265/6	2
Virgin Islands	130/1	2
Total		28

Complete set of 28 stamps 9·00 8·50

Index